307

D1135087

The Many-Body Problem

THE MANY-BODY

PROCEEDINGS OF THE SYMPOSIUM
ON THE MANY-BODY PROBLEM
HELD AT STEVENS INSTITUTE OF TECHNOLOGY,
HOBOKEN, NEW JERSEY, JANUARY 28-29, 1957

INTERSCIENCE PUBLISHERS

New York, London

PROBLEM

Edited by Jerome K. Percus

The Courant Institute of Mathematical Sciences

New York University, New York, New York

a division of John Wiley & Sons

1963

Library of Congress Catalog Card Number: 62-21629
Printed in United States of America

Preface

In the early part of 1957, a Symposium was held at the Stevens Institute of Technology for the purpose of bringing together workers in the numerous rapidly moving fields of many-particle physics. The timing was, *a posteriori*, most suitable. The fundamentals of the Brueckner theory had been solidified, and a basic understanding of electron correlations in a plasma was at the point of being achieved, as was that of superconductivity, with its manifold implications for other many-body systems. It was also, as E. Montroll pointed out, the centenary of Statistical Mechanics, and one of the directions of the second century was evident in the emerging numerical data on classical rigid sphere and helium lambda point transitions.

The gestation period of this volume has been very long. A number of rather lengthy connecting sections have therefore been inserted by the Editor with the intention of bringing the discussion somewhat forward in time. These relate in the main to general methodology, with attendant advantages and disadvantages, notable among the latter being the frequent yet always unexpected difficulties when specific cases are under examination. The extent to which the unallocated material represents an original contribution is, to put it charitably, uncertain, for in a rapidly moving field there is a large body of knowledge of undetermined origin constantly "in the air". There has at least been an effort to include references through the end of 1958, when the body of the text was completed, as well as a scattering of newer publications. Major parts of Chaps. I and XIII were used in a course in 1958 and should be without significant error; such optimism in the remaining survey chapters is not warranted.

The distribution of responsibility for the tardiness of the publication is extensive. Even larger is the list of individuals who have given of their time and efforts on behalf of the Symposium and the Proceedings. The Editor wishes to acknowledge the contributions of President J. Davis and members of the administrative staff; of the Symposium Committee (D. Finkelstein, J. Percus, F. Pollock, G. Yevick); of E. Jeschke and A. de Graw; E. Farber, J. Neidhart, M. Rehfeld, and M. Rozmarinowski, all of Stevens Institute of Technology; of J. Apeland and C. Engle of New York University; and of numerous others without whose aid a difficult task would have been quite impossible.

* * *

Due to the well-known innate perversity of inanimate objects — and some animate ones as well — there has been another long delay in the publication of this volume. Since most of the topics here included have seen the light of day — or of a large number of days — several chapters are now presented by abstract alone. To maintain a sense of balance, a number of editorial sections have been excised as well. It is to be hoped that the value of the Proceedings is not impaired by these alterations.

JEROME K. PERCUS

The Courant Institute of
Mathematical Sciences
New York University, New York
> 1963

Authors

B. J. Alder
Lawrence Radiation Laboratory, University of California, Livermore, California

M. K. Banerjee
Palmer Physical Laboratory, Princeton University, Princeton, New Jersey

H. A. Bethe
Laboratory of Nuclear Studies, Cornell University, Ithaca, New York

N. N. Bogoliubov
Steklov Mathematical Institute, Academy of Sciences, Moscow, U.S.S.R.

Leon N. Cooper
Department of Physics, Brown University, Providence, Rhode Island

C. De Dominicis
Service de Physique Mathématique, Centre d'Études Nucléaires de Saclay, France

Joachim B. Ehrman
Nucleonics Division, U.S. Naval Research Laboratory, Washington, D. C.

Leonard Eyges
Lincoln Laboratory, Massachusetts Institute of Technology, Lexington, Massachusetts

Louis Goldstein
Los Alamos Scientific Laboratory, University of California, Los Alamos, New Mexico

Eugene P. Gross
Brandeis University, Waltham, Massachusetts

Kerson Huang
Department of Physics, Masssachusetts Institute of Technology, Cambridge, Massachusetts

Robert Jastrow
Goddard Space Flight Center, Institute for Space Studies, National Aeronautics and Space Administration, New York, New York

T. D. Lee
Department of Physics, Columbia University, New York, New York (formerly Institute for Advanced Study, Princeton, New Jersey)

C. A. Levinson
Department of Physics, Weizmann Institute of Science, Rehovoth, Israel (formerly Palmer Physical Laboratory, Princeton University, Princeton, New Jersey)

A. A. Maradudin
Westinghouse Research Laboratories, Pittsburgh, Pennsylvania (formerly Institute for Fluid Dynamics and Applied Mathematics, University of Maryland, College Park, Maryland

P. C. Martin
Lyman Laboratory of Physics, Harvard University, Cambridge, Massachusetts

E. W. Montroll
IBM Research Center, Yorktown Heights, New York (formerly Institute for Fluid Dynamics and Applied Mathematics, University of Maryland, College Park, Mary-land)

Lars Onsager
Sterling Chemistry Laboratory, Yale University, New Haven, Connecticut

Jerome K. Percus
The Courant Institute of Mathematical Sciences, New York University, New York

David Pines
Department of Physics, University of Illinois, Urbana, Illinois

V. V. Tolmatchev
Karpov Institute of Physical Chemistry, Moscow, U.S.S.R.

S. V. Tyablikov
Steklov Mathematical Institute, Academy of Sciences, Moscow, U.S.S.R.

T. Wainwright
Lawrence Radiation Laboratory, University of California, Livermore, California

G. H. Weiss
Institute for Fluid Dynamics and Applied Mathematics, University of Maryland, College Park, Maryland

C. N. Yang
Institute for Advanced Study, Princeton, New Jersey

George J. Yevick
Department of Physics, Stevens Institute of Technology, Hoboken, New Jersey

P. R. Zilsel
Department of Physics, Western Reserve University, Cleveland, Ohio (formerly McMaster University, Hamilton, Ontario, Canada)

D. N. Zubarev
Steklov Mathematical Institute, Academy of Sciences, Moscow, U.S.S.R.

Contents

PART THREE

PART FOUR

PART FIVE

PART SIX

Part One

CHAPTER I

Multiple Scattering Methods

JEROME K. PERCUS

A. Basic Formulation

1. *Introduction*

Many of the properties of atoms [1], nuclei [2], and fluids [3] give evidence for the inadequacy of a picture in which each particle of a many-body system moves independently of the others, albeit via a force field depending upon some average parameters of the whole system. Thus, explicit correlations between particles must be taken into account. Part One will be devoted to treatments of the many-body problem which have arisen from investigations of the phenomenon of multiple scattering. In other words, a literal attempt is made to reduce the study of a complex system with two-body interactions to that of a sequence of two-body collisions; these two-body collisions are occasioned by effective interactions, presumably solvable, of a nature similar to that of real pair interactions. (Imposition of an external potential, as in an atom, in principle requires only minor modifications). An obvious advantage of such an approach is that difficulties due to singularities of the interaction potential (e.g., hard sphere repulsion) are relegated to the level of the two-body problem, in which the availability of exact or nearly exact solutions is little influenced by the existence of singularities. Another advantage of the fully developed formalism, although not specific to the multiple scattering approach, lies in the elimination of unphysical terms pyramiding as powers of the particle number, a common and distressing attribute of ordinary perturbation methods. The development presented here will be based principally on the papers of Lax [4],

3

Watson, and collaborators [5]–[10], and Brueckner and collaborators [2], [11]–[19].

2. *Single scattering*

Consider first the stationary state scattering of a spinless single particle by a potential V:

$$[T+V(\mathbf{x}, \mathbf{p})]\psi = E\psi \tag{1}$$

where T may be imagined to be $p^2/2m$, but the specific form will not be utilized. Physically, we know that ψ (unnormalized) can be represented as

$$\psi = \varphi + \psi^{\mathrm{sc}} \tag{2}$$

where φ is an incoming wave satisfying the "unperturbed" equation

$$T\varphi = E\varphi \tag{3}$$

and ψ^{sc} is the outgoing scattered wave. If the interaction is so long-range that it cannot be neglected at any point, then this separation becomes conceptual rather than physical. In terms of the outgoing wave Green's function for the unperturbed problem: $(E-T)\,G(\mathbf{x}, \mathbf{x}') = \delta(\mathbf{x}-\mathbf{x}')$ (with, e.g., positive radial mass flow at large x as boundary condition), or in operator form (defining $\langle\mathbf{x}|G|\mathbf{x}'\rangle = G(\mathbf{x}, \mathbf{x}')$)

$$(E-T)\,G = 1, \tag{4}$$

eqs. (1) and (2) may be rewritten as

$$\psi = \varphi + GV\psi \tag{5}$$

If T is time reversible, G is not Hermitian, but symmetric; for example [20], if $T = p^2/2m$, one has $G(\mathbf{x}, \mathbf{x}') = -(4\pi|\mathbf{x}-\mathbf{x}'|)^{-1} \cdot \exp\left[(i/\hbar)(2mE)^{\frac{1}{2}}|\mathbf{x}-\mathbf{x}'|\right]$. Equation (5) represents a feedback process: due to the incoming φ, a net ψ is produced; ψ, surrounding V, creates a source of strength $V\psi$ and this, via the propagator G, propagates the outgoing wave $\psi^{\mathrm{sc}} = GV\psi$, which together with φ comprises ψ.

The prescription one obtains [21] for the operator G is

$$G = 1/(E+i\xi-T) \tag{6}$$

where ξ is an arbitrarily small positive number, to be taken as zero after all computations are performed; coupled with normalizability,

ξ ensures an outwardly traveling wave. The solution of the scattering problem can then be written down formally in a variety of ways. If we introduce the wave operator Ω and scattering operator t

$$\psi = \Omega\varphi \qquad \psi^{sc} = Gt\varphi \tag{7}$$

then we have at once the interrelations

$$\Omega = 1+Gt \qquad t = V\Omega \tag{8a}$$

$$t = V+VGt \tag{8b}$$

which may be solved as

$$\Omega = 1/(1-GV)$$
$$t = (1-VG)^{-1}V = V(1-GV)^{-1} \tag{9a}$$

and also as

$$t = V+V(E+i\xi-T-V)^{-1}V \tag{9b}$$

It is important to note, from eq. (5), that it is not *necessary* that eqs. (8) be true as operator relations; in considering the transition from a given initial φ to ψ, they need only hold when applied to φ itself. In fact, since Ω depends on E, through G, the operator which transforms the set of incoming states cannot be Ω, but, indexing the incoming states by k, must be U, defined by

$$\langle k'|U|k\rangle = \langle k'|\Omega(E_k)|k\rangle \tag{10}$$

For example, from ordinary phase shift analysis [22] for $T = p^2/2m$ and spherically symmetric V, we know that the asymptotic (large x) expression for U is given by

$$(U-1)|e^{i\mathbf{k}\cdot\mathbf{x}}\rangle = (e^{ikx}/2ikx)\sum_l(2l+1)[e^{2i\delta_l(E_k)}-1]P_l(\mathbf{k}\cdot\mathbf{x}/kx) \tag{10'}$$

where $E_k = \hbar^2k^2/2m$. However, when the situation here considered is merely a subsystem of a larger system, it will be necessary to consider off-energy-shell propagation, i.e., $\Omega(E)|k\rangle$, where $E \neq E_k$.

In the Born approximation (small V), we have $\Omega = 1+GV$, so that one can say that t is that operator (written as $V+VGV+VGVGV+,\ldots$, t is clearly symmetric if T and V are) which, when used instead of V in the Born approximation, gives the correct scattering. Also, in the full expansion of (9a), $\Omega = 1+GV+GVGV+GVGVGV+\ldots = 1+Gt$, the nth term may be visualized as consisting of n successive single interactions with n intermediary propagations. Thus, t is the equivalent potential when only a composite single scattering is conceived; t is well-behaved irrespective of singularities in V and convergence of various power series.

3. *Multiple scattering* [4], [5], [6]

Suppose the scatterer to be a system of A particles, with Hamiltonian H_s; the interaction potential with an incoming particle is to consist of the sum of separate interaction potentials with the particles of the scatterer: $V = \sum_1^A V_i$, so that

$$(H_s + T + \sum V_i)\psi = E\psi \qquad (11)$$

where E is the total energy of scatterer and incoming particle. We again inquire as to the relation between the total ψ and the "incoming" φ (scatterer plus incoming particle) which satisfies eq. (11) with the interaction V turned off; it will be explicitly assumed that the full system (11) has no bound or rearrangement states near energy E. In particular, we wish to decompose the interaction of particle and compound scatterer into a set of elementary particle-particle interactions. Now introducing the elementary scattering operators

$$t_i = V_i + V_i\, G\, t_i \qquad (12a)$$

$$\text{or} \qquad t_i = V_i\, (1 - GV_i)^{-1} \qquad (12b)$$

where

$$G = (E + i\xi - H_s - T)^{-1} \qquad (13)$$

we would expect, on physical grounds, since t_i already includes any number of successive interactions with V_i, that the complete wave operator Ω will simply be the sum of the various possibilities of successive scatterings t_i, with the proviso that no two successive scatterings be from the same particle:

$$\Omega = 1 + \sum Gt_i + \sum_{i_2 \neq i_1} Gt_{i_1} Gt_{i_2} + \sum_{\substack{i_3 \neq i_2 \\ i_2 \neq i_1}} Gt_{i_1} Gt_{i_2} Gt_{i_3} + \ldots \qquad (14)$$

Equation (14) is correct. To prove this most profitably, we proceed as follows. If

$$\Lambda_j = 1 + \sum_{i_1 \neq j}^{} G\, t_{i_1} + \sum_{\substack{i_1 \neq j \\ i_2 \neq i_1}}^{} G\, t_{i_1}\, G\, t_{i_2}$$

$$+ \sum_{\substack{i_1 \neq j \\ i_2 \neq i_1,\, i_3 \neq i_2}}^{} G\, t_{i_1}\, G\, t_{i_2}\, G\, t_{i_3} + \ldots \qquad (15)$$

denotes the result of all scatterings which do not end up with a composite single scattering on particle j, then according to eq. (14),

$$\Omega = 1 + \sum G t_j \Lambda_j \qquad (16)$$

On the other hand, from definition (15) itself,

$$\Lambda_j = 1 + \sum_{i \neq j} G t_i \Lambda_i \qquad (17)$$

Thus, eq. (16) may also be written as

$$\Omega = \Lambda_j + G t_j \Lambda_j \qquad (18)$$

which may again be interpreted by saying that $\Lambda_j \varphi$ represents the incoming wave arriving at particle j, and this together with its scattering by particle j produces the overall state at particle j; note however that G is the propagator for the unperturbed system and not for the system with V_j alone turned off (related to the fact that previous scattering by all V_i is already included in $\Lambda_j \varphi$). Coupling eqs. (12a) and (18),

$$V_j \Omega = t_j \Lambda_j \qquad (19)$$

which enables us to write eq. (16) as

$$\Omega = 1 + G \sum V_i \Omega \qquad (20)$$

Noting that eq. (20) merely expresses (8a) for the interaction potential $\sum V_i$, then letting $\xi \to 0$ as originally prescribed [23], we have verified the validity of eq. (14), or equivalently, of the pair (16), (17).

The relation of t_i to a true elementary scattering on particle i is somewhat imprecise, due both to the fact that we cannot divide $G^{-1} = E + i\xi - H_s - T$ into a two-body part and a constant, and to the possible off-energy-shell character of the propagation, i.e., the state being acted on may not have total energy E. Under certain conditions, both difficulties may be removed. Let us call the energy difference δ, so that

$$G = (\langle H_s \rangle + \langle T \rangle + \delta + i\xi - H_s - T)^{-1} \qquad (21a)$$

where expectations are taken in the initial state for t_i. If the impulse approximation [24] is valid, the binding of particle i to the scatterer is ineffective during the scattering process, and (21a) becomes

$$G' = (\langle T_i \rangle + \langle T \rangle + \delta + i\xi - T_i - T)^{-1} \qquad (21b)$$

Further, if the energy dependence of the scattering is weak, matrix elements of t_i may be evaluated at nearby incoming energy $\langle T \rangle'$; choosing

$$\langle T \rangle' = \langle T \rangle + \delta \qquad (21c)$$

then t_i represents a real two-body scattering process.

It is convenient and valuable in the multiple scattering problem to decompose the scattering into coherent and incoherent parts. By a coherent scattering process, we shall mean one in which the state of the scattering medium is left unchanged — does not react to the scattered particle — and, if a real process, is thus certainly elastic; the remaining processes are incoherent. Taking only overall coherent scattering into account, the scatterer simply acts as a medium through which the incoming wave is refracted (with absorption and diffusion in momentum as well) as in optics. In the important special case in which $H_s + T$ and the interaction potential V_j are translation invariant, and the unperturbed state is an eigenstate of total momentum (each particle in the scatterer thus uniformly distributed), momentum is conserved in any scattering, so that the momentum of the coherently scattered particle remains unchanged: coherent scattering then consists only of forward scattering, and the incoming particle passes "straight through" the medium. For the time being, we shall regard the incoming particle as distinguishable from the scattering particles, in order that forward exchange scattering, and its generalization for non-uniform media, need not be taken into account.

The advantage of the separation into coherent and incoherent components is readily expressed. From one point of view, if the state of the medium is changed only with difficulty (e.g., requires a large energy shift) then the scattering by $\sum V_i$ is principally coherent, and the incoherent scattering may reasonably be regarded as a correction term. For example, for a low energy nucleon scattering on a nucleus in the independent particle (shell model) approximation, a struck nucleon has, due to the Fermi statistics, relatively few states available with a nominal acquisition of energy; regarding the scattered nucleon as one normally present in the nucleus, the effect is to further validate the independent particle model [25]. From another point of view, the incoherent scattering from various elementary scatterers is essentially uncorrelated and hence tends to cancel for a large system, compared to the coherent scattering; more or less local excitations do however remain, so that some energy is transferred to the scattering medium. It should be noted that unless the center of mass of a finite scatterer is sufficiently constrained, final states will proliferate in a real elastic scattering process; envisaging very large systems, such a constraint may be assumed, and elastic becomes coherent — or one applies the term coherent to internal degrees of freedom alone.

Given a scattering represented by the operator S, the coherent portion S_c will be defined by those matrix elements that are diagonal with respect to the states of the scatterer (or in the case of degeneracy, perhaps with respect to a subset of states of equal energy). Explicitly, if the states of the uncoupled scattering medium and scattered particle (distinguishable from the particles in the medium; otherwise, (22) must be symmetrized — see also Takeda and Watson [6]) are indexed by m and k respectively, then

$$\langle m'k'|S_c|mk \rangle \equiv \langle mk'|S|mk \rangle \delta_{mm'} \tag{22}$$

We observe that, G being itself diagonal with respect to the scatterer, the relation $\Omega = 1 + Gt$ between the total wave and scattering operators implies the identical relation

$$\Omega_c = 1 + Gt_c \tag{23}$$

between their coherent components. Now if $\psi_c \equiv \Omega_c \varphi$ were known, one might reasonably expect the remaining "relatively small" incoherent scattering to be obtainable by an appropriate perturbation procedure. Since ψ_c actually requires the complete solution of the problem for its determination, this is little help; however, a good head start may be obtained in the following fashion.

4. *Approximate formulation*

Let $\bar{V}_c$ be that coherent operator which, alone, would give rise to the coherent scattering $\psi_c = \Omega_c \varphi$:

$$\Omega_c = 1 + G\bar{V}_c \Omega_c \tag{24}$$

or simply

$$(H_s + T)\varphi = E\varphi$$
$$H'\psi_c \equiv (H_s + T + \bar{V}_c)\psi_c = E\psi_c \tag{25}$$

If the common state of the scatterer for "incident" φ and coherent ψ_c is θ_m, with energy E_m, then integrating with θ_m^*, eq. (25) may be interpreted as the propagation of a wave of energy $E - E_m$ and wave function ψ_c/θ_m through the "optical model" potential

$$V^{\text{opt}} \equiv \int \theta_m^* \, \bar{V}_c \, \theta_m \, d\tau_s \tag{26}$$

Since $\bar{V}_c$ is in general non-Hermitian, V^{opt} is a complex potential as well, accounting for the loss of coherent amplitude in the real scattering process, the scatterer being left in an excited state.

We shall determine $\bar{V}_c$ in an indirect manner. It is reasonable to assume that $\bar{V}_c$ can be decomposed

$$\bar{V}_c = \sum U_{ci} \tag{27}$$

into coherent potentials U_{ci} associated with each particle in the scatterer, such that the residual potentials

$$\delta V_i \equiv V_i - U_{ci} \tag{28}$$

are random with respect to each other, in the sense that the coherent part of a product of different δV_i is very small. Let us find the consequences of this assumption. We may reconstruct the scattering problem by considering ψ_c of eq. (25) as the unperturbed initial state, with the interaction potentials δV_i then turned on. If primes denote quantities taken with respect to H' of eq. (25) as the unperturbed Hamiltonian,

$$G' = (E + i\xi - H_s - T - \bar{V}_c)^{-1} \tag{29a}$$

$$t_i' = (1 - \delta V_i G')^{-1} \delta V_i \tag{29b}$$

we now have, from (14),

$$\psi = (1 + \sum G' t_i' + \sum_{i \neq j} G' t_i' G' t_j' + \ldots) \psi_c \tag{30}$$

or, extracting the coherent part, using the relative randomness of the δV_i,

$$\psi_c \sim (1 + G' \sum t_{ci}') \psi_c \tag{31}$$

Thus, in the present approximation, the condition that the U_{ci} have already accounted for the full coherent portion of ψ becomes simply

$$t_{ci}' \sim 0 \tag{32}$$

that no elementary coherent scattering remains.

To make use of eq. (32) in obtaining $\bar{V}_c = \sum U_{ci}$, we see from

$$t'_i = [1-(V_i-U_{ci})G']^{-1}(V_i-U_{ci}) \tag{33}$$

that, after some algebra,

$$t'_i = (1-V_iG')^{-1}V_i(1-G'U_{ci})-U_{ci}-(1-V_iG')^{-1}U_{ci}G't'_i \tag{34}$$

The compound scattering factors of the form $(1-V_iG)^{-1}$, which are required to remove physically irrelevant singularities in V, represent high momentum terms. If a well-behaved function (composed, e.g., of U's and t's) does not contain coherent terms, they would not be expected to enter on applying the factor $(1-V_iG')^{-1}$. Thus, taking the coherent part of eq. (34), condition (32) yields the desired relation

$$U_{ci} = [(1-V_iG')^{-1}V_i]_c(1-G'U_{ci}) \tag{35}$$

For a general system, eq. (35) together with (27) and (29a) constitute a self-consistent set of relations of the Hartree type for the determination of the effective potentials U_{ci}; in practice, of course, the various inverses are quite impossible to perform unless one uses simplified models for the scatterer and its state sequence. Since the diagonality implicit in the coherence concept [eq. (22)] is with respect to the scatterer alone, eq. (35) is not diagonal in the states of the scattered particle. With the momentum conservation resulting in the case of a uniform scatterer and relative coordinate interactions V_i, however, full diagonality is present (except perhaps for discrete indices corresponding to spin, isotopic spin, etc.), so that only a set of algebraic equations for the U_{ci} have, in principle, to be solved.

Assuming that the approximate U_{ci} have been obtained, as well as the corresponding approximate coherent wave function ψ_c defined by eq. (25), the complete solution of the scattering problem then follows by perturbation, eq. (14) or (16), (17), with the properties of the state ψ_c replacing those of φ, and with imposition of the incoherent interaction potential δV_i instead of V_i. In other words, gathering together the definitions, if

$$(H_s+T+\bar{V}_c)\psi_c = E\psi_c \tag{36a}$$

$$\text{where} \quad \bar{V}_c = \sum U_{ci} \tag{36b}$$

$$\text{and} \quad U_{ci} = [(1-V_iG')^{-1}V_i]_c(1-G'U_{ci}) \tag{36c}$$

$$\text{with} \quad G' = (E+i\xi-H_s-T-\bar{V}_c)^{-1} \tag{36d}$$

then if

$$\Omega' = 1 + \sum G' t'_j \Lambda'_j \tag{37a}$$

$$\Lambda'_j = 1 + \sum_{i \neq j} G' t'_i \Lambda'_i \tag{37b}$$

where $\qquad t'_i = [1 - (V_i - U_{ci}) G']^{-1} (V_i - U_{ci}) \tag{37c}$

for the remaining scattering, $\psi = \Omega' \psi_c$ satisfies the scattering equation $(H_s + T + \sum V_i)\psi = E\psi$.

The solution (36), (37) is exact (although ψ_c no longer means precisely $\Omega_c \varphi$), and in practice a perturbation expansion may be expected to converge quite rapidly whenever the scattering is predominantly coherent, for this effect has been relegated to the propagator G'. Now if $t'_{ci} = 0$ were satisfied exactly, the additional coherent correction $\Omega'_c = 1 + \sum G' t'_{ci} + \sum_{i \neq j} G'(t'_i G' t_j)_c + \ldots$ would have no contribution in first order, and very little in any term $G' t'_i G' t'_j G' t'_k \ldots$ in which all indices occur just once. To recover this desirable state of affairs, negated by the form of (36c), an approximation (part of which is deferred until later) has been extensively used [5]–[19]. For a class of scatterers in which the scattering "material" (mean density, etc.) remains constant as the particle number A increases, G' and $\bar{V}_c$ should be essentially independent of A, while $U_{ci} \sim (1/A) \bar{V}_c$. Thus in eq. (34) [equivalent to (37c)], the term $[1 + (1 - V_i G')^{-1} U_{ci} G'] t'_i$ may be reduced to t'_i. But then, according to (34) and (35), t'_i achieves the form $U_i - U_{ci}$: the scattering is totally incoherent; it is easily seen that (36c) and (37c) are accordingly replaceable by

$$U_i = V_i + V_i G' t'_i \tag{38a}$$

$$t'_i = U_i - U_{ci} \tag{38b}$$

Let us explicitly find the effect of approximation (38); from (37a), (37b), we have

$$\Omega' = (1 + G' t'_i) \Lambda'_i \tag{39}$$

for any i. Further, using (38b), and rewriting (38a) as

$$V_i (1 + G' t'_i) = t'_i + U_{ci} \tag{40}$$

it follows that

$$\sum (V_i - U_{ci}) \Omega' = \sum (V_i - U_{ci})(1 + G' t'_i) \Lambda'_i \\ = \sum [(1 - U_{ci} G') t'_i] \Lambda'_i \tag{41}$$

but from (37a) and (36d), letting $\xi \to 0$ when applied to ψ_c,

$$(E-H_s-T-\sum U_{ci})\Omega'\psi_c = \sum t_i'\Lambda_i'\psi_c \tag{42}$$

Subtracting (41), applied to ψ_c, from (42) finally yields

$$(E-H_s-T-\sum V_i)\Omega'\psi_c = \sum U_{ci}G't_i'\Lambda_i'\psi_c \tag{43}$$

The adequacy of eq. (43) as particle number $A \to \infty$ is readily assessed, for $\sum U_{ci}G't_i'\Lambda_i' \sim (1/A)\,\bar{V}_c\sum G't_i'\Lambda_i' = (1/A)\,\bar{V}_c(\Omega'-1)$; since $(\Omega'-1)\psi_c \sim \psi-\psi_c$, the incoherent part of ψ, does not exceed ψ in magnitude, it appears that the right-hand side of (43) may be neglected as $A \to \infty$.

It is interesting to observe that if the propagator G' were defined, in an involved self-consistent way, by the diagonal part of $[E+i\xi-H_s-T-\bar{V}_c+\sum U_{ci}G't_i'\Lambda_i'(\Omega')^{-1}]^{-1}$, the right-hand side of eq. (43) would not appear at all. Considerations of this type will be pertinent in Sect. B2.

5. *Bound states*

Having multiple scattering as a background, we now proceed to the bound state many-body problem, with pair interaction potentials. The problems to be considered must include a scattering interpretation for bound state perturbations, the simultaneous turning on of all pair interactions in the medium, and the effect of quantum statistics as dictated by the impossibility of choosing a distinct scattered particle. For convenience in terminology, we will often use the expression "scattering" when the process actually referred to is of a standing wave or reaction character.

If φ is a normalized bound state of an unperturbed or free Hamiltonian H_F:

$$H_F\varphi = \mathscr{E}\varphi \tag{44}$$

to which an interaction potential V is added, we require for the corresponding bound state ψ:

$$H\psi \equiv (H_F+V)\psi = E\psi \tag{45}$$

Now if P is defined as the projection operator which projects out (annuls) the φ component of any function

$$Pf \equiv f-\langle\varphi|f\rangle\varphi \tag{46}$$

we may rewrite eq. (45) as

$$(E-H_F-PV)\psi = \langle\varphi|V\psi\rangle\varphi \tag{47}$$

and hence, since $PV\psi$ has no φ component, as

$$\psi-(E-H_F)^{-1}PV\psi = \langle\varphi|V\psi\rangle/(E-\mathscr{E})\varphi \tag{48}$$

It is convenient to normalize ψ so that

$$\langle\psi|\varphi\rangle = 1 \tag{49}$$

For then, taking the scalar product of eq. (48) with φ, we have at once [26]

$$E-\mathscr{E} = \langle\varphi|V\psi\rangle \quad (= \langle\varphi|t|\varphi\rangle) \tag{50}$$

and eq. (48) thus becomes

$$\psi = \varphi+GV\psi$$
$$\text{where} \quad G = (E-H_F)^{-1}P \tag{51}$$

The formalism of eqs. (51) is identical to that of eq. (5), except that G now refers to a bound state Green's function depending upon both the state φ and the energy E, with E to be determined by the subsidiary relation (50). With this modification, the definition of $t = V\Omega$ and succeeding developments may be taken over unchanged. Since the "source" $V\psi = t\varphi$ does not actually produce scattering, but merely modifies the initial field, it is customary to refer to t in this case as the reaction matrix or operator.

If φ happens to be degenerate (or nearly so), it is to be noted that $(E-H_F)^{-1}PV\psi$ in (48) may introduce small denominators and a consequent very slow convergence, if any at all, of the iterative eq. (51). In such a case, one chooses P to project out all states φ_r degenerate with φ and has to solve, instead of (50) and (51),

$$\psi-GV\psi = \sum_r \langle\varphi_r|\psi\rangle\varphi_r$$
$$\langle\varphi_r|V\psi\rangle = (E-\mathscr{E})\langle\varphi_r|\psi\rangle \tag{52}$$
$$G = (E-H_F)^{-1}P$$

In general the solution of (52) proceeds as is usual in degenerate perturbation theory [27]: the "correct linear combinations" φ_r are those which diagonalize the finite matrix $\langle\varphi_r|V|\psi_{r'}\rangle$; the corresponding ψ_r can then be normalized such that $\langle\varphi_r|\psi_{r'}\rangle = \delta_{rr'}$, and so for each φ_r, eq. (52) reduces to the pair (50), (51). If degeneracy is removed in the first-order approximation, the φ_r are such correct combinations if

$$\langle \varphi_r | V | \varphi_{r'} \rangle \quad \text{diagonal}, \qquad \langle \varphi_r | \varphi_{r'} \rangle = \delta_{rr'} \tag{52'}$$

for the perturbation series then guarantees (52') with $\psi_{r'}$ replacing $\varphi_{r'}$. For degeneracy first removed in higher order, conditions (52') must be appropriately augmented.

Now we are prepared to consider an A-body system with $\frac{1}{2}A(A-1)$ pair interaction potentials v_α, α denoting the unordered pair i, j; any one-body (external) potentials are included with the kinetic energy. The corresponding t_α may be sequentially applied by a direct transcription of the multiple scattering method. Thus, taking φ to be the state of an independent particle system, $H_F = \sum T_i$ (where T_i can be just the kinetic energy of the ith particle if fixed — e.g., periodic, Dirichlet, Neumann, etc. — boundary conditions are employed, but should otherwise be an operator with bound states, a barrier being erected for this purpose, if necessary), we may solve

$$\left(\sum T_i + \sum v_\alpha \right) \psi = E \psi \tag{53}$$

at once in the form $\psi = \Omega \varphi$ with

$$\begin{aligned}
\Omega &= 1 + \sum G t_\alpha \Lambda_\alpha \\
\Lambda_\alpha &= 1 + \sum_{\beta \neq \alpha} G t_\beta \Lambda_\beta \\
t_\alpha &= v_\alpha + v_\alpha G t_\alpha \\
G &= \left(E - \sum T_i \right)^{-1} P \\
E &= \mathcal{E} + \sum \langle \varphi | t_\alpha \Lambda_\alpha | \varphi \rangle
\end{aligned} \tag{54}$$

Since the full perturbation $\sum v_\alpha$ is symmetric, we know that as long as the "initial" state φ has the correct Fermi-Dirac (to which we will devote our major attention) or Einstein-Bose character, the same will be true for the "final" state ψ, even if the space of allowed wave functions is taken to be unrestricted by symmetry requirements. Such an unrestricted space must indeed be used, for the formulation of eq. (54) employs non-symmetric operators v_α, t_α, Λ_α. Over this full space, the state φ is in general degenerate; but since it is itself the correct linear combination of degenerate states under the action of the perturbation, one need not on this account consider degenerate perturbation theory, and P may be taken to annul all product states degenerate with φ.

In computing the energy E in (54), one must of course use the correct (anti-) symmetric state φ. Alternatively, if the $\chi_k(i)$ are a complete set of orthonormal eigenfunctions for the ith-particle unperturbed Hamiltonian T_i ($k =$ all indices):

$$T_i \chi_k(i) = \varepsilon_k \chi_k(i) \qquad (55)$$

and $\varphi_1 = \chi_{k_1^0}(1)\, \chi_{k_2^0}(2) \ldots \chi_{k_A^0}(A)$ is a typical product term of φ, one can (anti-) symmetrize φ_1 and place it in E. But $\sum t_\alpha \Lambda_\alpha$ in (54) is already symmetric, so that two symmetrizations are unnecessary; in other words, it suffices to write

$$E = \mathscr{E} + \eta \sum_\Pi (\pm 1)^\Pi \langle \Pi \varphi_1 | \sum t_\alpha \Lambda_\alpha | \varphi_1 \rangle \qquad (54')$$

where Π is a particle permutation, $1/\eta$ is the number of times $\Pi \varphi_1$ coincides with φ_1, and the sign $\pm$ is for Einstein-Bose or Fermi-Dirac statistics ($\eta = 1$ for Fermi-Dirac). Actually, not many of the permutations will contribute, for t_α, from the defining relations in (54), is clearly diagonal with respect to all particles but the pair α (P, annulling all states degenerate with φ, is itself diagonal); thus, for a typical term $t_\alpha G t_\beta$ in the expansion of $\sum t_\alpha \Lambda_\alpha$, only a Π which exchanges the four (or three) particles α, β can yield a non-vanishing result.

For example, the first-order energy correction now reads $E = \mathscr{E} + \sum_\alpha (1 - \tfrac{1}{2}\delta_{\varphi_1, \Pi_\alpha \varphi_1}) \langle \varphi_1 \pm \Pi_\alpha \varphi_1 | t_\alpha | \varphi_1 \rangle$, where Π_α interchanges the pair α. Since, operating on $\mathbf{x}_1, \mathbf{x}_2, E - \sum T_i$ in G becomes $\varepsilon_{k_1^0} + \varepsilon_{k_2^0} - T_1 - T_2$ to lowest order, the determination of $t_{12} | \chi_{k_1^0}(1)\, \chi_{k_2^0}(2) \rangle$ is a straightforward two-body problem, and the energy contributions in E are separate two-body energy shifts. For a large system, and only short-range translation-invariant two-body forces without localized bound states, the relative coordinate bound states are just standing waves in the enclosure. Since the spin-independent relative coordinate states of angular quantum number l are given asymptotically, from (10') by $\left(e^{2i\delta_l} e^{ikx} + (-1)^{l+1} e^{-ikx} \right)$ $\times P_l(\cos\theta)/x$, (scattered plus incoming) a relative coordinate box of radius R will support a standing wave for which $kR = \tfrac{1}{2}\pi l - \delta_l(k)$. This produces an energy shift, due to the interaction, of $(\hbar^2/\mu) k \Delta k$ (for $T_{\text{rel}} = p^2/2\mu$) or [8, 28]

$$\langle \varphi_{k_\alpha l} | t_\alpha | \varphi_{k_\alpha l} \rangle = -(\hbar^2/\mu) k_\alpha \delta_l(k_\alpha)/R \tag{56}$$

where $\mathbf{k}_\alpha \hbar$ is the relative momentum of the pair α in φ_1 and $\varphi_{kl}(\alpha)$ has relative momentum $k\hbar$, angular momentum $l\hbar$, the other indices being irrelevant. It follows without difficulty by a transformation to plane wave functions that (for isotropic t_α)

$$\langle \varphi_1 \pm \Pi_\alpha \varphi_1 | t_\alpha | \varphi_1 \rangle = -(2\pi\hbar^2/\mu V) \sum (2l+1)[1 \pm (-1)^l] \delta_l(k_\alpha)/k_\alpha \tag{56'}$$

for spin-independent product functions; V is the system volume. Inclusion of spin dependence is trivially accomplished.

From the particle scattering viewpoint, product wave functions are the basic entities. Their use as intermediate states, in Fermi-Dirac statistics, instead of the rather small number of antisymmetric states, affects the value of t_α and, for low excitation, adversely affects the rate of convergence of Ω in eq. (54). Much of the difficulty may be avoided by the observation that in eq. (47) for the many-body case no alteration occurs if P is chosen not only to project out the states degenerate with φ but also to select the antisymmetric component of what remains; choosing P in this manner (or its analog in Einstein-Bose statistics), each action of G in (54) picks out an antisymmetric intermediate state. Computationally, the proliferation of components due to antisymmetrization can be annoying, but essentially the same advantage can be obtained if we isolate one of the major characteristics of an antisymmetric state. Thus, we may simply require that P both project out the product states $\Pi[\chi_{k_1^0}(1) \ldots \chi_{k_A^0}(A)]$ of φ and retain only component states $\chi_{k_1}(1) \chi_{k_2}(2) \ldots \chi_{k_A}(A)$ for which all k_j are different [29]; we shall henceforth use this revised definition.

The revised definition of P and G certainly affects the value of t_α. To be specific, consider t_{12}, which has matrix elements between states $g(1, 2) \chi_{k_3}(3) \ldots \chi_{k_A}(A)$ and $f(1, 2) \chi_{k_3'}(3) \ldots \chi_{k_A'}(A)$ only if $k_3' = k_3, \ldots, k_A' = k_A$. Hence, if the common state $\chi_{k_3}(3) \ldots \chi_{k_A}(A)$ is understood, there remains only the operator relation on the space of particles 1 and 2

$$t_{12} = v_{12} + v_{12} G_{12} t_{12}$$

where
$$G_{12} = (E_{12} - T_1 - T_2)^{-1} P_{12} \tag{57}$$

and
$$E_{12} = E - \sum_3^A \varepsilon_{k_i}$$

Here P_{12} projects out any two-body state $\chi_{k_1}(1)\,\chi_{k_2}(2)$ for which either k_1 or k_2 coincides with one of $k_3, \ldots, k_A$, which is diagonal, $(k_1 = k_2)$ or for which k_1, k_2 coincide with k_1^0, k_2^0 and all other k_i with k_i^0. Except for processes of very high excitation, it is generally an excellent approximation [30] to say that P_{12} projects out any one-body χ_k which is contained in φ (the unperturbed Fermi sea). The superior form (57) cannot, unfortunately, due to P_{12}, be readily treated in the fashion of (56'), unless of course v_α is weak enough to permit the Born approximation. But (57) may be rewritten with effective potential $P_{12}\,v_{12}\,P_{12}$, which, because of the excluded momenta, has a very short-range effect on any wave function; one may take advantage of this fact. For further discussion, see Bethe and Gold-stone [42] and Gomes, Walecka, and Weisskopf [30].

6. *Coherent contributions*

Although the interaction potential v_{ij} may be totally without exchange character, nonetheless due to the (anti-) symmetry of the true wave function, an interpretation of the interaction as being between ordered or product states $|k_1 k_2 \ldots k_A\rangle \equiv \chi_{k_1}(1)\,\chi_{k_2}(2)\ldots\chi_{k_A}(A)$ requires the possibility of particle exchange. Since all elementary transitions are two-body, at most a two-body exchange can occur in a single "scattering". This is often preliminarily accounted for by the observation that the replacement of the two-body potential, defined by [7], [8]

$$\langle k_i' k_j' | v_{ij} | k_i k_j \rangle \rightarrow \tfrac{1}{2}\langle k_i' k_j' | v_{ij} | k_i k_j \rangle \pm \tfrac{1}{2}\langle k_i' k_j' | v_{ij} | k_j k_i \rangle \qquad (58)$$

($\pm$ for Einstein-Bose or Fermi-Dirac statistics), leaves the solution to the Schrödinger equation unaltered, while automatically including two-body exchange transitions.

Similarly, in introducing the concept of the coherent component of an operator between such product states, the omnipresent exchange must be included. Now, since there is no fixed distinction between scattering medium and scattered particle for a many-body bound state, but since the "unperturbed" particles are all independent except for statistics, an appropriate definition of the coherent component is that it only includes terms for which at most one particle changes its state, and may change its label as well. Concentrating in the rest of this section on Fermi-Dirac systems of low excitation, for which coherent scattering so constructed should predominate: If S is a two-body operator, diagonal on all particles but i, j, we would define

$$
\begin{aligned}
\langle k_i' k_j' | S_c | k_i k_j \rangle \equiv & [(\delta_{k_i' k_i} + \delta_{k_j' k_j} - \delta_{k_i' k_i} \delta_{k_j' k_j}) \\
& + (\delta_{k_i' k_j} + \delta_{k_j' k_i} - \delta_{k_i' k_j} \delta_{k_j' k_i})] \langle k_i' k_j' | S | k_i k_j \rangle
\end{aligned}
\tag{59}
$$

(omitting the common states), with analogous expressions for multi-body operators. If S happens to have no matrix elements for the change of just one particle state, e.g., if the single-particle states are separately momentum eigenfunctions and S conserves total momentum and any necessary discrete quantities, then eq. (59) reduces to

$$
\langle k_i' k_j' | S_c | k_i k_j \rangle = \delta_{k_i' k_i} \delta_{k_j' k_j} \langle k_i k_j | S | k_i k_j \rangle + \delta_{k_i' k_j} \delta_{k_j' k_i} \langle k_j k_i | S | k_i k_j \rangle
\tag{59'}
$$

the diagonal and exchange-diagonal part of S in χ_k representation. If S fails only to conserve discrete quantities like spin, eq. (59') may nonetheless be chosen by definition, leaving specific spin flip effects as lesser corrections.

We are now prepared to improve the perturbation treatment (54) by isolating a significant portion of the interaction potential at the outset, solving with its imposition alone, and applying the remainder as perturbation. Suppose in general that this "model" potential has the form $\sum V_i$, where each V_i is a one-body potential. If the intermediate Hamiltonian

$$
H' = \sum T_i + \sum V_i
\tag{60}
$$

is introduced, its eigenstates may be constructed from the one-body states $\chi_k'(x_i)$:

$$
(T_i + V_i) \chi_k'(i) = \varepsilon_k' \chi_k'(i)
\tag{61}
$$

By diagonal (and coherent) we shall mean diagonal (and coherent) with respect to these χ'. A typical V_i may be a shell model potential for a finite nucleus, a coordinate-independent effective mass type of correction for a uniform system, or a self-consistent coordinate and momentum-dependent potential for a general non-uniform system; in the first two cases, the χ' are fixed at once without a self-consistency requirement.

Now commencing with a state and energy satisfying

$$
(\sum T_i + \bar{V}_c) \psi_c = E_c \psi_c
\tag{62}
$$

where, in order that ψ_c be constructed from the χ'_k of (61), $\bar{V}_c$ and $\sum V_i$ need only coincide on ψ_c,

$$\bar{V}_c \psi_c = \sum V_i \psi_c \tag{63}$$

the turning on of the perturbation proceeds precisely as in (54). That is, $\sum T_i \varphi = \mathscr{E}\varphi$ is replaced by (62), and we must be able to write $\bar{V}_c$ as the sum of two-index terms, say

$$\bar{V}_c = \sum u_{c\alpha} \tag{64}$$

The decomposition is thus far any which suits our fancy, e.g., $u_{cij} = (V_i + V_j)/(A-1)$ will do. Then, $\psi = \Omega' \psi_c$ satisfies $(\sum T_i + \sum v_\alpha)\psi = E\psi$, with perturbation from an effective medium:

$$G' = (E - \sum T_i - \sum V_i)^{-1} P' \tag{65a}$$

$$t'_\alpha = (v_\alpha - u_{c\alpha}) + (v_\alpha - u_{c\alpha}) G' t'_\alpha \tag{65b}$$

$$\Omega' = 1 + \sum G' t'_\alpha \Lambda'_\alpha \tag{65c}$$

$$\Lambda'_\alpha = 1 + \sum_{\beta \neq \alpha} G' t'_\beta \Lambda'_\beta \tag{65d}$$

$$E = E_c + \sum \langle \psi_c | t'_\alpha \Lambda'_\alpha | \psi_c \rangle \tag{65e}$$

P' serving to project out both ψ_c and doubly occupied one-body states χ'_k. Alternatively, one may perturb both by two-body reaction operators and one-body effective potentials, thus dispensing with the decomposition (64).

For a physical situation in which coherent virtual scattering is predominant, a rational choice for the V_i and $u_{c\alpha}$ is again one which removes all coherence from the perturbation operator t'_α. In fact, if this is so, it is easy to see that both first- and second-order perturbations vanish in $E = E_c + \langle \psi_c | \sum t'_\alpha + \sum_{\beta \neq \alpha} t'_\alpha G' t'_\beta + \ldots | \psi_c \rangle$, because t'_{ij} must change both states χ'_{k_i} and χ'_{k_j}, while G' vanishes whenever two-particle states coincide. Once more, as in (34), eq. (65b) can be solved as $t'_\alpha = (1 - v_\alpha G')^{-1} v_\alpha (1 - G' u_{c\alpha}) - u_{c\alpha} - (1 - v_\alpha G')^{-1} G' t'_\alpha$ and $t'_{c\alpha} = 0$ approximated by $u_{c\alpha} = [(1 - v_\alpha G')^{-1} v_\alpha]_c (1 - G' u_{c\alpha})$. Let us further note that for a large system, $\langle \bar{V}_c \rangle \sim E_c - \mathscr{E}$ will vary as particle number A (i.e., energy per particle depends only upon intensive parameters such as density), $u_{c\alpha}$ as $1/A$, and correspondingly (if no elements of G' increase as A) reduce the expression for $u_{c\alpha}$ to $[(1 - v_\alpha G')^{-1} v_\alpha]_c$. Hence, $u_{c\alpha}$ is the coherent part of $u_\alpha = (1 - v_\alpha G')^{-1} v_\alpha$, or

$$u_\alpha = v_\alpha + v_\alpha G' u_\alpha \tag{66a}$$

$$G' = (E - \sum T_i - \sum V_i)^{-1} P' \tag{66b}$$

u_α then simply represents the reaction operator modified by propagation in the medium.

We have assumed from the start that $\sum u_{c\alpha} = \sum V_i$ on that state ψ_c whose perturbation concerns us. How closely this holds as an *operator* relation determines how appropriate the same intermediate Hamiltonian is for obtaining other states as well, and also how effectively coherent perturbation terms are eliminated. An identity could easily be maintained if we were willing to allow the one-body potentials V_i diagonal dependence on other particles, but this would necessitate an extremely involved self-consistent procedure. Instead, let us simply note from (66) that, acting on any product term in ψ_c, u_{ij} is fully determined by k_i, k_j, since the only diagonal dependence of u_{ij} on other particles is via the factor $E - \sum_{n \neq i,j}(T_n + V_n) = (E - E_c) + \varepsilon'_{k_i} + \varepsilon'_{k_j}$; thus, u_{ij} acts as a pure two-body operator on ψ_c. Further, from definition (59), $\sum u_{c\alpha}$ is then a sum of one-body operators with additional diagonal dependence; upon application to ψ_c, this dependence reduces to a summation over the Fermi sea of states occupied in ψ_c. The result is that we may choose

$$\langle k'|V|k \rangle = \sum_l (\langle k'l|u|kl \rangle - \langle lk'|u|kl \rangle) \\ - \tfrac{1}{2} \sum_l (\langle kl|u|kl \rangle - \langle lk|u|kl \rangle) \delta_{k'k} \tag{67}$$

where l runs over the Fermi sea, and k belongs to it. Equation (67) has the form of a Hartree-Fock potential, together with its energy shift. The matrix element, for k an unoccupied state, is at our disposal, but if (67) is followed, then V becomes Hermitian.

Equations (61), (66), (67) represent a self-consistent process for the determination of u_α, basically a Hartree-type treatment for particle pairs in a particle medium. Relation (66) may be treated as in eq. (57). That is, considering u_{12} for definiteness, u_{12} is [via eq. (66b)] diagonal on particles 3 through A, which enter only via their total energy. Thus if the state to the right, upon which u_{12} is to act, has energy denoted by E_r, and particles 1, 2 are in states k_{1r} k_{2r}, one may write

$$\langle k_1 k_2 | G' | k_1 k_2 \rangle = [(E - E_r) + (\varepsilon'_{k_{1r}} - \varepsilon'_{k_1}) + (\varepsilon'_{k_{2r}} - \varepsilon'_{k_2})]^{-1} P' \tag{68}$$

and (66a) becomes a pure two-body relation, with implicit dependence on $E-E_r$. It is again not of the usual reaction operator form, and of course not experimentally determinable from two-body interactions, for P' also includes P_F, projecting out any state in the original Fermi sea. Equivalently, in the form $P_F u_\alpha = P_F v_\alpha + (P_F v_\alpha)(\ )^{-1} P_{12} P_F u_\alpha$, a highly non-local potential $P_F v_\alpha$ must be used. Further, a general two-body problem (without translation invariance) is a quite difficult one, in essentials like a three-body problem with ignorable center of mass.

In the special case in which the system is uniform and the interaction v_α is invariant to translation and any necessary discrete operations (or u_c defined to be diagonal on these), the V_i themselves become diagonal. Hence the self-consistency requirement on the states becomes evanescent, the $\chi'_k(i) = \chi_k(i)$ are simply the unperturbed free particle (with, e.g., periodic boundary conditions) states, $E_c = \mathscr{E} + \langle \varphi | \vec{V}_c | \varphi \rangle$ and only a translation-invariant two-body scattering problem is to be solved. The comparative simplicity of the computations [29], [42] recommends this model when feasible. In particular, a large closed-shell nucleus is not too far from a bounded uniform fluid. For such a system, then, rather than relinquish the simple plane wave states of unbounded or periodic boundary conditions, one may observe [12], [16] that a principal effect of restricting a particle to a region of volume V and surface area S is that the density of states in momentum space changes roughly to

$$\mathcal{N}(k)\,d^3k = [V/(2\pi)^3 - (S/64\pi^2 k)]\,d^3k \qquad (69)$$

One may then hope that much of the surface effect on such a ground state energy will be simulated by modifying the one-body summations according to eq. (69), with the states remaining uniform in the volume V. A much more detailed and less ad hoc alternative which centers about intermediate computation of t on the assumption of local homogeneity is now under intensive investigation [18].

Finally, after determination of the effective potential $\vec{V}_c$, the corresponding "unperturbed" state ψ_c and pair potential u_α, the many-body problem can be solved by the modified perturbation expansion of (65). However, t'_α is not quite totally incoherent, so that leading terms in the perturbation series do not vanish as originally intended. This may be remedied at the expense of some error by repeating the large A approximation which led to (38b); thus, we now consider the replacement of eqs. (65) by (67) together with †

$$\Omega' = 1 + \sum G' t'_\alpha \Lambda'_\alpha$$
$$\Lambda'_\alpha = 1 + \sum_{\beta \neq \alpha} G' t'_\beta \Lambda'_\beta \tag{70}$$

where $\quad t'_\alpha = u_\alpha - u_{c\alpha} \qquad u_\alpha = v_\alpha + v_\alpha G' u_\alpha$

$$G' = (E - \sum T_i - \sum V_i)^{-1} P'$$

We seek the error produced by the employment of eqs. (70). The procedure of eqs. (39)–(43), applied to an initially unspecified $\bar{\psi}_c$, may be imitated step by step; the only modifications are that eqs. (41) and (42) are replaced by

$$\sum (v_\alpha - u_{c\alpha}) \Omega' = \sum [(1 - u_{c\alpha} G') t'_\alpha - v_\alpha G' u_{c\alpha}] \Lambda'_\alpha$$
$$(E - \sum T_i - \sum V_i) \Omega' = (E - \sum T_i - \sum V_i) + P' \sum t'_\alpha \Lambda'_\alpha \tag{71}$$

so that finally

$$(E - \sum T_i - \sum v_\alpha) \Omega' \bar{\psi}_c - (E - \sum T_i - \sum V_i) \bar{\psi}_c$$
$$= (\sum V_i - \sum u_{c\alpha}) \Omega' \bar{\psi}_c - (1 - P') \sum t'_\alpha \Lambda'_\alpha \bar{\psi}_c \tag{72}$$
$$+ \sum (v_\alpha G' u_{c\alpha} + u_{c\alpha} G' t'_\alpha) \Lambda'_\alpha \bar{\psi}_c$$

Now to assess the degree of approximation, choose $\bar{\psi}_c$ such that $\Omega' \bar{\psi}_c$ coincides with the correct wave function ψ: $E\Omega' \bar{\psi}_c = (\sum T_i + \sum v_\alpha) \Omega' \bar{\psi}_c$. According to (72), $\bar{\psi}_c$ must then satisfy

$$[\sum T_i + \sum V_i + (1 - P') \sum t'_\alpha \Lambda'_\alpha - \sum (v_\alpha G' u_{c\alpha} + u_{c\alpha} G' t'_\alpha) \Lambda'_\alpha$$
$$+ (\sum u_{c\alpha} - \sum V_i) \Omega'] \bar{\psi}_c = E \bar{\psi}_c \tag{73a}$$

But since $(1 - P') \sum t'_\alpha \Lambda'_\alpha |\psi_c\rangle = \langle \psi_c | \sum t'_\alpha \Lambda'_\alpha |\psi_c\rangle \psi_c$, we have

$$[\sum T_i + \sum V_i + (1 - P') \sum t'_\alpha \Lambda'_\alpha] \psi_c = (E_c + \langle \sum t'_\alpha \Lambda'_\alpha \rangle) \psi_c \tag{73b}$$

$\langle \; \rangle$ denoting an average in the model state ψ_c. To first order perturbation, the energy E of (73a) then becomes

$$E = E_c + \langle \sum t'_\alpha \Lambda'_\alpha \rangle - \langle \sum u_{c\alpha} G' t'_\alpha \Lambda'_\alpha \rangle - \langle \sum v_\alpha G' u_{c\alpha} \Lambda'_\alpha \rangle$$
$$E_c = \langle \sum u_\alpha \rangle \tag{74}$$

For particle number A approaching ∞ at constant density, etc., we have noted that $u_{c\alpha} \sim 1/A$; one similarly expects u_α, $t'_\alpha \sim 1/A$,

† To agree with Brueckner's notation, let $\bar{V}_c \to V_c$, $u_{c\alpha} \to t_{c\alpha}$, $G' \to 1/e$, $\Lambda'_\alpha \to F_\alpha$, $\Omega' \to F$, $t'_\alpha \to I_\alpha$.

while Λ'_α, $G' \sim 1$. Hence the second correction term in eq. (74) should be roughly constant as $A \to \infty$ and so yield a vanishing energy per particle; the third correction term should behave similarly (on expanding v_α in a power series in u_α). Numerically [29], these corrections are quite small for extended nuclear matter of even moderate mass number (and higher order perturbation terms even smaller). As $A \to \infty$, there remains only the "unperturbed" model correction of (65e) or (73b); it indeed varies as A, although in idealized nuclear systems which have been investigated [14], [29], its relative contribution has turned out to be fairly small, as befits an expansion starting at third order. (Of course, while true for energy, this may not hold for other expectation values.) Consequently, one can for example eliminate one self-consistency problem by replacing E by E_c in the propagator G'; when properly interpreted, as in Secs. B3, and B4, this becomes not an approximation but a superior expansion method.

7. *Field theoretic methods*

An apparent drawback of the particle approach to the many-body problem is that the consequences of quantum statistics must be eliminated by various artifices in order that the particle "scattering" picture be useful. These artifices — the use of only a typical product state as initial state, the prohibition of repeated one-body intermediate states in the Fermi-Dirac case — are in fact completely effective. The physical picture however becomes a complicated one, with, e.g., the considerable interparticle correlations which are automatically present in a Boson or Fermion system being continually lost and reinserted in the perturbation calculation, and considerable excess verbiage is required. Envisaging the "scattering" to be between system-wide waves (e.g., symmetrized wave functions) rather than between particles (product wave functions) suffices to rectify the situation. The collective description thus implied will be treated in Part Three by methods specifically developed for collective motion. We indicate here how the formalism of second quantization, while identical both in substance and in explicit computational steps with the previous exposition, is intrinsically suited for analysis of multiple scattering effects in quantum many-body systems.

If a many-body system is characterized by one-body (kinetic

and potential energies) T_i and two-body interaction potentials v_{ij}, then if the $\chi_k(i)$ are a complete set of one-body states, taken for convenience as eigenstates of T_i, the system may be represented by the field Hamiltonian

$$H = \sum T_k \eta_k^* \eta_k + \tfrac{1}{2} \sum v_{kl,pq} \eta_k^* \eta_l^* \eta_q \eta_p$$
$$= T + \tfrac{1}{2} \sum \bar{v}_{kl,pq} \tag{75}$$

where the pure numbers T_k and $v_{kl,pq}$ are defined by

$$T_k = \langle \chi_k(i) | T_i | \chi_k(i) \rangle$$
$$v_{kl,pq} = \langle \chi_k(i) \chi_l(j) | v_{ij} | \chi_p(i) \chi_q(j) \rangle \tag{76}$$

and the non-zero anti-commutators (for Fermi-Dirac)or commutators (for Einstein-Bose) of the annihilation, η_k, and creation operators η_k^* satisfy

$$[\eta_k, \eta_l^*]_\pm = \delta_{kl} \tag{77}$$

Clearly, we may assume, as in eq. (58), that $v_{kl,pq} = \mp v_{kl,qp}$ and hence that $\bar{v}_{kl,pq} = \bar{v}_{kl,qp}$; we shall do so. Since H commutes with the total particle number operator $\mathcal{N} = \sum \eta_k^* \eta_k$, the total particle number may indeed be taken as fixed. Here $\mathcal{N}_k = \eta_k^* \eta_k$ represents the number of (undesignated) particles in state χ_k; customarily, one works in a representation in which all $\mathcal{N}_k$ are diagonal, so that the states of the system are specified as $\Phi = \sum_{\{N_k\}} \Phi(\dots N_k \dots) | \dots \mathcal{N}_k \dots \rangle$.

The fundamental entities which are "scattered" in this approach are the composite states or undesignated particles χ_k and not the individual particles; thus the term $\eta_k^* \eta_l^* \eta_q \eta_p$ signifies the scattering of states p, q into states k, l. This is, from the state scattering viewpoint, a four-body interaction, with each of the "bodies" p, q, k, l changing its quantum index (= occupation number, or excitation), and may be treated accordingly, using a four-body reaction operator. The preceding is more formal than physical, and we may obtain the reaction operator in precisely the same fashion as in the particle picture: Consider the object to be scattered (in this case, a pair p, q) as initially existing by itself in the system, and sum up all scattering processes it can then undergo. Now in the particle picture, the interaction of a particle pair i, j alone can produce no other particles, and so only the portion v_{ij} of the total potential enters into determination of the scattering matrix; however, for the initial state pair

p, q in the wave picture, other pairs will be produced so that the full potential is required.

Thus, p, q may be acted on by $\frac{1}{2}G(\bar{v}_{p'q',pq}+\bar{v}_{p'q',qp}) = G\bar{v}_{p'q',pq}$ to produce $p'q'$, and this in turn by $G\bar{v}_{p''q'',p'q'}$ to produce $p'q''$, and so forth. The net effect may be expressed most easily by saying that the scattering factors must matrix multiply with respect to their indices. Hence, the reaction matrix for determination of the state ψ from the interactionless state Φ is given by

$$\bar{t}_{kl,pq} = \bar{v}_{kl,pq} + \sum_{rs} \bar{v}_{kl,rs} G\bar{t}_{rs,pq}$$

$$\text{where} \quad G = (E-T)^{-1}P \tag{78}$$

or equivalently by

$$\bar{t}_{kl,pq} = \eta_k^* \eta_l^* \bar{t}_{kl,pq} \eta_q \eta_p$$

$$\text{and} \quad \bar{t}_{kl,pq} = v_{kl,pq} + \sum_{rs} v_{kl,rs} \eta_r \eta_s G\eta_s^* \eta_r^* \bar{t}_{rs,pq} \tag{79}$$

where P annuls the state Φ. Here $t_{kl,pq}$ is not a number but rather a diagonal operator; the corresponding non-diagonal four-index operator is uniformly indicated by a bar. The multiple scattering solution for the bound state wave matrix Ω of $\Psi = \Omega\Phi$ then proceeds as in Section A5, and we readily verify that

$$\Omega = 1 + \frac{1}{2}G \sum t_{kl,rs} \Lambda_{rs}$$

$$\text{with} \quad \Lambda_{rs} = \Omega - G \sum t_{rs,pq} \Lambda_{pq}$$

$$= 1 + \frac{1}{2}G \sum_{kl \neq rs, sr} t_{kl,pq} \Lambda_{pq} \tag{80}$$

$$\text{and} \quad E = \mathscr{E} + \frac{1}{2}\langle\Phi| \sum t_{kl,pq} \Lambda_{pq}|\Phi\rangle$$

with no spurious degeneracy ever arising, although real degeneracy will generally arise in all but the ground state.

Improvement of a perturbation expansion for eqs. (80) is again to be obtained by preliminary accounting of coherent terms, the appropriate definition of which depends upon the system under consideration. For a highly excited system (above the independent-particle ground state), Pauli principle restrictions in intermediate states are of little effect, so that singling out one class of transitions is not of great value; of course, in this case, the wide spread of unperturbed one-particle energies reduces the higher order perturbation terms through increase of typical denominators. For a weakly excited Fermi system, most of the one-particle states of the Fermi sphere are occupied in any intermediate state, so that the previous definition of the coherent part of an operator as that which allows at most one state to change does pick up the major contribution. Thus, with $f_{mn,rs}$ diagonal,

$$\text{if} \quad \bar{f}_{kl,pq} = \eta_k^* \eta_l^* f_{kl,pq} \eta_q \eta_p$$
$$\text{then} \quad f_{ckl,pq} = \delta(kl; pq) f_{kl,pq} \tag{81}$$

where $\delta(kl; pq) = 1 - (1-\delta_{ql})(1-\delta_{qk})(1-\delta_{pl})(1-\delta_{pk})$ vanishes unless at least one final state coincides with an initial state, and then is unity; if $\bar{f}$ conserves momentum, and Φ as well as the χ_k are momentum eigenstates, one appends conservation of discrete variables to (81) and so defines

$$f_{ckl,pq} = (\delta_{kp}\delta_{lq} + \delta_{kq}\delta_{lp}) f_{kl,pq} \tag{81'}$$

For a weakly excited (condensed) Bose system, on the other hand, most one-particle state components are in the ground state, say χ_0, and we would do well to define the coherent or principal scattering part by the condition [31] that at least one initial state and one final state be χ_0:

$$f_{ckl,pq} = (\delta_{ko} + \delta_{lo} - \delta_{ko}\delta_{lo})(\delta_{po} + \delta_{qo} - \delta_{po}\delta_{qo}) f_{kl,pq} \tag{82}$$

with only components of the form $f_{ko,ko}$ appearing in the analog to (81'). Definitions (81) and (82) satisfy the important condition that the coherent part of a sum of two-body operators be (subsuming diagonal parts) a sum of one-body operators.

Now one can proceed as in the particle analysis. For either Fermi-Dirac or Einstein-Bose systems, the effective coherent potential is again defined as in (63), with modified propagator and reaction matrix as in (66), and is thereby a self-consistent external potential patterned after eq. (67). The solution for the modified Hamiltonian may then be expanded exactly perturbationwise, or approximately as in eqs. (70), (74), with analogous accompanying remarks. Thus, using (74) as $A \to \infty$, the two leading terms in the perturbation energy above that of the model state vanish not only for a Fermion ground state, but by virtue of (82), for a Boson ground state as well. A difference is that, here, the accounting procedure is somewhat simplified over that involved in the particle scattering approach, where both particle number and state are retained. Aspects of the second quantization treatment will be further considered in Sect. B4.

B. Further Developments

1. *The resolvent operator*

As an alternative approach to the bound state problem for the Hamiltonian H, let us consider the total Green's function

$$W(E) = (E-H)^{-1} \qquad (83)$$

a function of the complex variable E; except for sign, this is the resolvent operator, much used by mathematicians [32] in their investigations of spectra of linear transformations. $W(E)$ is seen to be non-singular except at the eigenvalues E_s of H, which may indeed be recognized as the poles of $W(E)$. Use of the identity

$$W(E)\,W(E') = (1/E'-E)(W(E)-W(E')) \qquad (84)$$

facilitates proof that

$$Q_{\{m\}} = (2\pi i)^{-1} \oint_{\{E_m\}} W(E)\,dE \qquad (85)$$

is the projection onto the linear space generated by the eigenvectors $\{\bar{\psi}_m\}$, the integration enclosing only the poles $\{E_m\}$, and it follows that

$$f(H) = (2\pi i)^{-1} \oint f(E)\,W(E)\,dE, \qquad (86)$$

the integration enclosing all poles; eqs. (84), (85) hold as well for multiple poles (degenerate eigenvalues).

Since we envisage only prosaic discrete spectra, and are quite content to dispense with rigor, rather elementary matrix methods will here replace methods of complex analysis.
If

$$\begin{aligned} H &= H_F + V \\ H_F \varphi_m &= \mathscr{E}_m \varphi_m \end{aligned} \qquad (87)$$

we wish to perturb the bound states φ_m of H_F to the corresponding normalized bound states $\bar{\psi}_m$ of H. We first examine the form of the singularities of $W(E)$; clearly

$$\langle \varphi_m | W(E) | \varphi_n \rangle = \sum_r \langle \varphi_m | \bar{\psi}_r \rangle \langle \bar{\psi}_r | \varphi_n \rangle / (E - E_r) \qquad (88)$$

so that as E approaches a non-degenerate eigenvalue, say E_s, the matrix element approaches $\langle\varphi_m|\bar{\psi}_s\rangle\langle\bar{\psi}_s|\varphi_n\rangle/(E-E_s)$, proportional to the projection onto $\bar{\psi}_s$, but with a proportionality factor of infinity. A simple way of making eq. (88) finite at its poles is to divide by a quantity which itself has a pole $1/(E-E_s)$. In particular, let subscript d denote the diagonal part in the φ_m representation:

$$\langle\varphi_m|F_d|\varphi_n\rangle = \langle\varphi_m|F|\varphi_m\rangle\delta_{mn} \tag{89}$$

a notation which, for degenerate $\{\varphi_m\}$, depends upon the particular sequence of $\{\psi_m\}$ chosen, and define

$$\Omega(E) = W(E)\,W_d(E)^{-1} \tag{90}$$

it is clear that, if E_s is non-degenerate, then as $E \to E_s$,

$$\lim \quad \langle\varphi_m|\Omega(E)|\varphi_n\rangle = \langle\varphi_m|\bar{\psi}_s\rangle/\langle\varphi_n|\bar{\psi}_s\rangle \tag{91}$$

Thus,

$$\Omega(E_s)\varphi_s = \bar{\psi}_s/\langle\varphi_s|\bar{\psi}_s\rangle = \psi_s \tag{92}$$

normalized so that $\langle\varphi_s|\psi_s\rangle = 1$. Hence $\Omega(E_s)$ is identical in its action on φ_s as Ω of Sec. A 5, although not in its action on anything else. The relation of $\Omega(E)$ to the Brillouin-Wigner Ω [eqs. (9a), (51)] is most directly obtained by defining, for non-degenerate φ_n,

$$\langle m|\Omega_n^B(E)|n\rangle = \langle m|1+(E-H_F)^{-1}P_n V+[(E-H_F)^{-1}P_n V]^2+...|n\rangle \tag{93}$$

where P_n projects out φ_n, and noting that the index n is present exactly once in the matrix expansion of each term of (93). Hence, multiplying by $\langle n|W_d(E)|n\rangle = \langle n|(E-H_F)^{-1}+(E-H_F)^{-1}V(E-H_F)^{-1}+\ldots|n\rangle$ which necessarily has an index n on the left, we obtain simply $\langle m|(E-H_F)^{-1}+(E-H_F)^{-1}V(E-H_F)^{-1}+\ldots|n\rangle$ or $\langle m|W(E)|n\rangle$, proving the identity of $\Omega_n^B(E)$ and $\Omega(E)$ of eq. (90), acting on $|n\rangle$.

To locate the eigenvalues E_s in the context of this presentation, we recognize them as the poles of $W_d(E)$. Now if

$$t(E) = V\Omega(E) \tag{94}$$

we have from $(E-H_F)W(E) = 1+VW(E)$,

$$(E-H_F)\,\Omega(E)\,W_d(E) = 1+t(E)\,W_d(E) \tag{95}$$

taking the diagonal part of eq. (95) and noting that $\Omega_d(E) = 1$, it follows that $(E-H_F)\,W_d(E) = 1+t_d(E)\,W_d(E)$, whence

$$W_d(E) = (E-H_F-t_d(E))^{-1} \tag{96}$$

In other words, applying (96) to φ_s, the eigenvalues are characterized by

$$E_s = \mathscr{E}_s + \langle \varphi_s | t_d(E_s) | \varphi_s \rangle$$
$$t(E) = V\Omega(E) \tag{97}$$

which is of course the same condition as eq. (50). Thus far, degeneracy of the unperturbed set $\{\varphi_m\}$ causes no difficulty; any normalized linear combination of degenerate φ_s will certainly serve equally well in (97).

2. A general method for bound states

We proceed further, along the lines of a very formal development due to Riesenfeld and Watson [8]. The observation is made that if $\varDelta$ is any diagonal operator, then writing $H = (H_F + \varDelta) + (V - \varDelta)$, the unperturbed eigenspace is unchanged, while allowing a preliminary subtraction of some "optimal" diagonal part of V. This is recognized as the process which was employed previously with respect to coherent components in uniform many-body systems, and $\varDelta$ is the optical model potential; the generalization of $\varDelta$ to one-body sums, more appropriate for non-uniform many-body systems, will not be considered at this time. It is convenient to introduce

$$M(E) = W(E)(E - H_F - \varDelta) \tag{98}$$

again we have

$$\Omega(E) = M(E) M_d(E)^{-1} \tag{99}$$

From (98), we obtain by simple algebra the basic relation

$$M(E) = 1 + (E - H_F - \varDelta)^{-1}(V - \varDelta) M(E) \tag{100}$$

and the corresponding perturbation expansion

$$M(E) = 1 + G(E)(V - \varDelta) + G(E)(V - \varDelta)G(E)(V - \varDelta) + \cdots$$
$$G(E) = (E - H_F - \varDelta)^{-1} \tag{101}$$

to which (97) is again to be appended.

Any approximate computation of $\Omega(E)$ as the quotient in (99), followed by the limit $E \to E_s$, is subject to considerable uncertainty. In the special case, however, in which $\varDelta$ may be chosen such that $M_d(E) = 1$ on the selected unperturbed state φ_s, we see from (98) that $E - H_F - \varDelta$ must vanish on the same state, and from (99) that $M(E_s)\varphi_s$ is an eigenstate; hence if $\quad \langle s|M(E_s)|s\rangle \quad$ is finite

then $\quad E_s = \mathscr{E}_s + \langle s|\Delta|s\rangle$

$$G(E_s) = [\langle s|H_F+\Delta|s\rangle - (H_F+\Delta)]^{-1} \tag{102}$$

and $\quad \psi = \text{constant} \quad M(E_s)|s\rangle$

The simple result is due to the absence of energy shift from $H_F+\Delta$ to H. Even if (102) does not hold, one can directly convert (99), (101), via the process of eq. (93), to the corresponding Brillouin-Wigner form [treating degeneracy of the unperturbed set as in (52), (52′)]. There are a number of ways of choosing Δ to improve the convergence of the perturbation series under varying conditions. Thus, with $\Delta = E_s - \mathscr{E}_s$, the Rayleigh-Schrödinger expansion is in principle obtained; an E-dependent change of constant Δ yields the Eden-Francis form [33], and a panoramic state generalization, $\Delta = \sum(E_p - \mathscr{E}_p)Q_p$, is due to Tanaka and Fukuda [34], [35]. In an ingenious approach used by Swiatecki [36] in the nuclear problem, with $H_F = \sum p_i^2/2m$, Δ is the sum of one-body terms: $\sum f(p_i)$, with n parameters in f (e.g., two for constant potential plus effective mass) adjusted to annul the leading terms in the expansion of the energy of n given states.

As mentioned in Sect. A2, if one is interested in a specific state, say ψ_s emanating from φ_s, a relation of the form (101) is sufficient but not at all necessary. Indeed

$$M(E) = 1 + (E-H_F-\Delta)^{-1}(PVM(E)) \tag{103}$$

will suffice, contingent only upon the satisfying of

$$(1-P)[VM(E_s)]|s\rangle = \Delta M(E_s)|s\rangle \tag{104}$$

here P is a *linear operator on operators*. To verify (103), multiply on the left by $E-H_F-\Delta$ and apply to φ_s; we have

$$(E-H_F-V)M(E)|s\rangle = [\Delta M(E)-(1-P)(VM(E)]|s\rangle$$
$$+(E-H_F-\Delta)|s\rangle \tag{105}$$

Thus, $M(E)|s\rangle$ satisfies its proper equation (see eq. (98)) as $E \to E_s$, if (104) holds. We shall restrict our consideration to the special case in which

$$\langle s|P(VM(E))|s\rangle = 0 \tag{106}$$

It follows from (103) that $\langle s|M(E)|s\rangle = 1$, so that $M(E) = \Omega(E)$ is the wave operator. Further, eq. (105) then implies that $\langle s|E_s - H_F - \Delta|s\rangle = 0$, or

$$\psi_s = \Omega(E_s)\,\varphi_s$$
$$E_s = \mathscr{E}_s + \langle s|\Delta|s\rangle \tag{107}$$

as in (102) — the optical model energy is that of the real system. Due to the form of P, the term $\langle s|(E-H_F-\Delta)^{-1}|s\rangle$ will fortunately not appear in the expansion of (103).

The Brillouin-Wigner expansion is obtained by choosing $P = P_s$, the projection off φ_s, so that [from (104) and (107)] $\langle m|\Delta|m\rangle = 0$ for $m \neq s$ and $E_s = \mathscr{E}_s + \langle s|V\Omega(E_s)|s\rangle$; it may be regarded as the prototype for eqs. (103)–(107). The formulation in general is a very powerful one, and it is not *necessary* that $P|s\rangle = 0$. In applications, one will choose P to improve the convergence of the perturbation expansion of (103):

$$\Omega(E) = 1 + G(E)P(V) + G(E)P[VG(E)P(V)]$$
$$\qquad + G(E)P\{VG(E)P[VG(E)P(V)]\} + \ldots \tag{108}$$
$$G(E) = (E - H_F - \Delta)^{-1}$$

and then determine the diagonal Δ from eq. (104) which, multiplied by $\langle m|$, yields

$$\langle m|\Delta|m\rangle = \langle m|(1-P)[V\Omega(E_s)]|s\rangle / \langle m|\Omega(E_s)|s\rangle \tag{109}$$

the case $m = s$ does not occur in the expansion, but serves to evaluate the energy in eq. (107).

As an example (Feenberg [37]), we may define $P(VF)$ by the condition that whenever F is a polynomial of V's and of diagonal operators, then $\langle m|P(VF)|n\rangle = \langle m|V\bar{F}|n\rangle$, where $\bar{F}$ retains only those matrix elements in the expansion of F which do not include the state m. The resulting elimination of matrix elements which are superfluous from the secular determinant viewpoint may be expected to speed convergence of (108). To determine the appropriate Δ, we note that in (108), the iterated factors P now require all intermediate states in each term to be different; hence $\langle m|(1-P)(V\Omega)|s\rangle$ contains those terms in which precisely one intermediate state is m. It follows as in the discussion of eq. (93) that

$$\langle m|(1-P)(V\Omega)|s\rangle = \langle m|V\Omega|m\rangle\langle m|\Omega|s\rangle \tag{110}$$

and so from condition (109),

$$\Delta = [V\Omega(E_s)]_d \tag{111}$$

valid for any s. Since (106) is clearly satisfied, then eq. (107) holds true and $E_s = \mathscr{E}_s + \langle s|V\Omega(E_s)|s\rangle$.

The problem may also arise of selecting a P to accommodate a convenient choice of Δ. Thus, if we wish to obtain the Rayleigh-Schrödinger expansion, Δ must be a constant, the energy shift in state s. Now if $\langle m|\Delta|m\rangle$ of (109) is to be independent of m, it is clear that $1-P$ should insert only s-dependent terms; indeed, suppose [15] that P, applied to a product of V's and diagonal operators, subtracts out all s state expectations which start from the left:

$$(1-P)(VD_1VD_2VD_3\ldots V) = \langle s|V|s\rangle D_1VD_2\ldots V$$
$$+\langle s|VD_1V|s\rangle D_2V\ldots V+\ldots+\langle s|VD_1V\ldots V|s\rangle \tag{112}$$

Then $\Omega(E)$ of (108) contains terms in which internal expectations are taken in all possible ways (since $\langle s|\ldots|s\rangle$ is trivially a diagonal operator, there will be expectations within expectations as well), for each must start at some point; the sign of a given term is -1 for an odd number of expectations, $+1$ if even. It is apparent that $\langle s|P(V\Omega(E)|s\rangle = 0$, since for every term $\mathscr{T}$ in $P(V\Omega)$, $\langle s|\mathscr{T}|s\rangle$ also appears in $P(V\Omega)$ with a minus sign; thus (107) is valid. Finally, and crucially,

$$\langle m|(1-P)(V\Omega(E)|s\rangle/\langle m|\Omega(E)|s\rangle = \langle s|V\Omega(E)|s\rangle \tag{113}$$

since each expectation on the left of $(1-P)(V\Omega)$ must be accompanied on the right by the full set of Ω. Hence, from (109), $\Delta = $ constant $= E_s - \mathscr{E}_s$, and

$$G = (\mathscr{E}_s - H_F)^{-1} \tag{114}$$

as desired. If $E_s = \mathscr{E}_s + \langle s|V\Omega|s\rangle$ is expanded out, various simplifications occur; these may be more easily realized [15] if instead $H_F + \langle s|V|s\rangle$ is perturbed by $V - \langle s|V|s\rangle$, for then all one-term expectations vanish. Of course, all terms with zero denominator must cancel and so may be dropped at the outset.

Let us return explicitly to the many-body problem. While there is no difficulty in merely substituting $V = \sum v_\alpha$ in the above, we know that singular potentials may also be encompassed if reaction operators t_α are available, and convergence enhanced by preliminary coherent subtraction. We may literally add up all successive identical scatterings in the perturbation expansion (108), or more concisely write down a multiple scattering series for (100):

$$\Omega = 1 + G \sum P(t_\alpha \Lambda_\alpha)$$
$$\Lambda_\alpha = 1 + G \sum_{\beta \neq \alpha} P(t_\beta \Lambda_\beta)$$
$$\text{where} \quad t_\alpha = v_\alpha(1 + GP'(t_\alpha))$$
$$G = (E - T - \Lambda)^{-1} P_s$$

(115)

some formal advantages accruing from a possible distinction between P and P'. Here H_F has been replaced by $T = \sum T_i$ and a projection off state s, P_s, has been included, via G, so that eq. (106) and thereby (107) are valid. Treating eqs. (115) as we did in the sequence (16)–(19), we readily find

$$v_\alpha \Omega = t_\alpha \Lambda_\alpha + v_\alpha G[P(t_\alpha \Lambda_\alpha) - P'(t_\alpha)\Lambda_\alpha] \tag{116}$$

which reproduces $\sum v_\alpha \Omega = (E - T - \Lambda)(\Omega - 1) + \Lambda\Omega$ on φ_s if $\Lambda\Omega = \sum (1 - P_s P)(t_\alpha \Lambda_\alpha) + \sum v_\alpha G(P(t_\alpha \Lambda_\alpha) - P'(t_\alpha)\Lambda_\alpha)$ on φ_s. Hence

$$\langle m|\Lambda|m\rangle\langle m|\Omega|s\rangle = \langle m| \sum (1 - P')(t_\alpha)\Lambda_\alpha$$
$$+ \sum (v_\alpha G - 1)(P(t_\alpha \Lambda_\alpha) - P'(t_\alpha)\Lambda_\alpha)|s\rangle \tag{117a}$$
$$E_s = \mathcal{E}_s + \langle s| \sum [t_\alpha \Lambda_\alpha + v_\alpha G(P(t_\alpha \Lambda_\alpha) - P'(t_\alpha)\Lambda_\alpha)]|s\rangle \tag{117b}$$

(with $m \neq s$), replacing eq. (109). If P does not interfere with an over-all two-body scattering: $P[v_\alpha GP(t_\alpha F)] = P[v_\alpha GP'(t_\alpha)F]$, and if the energy is closed with respect to P: $\langle s|P[v_\alpha GP(F)]|s\rangle = 0$, then (117b) reduces as expected to $E_s = \mathcal{E}_s + \langle s| \sum t_\alpha \Lambda_\alpha|s\rangle$.

The appearance of the anomalous term $P(t_\alpha \Lambda_\alpha) - P'(t_\alpha)\Lambda_\alpha$ in eqs. (117) is striking; its multiplication by v_α is annoying, for this gives rise to a possible singular form which, if real, must be mitigated by expansion of v_α in a series in t_α. An alternative formulation eliminates this feature at the cost of a more complex form of self-consistency, namely we retain eqs. (115) except for the definition of t_α, which is replaced by

$$t_\alpha = v_\alpha + v_\alpha GP(t_\alpha \Lambda_\alpha)\Lambda_\alpha^{-1} \tag{118}$$

We see now that $v_\alpha \Omega = t_\alpha \Lambda_\alpha$, so that eqs. (117) become simply

$$\langle m|\Lambda|m\rangle = \langle m| \sum (1 - P)(t_\alpha \Lambda_\alpha)|s\rangle / \langle m|\Omega|s\rangle \tag{119a}$$
$$E_s = \mathcal{E}_s + \langle s| \sum t_\alpha \Lambda_\alpha|s\rangle \tag{119b}$$

The foregoing certainly applies to (Fermi-Dirac or) Einstein-Bose many-body systems if (anti-) symmetric states are employed throughout. But from the particle scattering point of view, one prefers to use many-body product states $\chi_{k_1}(1) \ldots \chi_{k_A}(A)$ of the unperturbed Hamiltonian as intermediate states; indeed, one can use these even when the concept of diagonality (of Δ) is involved [eqs. (117), (119)], for an operator diagonal on product states, which is also symmetric in the particles, is automatically diagonal on (anti-) symmetric functions. On the other hand, by virtue of the projection P_s, the initial φ_s is guaranteed never to occur as an intermediate state, a statement which is unaltered if P_s is extended to project out product states of φ_s. Thus s as initial or final state may always refer to the correct (anti-) symmetric combination and in fact must do so if the expressions for $\langle m|\Delta|m\rangle$ and $E_s - \mathscr{E}_s$ are to remain valid.

The formulations (115), (117) or (115), (118), (119) provide a rich source of perturbation expansions (which however are not in notably short supply). The coherent decomposition of eq. (70) for a uniform Fermi-Dirac medium is a special case obtained by choosing $P' = 1$ and P to remove all diagonal (coherent) matrix elements of the t_α from any expansion in the t_α one which it operates; in particular, $P(t_\alpha) = t_\alpha - t_{c\alpha}$. In this case, since the coherent terms are already removed in Λ_α [see eq. (115)], we have $P(t_\alpha \Lambda_\alpha) = P(t_\alpha)\Lambda_\alpha$, and (115), (117) reduces to

$$\langle m|\Delta|m\rangle = \sum \langle m|(1 - v_\alpha G)t_{c\alpha} \Lambda_\alpha|s\rangle / \langle m|\Omega|s\rangle \tag{120a}$$

$$E_s = \mathscr{E}_s + \sum \langle s|(t_\alpha - v_\alpha G t_{c\alpha}) \Lambda_\alpha|s\rangle \tag{120b}$$

$$\text{where} \qquad t_\alpha = v_\alpha + v_\alpha G t_\alpha \tag{120c}$$

The approximation, eqs. (70)–(74), previously made, corresponds to replacing Λ_α by Ω in (120a), presumably a $1/A$ correction, and neglecting $v_\alpha G$ compared to unity in (120a), (120b), of less obvious validity. On the other hand, from both (115), (117) and (118), (119), with $P' = P$ as above,

$$\langle m|\Delta|m\rangle = \sum \langle m|t_\alpha|m\rangle\langle m|\Lambda_\alpha|s\rangle / \langle m|\Omega|s\rangle$$

$$E_s = \mathscr{E}_s + \sum \langle t_\alpha \Lambda_\alpha\rangle \tag{121}$$

$$\text{where} \qquad t_\alpha = v_\alpha + v_\alpha G(t_\alpha - t_{c\alpha})$$

the coherent subtraction of (38) now being relevant, and only the $\Lambda_\alpha \to \Omega$ replacement is necessary. For comparison with eqs. (71)–(74), we of course write $E_s = \mathscr{E}_s + \sum \langle t_{c\alpha} \rangle + \sum \langle (t_\alpha - t_{c\alpha}) \Lambda_\alpha \rangle = E_c + \sum \langle (t_\alpha - t_{c\alpha}) \Lambda_\alpha \rangle$.

3. *The unlinked cluster problem: particle viewpoint*

The question of convergence of perturbation series expansions has thus far been left open. This question has many facets, few of which can be treated in a definitive fashion; attention must then be suitably restricted. In particular, since the characteristics of principal interest in a many-body system per se are those which are valid for arbitrarily large particle number at fixed density, one would like convergence of any series for the energy per particle to be uniform as $A \to \infty$.

Dependence on Large Particle Number. Consider the Brillouin-Wigner expansion (50), (51), with many-body potential $V = \sum v_\alpha$. The propagator $G = (E - H_F)^{-1} P$ is guaranteed to vanish on the unperturbed state (for which $H_F = \mathscr{E}$ might cause $(E - H_F)^{-1}$ to be quite large), but nothing prevents G from becoming infinite if E coincides with another unperturbed energy; a crossing of levels in this fashion then certainly interferes with convergence. But take the ground state of a free Fermi-Dirac system at fixed density ρ as an example. While the level spacing near the ground state varies as $\rho^{2/3} A^{-1/3}$, $E - \mathscr{E}$ will presumably increase as A for large A; hence for positive perturbation energy, E will repeatedly cross unperturbed levels. The phenomenon is enhanced on perturbing a free Einstein-Bose system.

For negative (attractive) perturbations in the ground state, the denominator $E - H_F$ will never vanish, although its doing so for excited states still suggests convergence difficulties. From another point of view, one sees that due to the corresponding variation of $E - \mathscr{E}$, then $G \sim 1/A$ for large A at fixed intermediate state excitation. Now as will be shown, very few terms in the perturbation expansion contribute under these circumstances to a constant ratio of $(E - \mathscr{E})/A$ as $A \to \infty$, most terms yield zero. This implies that the bulk of the series has effect only when taken together in at least A orders of perturbation, i.e., that convergence becomes infinitely slow.

The difficulty in all cases resides in the fact that the perturbation becomes too large as $A \to \infty$, and the increase of $E - \mathscr{E}$ in the propagator is the focus of the difficulty. This suggests arranging matters such that the energy denominators, evaluated at the desired unperturbed state φ, vary only slowly with A; the same will then be true at any unperturbed state of fixed excitation energy. Precisely this objective is achieved by the various optical (or coherent-subtraction) models of Section B2, for they shift the starting point so that the denominator $E - T - \Delta$ (or $E_c - T - \sum V_i$) vanishes on the initial state. Hence $G \sim 1$, and the above objections are removed.

This tale does not yet have a happy ending. For example, taking $G' = (E_c - T - \sum V_i)^{-1} P'$ in (70), (74) as $A \to \infty$, first- and second-order ground state energy perturbations vanish, the third-order perturbation is small and varies as A, but the fourth-order one contains a contribution increasing as A^2, at constant density. Such terms (diagrammatically interpreted by Bethe [38] in the wave picture) are clearly not physical, and must simply mirror a lack of convergence in the infinite-body limit. One may try to set up a unique prescription for elimination of such terms in the final expansion, or modify the formulation such that the terms automatically disappear. The former is complicated by uncertainty in the final disposition of a term, e.g., A^2 may simply cancel on insertion of A dependence of t' and G' in the complete series, may ultimately contribute as in $A^2 - A^3 + A^4 \ldots = A^2/1 + A$, or as in $A^2 - A^3 + \frac{1}{2} A^4 \ldots = A^2 e^{-A}$ have no net contribution. The latter is preferably done in a t-operator expansion, but is more easily accomplished in a direct expansion in terms of the potential v, which is then to be converted to the guaranteed nonsingular t's; we shall consider both possibilities. First however we must catalog the A dependence of the various terms.

The approximation (74) to the particle-multiple scattering formulation of the bound state problem is, even as $A \to \infty$, only a first-order result unless one can identify $\sum u_{c\alpha}$ and $\sum V_i$ by a further involved self-consistency condition; we shall therefore use it with the modified propagator $G' = (E_c - T - \sum V_i)^{-1} P'$. The form at any rate is certainly typical of multiple scattering transcriptions. The large A energy shift from that of the decoupled state φ is then given by (dropping prime superscripts)

$$\Delta E = \langle\varphi|\sum u_{c\alpha}|\varphi\rangle + \langle\varphi|\sum t_{\alpha_1} + \sum_{\alpha_1 \neq \alpha_2} t_{\alpha_1} G t_{\alpha_2} + \ldots$$

$$+ \sum_{\alpha_1 \neq \alpha_2 \cdots \neq \alpha_h} t_{\alpha_1} G t_{\alpha_2} \ldots G t_{\alpha_h} + \ldots|\varphi\rangle \tag{122}$$

with $t_\alpha = u_\alpha - u_{c\alpha}$. We wish to analyze this expression as a function of particle number A; hence the situation we envisage is a uniform one (with, say periodic boundary conditions and momentum-conserving interaction) in the ground state, so that we can let A grow at constant density $\rho = A/V$ and expect physically that ΔE will grow as A. Now since u_{ij} is diagonal in all particles but i, j, its matrix elements depend on the transition of the one-body states of i and j, all other particle states being fixed; since presumably $\sum_\alpha \langle\varphi|u_{c\alpha}|\varphi\rangle = \langle \bar{V}_c\rangle \propto A$, the diagonal elements of u_α and hence typical matrix elements of u_α and t_α should vary as $1/A$. Such indeed is the dependence of matrix elements of $v(\mathbf{x}_i - \mathbf{x}_j)$ for nonsingular v. Further, G, here depending only upon the excitation energy of the product state upon which it acts, should not vary with A. Then, except for the general diagonal-state dependence of t_α and G, a typical product of matrix elements in $\langle\varphi|t_{\alpha_1} G t_{\alpha_2} \ldots G t_{\alpha_h}|\varphi\rangle = \langle \sum (\pm 1)^\Pi \Pi \varphi_1|t_{\alpha_1} G t_{\alpha_2} \ldots G t_{\alpha_h}|\varphi_1\rangle$ may be depicted as a set of scatterings from the pair $\chi_k(i) \chi_l(j)$ to $\chi_{k'}(i) \chi_{l'}(j)$, with the matrix element of $t_\alpha = t_{ij}$ depending only on k, l, k', l'. There is, further, the boundary condition that the state $\chi_k(i)$ in φ before the first scattering of i and $\chi_{k'}(i)$ after its last scattering are fixed (for an exchange term, k need not equal k'). We shall assume here that $h \ll A$.

It is convenient to divide the particles of such a product term into irreducible clusters, depending on the pairs $\alpha_1, \ldots, \alpha_h$, such that each particle scatters solely within its own particle cluster, each cluster contains at least one scattering, and its final substate is a permutation of the initial substate. Fig. 1 illustrates three representations (particle channels collapsed to points in diagram b, interaction lines to points in diagram c) of a typical non-exchange matrix element in the three-body cluster $t_{12} G t_{23} G t_{13}$. Consider all matrix elements represented by a given cluster of b particles, with b' ($\geq b/2$) pair interactions, and suppose that particle j enters into p_j pair interactions, so that $\sum p_j = 2b'$. Due to the boundary conditions, there will then be $p_j - 1$ one-particle states associated with j to be summed over. On the other hand, each pair interaction introduces a momentum space δ function, thereby decreasing by one (except for discrete indices, such as spin) the state indices to be summed; one of these δ functions is rendundant due to the automatic momentum conservation between initial and final states.

Thus, there are $\sum (p_j - 1) - b' + 1 = (2b' - b) - b' + 1 = b' - b + 1$ one-body summations to be made, and since, with plane wave expansion states, $\sum_k \to V \int d^3k \propto A$, a factor of $A^{b'-b+1}$ is inserted. Finally, similar terms in $t_{\alpha_1} G \ldots G t_{\alpha_h}$ may be obtained by choosing the b particles in any fashion from all A; except for a constant factor (recalling that $h \ll A$), there are A^b such geometrically (under permutation) identical clusters possible. Combining the contributions

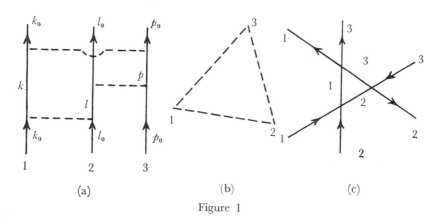

Figure 1

due to pair number ($t \propto 1/A$), state summation, and geometrically identical clusters, the variation with A due to a single geometrical (unindexed) cluster is given by $A^{-b'} A^{b'-b+1} A^b = A$. All geometrically identical terms of a diagram of d clusters (which, except for a geometrical permutation factor, accumulate terms independently) thereby give rise to a term in ΔE which goes as A^d. Hence, any diagram containing disconnected ($d > 1$) or "unlinked" clusters imparts an anomalous A dependence to ΔE; since eq. (122) is a typical multiple scattering result, this conclusion is not restricted to the approximation (70)–(74). One notes incidentally that if $G \sim 1/A$, as in an unmodified Brillouin-Wigner expansion, the above is altered to A^{d+1-h}, and only completely disconnected terms ($d = h$) contribute, raising a complementary problem previously mentioned.

Linked Diagram Expansion. The simplest formal method of eliminating terms of more than one cluster in the perturbation energy is to use the structure-modifying operator P of (108), (109) or (115), (117). We first consider a direct expansion in the potential, (107)–(109), where now $V = \sum v_\alpha$. Further, to avoid some difficulties which are not pertinent to the present discussion, we limit ourselves to the special case of the ground state of an Einstein-Bose system; thus $|0\rangle$, the state to be perturbed, has all particles in the same one-body state χ_0. A matrix element $\langle m|\Gamma|0\rangle$, where m is a product state and Γ a product of G's and v_α's, will be termed linked to the final state if no final sub-state of a geometrical cluster contained therein coincides with a permutation of its initial substate (i.e. here, all χ_0's). The claim is now made that if P^L in (108), (109) retains only matrix elements linked to the final state, then as $A \to \infty$, Δ is literally a constant. According to (107), (109), we must then have

$$\Delta = E_0 - \mathscr{E}_0 = \langle 0| \sum v_\alpha \Omega(E_0)|0\rangle \qquad (123)$$

First, let us describe the energy shift of (123). Clearly, $\langle m|\Omega|0\rangle = \langle m|\{1+GP^L(\sum v_\alpha)+GP^L[\sum v_\alpha GP^L(v_\beta)]+ \dots\}|0\rangle$ consists of all diagrams in which no intermediate or final substate of a single cluster is composed of all χ_0. But v_α can change the states of at most two particles; in order for $\langle 0|v_\alpha|m\rangle\langle m|\Omega|0\rangle$ to contribute to (123), m can then have at most two particles in states other than χ_0. Hence, either $\langle m|\Omega|0\rangle$ contains only one cluster to which v_α is connected or (impossible in the event of momentum conservation) two clusters joined by v_α as the final interaction. It follows that, $E_0 - \mathscr{E}_0$ consists precisely of all single clusters or linked diagrams, with $|0\rangle$ prohibited as intermediate state.

To prove that $\langle m|\Delta|m\rangle$ of (109) has the value given by eq. (123), it must be shown that

$$\langle 0| \sum v_\alpha \Omega|0\rangle\langle m|\Omega|0\rangle = \langle m|(1-P^L)(\sum v_\alpha \Omega)|0\rangle \qquad (124)$$

Now $\langle m|(1-P^L)(\sum v_\alpha \Omega)|0\rangle$ contains those terms for which the final interaction "closes" either a single cluster or a pair of clusters in the sense of repeating their initial substate; it is therefore composed of those terms that would yield $\langle 0| \sum v_\alpha \Omega|0\rangle$ if appearing by themselves, in parallel with diagrams linked to the final state which would comprise $\langle m|\Omega|0\rangle$ if unaccompanied. It is not quite true that all such combinations are present, for the total number of particles in clusters is limited by A, not by $2A$. However, for m of fixed excitation, as $A \to \infty$ the residual terms will not contribute (similar to the statistical mechanical cluster expansion for free energy at constant particle number). Equation (124) will thereby be established if it can be shown that the sum of the contributions of two disconnected components of a diagram, as the relative order of the interactions varies (e.g., $v_{12}Gv_{23}$ and $Gv_{45}Gv_{46}$ combine as $v_{12}Gv_{23}Gv_{45}Gv_{46}$, $v_{12}Gv_{45}G$ $v_{23}Gv_{46}$, and $v_{12}Gv_{45}Gv_{46}Gv_{23}$), equals the product of the separate contributions of the two components.

Consider then a diagram with all intermediate one-body states, and hence all v_α matrix elements, fixed. In the present case, if (123) is valid, the propagator $G = (E_0 - T - \varDelta)^{-1}P_s$ becomes $-(T - \mathscr{E}_0)^{-1}$: the denominator is simply the excitation energy above the initial unperturbed state, or if G occurs after the rth interaction, $G = -(\varDelta E_1 + \varDelta E_2 + \ldots \varDelta E_r)^{-1}$, where $\varDelta E_n$ is the two-body change in kinetic energy at the nth interaction. Now the aggregate contribution of propagators to a diagram with a propagators may be written as

$$(\varDelta E_1)^{-1}(\varDelta E_1 + \varDelta E_2)^{-1} \ldots (\varDelta E_1 + \varDelta E_2 + \ldots + \varDelta E_a)^{-1}$$

$$= \int \underset{0\rangle s_a\rangle \cdots \rangle s_1\rangle - \infty}{\ldots \ldots \ldots} \int \exp (s_1 \varDelta E_1 + \ldots + s_a \varDelta E_a)\, ds_1 \ldots ds_a \qquad (125)$$

If one multiplies (125) by the corresponding contribution of a b-propagator diagram, with integration variables $t_1, \ldots, t_b$, the combined region of integration may be decomposed into all subregions characterized by ordered sequences of $s_1, \ldots, t_b$ in which the orderings $s_1 \langle \ldots \langle s_a, t_1 \langle \ldots \langle t_b$ are separately maintained. Since the v_α matrix elements are identical for a composite diagram and a product of components, it readily follows that all contributions of the two disconnected components add up to the product of the contributions, as desired.

Summing up, then, if the propagator $G = (\mathscr{E}_0 - T)^{-1}$ is used, thereby yielding a Rayleigh-Schrödinger expansion, the diagrams contributing to the ground state energy of an Einstein-Bose many-body system are, in the $A \to \infty$ limit, precisely those which are linked, without $E = \mathscr{E}_0$ intermediate states. Looking back to the general

Rayleigh-Schrödinger prescription (112)–(114), it appears fortuitous that only single matrix elements are needed rather than products. This is a consequence of the identity of all one-body states in the independent particle Einstein-Bose ground state, and may be achieved for more general Einstein-Bose or Fermi-Dirac states only by the introduction of certain fictitious states which are more appropriately discussed from the wave scattering viewpoint.

Turning now to the multiple scattering approach of (115), (117), an immediate difficulty arises since the prohibition against repeating an initial substate appears difficult to extract when intermediate states are buried inside reaction operators; that is, P^L *does* interfere with an over-all two-body scattering. An obvious way out is to stop the interaction chain leading to the definition of t_α when *either* another pair of particles interacts *or* an initial two-body wave function is produced (or both). There will then be two types of reaction operator, one of which, $t_{I\alpha}$, requires a change in the interaction pair before and after, while the other, $t_{c\alpha}$ (a generalized coherent component) does not. Formally, eqs. (115), (117) are therefore replaced by

$$\Omega = 1 + G \sum_\beta P(t_{I\beta}\Lambda_\beta) + G \sum_\beta P(t_{c\beta}\Lambda_\beta)$$

$$\Lambda_\alpha = 1 + G \sum_{\beta \neq \alpha} P(t_{I\beta}\Lambda_\beta) + G \sum_\beta P(t_{c\beta}\Lambda_\beta) \qquad (126)$$

$$t_{I\alpha} + t_{c\alpha} = v_\alpha[1 + GP'(t_{I\alpha})]$$

with

$$\langle m|\Delta|m\rangle\langle m|\Omega|s\rangle =$$

$$\langle m| \sum (1-P)\,(t_{I\alpha}\Lambda_\alpha + t_{c\alpha}\Lambda_\alpha) + \sum v_\alpha G[P(t_{I\alpha}\Lambda_\alpha) - P'(t_{I\alpha})\Lambda_\alpha]|s\rangle$$

$$E_s = \mathscr{E}_s + \langle s| \sum (t_{I\alpha}\Lambda_\alpha + t_{c\alpha}\Lambda_\alpha) + \sum v_\alpha G[P(t_{I\alpha}\Lambda_\alpha) - P'(t_{I\alpha})\Lambda_\alpha]|s\rangle \qquad (127)$$

When, as above, $t_{I\alpha}$ and $t_{c\alpha}$ are components of a single t_α, one may write

$$t_{c\alpha} = P_c(t_\alpha) \qquad t_{I\alpha} = (1-P_c)(t_\alpha)$$

$$t_\alpha = v_\alpha[1 + GP'(t_\alpha - t_{c\alpha})] \qquad (128)$$

For somewhat similar considerations, see Tobocman [37].

In the present case then of an Einstein-Bose ground state, we may choose $P = P^L$ to retain only elements linked to final state, $P' = 1$, and P_c to insist on a $\chi_0 \chi_0$ two body final state; it is clear that P^L can only eliminate terms with clusters ending in bunches of χ_0 states, but that $t_{I\alpha}$ cannot contribute to such an ending. Hence, the anomalous term $P^L(t_{I\alpha}\Lambda_\alpha) - t_{I\alpha}\Lambda_\alpha$ vanishes, and (127) reduces to $E_s = \mathscr{E}_s + \langle s| \sum t_{c\alpha}\Lambda_\alpha|s\rangle$, with a similar form for $\langle m|\Delta|m\rangle$; the structure is essentially identical with (107), (109), (110). The analysis proceeds precisely as does that of eq. (123), leading again to the conclusion that Δ is a constant, the energy shift (so that a Rayleigh-Schrödinger propagator ensues), together with a reaction operator linked cluster expansion, as required. This result remains unchanged as long as P_c includes $\chi_0 \chi_0$ final state matrix elements; for example, the coherence definition of (82) can absorb such an alteration, and so becomes appropriate for a Rayleigh-Schrödinger expansion — as well as necessary for convergence.

The case of a ground state other than an Einstein-Bose one is considerably more complicated from the particle viewpoint; reasonably straightforward treatments [8]–[10] that eliminate undesirable unlinked terms as well as spurious scattering singularities tend to introduce quite complex propagators, necessitating approximations before one can write down a perturbation series. Thus, if P_c selects the coherent (= diagonal) part of t_α, one may choose $P' = 1$, $P = P^L(1 - P_c)$ in eqs. (115), (117), thereby guaranteeing a linked expansion $E_s - \mathscr{E}_s = \langle s|P^L(\sum t_\alpha\Lambda_\alpha)|s\rangle$ for the energy, but yielding the simple expression $\langle m|\Delta|m\rangle = \langle m| \sum t_\alpha|m\rangle$ (with Brillouin-Wigner denominators) only on approximating as we did for eq. (120). Utilization of the wave scattering picture permits considerably more satisfactory treatments, and we now return to this point of view.

4. The unlinked cluster problem: wave viewpoint

In assessing the large A dependence of a perturbation solution, the intensive properties of the system are to be held fixed, a condition most easily realized by considering the ground state at fixed density. A satisfactory analysis of the Einstein-Bose case has been obtained; let us therefore turn our attention in the main to the ground state of a uniform Fermi-Dirac medium, and for this purpose introduce the second quantized or wave-multiple scattering formulation. In the coherent-subtraction procedure of eqs. (70)–(74) [using the notation of Section A7 and of the footnote to eq. (70)] with approximate propagator, and v chosen such that $\bar{v}_{kl,pq} \, (= \bar{v}_{lk,qp}) = \bar{v}_{kl,qp}$, if

$$F = 1 + \tfrac{1}{2}G \sum \bar{I}_{kl,pq} F_{pq}$$
$$F_{kl} = 1 + \tfrac{1}{2}G \sum_{rs \neq kl,\,lk} \bar{I}_{rs,pq} F_{pq} \qquad (129)$$

where
$$\bar{I}_{kl,pq} = \bar{v}_{kl,pq} + \sum_{rs} \bar{v}_{kl,rs} G \bar{I}_{rs,pq}$$
$$G = (E_c - T - \sum_{l \in \Phi_0,\,k} \bar{I}_{kl,kl} \eta_k^* \eta_{\mathbf{k}})^{-1} P$$
$$\bar{I}_{kl,pq} = \bar{I}_{kl,pq} - \bar{I}_{kl,kl}(\delta_{kp}\delta_{lq} + \delta_{kq}\delta_{lp})$$

we have for the principal part, as $A \to \infty$, of the energy of Ψ_o, perturbed from Φ_0,

$$E = E_c + \tfrac{1}{2} \sum \langle \Phi_0 | \bar{I}_{kl,pq} F_{pq} | \Phi_0 \rangle$$
$$E_c = \langle \Phi_0 | T + \sum \bar{I}_{kl,kl} | \Phi_0 \rangle \qquad (130)$$

The energy change $E - E_c$, basically a first-order correction, is now

$$\Delta E = \sum_{\nu > 2} 2^{1-\nu} \sum \langle \Phi_0 | \bar{I}_{k_1 l_1, \, p_1 q_1} G \bar{I}_{k_2 l_2, \, p_2 q_2} \cdots G \bar{I}_{k_\nu l_\nu, \, p_\nu q_\nu} | \Phi_0 \rangle \quad (130')$$

where adjacent state pairs cannot be the same; this form is typical of any exact formulation as well.

In eq. (130′), the $\nu = 1$ and 2 terms vanish identically. The general element of the νth term may be depicted as a "scattering" of states $p_\nu q_\nu$ into the pair $k_\nu l_\nu$, then of $p_{\nu-1} q_{\nu-1}$ into $k_{\nu-1} l_{\nu-1}, \ldots$, and finally of $p_1 q_1$ into $k_1 l_1$. Diagrammatically, an elementary term $\bar{I}_{kl,pq}$ may be indicated as shown; using only one of $\bar{I}_{kl,pq}$ and $\bar{I}_{lk,qp}$ avoids factors of $\tfrac{1}{2}$. These are then to be joined, with the boundary condition that,

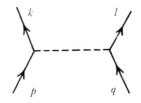

Figure 2

for ΔE, the first appearance of a one-body state not in Φ_0 must be a creation, the last an annihilation; the reverse holds for states in Φ_0.

The numerical value of an element of the νth sum is then given by the product of the diagonal $I_{kl,pq}$'s and G's contained therein, if we also append ± 1 (due to the anticommutativity) depending on whether the final one-body states are an even or odd permutation of those initially in the same scattering channels. Diagrams containing initial, intermediate, or final states with one-body repetitions are to be given the coefficient zero; however, if regarded as special confluences as state indices are permitted to roam freely, they are guaranteed to cancel in pairs and so may be included.

Except for the fact that particle indices are no longer carried along as excess baggage, the typical νth order element (and diagram) coincides with the typical product of matrix elements in an expansion via the particle picture; this is as it must be. Correspondingly, taking G to be of order unity, $I_{kl,pq}$ of order $1/A$, and each state summation to introduce a factor of A, any geometrical diagram composed of d disconnected parts leads to a term of order A^d; a redefinition of propagator and reaction operator must then be introduced to eliminate the possibility $d > 1$. Now a formulation employing only linked diagrams will generally arise from the realization that a propagator, or the energy, may be written as a quotient of contributions from all diagrams by those of unlinked portions. The set of all diagrams must therefore include juxtapositions of independently constructed diagrams; not only may we obtain intermediate states excluded by the Pauli principle (but allowed from the particle viewpoint) but also "states" in which, e.g., a χ_k originally present in Φ_0 is annihilated more than once before being created again. These fictitious states appear more innocuous if we transform to a particle-hole description of states.

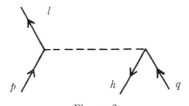

Figure 3

For an unperturbed Fermi-Dirac ground state Φ_0, an excited state may be specified by enumerating the "particles", one-body states p

not contained in Φ_0, and "holes", missing states h originally in Φ_0. Hence η_h is described as creating a hole h, while η_h^* annihilates the hole. Diagrammatically, the direction of a hole line is to be reversed; an elementary term $I_{kl,pq}$, a scattering of particle p into particle l while particle q annihilates hole h, is illustrated. Using this description, the excitation energy $\mathscr{E}(\ldots, p_i, \ldots, h_j, \ldots) - \mathscr{E}_0$ of an intermediate state with particles p_i and holes h_j is simply

$$\mathscr{E}(\ldots, p_i, \ldots, h_j, \ldots) - \mathscr{E}_0 = \sum \varepsilon_{p_i} - \sum \varepsilon_{h_j} \tag{131}$$

and a return to the ground state at some intermediate stage is recognized by the absence of both particles and holes. The sign of a diagram no longer depends on the explicit states represented, but is determined simply by the number of individual internal hole lines (those both annihilated and created; no others occur in $\Phi_0 \Phi_0$ matrix elements) plus the number of closed loops formed by particle and hole lines. Following the recipe of (131) for evaluating propagators, diagrams with more than one hole simultaneously in the same state are guaranteed to cancel in pairs (just interchange the termini of identical holes); but these include the fictitious states mentioned above, which thereby appear as the hole analog of Pauli-excluded states and offer no further difficulty.

The result of the foregoing redescription is that the juxtaposition of *any* two diagrams is itself an allowed diagram. Secure in this knowledge, one may repeat the direct (potential expansion) perturbation analysis of (123)–(125), applied now to a Fermi-Dirac ground state. There are obvious transcriptions to be made, e.g., linked to final state now means literally that all subdiagrams end with unterminated lines at the final state, a criterion with the welcome distinction of depending only on the geometrical diagram, not on specific states. The conclusion is again that the energy change is the sum of all connected Φ_0, Φ_0 matrix elements, with the Rayleigh-Schrödinger propagator — the reciprocal of (131) with sign reversed — being employed. Application to perturbation of excited Fermi-Dirac states may be made by referring particles and holes to the unperturbed Φ instead of to the ground state; states degenerate to Φ must however be explicitly omitted. In the special case of a single excitation for a spin-independent translation-invariant potential, one can also refer the description to the ground state Φ_0, for a single particle line uniquely characterizes the state Φ, just as the absence of particles and holes did when Φ was the ground state. Einstein-Bose states of low excitation may be similarly treated if a special sign convention is used for the fictitious states.

This first step, the expression of the energy in a direct potential expansion by the linked Rayleigh-Schrödinger form, is a crucial one, and has been accomplished in various other ways which have some advantage in giving the practitioner more direct control over the reductions he performs. Let us consider the analytical approach of Hugenholtz [41], using the unadulterated resolvent operator formulation and particle-hole picture, for the ground state of a Fermi-Dirac system. Again introducing the resolvent $W(z) = (z-H_F-V)^{-1}$, where $H_F \Phi_0 = \mathscr{E}_0 \Phi_0$ and $V = \frac{1}{2} \sum \bar{v}_{kl,pq}$, the perturbed energy E_0 is recognized as the lowest pole of the diagonal element $W_{a0}(z) \equiv \langle \Phi_0 | W(z) | \Phi_0 \rangle$; clearly

$$W_{a0}(z) = 1/(z-\mathscr{E}_0) + \langle \Phi_0 | G(z)VG(z) + G(z)VG(z)VG(z) + \ldots | \Phi_0 \rangle \tag{132}$$

where $G(z) = (z-H_F)^{-1}$.

To analyze (132), the convolution operation

$$f(z) * g(z) = (2\pi i)^{-1} \oint f(z-\zeta)g(\zeta)\,d\zeta \tag{133}$$

is introduced, the contour in the complex plane encircling the poles of g but not those of f. It may be shown that if we consider particle-hole diagrams corresponding to matrix elements $F(z)$ of the form $\langle \Phi_1 | G(z + \mathscr{E}_0) | \Phi_1 \rangle \langle \Phi_1 | U_1 | \Phi_2 \rangle \langle \Phi_2 | G(z + \mathscr{E}_0) | \Phi_2 \rangle \ldots \langle \Phi_{n-1} | U_n | \Phi_n \rangle \langle \Phi_n | G(z+\mathscr{E}_0) | \Phi_n \rangle$, then if $F(z)$ represents the sum of all ways in which a subdiagram $A(z)$, disconnected from another subdiagram $B(z)$, can be juxtaposed with $B(z)$ (the order of the scattering points of A with respect to B inducing the various possibilities), we have

$$F(z) = A(z) * B(z) \tag{134}$$

This means that if α and β are incoming sets of lines, γ and δ outgoing, then $\langle \gamma\delta | F(z) | \alpha\beta \rangle = \langle \gamma | A(z) | \alpha \rangle * \langle \delta | B(z) | \beta \rangle$, which follows fairly easily from the elementary convolution

$$\langle \alpha | G(z+\mathscr{E}_0) | \alpha \rangle * \langle \beta | G(z+\mathscr{E}_0) | \beta \rangle = \langle \alpha\beta | G(z+\mathscr{E}_0) | \alpha\beta \rangle \tag{135}$$

a consequence of the relation $\langle \alpha | H_F | \alpha \rangle + \langle \beta | H_F | \beta \rangle = \langle \alpha\beta | H_F | \alpha\beta \rangle + \mathscr{E}_0$.
Now if $C(z)$ is, except for two factors of z, the connected or linked
part of $W_{d0}(z + \mathscr{E}_0)$

$$C(z) = \langle \Phi_0 | [V + VG(z + \mathscr{E}_0)V + VG(z + \mathscr{E}_0)VG(z + \mathscr{E}_0)V + \cdots]_{\text{con}} | \Phi_0 \rangle \tag{136}$$

$W_{d0}(z + \mathscr{E}_0)$ is obtained by juxtaposing diagrams of $C(z)$ in all possible
ways; hence

$$W_{d0}(z + \mathscr{E}_0) = 1/z + \frac{1}{1!} C(z)/z^2 + \frac{1}{2!} [C(z)/z^2] * [C(z)/z^2]$$

$$+ \frac{1}{3!} [C(z)/z^2] * [C(z)/z^2] * [C(z)/z^2] + \cdots \tag{137}$$

$$\equiv \exp * [C(z)/z^2]$$

Observing that $*$ is an associative operation, like ordinary multiplication, and that $1/z$ acts as unit: $1/z * g(z) = g(z)$, then if one sets
$C(z) = C(0) + zh(z)$ where h is regular at $z = 0$, eq. (137) may be
written instead as

$$W_{d0}(z + \mathscr{E}_0) = (\exp * [C(0)/z^2]) * (\exp * [h(z)/z]) \tag{137'}$$

But one readily evaluates $\exp * [C(0)/z^2]$ as $1/[z - C(0)]$; thus
$W_{d0}[z + \mathscr{E}_0 + C(0)] = (1/z) * (\exp * [h(z)/z])$, or

$$W_{d0}[z + \mathscr{E}_0 + C(0)] = 1/z + \frac{1}{1!} (h(z)/z) + \frac{1}{2!} [h(z)/z] * [h(z)/z] + \cdots \tag{137''}$$

The pole of the function W_{d0} which reduces to $\mathscr{E}_0$ on turning off the
interaction is then determined by $z = 0$ or

$$E_0 = \mathscr{E}_0 + C(0) \tag{138}$$

fully linked, the desired result. One can obtain the corresponding
wave function in similar fashion [following eq. (90)], and with
somewhat greater difficulty analyze the excited states, still maintaining the ground state particle-hole description.

On the other hand, the elimination of unlinked diagrams can also
be carried out under the aegis of the usual quantum field theory
concepts. Thus, Goldstone has shown [42], and this is spelled out in
detail in Bethe's discussion [38], how such elimination corresponds

to an explicit normalization of the wave function, in a form which arises from the adiabatic switching-on method for the determination of bound states.

With the problem of unlinked clusters thus overcome, further diagram compressions may be made at leisure. For example, the formal technique of (126)–(128) may be employed to introduce a reaction matrix. Since a continued series of pair interactions is closed on scattering by a pair of holes, the usual reaction operator t_I involves only particles; those, t_c, ending with holes are not barred from repeated scattering. Further coherent subtractions may similarly be made. The formal technique possesses a certain amount of rigidity, and certainly for the purpose of discovering diagram reductions, it is best to decide on those composite units which will best mirror the anticipated nature of the system, and then visually introduce these units into the linked diagram structure. For highly singular potentials, where the multiple scattering point of view is necessary, Goldstone [38], [42] eliminates successive two-body potential interactions in the expansion by the direct introduction of the reaction operator $\tilde{t}$; total elimination of coherent terms then poses considerable difficulties, and preliminary elimination of a mean one-body potential, then to be reinserted as a one-body perturbation, may be most expedient [39].

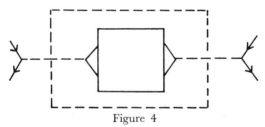

Figure 4

Almost diametrically opposite, for well-behaved potentials, but strongly collective system behavior, Hubbard [43] eliminates medium polarization effects by replacing the subgraph shown by an equivalent interaction; convergence for singular potentials is then poor. Under similar circumstances, in the sense that the reaction of the medium is important, Hugenholtz [41] takes into account self-energy (i.e., coherent) modifications of the propagator. For further (e.g., ring) reductions, see Chap. VIII, Sec. 2.

It is of course vital that diagram compressions have physical meaning and justification, and not be used simply because they can be used. A number of years ago, the writer successfully summed all series-parallel diagrams of classical statistical mechanics, obtaining a new basic link in terms of which diagrams start at the fourth order. The domain of utility of this summation has evaded him to this day.

5. *Model Hamiltonians*

Much of the improved convergence for energy expansions in the approximation methods we have discussed resulted from perturbing not the initial uncoupled system, but rather a model so determined that its energy was already nearly correct. A wave function was obtained incidentally, and although it too was effectively close to correct in that it reproduced expectations such as the energy, no claim was made for the literal accuracy of the wave function after a few perturbation terms. Indeed, in the many-body problem, such literal accuracy will not occur (see, e.g., Bethe [29]). To indicate why this is so, consider the perturbation of the ground state of an independent-particle Einstein-Bose system by a sum of one-body potentials. If the new one-body ground state (normalized by $\langle \psi_0|\psi_0\rangle = 1$) is given by $\psi_0(i) = (1-\lambda)\varphi_0(i) + \sum_{k\neq 0}\lambda_k\varphi_k(i)$, then clearly

$$\prod_i \psi_0(i) = (1-\lambda)^A \prod_i \varphi_0(i) + A^{\frac{1}{2}}(1-\lambda)^{A-1}\sum_k \lambda_k[\sum_j A^{-\frac{1}{2}}\varphi_k(j)\prod_{i\neq j}\varphi_0(i)]$$
$$+A(1-\lambda)^{A-2}\sum_{kl}\lambda_k\lambda_l[\sum_{jj'}A^{-1}\varphi_k(j)\varphi_l(j')\prod_{i\neq j,j'}\varphi_0(i)] + \ldots \quad (139)$$

The Fermi-Dirac result is similar except for the powers of A in the coefficients and the meaning of λ. The point is that for large A, the leading term $\langle \prod_i \psi_0(i)|\prod_i \varphi_0(i)\rangle$ in (139), as well as succeeding terms, all have factors of $(1-\lambda)^A \sim e^{-A\lambda}$. The number of perturbation terms required to pick up most of the normalization hence increases rapidly with A, a phenomenon not restricted to the special case chosen here but characteristic of systems of very many degrees of freedom.

The poor convergence of the wave function in a perturbation series need not imply the same for physically important expectations involving only a few particles at a time. The energy shift under a perturbation δV requires, as we know, only $\langle \varphi|\delta V|\psi\rangle/\langle \varphi|\psi\rangle$, which for two-body potentials extracts from ψ components differing from φ

by at most a two-body change — just the beginning of the series. Although there are many more ways in which multi-body changes can occur, they are not needed for this purpose. One can thus visualize a two-step transformation from uncoupled wave function φ to real ψ: first from φ to a simple model φ^M which effectively reproduces up to two-body changes, then from φ^M to ψ by a complicated poorly convergent transformation which however does not further alter relevant expectation values. Detailed knowledge of the energy for a system with two-body forces is in fact enough to determine the two-body distribution function (and hence any pair expectations), in the sense that the variational derivative with respect to the two-body potential in $V = \sum v_\alpha$ yields

$$\tfrac{1}{2}\langle \mathbf{x'}\mathbf{y'}|\hat{n}^{(2)}|\mathbf{x}\mathbf{y}\rangle = \delta E/\delta\langle \mathbf{x}\mathbf{y}|v|\mathbf{x'}\mathbf{y'}\rangle \qquad (140)$$

A number of investigations have been made into the practicability of setting up a model Hamiltonian to reproduce energy and other physically significant quantities of specified systems with a minimum of detailed solution of the Schrödinger equation — aside from the large category of empirical models typified by the shell model in nuclei. That is, part of the simulation is accounted for by the model wave function, part by a model Hamiltonian of which it is an eigenfunction; other observables must be correspondingly transformed. In general, this objective is accomplished by giving the model Hamiltonian available parameters, while maintaining sufficient invariance. (e.g., rotational) that the model states may be described by quantum numbers similar to those of the true states; if all levels were precisely reproduced, the model would then be a unitary redescription of reality. For such a determination, general iterative techniques of solution are still necessary, but if the model has enough "meat", these should converge rapidly for the quantities under consideration.

Perturbation Approach. Suppose that the Hamiltonian $H = H_F + V$ is to be simulated by the model $H^M = H_F + \Delta$ (with the same boundary conditions), presumed solvable; when Δ is diagonal with respect to the states of H_F, no self-consistency problem for the model states will arise — they are independent of Δ. If H^M retains a sufficient number of invariances, the reproduction of an energy level of H by H^M guarantees that of the quantum indices as well. Now for a bound state ψ_s emanating from a model state φ_s^M, the condition that the energy level E_s be unchanged is of course that

$$\langle \varphi_s^M | V - \Delta | \psi_s \rangle = 0 \qquad (141)$$

where $\psi_s = \Omega_s \varphi_s^M$, normalized according to $\langle \psi_s | \varphi_s^M \rangle = 1$, is to be found from

$$\psi_s = \varphi_s^M + (E_s - H_F - \Delta)^{-1} P_s (V - \Delta) \psi_s \qquad (142)$$

solved in any appropriate fashion. This is to some extent a generalization, albeit inexplicit, of the optical model approach of Sec. B2. It is to be observed that since energy is unchanged, the expansion (142) is simultaneously Brillouin-Wigner and Rayleigh-Schrödinger; as a transformation from H_F, however, this is not the case.

If the model potential Δ contains free parameters, these parameters may be adjusted to achieve various objectives. For example, if attention is restricted to a single state and energy level, the n parameters in Δ may be adjusted to annul the first n perturbation terms when (142) is inserted into (141); the remaining perturbation energy from the model should then be small. On the other hand, n parameters are certainly sufficient to assure identity of n energy levels for model and real system; since the perturbation energy for a model so chosen should converge quite rapidly, the self-consistency condition (141) that it converge to zero may not be too onerous. Let us briefly consider a few special cases of this procedure applied to the many-body $H = \sum T_i + \sum v_\alpha$, generally with $H_F = \sum T_i$, $V = \sum v_\alpha$.

Suppose that Δ contains just one parameter (e.g., is a constant, the well depth for a primitive optical model); then one can force the ground state energy of H and H^M to coincide [33]. From (141), a single condition results, which for Δ diagonal becomes

$$\langle \varphi_0^M | \Delta | \varphi_0^M \rangle = \langle \varphi_0^M | V \Omega_0 | \varphi_0^M \rangle \qquad (143)$$

The remaining diagonal elements of Δ are buried inside the right-hand side of (143).

If Δ contains two parameters, say a constant plus effective mass: $\Delta = U_0 + (2/m^* - 2/m) \sum p_i^2$, and $T_i = p_i^2/2m$, then both the ground state and a low excited state may be matched in energy with the model. Swiatecki [36] applies this by computing (142) to second order, and

employing (141) together with its derivative with respect to unperturbed excitation energy, evaluated in the ground state.

Going a large step further, if $\varDelta = \sum U_i$, a sum of similar diagonal
operators with an infinite number of available parameters, to wit
the functions U_i themselves, we may ask [33] for the whole energy
spectrum to be reproduced. Hence (141) is replaced by

$$\sum \langle \varphi_s^M | U_i | \varphi_s^M \rangle = \langle \varphi_s^M | \sum v_\alpha \Omega_s | \varphi_s^M \rangle \qquad (= \varDelta E_s) \qquad (144)$$

for all s. If each U_i were to depend only on particle i, the left-hand
side of eq. (144) would be an additive function of the momenta
present in φ_s^M; $\varDelta E_s$ does not in general have this form, illustrating
only that the infinities belonging to $\varDelta$ functions of one variable and to
one function of $\varDelta$ variables are really different in physics. Thus U_i
may be indexed by particle number i (and the U_i permute under a
particle permutation), but it is actually dependent on all particles, or
if one prefers, state-dependent.

If interest is centered upon one particle in an $\varDelta$-body system [33],
one may choose

$$H^M = H(A-1) + (T_A + U_A)$$
$$H(A-1) = \sum_{i<A} T_i + \sum_{i<j<A} v_{ij} \qquad (145)$$

and try to identify the spectra of H^M and H. U_A, operating on particle
A alone, is thus a type of shell model potential appropriate to a
closed-shell-plus-one nucleus. As model wave functions for excitation
of particle A, we have $\varphi_s^M = \psi_0(A-1) \chi_s(\mathbf{x}_A)$, anti-symmetric only on
particles $1, \ldots, A-1$. Since the perturbation is $\sum v_{iA}$, then for
diagonal model potential U_A, (141) reduces to

$$\langle \chi_s | U_A | \chi_s \rangle = \langle \psi_0(A-1)\chi_s(\mathbf{x}_A) | \sum v_{iA} \Omega_s | \psi_0(A-1)\chi_s(\mathbf{x}_A) \rangle \qquad (146)$$

apparently determining the one-body U_A in principle, while the practical computation of Ω_s remains as no mean task. However, although
the final wave function necessarily remains anti-symmetric on $A-1$
particles, it may either be totally anti-symmetric, or it may belong to the
$\{A-1, 1\}$ representation of the symmetric group (with vanishing antisymmetric component), depending upon the choice of χ_s. Thus, not all
diagonal elements of U_A are obtained; in particular, if χ_s is occupied

almost fully in the one-body density matrix for $\psi_0(A-1)$, one could scarcely perturb to an anti-symmetric wave function.

In the event of near degeneracy of either unperturbed or model states, the degenerate perturbation method of (52) becomes appropriate. Perturbing from $H^M = H_F + \varDelta$ to $H = H_F + V$, the correct linear combinations φ_s of the φ_r^M are now fixed by the trivial diagonality condition $\langle \varphi_s | V - \varDelta | \psi_r \rangle = (E_s - E_s^M) \delta_{rs} = 0$, or $\langle \varphi_s | \varDelta \varOmega_r | \varphi_r \rangle = \langle \varphi_s | V \varOmega_r | \varphi_r \rangle$. If $\varDelta$ is taken to be diagonal with respect to the n-fold φ_r, the explicit combinations of φ_s^M and the n diagonal elements of $\varDelta$ are then determined in principle. It is far simpler to choose the φ_r once and for all as eigenfunctions of H_F, and to assume only that $\varDelta$ takes the n-dimensional model space $\mathscr{M}$ of the φ_s into $\mathscr{M}$; the n^2 relevant elements of $\varDelta$ are then given by the self-consistency condition

$$\langle \varphi_s | \varDelta | \varphi_r \rangle = \langle \varphi_s | V \varOmega_r | \varphi_r \rangle \qquad (147a)$$

$$\varOmega_r = (E_r - H^M)^{-1} P (V - \varDelta) \varOmega_r + 1 \qquad (147b)$$

With $\varDelta$ known, the model wave functions are those of $H^M = H_F + \varDelta$, but need not be computed.

The additional structure which $\varDelta$ receives in (147a), with corresponding initial mixing of model states, allows $\varDelta$ to more closely mirror reality, and suggests the utility [33], [36] of (147) in constructing a model for an n-state sequence in which degeneracy plays no role. A consequence is that matrix elements of an observable O operating only on the space $\mathscr{M}$ are also reproduced, for if $Q = 1 - P$ is the projection onto $\mathscr{M}$, then since $Q\varOmega_r = Q$, one has $\langle \psi_s | O | \psi_r \rangle = \langle \psi_s | Q O Q | \psi_r \rangle = \langle \varphi_s | O | \varphi_r \rangle$. It is of course necessary to iterate eq. (147b), and this may be done in many ways; an alternative form [36] follows from the observation that $(H_F + V) \varOmega_s \varphi_s^M = E_s \varOmega_s \varphi_s^M = \varOmega_s E_s \varphi_s^M = \varOmega_s (H_F + \varDelta) \varphi_s^M$, so that acting on $\mathscr{M}$,

$$[H_F, \varOmega] = \varOmega(QVQQ) - V\varOmega \qquad (148)$$

determining the full n-level transformation. The boundary condition $Q\varOmega = Q$ is required for uniqueness.

Variational Method. A more recent approach due to Skyrme [44] is directed towards a variational model determination. The basic novelty is that, for this purpose, the model space is taken as distinct from real space. In other words, q denoting real space and ξ the model space, we want to choose a model Hamiltonian $\mathscr{H}^M$ with available parameters such that the energies e_s of some sequence of eigenstates

$$\mathscr{H}^M \varphi^M_s(\xi) = e_s \varphi^M_s(\xi) \tag{149}$$

match the energies of the corresponding real sequence

$$H\psi_s(q) = E_s \psi_s(q) \tag{150}$$

To accomplish this, it is observed that for those s for which the energies are matched, the eigenfunction equation in the compound space

$$(H - \mathscr{H}^M) F(q, \xi) = 0 \tag{151}$$

will have the solutions

$$F(q, \xi) = \sum a_s \psi_s(q) \varphi_s(\xi) \tag{152}$$

with constants a_s. Thus, if an F can be found to satisfy eq. (151), we will have $e_s = E_s$ for those terms s represented, and indeed, including normalization, the ψ_s will then be given by

$$\begin{aligned}
\psi_s(q) &= \mathscr{N}_s^{-1} \int \varphi^*_s(\xi) F(q, \xi) \, d\xi \\
\mathscr{N}_s^2 &= \int F^*(q, \xi') \varphi_s(\xi') \varphi^*_s(\xi) F(q, \xi) d\xi \, d\xi' \, dq
\end{aligned} \tag{153}$$

In approximations, F will of course be set up to have a large component at the desired value of s.

Equation (151) may be expressed by a variational principle in many ways; simplest is

$$\delta(I/D) = 0$$

$$I = \int F^*(q, \xi)(H - \mathscr{H}^M)^2 F(q, \xi) \, dq \, d\xi \tag{154}$$

$$D = \int F^*(q, \xi) F(q, \xi) \, dq \, d\xi$$

and I/D is stationary at the absolute minimum of zero. The stationary value for an approximation is then a measure of the error of the energy determination, for clearly (the smallest member of a sum does not exceed the average)

$$\text{Min} \quad (E_r - e_s)^2 \leq I/D \tag{155}$$

there is at least one eigenvalue of H closer than $(I/D)^{\frac{1}{2}}$ to one of $\mathscr{H}^M$. If $F(q, \xi)$ is allowed only a few components φ_s, this is a fairly restrictive condition. With a little more effort, one can do far better; from the completeness of the full set of φ_s and the diagonality of $\mathscr{H}^M$ on φ_s, one has $I = \sum_s \int [\int F^*(q, \xi')\varphi_s(\xi') \, d\xi' \, (H-e_s)^2 \int F(q, \xi)\varphi_s^*(\xi) \, d\xi] \, dq = \sum_s \mathscr{N}_s^2 \int \psi_s^*(q)(H-e_s)^2\psi_s(q) \, dq$, the approximate ψ_s being defined as in (153). Hence $\int \psi_s^*(q)(H-e_s)^2\psi_s(q) \, dq \leqq I/\mathscr{N}_s^2$, or if as in the Weinstein error estimate for energy [45], E_s is defined as the closest eigenvalue to e_s, then for any s,

$$|E_s - e_s| \leqq I^{\frac{1}{2}}/\mathscr{N}_s \tag{156}$$

Several forms are available in which to carry out variational approximations. Thus, parameters c_α may be introduced in $\mathscr{H}^M$ as

$$\mathscr{H}^M = \sum c_\alpha h_\alpha \tag{157}$$

where the h_α are known and Hermitian. Variation with respect to the c_α then yields the equations

$$\sum_\beta \langle h_\alpha h_\beta \rangle c_\beta = \langle h_\alpha H \rangle \tag{158}$$

where the expectation is with respect to the function F. Even for a fixed "model" F, one could in principle in this fashion secure exact results if a complete set of h_α were used. In practice, one would rather vary both $\mathscr{H}^M$ and F within physically reasonable classes; for solvable $\mathscr{H}^M$, the desired energies would then be approximately those of $\mathscr{H}^M$, which have functions given more poorly by eq. (153). This technique has been used to advantage [44] in determining the moments of inertia for nuclear rotational levels.

6. Concluding remarks

The preceding survey has been somewhat formal. In applying the concepts and methods, a number of interesting questions of physical import arise. Thus, we have seen that the coherent portion of a uniform system may be simulated by a one-body velocity-dependent potential $\bar{V}_i \sim \sum u_{cij}$ which, if regular and isotropic, can to first order be regarded as a change in the effective mass of the particles: $T_i + \bar{V}_i = p_i^2/2m + (a+bp_i^2 + \ldots) = a + p_i^2/2m^* + \ldots$ (see also Riesenfeld and Watson [8]). A discussion of the significance of this concept is presented in Chap. VII, Sec. 1. Of course, one would have a rigorous formulation if the effective mass were state-dependent; in cases in which the particles have discrete degrees of freedom, one should also have the effective mass depend at least on the discrete quantum number whenever changes in the latter are of importance. In Chap. VI, Ehrman shows that this is necessary for a hard sphere Fermi gas, with spin $\frac{1}{2}$, and leads to altered magnetic properties. The convergence of the multiple scattering series depends upon the effect of multiple collisions, and the extent to which they are included in coherent contributions. This topic is discussed in Chaps. IV, V, and VII, Sec. 2.

To avoid severe computational difficulties, one tries if possible to work with a uniform system. The transition from a free (constrained only by a boundary) to a bound system under the hypothetical increase of attractive interparticle forces cannot in this case be evidenced by a clumping of particles at sufficiently low density. One knows that a uniform system in any region of the E/A vs. V/A curve which is concave downwards is unstable, for a lower energy may be obtained by breaking the volume into subvolumes of differing density; thus a branching of the system's ground state must occur as the attraction is turned on to such a point. Restricting ourselves to uniform systems, singularities are then expected in the computations. The nature and meaning of these singularities and the extent to which a given method is valid on both sides of the transition are discussed at length in Chap. VII, Secs. 3 and 4.

For long-range forces, such as Coulomb forces, the concept of a collision is less well defined, and so, modifications of the multiple scattering approach are of importance. The form of these modifications and their relation to more direct collective approaches are considered in Chap. VII, Sec. 5.

Notes and References

1. See, e.g., J. C. Slater, *Phys. Rev.* **81**, 385 (1951).
2. K. A. Brueckner, R. J. Eden, and N. C. Francis, *Phys. Rev.* **98**, 1445 (1955); **99**, 76 (1955); **100**, 891 (1955).
3. L. S. Ornstein and F. Zernike, *Proc. Acad. Sci. Amsterdam* **17**, 793 (1914).
4. M. Lax, *Rev. Mod. Phys.* **23**, 287 (1951); *Phys. Rev.* **85**, 621 (1952). See also L. Foldy, *Phys. Rev.* **67**, 107 (1945).
5. K. M. Watson, *Phys. Rev.* **89**, 575 (1953); N. C. Francis and K. M. Watson, *Phys. Rev.* **92**, 291 (1953).
6. G. Takeda and K. M. Watson, *Phys. Rev.* **97**, 1336 (1955).
7. K. M. Watson, *Phys. Rev.* **103**, (1956).

8. W. B. Riesenfeld and K. M. Watson, *Phys. Rev.* **104**, 492 (1956).
9. R. Karplus and K. M. Watson, *Phys. Rev.* **107**, 1205 (1957).
10. W. B. Riesenfeld and K. M. Watson, *Phys. Rev.* **108**, 518 (1957).
11. K. A. Brueckner, C. A. Levinson, and Mahmoud, *Phys. Rev.* **95**, 217 (1954).
12. K. A. Brueckner, *Phys. Rev.* **96**, 508 (1954).
13. K. A. Brueckner and C. A. Levinson, *Phys. Rev.* **97**, 1344 (1955).
14. K. A. Brueckner, *Phys. Rev.* **97**, 1353 (1955).
15. K. A. Brueckner, *Phys. Rev.* **100**, 36 (1955).
16. K. A. Brueckner and W. Wada, *Phys. Rev.* **103**, 1008 (1956).
17. K. A. Brueckner, *Phys. Rev.* **103**, 1121 (1956).
18. K. A. Brueckner and J. L. Gammel, *Phys. Rev.* **105**, 1679 (1957); **109**, 1023 (1958); **109**, 1040 (1958). Brueckner, Gammel, and Weitzner, *Phys. Rev.* **110**, 431 (1958).
19. K. A. Brueckner, *Phys. Rev.* **110**, 597 (1958).
20. See, e.g., A. Sommerfeld, *Partial Differential Equations of Physics*, Academic, New York, 1949, p. 49.
21. B. Lippmann and J. Schwinger, *Phys. Rev.* **79**, 469 (1950).
22. See, e.g., N. F. Mott and H. S. W. Massey, *Atomic Collisions*, Oxford, New York, 1949, 2nd ed., p. 24.
23. See however L. L. Foldy and W. Tobocman, *Phys. Rev.* **105**, 1099 (1957).
24. G. F. Chew and M. L. Goldberger, *Phys. Rev.* **87**, 778 (1952).
25. V. Weisskopf, *Science* **113**, 1 (1951).
26. L. Brillouin, *J. phys. radium* 4, 1 (1933), E. Wigner, *Math. u. naturw. Anz. ungar. Akad. Wiss.* **53**, 477 (1935).
27. See, e.g., E. U. Condon and G. H. Shortley, *Theory of Atomic Spectra*, Cambridge, New York, 1953, p. 30.
28. N. Fukuda and R. G. Newton, *Phys. Rev.* **103**, 1558 (1956).
29. H. A. Bethe, *Phys. Rev.* **103**, 1353 (1956); see also R. J. Eden, *Proc. Roy. Soc.* **A235**, 408 (1956).
30. Gomes, Walecka, and Weisskopf, *Annals of Physics*, **3**, 241 (1958).
31. K. A. Brueckner and K. Sawada, *Phys. Rev.* **106**, 1117 (1957); 1128 (1957).
32. See e.g., M. H. Stone, *Linear Transformations in Hilbert Space*, American Mathematical Society, New York, 1932, Chap IV.
33. R. J. Eden and N. C. Francis, *Phys. Rev.* **97**, 1366 (1955).
34. H. Tanaka, *Progr. Theoret. Phys.* (*Kyoto*) **13**, 497 (1955).
35. N. Fukuda, *Phys. Rev.* **103**, 420 (1956).
36. W. Swiatecki, *Phys. Rev.* **101**, 1321 (1956).
37. E. Feenberg, *Phys. Rev.* **74**, 206 (1948).
38. H. A. Bethe, Chap. II, this volume.
39. W. Tobocman, *Phys. Rev.* **107**, 203 (1957).
40. See, e.g., P. M. Morse and H. Feshbach, *Methods of Theoretical Physics*, Mc Graw-Hill, New York, 1953 p. 1005; see also [15], [39].
41. N. M. Hugenholtz, *Physica* **23**, 481, 533 (1957); we have changed the notation somewhat.

42. J. Goldstone, *Proc. Roy. Soc.* (*London*) **A239**, 267 (1957); H. A. Bethe and J. Goldstone, *Proc. Roy. Soc.* (*London*) **A238**, 551 (1957).
43. J. Hubbard, *Proc. Roy. Soc.* (*London*) **A240**, 53 (1957); **A243**, 336 (1958); **A244**, 199 (1958).
44. T. H. R. Skyrme, *Proc. Roy. Soc.* (*London*) **A239**, 399 (1957); *Proc. Phys. Soc.* (*London*) **A70**, 433 (1957).
45. D. H. Weinstein, *Proc. Nat. Acad. Sci. U. S.* **20**, 529 (1934).

CHAPTER II

Derivation of the Brueckner Theory[†]

H. A. BETHE

1. *Introduction*

The approach of Brueckner and his collaborators has been very successful in explaining the properties of many-body systems with strong interactions. In particular, the consistency of the shell model picture of nuclear structure with the strong short-range exchange nature of nuclear forces has been established. However, the very formal nature of much of this theory has reduced its availability to the population of physicists. Recently, a derivation has been given by Goldstone [1], of Cambridge, which is simple, clarifies the concepts, and is flexible, permitting the possibility of other approaches.

2. *The model potential*

We consider the ground state of a closed-shell nucleus, finite in extent, but large. We start by defining a nucleon potential V. This is to be a one-body potential, each nucleon moving within it, and is subject to two requirements: (1) V keeps the nucleons confined in space, and (2) V is momentum-dependent and so must be regarded as a potential matrix $\langle \mathbf{r}'|V|\mathbf{r} \rangle$ or $\langle \mathbf{k}'|V|\mathbf{k} \rangle$. Otherwise, we can choose V to suit our fancy. The choice of V will have the purpose of making the perturbation theory rapidly convergent, but there will be no self-consistency problem, since a self-consistent V in the context of this theory cannot be obtained. In this potential alone, which may be regarded as a shell model potential, each nucleon will have an energy

[†] Composed from tape recordings and augmented by the editor.

E_n in its nth state; for the hypothetical case of an infinite (uniform) nuclear medium, V is diagonal in the wave number k and E is a function of k alone.

Now we may consider the nucleons in this "model" potential V with its corresponding wave functions, and treat the difference between the actual interaction and the model interaction as a perturbation. Either time-independent or time-dependent perturbation theory is appropriate, for, the nucleons already being bound in the unperturbed potential, the adiabatic theorem [2] holds with no further hypothesis; that is to say, if the perturbation is turned on arbitrarily slowly, reaching its full value at $t = 0$, then the state at $t = 0$ is the correct perturbed state. Moreover, the full power of field theory techniques and Feynman diagrams can be used, for in a finite system no divergences will appear.

The main problem solved by Goldstone is that of the unlinked clusters, which are completely eliminated in his treatment, unlike previous derivations in which explicit eliminations were required at each stage. Brueckner observed that straightforward perturbation theory allows processes like: a nucleon in state m occupied in the many-body model wave function is excited to state n outside it, a nucleon in state r initially occupied is excited to state s outside, nucleon in state n returns to m, nucleon in state s returns to r. The apparent correlation which results is certainly not physical; furthermore for A nucleons, the contribution to the energy goes as A^2 instead of A (for fixed density). In a properly formulated theory, such processes should be cancelled by higher order terms, and Brueckner showed explicitly [3] how this occurred in the first few orders of perturbation. By suitable handling of Feynman diagrams, the nature of the cancellation will now be generally clarified.

3. The linked cluster expansion

The nuclear forces will be regarded as strictly two-body in nature; there is no clear evidence that many-body forces are required as well. In terms of the matrix elements of the two-body potential v and the model potential V, the second quantized Hamiltonian for the nuclear Fermions becomes

$$H = H_0 + H_1$$

$$H_0 = \sum_n E_n \eta_n^+ \eta_n \tag{1}$$

$$H_1 = \sum_{r<s} \langle rs|v|mn\rangle \eta_r^+ \eta_s^+ \eta_n \eta_m - \sum \langle r|V|m\rangle \eta_r^+ \eta_m$$

the states m, n, r, s represented are those of a single particle in the model potential V, and η_n, η_n^+ are the annihilation and creation operators for these states. For convenience, we take the vacuum state as the lowest state of the system under the model potential V alone — the Fermi sea. One-particle model states not contained in the vacuum state will be designated as "particles" or "excited states", missing states in the vacuum as "holes" (given respectively by $k>$ and $k<k_F$ for an infinite system), and pictured accordingly; the characterization of η_n, η_n^+ is thus reversed for holes.

According to the adiabatic theorem [2], if the perturbation is turned on at $t = -\infty$ with amplitude $e^{\alpha t}$, then at $t = 0$, the perturbed ground state (non-normalized) and energy perturbation are given by the limit $\alpha \to 0$ of

$$\Psi_0 = U_\alpha \Phi_0 / \langle \Phi_0 | U_\alpha | \Phi_0 \rangle$$

$$\Delta E_0 = \langle \Phi_0 | H_1 U_\alpha | \Phi_0 \rangle / \langle \Phi_0 | U_\alpha | \Phi_0 \rangle \tag{2}$$

where

$$U_\alpha = \sum_{h=0}^{\infty} (-i)^h \int_{0 > t_1 > t_2 \cdots > t_h} H_1(t_1) H_1(t_2) \dots H_1(t_h) e^{\alpha(t_1 + \cdots + t_h)} \, dt^h \tag{3}$$

Here, $H_1(t)$ denotes H_1 with η_n replaced by $\eta_n(t) = \eta_n e^{-iE_n t}$, Φ_0 is the vacuum state, and we choose $\hbar = 1$.

Figure 1

The analysis of Wick [4] is used to express eqs. (2) and (3) by means of Feynman diagrams. Wick's contraction symbol turns out to vanish for one time ordering [5], and this is reflected in the diagrams by the condition that particles must be produced before they can be annihilated, with the reverse for holes. The fundamental one-body diagrams involve two states, appearing in Fig. 1 as scattering of a particle state, scattering of a hole, pair production, and pair annihilation. The fundamental diagrams corresponding to the two-body potential interaction and model potential interaction are then typified in Fig. 2. In the special case of infinite nuclear matter, momentum is conserved in each interaction: $\mathbf{k}_r + \mathbf{k}_n = \mathbf{k}_s + \mathbf{k}_m$ and $\mathbf{k}_m = \mathbf{k}_n$, respectively, which simplifies the summing up of the contributions, but this is not generally the case.

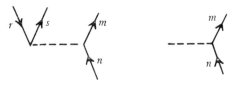

Figure 2

Now the prescription for writing down the hth order integral contribution to $\langle \varPhi_b | U_\alpha | \varPhi_0 \rangle$ from eq. (3) is as follows. We draw all diagrams in which h interactions (dashed lines) occur, such that there are no lines at the earliest time, and just those particle and hole lines at the latest time which represent the unperturbed state $\varPhi_b$. To the interactions (Fig. 2) we associate the matrix elements between incoming and outgoing states: $\langle sm|v|rn \rangle$ and $\langle m|-V|n \rangle$, as well as phase factors for the interaction time: $e^{i(E_s + E_m - E_r - E_n)t} e^{\alpha t}$ and $e^{i(E_m - E_n)t} e^{\alpha t}$. Further, each diagram is multiplied by $(-1)^{w+z}$ where w is the number of internal (terminated at both ends) hole lines and z the number of closed loops. The product of the factors of each such distinct diagram is finally integrated over its ordered time sequence from $-\infty$ to 0, and the total contribution is thus obtained. For the numerator of ΔE_0, one ends by closing the diagram with an unintegrated $H_1(0)$, and this is the only change.

Most of the diagrams are unlinked or disconnected. A portion of such a diagram is shown in Fig. 3, in which two nucleon pairs are produced and annihilated in the presence of a hole. In general, setting aside the portion of a diagram connected to the final state, the remainder consists of a set of disconnected vacuum-to-vacuum subdiagrams, such as in the right-hand side of Fig. 3. Moreover, each such Φ_0-to-Φ_b connected diagram is accompanied by the full set of vacuum-to-vacuum diagrams (including the blank case). If one takes a given connected vacuum subdiagram and constructs all diagrams obtained by moving its interaction times to all intermediate time positions in the big diagram in which it is located, maintaining the time ordering of the subdiagram itself, and adds up all these cases,

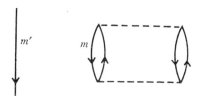

Figure 3

it is clear that the result is simply to separate the time ordering of the subdiagram from that of the remaining diagram. In other words, the integral of the subdiagram occurs as a factor of the sum of the integrals of the diagrams containing it. In this way, we may show that the full vacuum-to-vacuum matrix element $\langle \Phi_0 | U_\alpha | \Phi_0 \rangle$, being precisely the sum of such vacuum subdiagrams, is a factor of $\langle \Phi_b | U_\alpha | \Phi_0 \rangle$ and that the remaining factor consists of all diagrams without disconnected vacuum-to-vacuum components. Therefore, eq. (2) may be rewritten as

$$\langle \Phi_b | \Psi_0 \rangle = \langle \Phi_b | U_\alpha | \Phi_0 \rangle_L$$
$$\Delta E_0 = \langle \Phi_0 | H_1 U_\alpha | \Phi_0 \rangle_L \qquad (4)$$

where L indicates that only linked or connected diagrams (to the final state) are to be used.

In the above procedure, it is vital that no preliminary evaluations or reductions be made. More importantly, the Pauli principle is not used, and cannot be used, to restrict intermediate states. The reason for this is that in order to remove the vacuum subdiagrams as factors, the states which are summed over in computing their total contribution must vary independently of the states in the remainder of the diagram. But if, for example, the value of m in Fig. 3 is not allowed to become m' because there would then be two holes in state m', the process will not go through. Furthermore, a shift in time of a subdiagram might give a disallowed diagram if two states thereby coincide at the same time, and this too would invalidate the process. Of course, we know that if initial and final state obey the Pauli principle, and this the diagrams readily guarantee, then it is not necessary to restrict the intermediate states. What will simply happen is that contributions from Pauli-violating diagrams will be canceled by corresponding exchange diagrams. Thus, Fig. 3, for $m' = m$, yields Fig. 4 by exchange in state m, and the two diagrams, having opposite signs, cancel. But Fig. 3 is disconnected and hence eliminated in the Goldstone reduction, while Fig. 4 is linked and remains. It is therefore

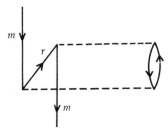

Figure 4

not permissible to employ the Pauli principle at the outset to eliminate both diagrams. Stated differently, the diagrams that are retained, in the linked cluster expansion, will include many which violate the Pauli principle.

Once the linked cluster reduction has been made, the parameter α, which was required in order to turn on the potential, can be dispensed with, although this is not possible before the reduction. It is easy to see that, performing the time integrations of a diagram from earliest time (vacuum) up, successive denominators of $\alpha + i(E - E_0)$ are introduced, where E is the energy of the intermediate state following each integration and E_0 is the energy of the vacuum state. If there is a closed vacuum subdiagram, E can return to E_0 at an intermediate state, and so the limit $\alpha \to 0$ cannot be carried out term-wise. But when these subdiagrams have been eliminated, $E - E_0$ must be positive. This is due to the fact that, in any intermediate state, particles have been removed from the Fermi sea and placed into "excited" states — by which the energy of the system is increased. Thus α may be taken as zero and only the usual energy denominator remains. One can describe the result by saying that ordinary Schrödinger perturbation theory, in which (as opposed to the Brillouin-Wigner form [6]) all energy denominators are differences between unperturbed energy levels, remains valid when only linked clusters are retained in the theory.

4. *The Hartree method*

Let us examine the choice of the one-body potential V which until now has remained arbitrary. In addition to the actual one-body potential due to V, there is an effective one-body interaction, in which a particle k (Fig. 5) interacts, by means of v, with a particle in the Fermi sea, leaving this particle in its normal state n, so that the matrix element is $\langle rn|v|kn\rangle$. Owing to this interaction, and its exchange counterpart, the Fermi sea gives rise to an average one-body interaction. The three one-body terms are indicated in Fig. 5. With

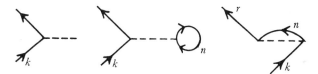

Figure 5

appropriate signs (negative for the exchange diagram), they always occur together. A special case is that of first-order processes, in which k is also a state in the Fermi sea; thus a single interaction can produce and reabsorb two states from the sea. Now we may choose V to cancel the equivalent one-body terms:

$$\langle r|V|m\rangle = \sum_n (\langle rn|v|mn\rangle - \langle rn|v|nm\rangle) \qquad (5)$$

summed only over states n in the sea; we thus obtain the Hartree method.

This definition of V then accounts for the average two-body potential seen by a given particle in the "unperturbed" many-body state, and the diagrams of Fig. 5 will cancel and will therefore no longer appear. In second order, only the diagrams of Fig. 6b occur; in third and higher order, diagrams of the type shown in Fig. 6c are

cancelled by corresponding diagrams involving $-V$. The first-order
diagrams shown in Fig. 6a are doubly cancelled by $-V$ and hence
occur with reversed sign, giving rise to the familiar first-order Hartree
approximation energy of

$$E = E_0 + \Delta E = \sum_n \langle n|T|n \rangle + \tfrac{1}{2} \sum_n \langle n|V|n \rangle \qquad (6)$$

where T is the kinetic energy.

The question of course is whether the correlation effects given by
second- and higher order terms are sufficiently small, so that our
perturbation series will converge in a practical way. Euler [7] in 1935,
and then again Huby [8] in 1948, did calculations by means of ordinary
perturbation theory (not Hartree; ordinary perturbation theory is
defined by setting $V = 0$) in which they found first- and second-order
perturbation energies for nuclei. Swiatecki has recently remarked [9]
that these calculations converge much better than had been supposed,

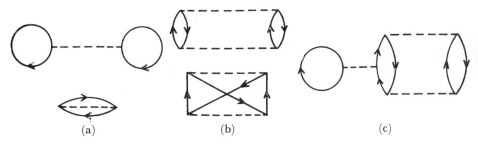

Figure 6

if one looks at them in the right way; that is, if one considers for
example just the attractive part of the interaction, its effect in second
order is quite small compared to that in first. The same is true of the
repulsive part, but these facts are masked by the near cancellation of
first-order attractive and repulsive contributions. If one considers the
multidimensional *wave function*, computations indicate [10] that
unperturbed and perturbed ground states may be practically orthogonal, but this is of little effect.

One can do still better in the Hartree approximation than with the
straight perturbation approximation, and the Hartree approximation
has the property of giving an effective mass smaller than the normal

mass, so that higher order corrections tend to be further minimized. For conventional forces — exponential-type or Yukawa-type exchange forces — the use of the Hartree approximation is perfectly satisfactory; one can get a perturbation theory which converges rapidly and one really wouldn't need to worry about a more powerful method. It is very strange that this was found out only now, but it seems to be the case. There is the question of whether or not conventional exchange forces will give you the right nuclear binding energy, but that is different from the question of convergence of the mathematical method.

5. *The reaction matrix*

There are interactions, and these are the interactions we now believe in, which are strongly singular at small distances — in particular, the repulsive core which was introduced by Jastrow [11]. Such interactions cannot be treated by the Hartree approximation for the simple reason that the expectation value of the potential, and indeed of all matrix elements of the potential, is infinite; you clearly cannot build a perturbation theory on that. It is with respect to these potentials that the Brueckner method is not only more powerful but also absolutely necessary, because it will give you finite results.

The Brueckner method is appropriate for singular potentials because it takes together any number of interactions of two particles, and adds up the contributions of all these ladder-type diagrams; the resulting reaction matrix is perfectly finite, even for interactions with repulsive cores. Thus, in Fig. 7, considering the interaction of particles r and k, we take not only the direct interaction, but also permit r and k to be excited to arbitrary excited states, and interact several times with each other before interacting with other particles. The reaction matrix $\langle ps|t|kr \rangle$ is precisely the sum of all such ladder diagrams between the initial state kr and final state ps. The reason that this device is necessary is that the matrix elements, e.g., for a repulsive core, have very large very high frequency components, and what one does by using this device is to take properly into account the possibility that two particles will hit each other into very high momentum states for a short time, interact strongly and repeatedly in these high momentum states (i.e., at close distances), then get out of the high momentum states and back into normal momentum states.

Unfortunately, as one does this trick, one can do it only for the interaction between particles; one cannot do it simultaneously for the interaction between particles and holes.

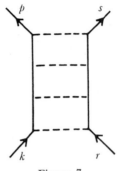

Figure 7

The interaction between particles k and r may take place for two particles normally in the Fermi sea. For instance, if $p = k$, $s = r$, the ladder of Fig. 7 will correspond to the upper graph in Fig. 6, first order, if it has one rung; to the upper picture in Fig. 6, second order, if it has two rungs, etc.

The interaction may also occur in a manner similar to the third-order diagram of Fig. 6. In this case, state k represents a particle in

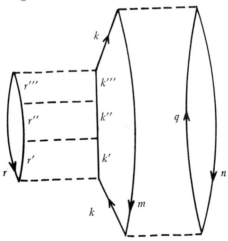

Figure 8

an excited state, and state r is a state in the Fermi sea. The full ladder diagram corresponding to this sequence is shown in Fig. 8. In this case, one must be careful about the energy denominators. In any intermediate state of the ladder diagram, in addition to particles in states k' and r', there is a particle in state q, and holes in states m, n, and r. The energy of excitation compared with the ground state energy is, therefore,

$$E(k') + E(r') + E(q) - E(r) - E(m) - E(n) \qquad (7)$$

This depends not only on the states k' and r' now occupied, and the states k and r from which the two particles came, but also on the empty states m and n and the filled state q.

Now if one wants to talk about a reaction matrix, this must depend only upon the interaction of the two particles r and k which interact with each other. It is therefore not possible to consider at the same time all the other particles which have been made. The only way to consider them and actually take them into account is by using the correct energy for the intermediate states, that is, to consider the process as one which is off the energy shell. Explicitly, the energy denominator may be written

$$E(k') + E(r') - E(k) - E(r) + \delta \qquad (8)$$

where

$$\delta = E(k) + E(q) - E(n) - E(m) \qquad (9)$$

The actual expression for the sum of the ladder diagrams is

$$\langle rs|t|mn \rangle = \langle rs|v|mn \rangle$$
$$+ \sum \frac{\langle rs|v|m'n' \rangle \langle m'n'|v|mn \rangle}{(E_m + E_n - E_{m'} - E_{n'} - \delta)}$$
$$+ \sum \frac{\langle rs|v|m''n'' \rangle \langle m''n''|v|m'n' \rangle \langle m'n'|v|mn \rangle}{(E_m + E_n - E_{m''} - E_{n''} - \delta)(E_m + E_n - E_{m'} - E_{n'} - \delta)} + \cdots \qquad (10)$$

where only particle states m', n', m'', n'' are summed over. Equation (10) may be rewritten as the integral equation

$$\langle rs|t|mn \rangle = \langle rs|v|mn \rangle$$
$$+ \sum \frac{\langle rs|v|m'n' \rangle \langle m'n'|t|mn \rangle}{(E_m + E_n - E_{m'} - E_{n'} - \delta)} \qquad (11)$$

This is the typical integral equation for a reaction matrix. The matrix t is of course a function of δ.

Although eq. (11) does allow for a reaction matrix from any initial state, it is sharply restricted to interaction ladders during which no other interaction takes place, for some energy denominators would otherwise be changed. Further, the interaction of a hole can occur in a ladder diagram only as in Fig. 9. Here initially we have a hole in

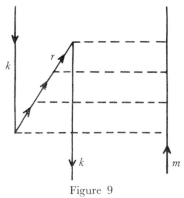

Figure 9

state k and a particle in state m. A second hole in k is created together with an extra particle r, which then is scattered by m via a reaction matrix. One does not properly consider the multiple interaction of holes, and so all the usual correction terms are still required to take account of these.

6. The Brueckner expansion

Now if one takes into account the off-energy-shell propagation, i.e., the specific fact that t is a function of δ, it is quite clear that it is no longer possible to invent a model potential V that will exactly compensate all t-matrix interactions with unexcited nucleons in the Fermi sea, as in Fig. 5. Thus, it is simply not possible to introduce a one-particle V which completely eliminates third-order graphs of the type given in Fig. 6, but with t interactions. This is why I said in the beginning that a self-consistent procedure such as originally envisaged by Brueckner and Levinson [12], who wanted to eliminate these third-order graphs, cannot be obtained. This has the advantage that one does not need to use special care in choosing V.

Let us now indicate the reaction matrix or sum of ladder diagrams by a wavy line, in which the dependence on δ is to be understood. It is clear that the full set of diagrams for the ground state energy will be obtained by removing all diagrams containing ladders of intermediate states of particles and no other intervening interactions, and then substituting a wavy line for each two-body dashed line. A wavy line can of course join a hole line to a particle — see Fig. 10 — or to another hole line. We now want to enumerate the diagrams that occur in the ground state energy; to do this, we must decide on the model potential V. Although V cannot be chosen to annul all effective one-body interactions due to the unexcited nucleon sea, still, if V is chosen as in eq. (5), with v replaced by t for some reasonable mean value of δ, the corrections should not be large and we shall not now consider them. Actually, Brueckner has pointed out [3] that, e.g.,

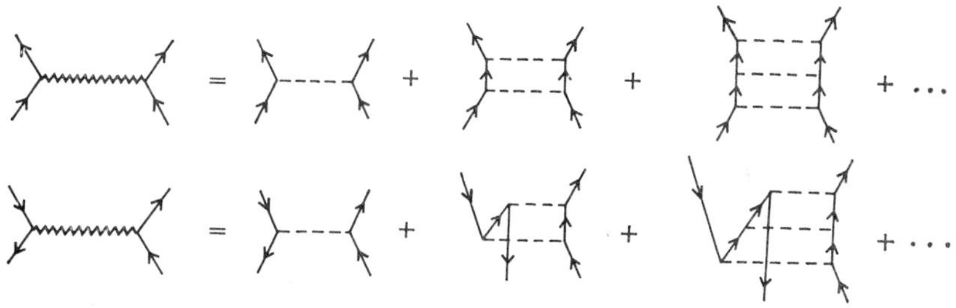

Figure 10

there are interactions in the fourth order which may largely compensate the effect of off-energy propagation in the lower orders. On the other hand, off-energy-shell propagation is useful to consider because in this way you avoid even the appearance of zero-energy denominators, which of course have no reason to appear in a theory which deals with the ground state. At any rate, there is little point in setting up a complicated self-consistent scheme to minimize the effect of off-energy-shell propagation.

Suppose that effective cancellation of the nucleon-sea contributions has been achieved by V. Then in first order, the wavy line analogues of Fig. 6 appear in the ground state energy, again with reversed sign, and they again contribute to the energy as in eq. (6). These innocent-looking diagrams, which give the main contribution to the energy, are in practice quite hard to calculate, owing both to the determination of the t matrix and to the self-consistency requirement, in whatever form we choose to take it. Next, we might think that a second-order diagram will appear; but there can be none, because these are already contained

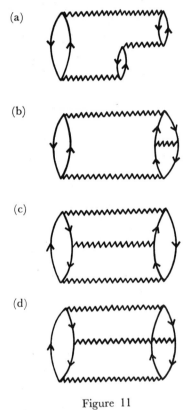

(a)

(b)

(c)

(d)

Figure 11

in ladder diagrams. Then there are third-order diagrams. The wavy line analogue to that in Fig. 6 is largely compensated by V, but there are several others. For example, as in Fig. 11a, you may create two nucleon pairs, destroy one and make a different pair, and then destroy the first pair. This is the linked cluster diagram first introduced by Brueckner in his paper on clusters [3]; it gives one of the main third-order contributions. (*Note added in proof*: It has been evaluated by Kohler [13].) Alternatively, after forming the first loop, you need not start a completely new loop but can have an interaction within one loop, which means that the hole is filled by a nucleon from another hole, and at the same time the excited particle goes into a different state (Fig. 11b); this can be shown to be an exchange diagram related to Fig. 11a. Next, you can let the particle of one pair interact with the hole of the other; for infinite matter, this means that the hole of the first pair is filled by a particle from the Fermi sea, while the particle of the second pair takes up the necessary momentum (Fig. 11c). This again is an exchange effect related to Fig. 11a. Finally, two holes may interact with each other, Fig. 11d — first, two pairs of nucleons are made, and then the holes are filled by two new particles from the sea, conserving momentum in the process (for infinite matter) without affecting the other sea particles. These then are all the possible third-order diagrams. In summary, you can either let the particles in one loop interact with each other, or have interactions between two loops in which at least one hole participates, or have three separate loops. Higher order terms may of course be enumerated similarly.

7. *Degenerate states*

If the ground state is not a closed shell, but contains a number of nucleons outside, then the degeneracy may be very high. As a simple example, suppose there are two extra particles outside the closed shell. Then in computing the perturbation energy in this case, you must start, not from the vacuum, but from a state in which two particles are already present. You can then go to any other final state in which two particles are again present, although not necessarily in the same magnetic substates as the original ones. Thereby, you get matrix elements from any two-particle state to any other two-particle state which is degenerate with it. This leads to a matrix, a Hamiltonian matrix, between any two degenerate states, which is just the tool of the shell theory physicists who then reduce this matrix and find the (model) states which the nucleus will actually take, as in spectroscopy. Of course, they use the potential v rather than the t matrices, and this procedure is valid only for well-behaved potentials.

One of the flexibilities of the theory is that you can choose what to call degenerate. You do not want to have energy denominators which are very small, and therefore you will choose to call degenerate any states which have approximately the same energy, approximately to the extent of the interaction energy. You will then get various unperturbed states which are associated with different diagonal elements of the energy and different interactions between them as in ordinary spectroscopy. This means then that the configuration interaction is taken fully into account between degenerate states. But the configuration interaction with excited configurations has already been taken into account in the derivation of the reaction matrix; it must therefore not be taken into account once more in an effort to improve energy levels. Hence the initial excited configurations cannot later be allowed to contribute elements to the Hamiltonian matrix.

Notes and References

1. J. Goldstone, *Proc. Roy. Soc. (London)* **A239**, 267 (1957).
2. M. Gell-Mann and F. Low, *Phys. Rev.* **76**, 350 (1951).
3. K. A. Brueckner, *Phys. Rev.* **100**, 36 (1955).
4. G. C. Wick, *Phys. Rev.* **80**, 268 (1950).
5. Since time ordering is not eliminated, the original method of A. Houriet and A. Kind, *Helv. Phys. Acta* **22**, 319 (1949), is also appropriate in this case.
6. L. Brillouin, *J. phys. radium* **4**, 1 (1933). E. Wigner, *Math. u. naturw. Anz. ungar. Akad. Wiss.* **53**, 477 (1935).
7. H. Euler, *Z. Physik* **105**, 553, (1937).
8. R. Huby, *Proc. Phys. Soc. (London)* **A62**, 62 (1949).
9. W. Swiatecki, *Phys Rev.* **101**, 1321 (1956).
10. H. A. Bethe, *Phys. Rev.* **103**, 1353 (1956).
11. R. Jastrow, *Phys. Rev.* **81**, 165 (1951).
12. K. A. Brueckner and C. A. Levinson, *Phys. Rev.* **97**, 1344 (1955).
13. S. Köhler, *Ann. of Phys.* **12**, 444 (1961).

CHAPTER III

The Many-Body Problem

K. A. Brueckner

(*Abstract*)

Each many-body system discussed presents problems of a special character which cannot be treated by perturbation procedures. The technique of solution in general is to solve exactly that feature of the system which presents a particular difficulty, while approximating those features which do not greatly affect quantitative and qualitative results. For strongly interacting Fermion systems — nuclear matter and liquid He^3 — pair correlation and exclusion effects are treated exactly, whereas other multibody correlations appear only through an average self-consistent field. Numerical results compare favorably with experimental values; the He^3 excitation curve is very flat, indicating imminent crystallization. In the electron gas, the high density screening effect can be treated rigorously, giving an exact expansion valid at high densities. Finally, in condensed He^4, pairwise correlation must be handled exactly, while the other particles are introduced only through statistics and a self-consistent field. A Landau type of spectrum for phonon excitation results.

CHAPTER IV

Energy of Interacting Fermi Systems

C. De Dominicis and P. C. Martin

1. *Introduction*

A number of procedures have recently been proposed for determining the ground state energy of interacting systems. Each of these procedures may be roughly characterized as an expansion in the ratio of the average distance between particles to a kind of effective mean free path in the medium. More precisely, the convergence of any of them requires that the effect of interactions on the statistical correlations already present with non-interacting particles be a small one. Generally speaking, this will be the case for one of two reasons. Either the interactions may be fairly weak and extend over a sizeable fraction of the volume, or they may be strongly repulsive but occupy only a small fraction of the volume. In either case, a perturbation theory which treats the effects of interactions on the correlations of successively larger numbers of particles may be expected to converge. We would like to report here on some investigations into the nature of this convergence for interactions which have one or the other of the properties just mentioned. In particular we wish to indicate the nature of convergence when the interaction potential is a small hard core and when it is a weak but longer ranged Yukawa potential.

2. *The hard core gas*

In the first of these cases, the hard core gas, the energy of the ground state is characterized by only one parameter, the ratio of the interaction radius, a, (twice the hard core radius or the distance of closest approach of two hard cores) to the interparticle spacing r_0. In practice it is more convenient to replace the latter by the wave length appropriate to the Fermi momentum, k_F, and use the parameter $k_F a$. The condition that the mean free path be long is the condition that $k_F a$ be small, and in that case, the energy may be expanded in powers of it. For a gas that has the spin degrees of freedom of a proton-neutron system, we have calculated this energy to third order in $k_F a$. To that order there are several contributions. Interactions in relative s states between each pair of particles give rise to an energy per particle

$$E = (k_F^2/2m)[(2/3\pi)k_F a(1+(1/10)(k_F a)^2)]$$
$$+12/35(11-2\ln 2)(k_F a/\pi)^2+2\pi(k_F a/\pi)^3$$

above the free-particle energy.

The last two terms [and therefore the only one of order $(k_F a)^2$] arise from statistical correlations in the Fermi gas. Interactions in relative p states give rise to an energy

$$E = (k_F^2/2m)[(k_F a)^3/\pi]$$

The result of successive interactions between different pairs of particles (in the nomenclature of Brueckner, three-particle clusters) gives an additional energy

$$E = (k_F^2/2m)[2\pi(k_F a/\pi)^3]$$

Some approximations made in evaluating the third-order terms may have led to an error as large as ten per cent. It will be seen from this separation, that at densities which are not too large, the many-particle terms are comparable to the corrections to the two-body terms. For a hard core interaction radius $a = 0.5 \times 10^{-13}$ cm and an interparticle spacing $r_0 = 1.2 \times 10^{-13}$ cm, the kinetic energy arising from this first term and higher order corrections is of the order of a few mev. With increasing density it clearly grows very rapidly. Thus, at least when there is no attraction outside the core, the limiting density for the validity of the perturbative procedure appears to be not much larger than the one observed in nuclear matter.

3. Yukawa interaction

It is probably worth remarking at the outset of a discussion of the convergence of these approximate treatments of weak interactions that Yukawa potentials, of the strength required by nuclear forces, can, at the observed nuclear density, be treated as weak. This is a point which has recently been stressed both by Swiatecki [1] and Bethe [2]. Since this is the case, none of the complicated procedures differ significantly from ordinary perturbation theory. We shall therefore, for these potentials, summarize our conclusions in terms of the ordinary perturbation expansion of the energy in powers of the potential. A number of these conclusions were already either implicit or explicit in calculations performed at an earlier stage by many authors, among them Van Vleck [3], Euler [4] and Huby [5].

The first approximation to the energy is just the potential energy of particles whose only correlations are due to their Fermi statistics. Their correlations contribute a potential energy which may be viewed in the familiar way, as the sum over all momenta of a Fermi gas of a potential which varies with momentum. It is of interest to determine from which states of relative angular momentum the important contributions to the direct and exchange potential energy originate. Qualitatively, we should expect that since the range of nuclear forces is only slightly larger than the interparticle spacing ($r_0 = 1.2 \times 10^{-13}$ cm), only a few states of relative angular momentum would be important. Quantitatively we find that s, p, and d states are the only significant ones. For a central Yukawa force, however, the contribution of the last of these is quite significant. In the neighborhood of the observed nuclear density it contributes about one-fifth as much potential energy as the s-state interaction, and for a Serber potential (no forces in odd states) it cuts the decrease in attraction between the bottom and top of the Fermi sea approximately in half. It is significant, therefore, that both the observed nucleon-nucleon scattering in d states and the observed large velocity dependence of the optical potential require less attraction than would be predicted by central Yukawa potentials fitting the observed s-wave scattering data.

The above considerations, based on first-order perturbation theory, are valid only if the higher order corrections are considerably smaller. We should like therefore to turn to a consideration of these higher order terms. Some of these results for second-order perturbation theory (a first approximation to the correlational energy) have also been obtained by Euler [4] and Huby [5] whose numerical values were different because they used different exchange mixtures and a larger nuclear radius. For a Serber mixture and the presently accepted density ($r_0 = 1.2 \times 10^{-13}$ cm), these terms contribute only ten per cent of the first-order energy. It is of interest to understand the mechanism by which this small correlational energy comes about. Actually, the ratio of the second-order contribution to that of the first-order depends upon two parameters, the strength of the two-body interaction and a function of the ratio of its range to the interparticle spacing. At the observed interparticle spacing it is possible to show that the Pauli principle has a rather large effect in reducing correlations. Were the Pauli principle inoperative, the correlational energy would be about four times as large and the procedure would be considerably less convergent. It should be remembered, however, that even with Pauli principle, the ratio of the correlational energy to the first-order energy is proportional to the potential strength, and if the potential were sufficiently large (whether or not it saturated) the Pauli principle would not be sufficient to make the successive terms small compared to the first. Not every system of Fermions is approximately a Fermi gas — there are crystals.

4. *Higher order corrections*

A treatment which takes account of all the correlations produced by interactions between a given pair of particles in the Fermi sea will include all of the second-order perturbation terms plus some higher order ones. To third order in the potential, however, there arise three additional kinds of terms which represent the interactions of more than two particles and which are not included. One of these represents successive interactions involving the correlations of each of the three possible pairs of three particles (Brueckner's three-particle cluster term). A second term describes the interaction of two particles, an interaction between the two vacated holes (one in which two other particles virtually scatter into the two vacated holes), followed by a third interaction in which the two particles originally virtually scattered go into the new holes. The third term represents a virtual scattering of two particles, a virtual forward scattering of one of the particles or holes by a third particle, and finally a second scattering of the first pair of particles which returns them to their holes. This last term may be looked upon as the effect of the average velocity-dependent potential of the remainder on the scattering of two. It is these corrections which Brueckner has tried to treat in a less perturbative way by means of a kind of self-consistency requirement.

We have already indicated that only the first two mechanisms contribute to a hard core gas at low densities. We wish now to indicate how large each of the three above corrections is for Yukawa forces with the Serber mixture. The first of them has been previously estimated for the same forces by Brueckner and his estimate revised by Bethe. A somewhat more careful examination indicates that the exchange terms are not as negligible as supposed and that this term contributes about one-tenth of the second-order energy. A calculation of the second kind of correction, which appears to have been omitted previously, indicates that it contributes an approximately equal amount. Together, these contribute a still rather small amount (about one Mev) which is fairly negligible. However, for the same potential, the remaining "self-consistent" corrections have opposite sign and are also less than one Mev.

It is easy to see that one greatly overestimates the magnitude of this last correction by approximating the velocity-dependent potential by the parabola which agrees with it at low energies and neglecting the exclusion principle. Not taking the exclusion principle into account overestimates the time each particle spends with a high momentum and consequently less attraction; making the quadratic approximation overestimates the difference in potential between the ground state and the fairly high momentum intermediate states which are favored when the exclusion principle is taken into account. The numerical effect is to overestimate the correction by a factor of eight.

With more realistic potentials we find that the contributions of the three terms discussed are somewhat larger than for the Yukawa potential considered here but still small enough to be treated by perturbation theory. Treating them that way, we have studied the predictions of the more realistic forces.

5. Concluding remarks

Whether or not there are short-range potentials for which, at higher densities, the "average" effects are so large that they cannot be treated perturbatively, while at the same time all other effects of more than two particles can be neglected, we do not know. We feel that the possibility of this situation requires further demonstration. Similarly, we feel that if this possibility does exist, then the question of the correct method for treating of the "average" field must be more thoroughly investigated. There is, in other words, a distinction between the nuclear problem and the familiar atomic problems. In the latter, a Hartree self-consistent procedure is a good one since many particles, which are not strongly interacting with a given one, contribute to the average potential that one experiences. These interactions favor forward scattering, and produce little correlation. In the nucleus, however, each particle interacts with only a few nearby particles, each of which may transfer a large momentum to it in a virtual scattering. It is this distinction which leads us to expect that the various many-particle effects will not differ vastly in magnitude when the forces have a short range.

Notes and References

1. W. Swiatecki, *Phys. Rev.* **101**, 1321 (1956).
2. H. A. Bethe, *Phys. Rev.* **103**, 1353 (1956).
3. J. H. Van Vleck, *Phys. Rev.* **48**, 367 (1935).
4. H. Euler, *Z. Physik* **105**, 553 (1937).
5. R. Huby, *Proc. Phys. Soc. (London)* **A62**, 62 (1949).

CHAPTER V

Saturation of Nuclear Forces

P. C. Martin and C. De Dominicis

1. Introduction

We would like to report here on an investigation into whether the forces between pairs of nucleons predict saturation of nuclear matter. Such an investigation really involves three distinct aspects: (a) what are the forces between nucleons; (b) is it possible to calculate the energy per particle predicted by these forces as a function of density; (c) do they predict a minimum energy at the observed density, or are the more complicated nuclear forces between many nucleons essential to understand this minimum. (We shall assume throughout that nuclear matter really would form with an interparticle spacing of about 1.2×10^{-13} cm and a binding energy per particle of about 16 Mev if there were no Coulomb forces.)

2. Method and results

Unfortunately, we do not know the answer to the first of these questions. What is certain is that these forces are very complicated. They contain a tensor force, they are different in the various charge and spin states and even in states in which the orbit and spin angular momentum are the same but their resultant different. Furthermore, at least the singlet s state's potential, which is attractive at low energies, becomes repulsive at higher ones. We may expect, however, that different potentials which fit all the observed scattering phase shifts for those momenta present in the nucleus would also predict about the same properties for the nucleus. This rather reasonable assumption appears to be borne out on a variety of potentials on which we have tested it. We have therefore taken the simplest potentials we could, which were compatible with the Feshbach-Lomon phase shifts [1] below 150 Mev and therefore at least qualitatively with the two-body scattering. We have also put the additional requirement on the singlet s-state potential: that it contain a hard core, 0.5×10^{-13} cm, and thus agree with the high-energy proton-proton scattering observations. In order to make calculations possible, all of the potentials were chosen to be separable.

The second question to be answered is whether it is possible to calculate the energy these forces predict. We have already indicated that in the neighborhood of the observed density, we would expect the methods outlined earlier [2] to be reliable. With hard cores and attractions present, however, it is hard to say to how much greater densities they remain so. Specifically, we have done the following. First we have solved exactly for the effect of the interaction on a pair of particles correlated by Fermi statistics. (This amounts to solving the Schrödinger equation for each pair of momenta in the Fermi sea, with the virtual intermediate states all restricted to lie outside that sea.) To the energy resulting from these interactions we have added the small effects of interactions involving more than two particles. We find these corrections with the aid of a simple perturbation theory suitably modified to make sense when a hard core is present.

The third question is what do these calculations predict. We find that they actually do predict saturation at a density between $1.1–1.2 \times 10^{-13}$ cm (where the calculations may be expected to be reliable). At the saturating radius, the interactions involving only one pair of particles at a time give rise to an energy per particle of 18 Mev. The corrections arising from interactions involving more than two particles give rise to an energy which reduces the binding energy by about three Mev.

3. Discussion of results

Probably more meaningful than the numerical results we have quoted are the qualitative features we find. In the first place, the effect of the hard core on the interaction energy in the singlet s state is quite small. This is in keeping with the expectation that interactions that predict the same phase shifts up to fairly high energies will predict about the same binding energy. It is amusing to note that at small densities, and with our potentials, up to the observed density, a singlet s-state potential which has a hard core predicts a greater attractive interaction energy. This rather paradoxical result can be understood by remembering that the outside attraction must be deepened in order that the potential yield the same scattering phase shifts at low energies. If there were no statistical correlations, the energies would be simply related to the phase shifts and consequently equal when the phase shifts are adjusted to agree. The effect of the statistical correlations, which reduce the binding energy, are greater on the more smoothly varying potential with no hard core. The derivative of the energy with respect to the density is, of course, quite different for the two potentials. With increasing density the repulsion of the hard core becomes effective, that is, momenta for which phase shifts of the two potentials differ become important, and the hard-core potential leads to saturation. If we were to consider only interactions in the singlet s, and triplet eigen s states, we would find saturation, but with a rather larger binding energy and smaller radius than is obtained. Numerically we find that this saturation occurs at a radius of 0.8×10^{-13} cm with a binding energy per particle of almost 30 Mev. At this density it is likely that terms involving more than two particles would be important. While they might alter the result they would not increase the nuclear radius to anywhere near 1.1–1.2×10^{-13} cm, since the many-particle corrections are certainly small at the larger radius.

In addition to the effect of the hard cores on interactions in relative s states, then, the quoted results, (and therefore the Feshbach-Lomon phase shifts and perhaps the nuclear forces), require a net repulsive force from states of higher angular momenta, in particular, from the p and d states. As far as the d states are concerned, we have already remarked that for central Yukawa forces, they would give a sizeable additional attraction. The Feshbach-Lomon phase shifts, however, predict a net repulsion instead of this attraction. On the one hand, they require a singlet d potential which is attractive but very much smaller; on the other hand they require a triplet eigen d potential which is both sizeable and repulsive. The smallness of the former might be attributed to a hard core, or to some non-locality or velocity dependence; the large repulsive value of the latter is certainly due mainly to the strong tensor force. This tensor nature of the triplet-state potential is an important feature in predicting saturation at a reasonable density. We know that as the density of a nuclear system increases, and as dynamical correlations are inhibited, the effect of the tensor forces must be small because the tensor potential, averaged over spins, vanishes. When the calculation is performed in eigenstates of the relative angular momentum, this decrease in energy relative to a central force is reflected in a partial cancellation of the eigen s and eigen d contributions. The presence of this large tensor force agrees with the ideas we have about the nucleon-nucleon interaction.

In the case of the Feshbach-Lomon phase shifts, an additional feature contributes to a decrease in the density at which nuclear saturation is predicted. When weighted by the appropriate spin factors and averaged, their phase shifts produce a very small repulsive scattering. However, for a large repulsive potential to give a repulsive phase shift equal in magnitude to that of an attractive potential, the repulsive potential must be considerably larger than the attractive one. When statistical correlations are taken into account, this repulsive contribution is increased further. In other words, a potential which reproduces the Feshbach-Lomon phase shifts must contain a small central odd-state repulsive potential, and a spin-orbit force. When statistical correlations are taken into account, the attractive correlational contribution of the spin-orbit force and central force are reduced, leaving only the repulsive effect of the central force.

It appears then that the properties of nuclear matter may be understood in terms of the forces between pairs of nucleons. To do this, however, one must invoke the full complication these forces require. In particular, the tensor nature of the triplet even force and the repulsion in odd states, as well as the repulsion at high energies in the singlet s state are all necessary to obtain saturation at a density small enough to agree with experiment.

ADDENDUM 1: *In reply to question on magnitude of wave function corrections*: One must distinguish here between corrections to the many-body wave function and the two-body kind of wave function. The corrections to the many-body wave function increase with the number of particles, that is, with very many particles it becomes extremely likely that some will be excited. This is not true when we speak of an effective two-body wave function or related correlation function obtained by integrating over the remaining coordinates. This two-body wave function, which contains the information of interest, differs from that for two free Fermions violently within the hard core, but only slightly in the remaining space. Whether one calls this a large difference is largely a question of terminology. Actually, I should add, the quantum mechanical effect of a hard core extends beyond the hard core effectively by a wave length, and for this reason the corrections are rather important and the three-body effects significant when the cores are still fairly far apart. On the other hand, the effect of three-body contributions with hard cores and attractive wells may be smaller, for the attraction allows the wave function to build up within a shorter distance of the core.

ADDENDUM 2: *In reply to question on comparison with Brueckner results*: I think our disagreement with Brueckner is, at present, really quite small. At the time that we performed our calculations, the apparent disagreement was much greater. At that time he argued that an *s*-wave potential containing a hard core and predicting the observed *s*-wave scattering by itself predicted saturation at a radius of 1.4×10^{-13} cm. He argued that this result followed from a self-consistent treatment of the problem. In fact it does not. The hard core has nowhere near that large an effect. Apparently, the extremely complicated machine calculations which take the statistical correlations into account have verified this point, for he reported here [3] that a potential with no forces in odd states, treated self-consistently, produced saturation at a spacing of less than 1×10^{-13} cm. That is what we find when we do not take account of the repulsion in odd states which Feshbach and Lomon propose.

The only remaining point of disagreement, and perhaps it would be better to call it doubt, is whether at separations lower than 1×10^{-13} cm, where the self-consistent corrections are large, it is really true that the other effects of more than two particles. can be neglected. For pure hard cores this is certainly not the case; for potentials containing attractions and repulsions, it certainly must be shown and has not been so far. The numerical diagreements indicated in the previous chapter pertain to the estimates for non-realistic potentials at densities of the order of 1.2×10^{-13} cm. They make it seem more possible to us, that with more realistic forces and higher densities, the so-called cluster terms might be quite important.

AUTHOR'S NOTE.[†] Since these calculations were performed the nuclear force picture has been significantly modified. Phase shifts have been determined which differ from, and are less repulsive in odd states than, the Feshbach-Lomon phase shifts. The nucleus therefore tends to saturate at considerably higher densities, where the hard core is more significant and the correction terms are more substantial. At these higher densities, less than 1.0×10^{-13} cm, the correction terms of a "self-consistent" kind amount to several Mev. The corrections due to three-particle clusters have not been adequately estimated. Perturbation calculations extending ours have been performed with the new potentials by Mozskowski. They appear to yield energies and radii which agree with those more recently obtained by Brueckner. The reliability of these calculations, i.e., the estimate of errors due to three-particle clusters at the higher densities is still unsettled.

Notes and references

1. H. Feshbach and E. Lomon, *Phys. Rev.* **102**, 891 (1956).
2. C. De Dominicis and P. C. Martin, Chap. IV, this volume.
3. K. A. Brueckner, Chap. III, this volume.

---

† This material has been added to the paper as it was originally presented in order to indicate recent relevant developments.

CHAPTER VI

Ferromagnetism of a Gas of Hard Sphere Fermions

JOACHIM B. EHRMAN

1. *Effective mass approximation*

A preliminary calculation on the magnetization of a gas of uncharged hard sphere Fermions of spin 1/2 has been carried out [1]. The calculation represents a generalization of the effective mass approximation of the Brueckner-Bethe theory [2, 3]. Two effective masses are introduced. For the model wave function of the chosen configuration, we take a Slater determinant of single-particle wave functions, each one of which has a definite component of spin along one fixed axis (called the z axis). Thus, we can always speak of particles with spin "up" and particles with spin "down," provided that we adopt the convention of referring to the main diagonal of the Slater determinant.

It is assumed that the Brueckner self-consistent potential which acts on one of the particles is quadratic in k, the wave number of the particle in question, but that the potential depends upon the spin orientation of the particle. (As mentioned above, the principal diagonal convention is understood.) Thus we have

$$V_+(k) = V_+(0) + k^2/2M_+^*$$ (1a)

and

$$V_-(k) = V_-(0) + k^2/2M_-^*$$ (1b)

where $V_+(k)$ is the potential for a particle with spin in the positive z ("up") direction, M_+^* is the effective mass for such a particle, and $V_-(k)$, M_-^* are similarly defined. The reason for using this spin-dependent effective mass approximation (s.d.e.m.a.) is the possibility that at a sufficiently high density, with the density fixed, the ground state of the system is not that in which one-half of the particles have their spin up and the other half down, i.e., it need not necessarily be the antiferromagnetic configuration. Physically, we can readily see how this *might* happen from a well-known result: simply the generalization of the first two terms of the power series expansion of the energy per particle in powers of the cube root of the density n. These two terms are the Fermi term (proportional to $n^{2/3}$) and the Lenz term (proportional to n). Let the diameter of each hard sphere be taken as the unit of length, i.e., let the interaction potential between particles i and j be given by

$$V(r_{ij}) = \begin{cases} + \infty & \text{for } r_{ij} < 1 \\ 0 & \text{for } r_{ij} > 1 \end{cases} \qquad (2)$$

where r_{ij} is the distance between the centers of sphere i and sphere j. Then, the energy per particle, $\bar{E}$, in a configuration in which all spin-up levels from $k = 0$ to $k = k_{f+}$ are occupied, and all spin-down levels from $k = 0$ to $k = k_{f-}$, is given by (where M is the mass of one particle):

$$M\bar{E} = \tfrac{3}{10}(k_{f+}^5 + k_{f-}^5)/(k_{f+}^3 + k_{f-}^3) + (2/3\pi)k_{f+}^3 k_{f-}^3 /(k_{f+}^3 + k_{f-}^3) \qquad (3)$$
$$+ \text{ terms of higher powers in the density.}$$

Now, as far as the first term (Fermi term) is concerned, the energy is lowest for a given density (i.e., given $k_{f+}^3 + k_{f-}^3$) if $k_{f+} = k_{f-}$. For the second term (Lenz [4] term), it is lowest if either $k_{f+} = 0$ or $k_{f-} = 0$, because then the s-wave portion of the repulsion is completely suppressed, which is obvious from the Pauli principle. Of course, this power series cannot be used at a density high enough for the second term to become comparable to or larger than the first. In the calculation done here, a power series is not used.

2. *Calculations and results*

The calculation is carried out by the Brueckner-Bethe theory, with the following simplifying assumptions, which were made merely for computational simplicity:

1. The quadratic dependence of $V_+(k)$ and $V_-(k)$ on k, as shown in eqs. (1a), (1b), is assumed to hold to arbitrarily high k, and M_+^*, M_-^*

are obtained by making $V_+(k)$ and $V_-(k)$ self-consistent at 0, k_{f+} and 0, k_{f-} respectively.

2. The effect of the Pauli principle in intermediate states is neglected.

3. Three-particle and higher particle clusters are neglected.

The following equations are used for the single-particle potentials:

$$V_+(k_i) = -(2\pi)^{-3} \int_0^{k_{f+}} \int\int d^3\vec{k}_j (4\pi/M_+^* k_{ij}) \sum_{l \text{ odd}} 2(2l+1)\delta_l(k_{ij})$$

$$-(2\pi)^{-3} \int_0^{k_{f-}} \int\int d^3\vec{k}_j (4\pi/M_0^* k_{ij}) \sum_{\text{all } l} (2l+1)\delta_l(k_{ij}) \qquad (4a)$$

$$V_-(k_i) = -(2\pi)^{-3} \int_0^{k_{f-}} \int\int d^3\vec{k}_j (4\pi/M_-^* k_{ij}) \sum_{l \text{ odd}} 2(2l+1)\delta_l(k_{ij})$$

$$-(2\pi)^{-3} \int_0^{k_{f+}} \int\int d^3\vec{k}_j (4\pi/M_0^* k_{ij}) \sum_{\text{all } l} (2l+1)\delta_l(k_{ij}) \qquad (4b)$$

Note that the phase shifts $\delta_l(k_{ij})$ rather than their tangents are used [5]. ($k_{ij} = \frac{1}{2}|\mathbf{k}_i - \mathbf{k}_j|$; M_0^* is the harmonic mean of M_+^* and M_-^*.)

The result of this calculation is as follows. We fix the sum of the densities n_+, n_- of spin-up and spin-down particles, and then we vary the difference of these two densities. If the densities are equal, the effective mass drops from the actual mass at zero density to zero effective mass at a value of $k_f = 1.90$ (0.164 of the density of close packing, for which $k_f = 3.47$). It turns out that if $k_f < 1.674$, then the lowest energy is obtained for $k_{f+} = k_{f-}$ (antiferromagnetic configuration), but if $k_f > 1.674$ (0.112 of the density of close packing), then the state of lowest energy is not that in which there is an equal distribution between the two Fermi seas. In that case, if one plots $n_+ - n_-$ against energy for fixed $n_+ + n_-$, instead of getting a minimum at 0 abscissa, one gets a local maximum. There may result a W-shaped curve (if the density is just a little above the critical value), or else a curve whose ordinate decreases whenever $|n_+ - n_-|$ increases, so that ferromagnetism may be obtained. Now the effective mass approximation, when we merely wish to make it self-consistent between 0 and k_f and pay no attention to values of $k > k_f$, is good to a value of k_f of almost 1.80. In view of the fact that the densities we are dealing with here ($k_f = 1.674$) are fairly close (~ 0.80 of the density at $k_f = 1.80$) to the density at which the effective mass approximation becomes really poor, no definite quantitative conclusions on the setting in of ferromagnetism should as yet be drawn.

Note added in proof: It has been shown in a more exact calculation by P. C. Martin that the power series of reference 1 is not correct to as many terms as given there. This is because Martin does not use the three simplifying assumptions which have been made above, and which must also be eliminated before a definite conclusion on the above problem can be drawn.

Notes and References

1. J. B. Ehrman, *Phil. Mag.* **2**, 404 (1957).
2. K. A. Brueckner and C. A. Levinson, *Phys. Rev.* **97**, 1344 (1955).
3. H. A. Bethe, *Phys. Rev.* **103**, 1353 (1956).
4. W. Lenz, *Z. Physik* **56**, 778 (1929).
5. W. B. Riesenfeld and K. M. Watson, *Phys. Rev.* **104**, 492 (1956). The author is very much indebted to Dr. W. Wada for bringing this point to his attention.

CHAPTER VII

Round Table on General and Nuclear Theory

Participants:

T. D. Lee, *Moderator*

H. A. Bethe	C. A. Levinson
R. Brout	P. C. Martin
K. A. Brueckner	D. Pines
K. Huang	L. J. Rainwater
R. Jastrow	V. F. Weisskopf
R. Karplus	C. N. Yang

1. The effective mass problem for the nucleus

V. F. Weisskopf: I would like to present a point which might be interesting to discuss in connection with the approaches we have heard. This is the problem of the effective mass, or perhaps more generally, the problem of the momentum-dependence of the potential in the independent particle model of the nucleus. I will present a very simple method to calculate this momentum dependence, and then I think it will be interesting to compare it with the more elaborate methods we have heard, to see whether or not there is agreement, and why.

The idea is the following. I make two assumptions — rather sweeping ones. First, that we have infinite nuclear matter, stable at a fixed density, with no boundary problems to be considered. Second, that the properties of this nuclear matter can be described by a true independent particle model, and this means by a Slater determinant of free particle wave functions. Certain conclusions may be drawn. For example, if a particle j has an energy given by its kinetic energy plus the potential of the well it is in,

$$E_j = T_j + U_j \qquad (1)$$

(you see that I am already making room for the possibility that U might depend on the momentum), then the mean energy per particle or negative packing fraction for this big chunk of nuclear matter is

$$-P = \bar{T}_j + 1/2\bar{U}_j \tag{2}$$

The factor of 1/2, familiar from the Hartree method, is due to the term U_j coming from the interactions of all other particles with j, so that merely taking the sum of the U_j would count each interaction twice.

Now in the limit of infinite nuclear matter, the energy per particle does not depend on the size of the nucleus, so P must equal the separation energy, the minimum work necessary to remove one particle from the nuclear matter:

$$P = S \tag{3}$$

On the other hand, the separation energy is just the energy from a particle at the top of the Fermi sea to the outside

$$S = -T_F - U_F \tag{4}$$

Since the mean kinetic energy $\bar{T}_j$ is given by $3/5 \, T_F$, we obtain one result right off by combining (2), (3), (4):

$$U_F - \bar{U}_j = 1/5 \, T_F + P \tag{5}$$

This tells us that U must depend on the momentum, for if not, the left side of (5) would be zero, and this would lead to a contradiction because both T_F and P are positive.

Knowing P and T_F, we can compute U_F and $\bar{U}_j$ from (2) and (5), but that is all. However, to see what this really means, suppose that the energy is quadratic,

$$U = U_0 + p^2 U_1 \tag{6}$$

identical with the assumption of an effective mass, with

$$1/2m^* = 1/2m + U_1 \tag{7}$$

From (5) and (6), by averaging and simple arithmetic,

$$m/m^* = 3/2 + 5/2 \, (P/T_F) \tag{8}$$

If one puts in the figures for nuclear matter: at the center of the nucleus, T_F (which depends only on the density) is 38 Mev at the Hofstadter [1] value of 1.72×10^{38} particles/cc, and P, from the volume term of the Weizsäcker mass formula [2], is 14 Mev, then $m/m^* = 2.42$, corresponding to an $m^* = 0.41\ m$; this is considerably smaller than the newest value, $m^* = 0.6\ m$, from the machines [3].

Let me suggest a possible explanation of this discrepancy, which also sheds a little light on the kind of reasoning used here. One point was jumped over rather lightly, namely that the separation energy, the difference between the Fermi energy in the well and the top of the well, was equal to the packing fraction. This assumption means that if a particle is removed, what is left is the next lowest nucleus.

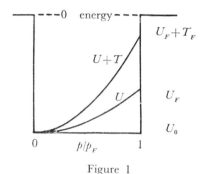

Figure 1

Of course, it is not, because it is actually a little too large and should shrink by the ratio $(A-1/A)^{1/3}$. The shrinking itself is really not serious, because we know that the volume is in stable equilibrium so that $dE/dV = 0$, and the shrinking after removal of the particle should therefore not change the energy. However, more serious is the assumption which I made that the wave function is a purely plane-wave Slater determinant (E is a function of the volume V alone, in this case). This means that after taking out the particle, the residual system differs from the $(A-1)$-particle nucleus only by an expansion. Actually, as we will see in Jastrow's talk [4], two nearby particles run around each other, so that if you remove one particle, the remaining particles sort of run around the particle which is no longer there. To reduce the remaining nucleus to its lower plane-wave state releases what one best calls a rearrangement energy X. Writing then instead of (3)

$$S = P+X \qquad (9)$$

and repeating the arithmetic,

$$m/m^* = 3/2 + 5/2[(P-X)/T_F] \qquad (10)$$

which does make m^* larger. It is interesting and perhaps a little disagreeable that in order to get the value $1/0.6$ for m/m^*, X must be taken as large as 10 MeV.

R. Karplus: One can continue this point of view a little further, and also introduce the fact of nuclear saturation in connection with the velocity-dependent potential by observing that it is closely related to the optical-model potential, which decreases greatly from about 40 MeV for very slow incident nucleons to about 10 or 15 Mev for relatively high energy incident nucleons. These positive energy measurements are consistent with the static effective mass value.

V. F. Weisskopf: In this connection, I should say that the quadratic dependence is evidently not true, for the potential, while quadratic for small p, certainly flattens out for high p. The experimental determinations, optical model for photoelectric and photomeson effects, as well as the calculations I have given, are relevant to the region around p_F. I would like to ask in what region the Brueckner result is valid.

K. A. Brueckner: The excitation energy we obtained was a function which was fitted self-consistently, no assumptions being made as to the form of the function. It then turned out that for low momentum, the effective mass ratio m^*/m was about 0.58, rising to about 0.63 for states near the Fermi surface — which makes the large value of your reciprocal ratio rather hard to understand. The quadratic approximation broke down rapidly as one got to twice the Fermi momentum, at which the one-body potential crossed the zero axis, become slightly positive, and thereafter remained small compared to the kinetic energy.

There are two comments I would like to make on your derivation of the effective mass. In the first place, I am puzzled as to how valid the argument really is. I know that if we take a saturated nucleus of

$A+1$ particles and remove one particle, leaving the nucleus behind in its lowest state, then the energy created is just the mean binding energy, since the mean binding energy per particle is the same for A particles as for $A+1$. But this does not reflect in any detail what the excitation spectrum is for the model particles, the uncertainty here being just in the appearance of a large rearrangement energy in a strongly correlated nucleus, which is somewhat difficult to estimate.

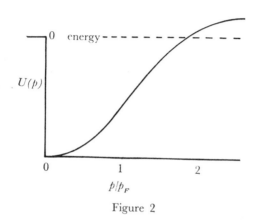

Figure 2

The other point is this: One of the original arguments on the magnitude of this so-called effective mass was given by Teller and Johnson [5], who argued that if there were no spin dependence of the nuclear forces to explain the neutron excess in large nuclei, or in other words, how the system resists the Coulomb repulsion of the protons, the effective mass would come out about 0.51. This is really not quite a safe argument since the forces are spin-dependent and indications are that somewhat more than half of the nuclear binding comes from the triplet interactions. Now Bethe pointed out recently that if one takes the nuclear forces, with neglect of the possible appearance of tensor forces, then to reconcile the spin dependence of nuclear forces with the observed symmetry energy, you need an effective mass of about unity. So I think that the effective mass that one deduces from the symmetry energy probably lies considerably above Teller's value, and can never get down as far as 0.41. Again, this is an argument for a large rearrangement energy.

2. On the magnitude of three-body effects

P. C. Martin: There is a question, insofar as the idea of these methods is concerned, which I think there is some difficulty in understanding. I should note that the results obtained by Brueckner and myself on related problems differ quite a bit, although this may very well be due to the nature of the potentials we have been using. At any rate, the philosophy of these methods seems to be that, somehow, the important effect is, as in a rare gas, the interaction between pairs of particles. Of course, even at low density, this is not good enough and so we must take into account the effect of a third particle on the scattering of a pair; there is an average effect of the third particle being around, and there is also an effect due to the fact that it may be correlated with the other two. Now what seems to be borne out by Brueckner's calculation, although not by mine, is that while the average effect of the third particle on the scattering of two (the effect of the particle sea on the potential of a pair, over and above the effect on the one-body potentials) is not large, the three-body correlation effects are very small. Thus the Hartree method would appear to have a distinct advantage over the low-density gas approximation. My question is that I really do not see how there can be so much difference between the average and the fluctuation effect of the third particle, where in fact the forces are strong and short-range.

K. A. Brueckner: I have essentially what I believe is the correct answer to this, although perhaps you will not agree. The first point is that part of the philosophy of all of these methods is that the extremely short-range repulsions, attractions, and so forth, are really never manifested directly in the interaction of particles, in the way they scatter, or in the way they move in nuclear matter. When a pair of particles gets close together, one sees only an integral effect on the wave function — the potential repeatedly acts before they separate, tending to smoothe out the effect of the potential. Hence one sees in actual scattering or in nuclear matter only the reaction matrix, a rather well-behaved nonsingular operator, whose matrix elements in the scattering case, and energy in the nuclear case, are also well-behaved. The fluctuation corrections to the potential have to do with multiple excitation of clusters of particles, and only the reaction matrix, expressing the screened effect of one particle on another, occurs in the successive interactions.

In general, the other particles in a system can interfere with a particle or a pair either by these successive scatterings, or they may have an effect because they act coherently (via forward scattering) as the binding medium of the nuclear matter. Now when a particle is bound, the binding effect is reflected in a strong shift in the exitation spectrum of the particles (30 or 40 Mev, as I previously mentioned [3]), manifesting itself in the way the particles interact. For this part of the interaction, there is no shielding effect of the multiple interactions of the potential, and so the precise excitation spectrum becomes important. This affects the value of the reaction matrix as well because high-momentum states are readily excited by the binding field. On the other hand, the incoherent scattering, via the reaction matrix, determines the cluster corrections, so these will be small, and small compared to the changes due to the shift in excitation spectrum. It seems to me then that there is a very basic difference in the way these corrections come in, which explains their very different magnitude.

P. C. Martin: In our work at least [6], we found corrections which are quite different. One may say that the strong short-range inter-actions are the ones which can lead to high-momentum interactions. When they do so, the change in kinetic energy is quite large but the change in potential energy relatively small. It seems that this singularity of potentials argues against self-consistency in the form that when two particles are close together, they act pairwise, and a third particle just does not get a chance. Probably there is so much involved in the various interactions that the situation will just have to be looked at further, numerically.

R. Jastrow: A question related to the point which Martin is making arises from the fact that in the variational calculation which we have done [4], a wave equation for the two-body correlation function is found. This contains terms which might be lumped with kinetic energy to yield an effective mass, but also contains terms coming from the potential, proportional in leading powers to the density, which modify the free space two-body interaction. If these additions are to be taken seriously, one wonders whether a similar (short-range) modification will show up in the Brueckner theory.

K. A. Brueckner: Since the methods are so different, as well as the way in which corrections appear, I am not sure that you can make a direct comparison. However, the effect of the velocity-dependence of the binding field can certainly be expressed as a change in the shape and range of the potential, in some approximate sense.

3. *The transition to a bound system*

C. N. Yang: I wish to make two comments and ask a question. The first comment is that there appears in London's book on super-fluids [7] a calculation that he made about 25 years ago in which he computed from a Lennard-Jones interaction between Helium atoms the density and binding energy per particle at zero temperature, for both He^3 and He^4. Now these calculations were done in a very physical, and compared to the developments of the last few years, by a very simple, physical argument, but the results obtained were remarkably good. This gives one the feeling — at least it gives me the feeling — that in order to justify a more sophisticated calculation, one needs much more than a quantitative agreement with experimental results.

The second comment I want to make is this. In our computation [8] of the energy per particle for both the Boson system and the Fermion system, one recognizes that the computation is in essence an asymptotic expansion. This can be seen immediately from the fact that, starting out with combinations which give nice integral powers, one ends up with fractional powers, which means that you cannot make an analytic continuation in which, for example, the parameter a — the scattering length — goes to negative values. This is obvious in the case of a Bose gas, because the result gives you a square root dependence on a. It is probably correct to say as well that for the Fermi case, you cannot make the analytic continuation for a reason which is well known: If you have pure attractive forces, without a repulsive core, in which the scattering length would be negative, you may get a collapsed state for an infinite system, even with Fermi statistics. All I want to say in this respect is that probably the calculation for a case in which there is a bound state, or in other words, in which the energy per particle is a negative quantity, is a quite different matter from that in the case in which the energy per particle is positive. If one makes a calculation and ends up with a negative result, one wonders whether it is possible to take the same potential and vary the parameters in it such that you can pass from a positive energy per particle to a negative energy per particle.

After these two comments, I would therefore like to ask Professors Brueckner and Bethe: In the Brueckner method for nuclear matter, one obtains a binding energy per particle. I realize of course that the method and the language used in Brueckner's method is quite different from that of the method which I discussed [8]. I would only like to ask whether they would have any comments about the question of the continuation of the energy from a positive value to a negative value.

K. A. Brueckner: I have a variety of comments. In the first place, I certainly agree that a calculation like this is not to be judged by its numerical agreement with experiment. One must show that what one has left out is small; one must show that the approximation method, as Bethe has emphasized [9], stands on its own feet. If one is forced by the numerical difficulty of the problem to make certain approximations, one must at least determine the errors introduced by these. If one does so, then one at least has a quantitative check on the accuracy of the method. Only after such a check has been made can the result then be compared with experiment, and some conclusions drawn from it.

The other comment is this. About the puzzling question you raise, that if one has repulsive forces and then turns the forces negative adiabatically, the energy of the system will drop, and finally reach (in the case of the nucleus, for example) a negative binding. This difficulty has also been repeatedly raised to us by Wigner, who is not a man to let a good point go by. One may consider the puzzle as follows: We compute an energy curve with a minimum which, in the case I mentioned previously [3], is at a separation of about 0.8 fermis, the energy then rising toward low density. What does this rise mean? How can the system then have higher energy than at the optimum density, which we say is the point at which the physical nucleus sits when we leave it alone — or, referring to Fig. 3, what does the rise *a-a-a* mean? If one takes an actual nucleus and removes the imaginary walls which one has for convenience imagined to confine it, then of course it will follow the lower curve *c-c-c*. If you push in the walls which confine it, then it will rise along the curve *b-b-b* all right; this makes physical sense, since on the high-density side it is being compressed and will necessarily follow the walls of the vessel.

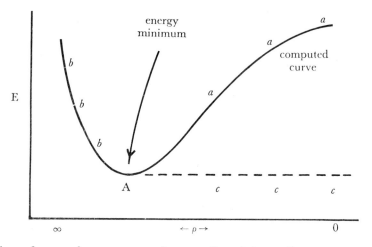

Figure 3. c-c-c denotes energy of system if confining walls are removed.

Now to make the problem more precise, we can pose the following situation: Suppose we take the system with repulsive forces alone, at density lower than that for an energy minimum with the full forces, and then turn the attractions on. Then what must happen is that the energy drops to the curve *c-c-c*. Physically, what would actually occur in a system like this is rather clear; it would condense. If one takes nuclear matter, puts it in a big box, and draws energy out of it when there are attractive forces present, or if one imagines that the attractive forces are turned on, the particles will condense into large clusters throughout the volume, and will form a nuclear liquid which only partially fills the total volume. Therefore, what does it mean when we get points on the curve *a-a-a*? We get these points because we deny the possibility of large scale condensation by terminating our cluster expansion at an early order. Therefore, I suspect that what is bothering

Yang and has bothered Wigner is that somewhere in our cluster expansion we must have divergences occurring, when we compute on the low-density side of the energy minimum.

There is another physical way of explaining what the curve a-a-a can mean, which is also mathematically equivalent to neglecting the effect of the high-order cluster corrections. Suppose that one takes a nucleus or a liquid. We know that we can compress on the high-density side and physically what happens is quite clear; we do work on the system and the energy rises. We can also draw the system out on the low-density side a short distance, in the sense that we can supercool a liquid, i.e., we can go into a state which is metastable. If we allow a small excitation or disturbance to occur, however, the system will immediately break into clusters, as a supercooled liquid will, and will then drop down to a lower energy corresponding to c-c-c, giving off energy in the process. Therefore the curve a-a-a can be physically reached by adiabatic transitions from the point of maximum stability. For example, a physical nucleus can be made to oscillate for some distance around the optimum density, adiabatically with no transitions occurring. Such transitions will actually occur if the system is forced to oscillate through too large amplitude and refuses to follow an adiabatic curve. Instead it undergoes fission or breaks into clusters.

What I would say then is that, in the low-density region, the curve a-a-a which we get has as physical meaning only that it can be reached by adiabatic expansion from the point A. The error we make in the energy along a-a-a must have to do with the appearance of singularities in the high-order cluster terms — these we neglect. In neglecting them, therefore, it makes some physical sense to say that the curve we compute here must lie above the correct energy curve. This leads to something else we have worried about in the past; when one computes a curve like this, we know that on the low-density side there must be large cluster corrections. How can we be sure that there are no high-order cluster corrections in the region of the energy minimum? We can not answer this with any reliability. All we know is that when we look at the cluster corrections in this region, they seem to be very small. We can not look at the cluster terms of high order and make any estimate of their convergence. The only answer I can make to these questions is that we have a physical picture of what this energy curve means. We have detailed calculations to partially bear out our view that in this region we are not making important errors by neglecting cluster corrections. This is the only response to this final question that I can make.

H. A. Bethe: I might add a completely different point, namely with respect to the question of when you can have a saturated state. It is of course perfectly true that in the case of a Bose gas, as soon as you have attraction, you get complete condensation into a region of the order of magnitude of the range of the forces. In the case of a Fermi gas, whether this happens or not depends on the details of the interaction between particles. If you have an interaction between particles, which is an ordinary force in the sense of old-fashioned nuclear theory — no repulsive core, no exchange character — then as we all know, you do not get saturation, but the mere fact of a negative scattering length does not mean that you do get collapse. If you have a negative scattering length in *s* states only, then you do get a finite binding energy — you do get saturation — and although you don't describe actual nuclear matter very well, you certainly have in this case a counterexample to any statement that a negative scattering length necessarily leads to infinite binding energy. It is only to such cases, in which there is saturation, that the theory of Brueckner and myself will apply. The state which makes real sense is the minimum of the curve, for there seems to be a variational principle which says that you ought to vary the density so as to get the point of maximum binding energy. Thus the physical meaning is attached to the minimum of the curve, and of course there is no physical meaning to any forces which do not give you saturation and which do not give you a minimum.

I don't know if between us, we have answered your worries.

C. N. Yang: I think that I understand the views that you take on this matter; I certainly agree with you that with a negative scattering length, it is not necessary for the system to collapse — we know that the actual nuclear system does not collapse. The question I have been raising is an academic one, as to how one justifies with confidence the calculation that one makes from the branch which is the high-density part. I might say that I am especially uncomfortable about this matter, because if you look into a gas which does lead to a binding energy per particle for an infinite system, and if you ask about the statistical mechanics of the system at zero temperature, you find that all the quantities which one usually uses are exponentially divergent.

More explicitly, the virial coefficients b_l by themselves become exponentially divergent. Now when you deal with a real physical system, you will absorb the exponential divergence in the fugacity parameter z, which, e.g., for systems with two-particle bound states, becomes exponentially vanishing. The cancellation is very delicate; a calculation in such a situation is therefore more suspect than that in a situation without such delicate cancellation. I agree that the statistical mechanical picture is not the simplest way of looking at the ground state, and my question only reflects an uncomfortable feeling borne out of looking at statistical mechanical problems. It makes me feel that I would like to examine in more detail a calculation which approaches this binding energy per particle in a system which has a bound state (infinite-body) from the high-density side. My feeling is that this is a situation that has to be handled with care, not that I know how to handle it.

V. F. Weisskopf: I would like to ask whether one could not invent such a system by taking your gas, which has of course a positive energy, and then give every particle a very long-range, very weak attraction, and slowly switch this on. It is hard to see at what range this will break down.

C. N. Yang: That is a very interesting suggestion, and we in fact started to look at such a system. The view is slightly different from the one expressed by Brueckner. The point is that if you have a very shallow attractive potential which extends to a very large distance, and with a hard core in the middle which prevents it from collapsing, then you can have a system which has a finite binding energy. In that case, you may compute the energy per particle, even though it is negative. The only reason it works in this case is that since the potential is so long and so shallow, the approximate value of the attrac-

tive potential energy can be computed independently of what the
wave function looks like — but I am not sure that this is the case with
the very deep attractive force of the nucleus.

H. A. Bethe: It is well known that the convergence of the method
is dependent on just the parameter you mentioned, the ratio of the
range to the average spacing between nucleons, and if you have
attractive forces, the method converges better the longer the range.
However, from explicit calculations you get the impression that for
the actual range and the actual density of nuclear matter, it still
converges very well. I think this is the best justification we can give
at the moment.

K. A. Brueckner: I would just like to repeat again that I suspect
very strongly that these methods do diverge as soon as one crosses the
energy line. They diverge somewhere in high order, just because the
system must exhibit some long-range cluster characteristics which is
simply ignored in these calculations. If you really were to do it correctly, really look at high-order terms, you would find that it diverges
out there. We can neglect this only on the basis of the physical argument which you make — but formally it probably does not work.

R. Karplus: I just wanted to mention that Watson has described a
theory of condensation [10] based on the linked-cluster expansion
of the partition function, in which at low pressure and density the
system behaves like a gas. As the pressure increases, the contributions
to the partition function shift — at first very slightly — and then all
of a sudden, at a certain pressure, they move throughout all clusters,
and there is a large region in which making the volume small does not
increase the pressure. Finally, the contribution comes essentially from
the cluster that contains all of the particles in the system, and then the
pressure increases very rapidly with further decrease in volume. This
was using the current many-body perturbation theory.

4. On the character of the interaction potential

T. D. Lee: May I exercise the right of a moderator in order to make
some comments. I think there is probable agreement, by various

methods, in the case of a repulsive force — a pure repulsive force with no attractive force. One can make statements concerning the behavior, statistically, of the whole energy spectrum. The question — if you have large attractive forces — of the exact characteristics of this potential, which will make the calculation, any calculation, possible to perform and evaluate, seems not to have been explicitly stated. It would also be very desirable to know that, for any method, there must be some region for which you can invent a potential to which this method does not apply. The very fact that we are not able to make a very concise statement concerning the validity is probably an indication that complete understanding of this problem is not yet in existence.

K. A. Brueckner: I would certainly agree with Lee's comments. As to what sort of potentials one could hope to study with our particular method, I think there are two conditions on this problem. First, one must be in the vicinity of the energy minimum, of the point of stability, because as I mentioned before, undoubtedly if one looks at high orders in the cluster expansion, one will eventually find divergences unless one is in a region in which the clustering tendency is small. The second condition one must impose on the potential is that it not have a very long range, like a Coulomb force, the reason in this case being that the screening effects which are so important in the Coulomb force problem actually appear in a divergence of the cluster expansion of the method we use for the nucleus. The cluster expansion which gives rise to the screening of the Coulomb force is actually an expansion which involves the coherent excitation of very large numbers of particles. This is the cluster expansion which Gell-Mann and I summed [11] in getting the properties of the electron gas, so in such a problem, one must introduce a special adaptation of the method, which first treats the long-range part of the interaction properly and gives the screening effect. After this is done, one has, like Bohm and Pines [12], a screened interaction left over to which perhaps one can apply the methods for treating short-range correlations which we use in the nucleus.

A third comment is this. One may ask how crystalline behavior can appear in such a calculation. Let me first say what I believe the conditions are, and then I'll quote an example which I think illustrates the feature I want to emphasize. One essential feature, and this was mentioned by Bethe [9], is that the system we compute must be able to be reached adiabatically from, in the infinite nuclear case, an assortment of particles moving in plane-wave states. That is, the energy we compute is in general the one reached adiabatically from the unperturbed system by turning the forces on; the state is the one reached by an adiabatic shift of this state. Now whenever a system occurs which cannot be reached adiabatically from our starting wave function, then we simply won't see it.

This difficulty actually shows up in the He³ calculation which I mentioned [3], in a very peculiar way. One knows that He³ tends to form a solid, at somewhat higher compression than normal density — if one compresses it somewhat, one finds a lower-energy crystalline state. Now we actually see strong indications of this, in our calculation, in the instability of the solutions. One finds, as I mentioned, that the excitation spectrum of He³ is almost flat — the effective mass is very large. If the excitation spectrum is so flat, this means that only a very small amount of energy is needed to take particles from the Fermi gas and put them into states of high momentum. Now the effect which we see increases with density. The spectrum becomes flatter and flatter as the density goes up, and finally if we push our calculations, we find a point where the spectrum is inverted, and it is energetically favorable for the particle to be in higher momentum states and therefore more localized in coordinate space. I would guess that this is the point at which it is energetically more favorable to put the particles in a sort of lattice, into a more highly-ordered structure than in a liquid.

This situation does not occur in the nucleus because the steep excitation spectrum and small effective mass means that one is very far away from forming any crystalline structure or solid in nuclear matter. One would have to compress a long way before the same spectral inversion would occur as in He³. One thus sees how one misses the solid state in these calculations, and one sees in the case of Helium indications of how it is trying to come in, in this phenomenon of spectral inversion. One perhaps has to choose a different unperturbed state to perturb adiabatically and reach the final perturbed wave function. Presumably one would take a more ordered state than a Fermi gas for the unperturbed system, and from this reach the proper solid.

5. *The free electron gas*

H. A. Bethe: Brueckner has mentioned the problems arising in the case of a long-range interaction, such as in electrons with a positive charge background. Brout, at Cornell, has done some further analysis of the solutions of Gell-Mann and Brueckner [11], and of Sawada [13], and has come to the conclusion that the problem takes on much the form of a Bohm-Pines plasma oscillation model [12]. Namely, you can separate out a part of the model that looks like a plasma oscillation, and indeed with coordinates which oscillate with a frequency similar to the plasma frequency. What you have left after removing the plasma oscillation energy is the correlation energy, which has been calculated by Sawada. This differs from that of the Bohm-Pines theory, and can be treated more adequately by the Gell-Mann-Brueckner method, so that one essentially gets the two aspects in the same theory — the oscillation aspect of Bohm and Pines and the zero point energy of Sawada.

D. Pines: I may just say to this that it is obvious that there must be a very close connection between the two methods, because the basic approximation that Bohm and I make is essentially the random phase approximation, and we separate out the interactions that take place at different momenta; this is also the basic approximation which Gell-Mann and Brueckner make. The question then arises as to the details of the calculations, and at least in the limit of very high density, Gell-Mann and I have established the identity of the two methods.

What is involved in the two methods is essentially this. We separate the Coulomb interaction into two parts [14]

$$V = \sum_{k < k_c} 2\pi e^2/k^2 \rho_k^* \rho_k + \sum_{k > k_c} 2\pi e^2/k^2 \rho_k^* \rho_k \qquad (11)$$

where k_c for the present is arbitrary. Now by suitable choice of the plasma coordinates, the first part can be treated as accurately as one likes, and can be shown in the high-density limit, for instance, to go over directly to what Gell-Mann and Brueckner get. The second part of the interaction is not treated with tremendous accuracy by per-turbation theory, and this evaluation by perturbation theory is the major approximation in our method.

What is desirable is to go beyond perturbation theory. Brueckner and Gell-Mann can do this at high densities, but the nub of the problem is to carry this over for intermediate densities. Our calcu-lation can be carried out for all densities, and by suitable choice of k_c, we can try to put as much of the interaction energy into the $k < k_c$ portion as possible, but this cannot be done accurately. So the whole question of a good calculation in the intermediate-density domain becomes one of good treatment of the high Fourier components of the interaction, not only for high density, as Brueckner and Gell-Mann did in this quite beautiful calculation, but for intermediate density as well.

R. Brout: I do not agree with Dr. Pines' statement that the bone of contention is for high k, which, of course, must be calculated in more detail, but rather for low k. It is this latter which I wish to discuss, as I think it is the heart of the matter.

The general form of the potential correlation energy can easily be shown to be an integral of a distribution function, $g(r)$, over a potential, where with zero mean potential things can be so normalized that $g(r)$ begins at zero and goes to one (here $n =$ density of electrons, total volume $= 1$):

$$E_{corr} \sim n^2/2 \int \left(g(r) - 1 \right) V(r) \, d\tau \tag{12}$$

or if $V(r)$ is Fourier analyzed then

$$E_{corr} \sim \sum_k 2\pi n^2 e^2/k^2 \int [g(r) - 1] e^{ikr} \, d\tau \tag{13}$$

We wish to examine the latter expression for small k where the exponential may permissibly be expanded, i.e., $k \ll \kappa$ where κ^{-1} is the screening length. For small k, one then finds that if the Fourier transform g_k is well-behaved around $k \sim 0$,

$$E_{corr}(k) \sim 2\pi e^2 n[1/\kappa^2 - 1/k^2], \qquad k \ll \kappa \tag{14}$$

The density dependence of κ^2 is like r_s where r_s is the mean inter-electronic distance in units of the Bohr radius. Thus, if a screening length exists, the correlation energy is necessarily of the above form with the density dependence as specified. $(n \propto r_s^{-3})$.

The theory of Bohm and Pines assumes the existence of a screening length, and establishes its density dependence by a variational argument [12]. However, the form of the correlation energy is not the above, but rather

$$E_{corr}(k) = (1/2)\hbar\omega_P - 2\pi n e^2/k^2 \qquad (15)$$

where ω_P, the plasma frequency, has a density dependence like $r_s^{-3/2}$. As eq. (14) is based on a dimensional argument, it appears that the Bohm and Pines theory does not take the proper form. However, the Gell-Mann, Brueckner [11], Sawada [13] theory does take the form (14) for small k. We conclude that the Bohm and Pines theory is suspect.

I should briefly like to discuss another aspect of the theory in terms of the Gell-Mann, Brueckner, Sawada Hamiltonian. This Hamiltonian allows only certain scattering processes to take place viz. two electrons scatter from the sea to above the sea, an electron and hole interchange, or two electrons scatter back into the sea, all without exchange. This Hamiltonian takes on a form in which it is possible to define normal coordinates η which I won't write down, but remark that these normal coordinates have the same structure as those of Bohm and Pines [15] except with an added restriction on the summation due to the restricted initial Hamiltonian. In order that the η are normal coordinates one comes upon a dispersion relation, which turns out to be identical in form to that of Bohm and Pines, again with a summation restriction. It is identical with the dispersion relation derived by Sawada using a scattering formalism. From this relation, Sawada concluded that the pairs have zero self energy. This, at least in part, is incorrect since it may be easily shown that in the limit as $k \to 0$, ω tends to ω_P. Thus, in the formalism of Gell-Mann, Brueckner, and Sawada one does recover plasma oscillations, and hence the nice physical features of the Bohm and Pines theory.

One might then ask: Why are the two theories at first sight inconsistent as first pointed out? I will conjecture that the answer lies in the following: The Hamiltonian H may be written as $H_{osc} + (H - H_{osc})$, where H_{osc} is an effective oscillator Hamiltonian so designed as to give the same commutation relations with η as does H. Thus $H-H_{osc}$ is a constant in η space and hence, if evaluated in the ground state, it is known. Thus, the ground state energy will not be simply the zero point energy of the oscillations, but rather will include $H-H_{osc}$. The conjecture is that this will be the energy calculated by Gell-Mann and Brueckner.

Note by R. Brout: The contribution of the plasma modes to the electron correlation energy was independently investigated by K. Sawada, K. Brueckner and N. Fukuda [16], and by R. Brout [17] immediately following the symposium. It was concluded that a plasma zero point energy *does* contribute to the energy for momentum transfer below a cutoff, fixed by the theory. The non-plasma oscillation part may be qualitatively described as a screened interaction. The physical model of Bohm and Pines is qualitatively correct, but the Gell-Man-Brueckner theory differs in some points of detail.

D. Pines: Perhaps at this point, I may make some further remarks on the connection between the approach which Bohm and I developed and the work of Brueckner and Gell-Mann; these have to do with the remarks of Brout on the limiting form of the energy as a function of momentum transfer. Let me recapitulate. He argues, and quite rightly, that the correlation energy can be written as the sum of energies associated with each momentum transfer k of the electrons, and that it is interesting to study this in the limit of low k, that is, for long wavelength momentum transfer. Thus

$$E = \sum_k v(k) \qquad\qquad 16$$

This is the part of the Hamiltonian that I treat. It is also the part that Brueckner and Gell-Mann treat. In both approaches, the approximation is made that the energy can be written as a simple sum arising from such momentum transfers, and that there is no coupling between a density fluctuation ρ_k and another $\rho_{k'}$, so that the energy can be solved separately for each momentum transfer.

The similarity in the basic approximation in the two approaches leads one to suspect that the two theories are probably very close in their physical content and, in fact, in their mathematical content.

Brout argues that the expression obtained from the Gell-Mann and Brueckner theory and the expression that Bohm and I got differ in their density dependence at low k. This is in fact not the case. One expression which has been compared for the Brueckner–Gell-Mann theory in the high-density limit, and for our theory in the same limit, is the leading term in $v(k)$, which in fact goes as a/k. The coefficient a is identical in the Brueckner–Gell-Mann theory and in mine.

The second point I want to make which concerns the close relationship between the theories is a comment on what Brout said, that the dispersion relation which Sawada got looks very much like the plasma dispersion relation, with the exception that the Sawada dispersion relation contains an apparent Pauli-principle restriction. Nozieres has pointed out to me that the Sawada Pauli-principle restriction, when one carries out a sum over all momentum states, identically cancels out, so that the dispersion relations of the two theories are identical. In other words, Brueckner and Gell-Mann have the plasmons in their theory. This leads one to suspect that the whole structure of the theories is very close, and I think that this will be established by the work of the coming months.

R. Brout: If it is indeed true that the Brueckner, Sawada, and Pines dispersion relations are identical, then the normal coordinates are the same, and so the restrictive subsidiary condition can be dispensed with too. The only remaining question is how to compute without the subsidiary conditions to make a direct independent check.

NOTE BY EDITOR: The foregoing section is presented to indicate the "atmosphere" as a basic understanding of the electron correlation problem was at the point of being achieved. Thus much of the discussion was elicited by the absence of plasma modes in the preprint (only a month prior) of Sawada's fundamental paper (*Phys. Rev.* **106**, 372(1957)) on the subject, a matter which was in fact corrected in a footnote to the published paper. To somewhat elucidate the differences of opinion which existed at the moment (and not much longer) we note that in Dr. Brout's opening remarks:

a. The cutoff wave number κ goes as $r_s^{-3/4}$, not as $r_s^{1/2}$; in fact, the first approximation of Bohm and Pines [12] to κ^2 is precisely $\kappa^2 = 2\pi n e^2/(\hbar\omega_P/2)$, so that eqs. (14) and (15) become identical. Equation (14) may thus be regarded as a heuristic approach to eq. (15).

b. Thus there is no low-density discrepancy. At high density, the short-range potential contribution, which does not appear in eq. (15), becomes important, and gives rise [18] to a $1/k$ term.

c. Due to this $1/k$ term, the Fourier transform g_k is not analytic at $k = 0$, and the expansion of eq. (14) is not valid. Generally, the ground state distribution transform has a branch point at $k = 0$.

The Editor wishes to thank the participants for their permission to include, at this very late date, the above discussion, which was something less than definitive.

6. *Concluding remarks*

T. D. Lee: Altogether, we have seen various different methods proposed by different authors — the Brueckner method, the binary collision method, the pseudopotential method, the collective mode method, and others. We see that in the dilute case, for a system of rather low density and, for example, an infinitely hard core of some radius, it is possible with several of these methods to obtain rigorous answers with respect to the energy and statistical-mechanical properties. We see from these results the difference between Einstein-Bose and Fermi-Dirac statistics, concerning say the behavior of the superfluid — which we have in one case, and do not have in the other case. Although these results are only for a dilute gas, it is very gratifying to me that they are indeed rigorous solutions.

On the other hand, for high density, we see various approximation methods proposed. While we are not completely sure of the validity of each of these methods, I would say that in each case they appear to be quite reasonable. It would be most desirable to seek the interrelationship of these various methods, and their limitations, if any.

I would conclude this discussion by wishing every success to all people on this side of the *rectangular* table, and on the other side.

Notes and references

1. B. Hahn, D. G. Ravenhall, and R. Hofstadter, *Phys. Rev.* **101**, 1131 (1956).
2. J. M. Blatt and V. F. Weisskopf, *Theoretical Nuclear Physics*, Wiley, New York, 1952, p. 227.
3. K. A. Brueckner, Chap. III, this volume.
4. R. Jastrow, Chap. XI, this volume.
5. M. H. Johnson and E. Teller, *Phys. Rev.* **98**, 783 (1955).
6. C. DeDominicis and P. C. Martin, Chap. IV, this volume.
7. F. London, *Superfluids*, Wiley, New York, 1954 Vol II, 55.
8. K. Huang, T. D. Lee, and C. N. Yang, Chap. X, this volume.
9. H. A. Bethe, Chap. II, this volume.
10. W. B. Riesenfeld and K. M. Watson, *Phys. Rev.* **104**, 492 (1956); *Phys. Rev.* **108**, 518 (1957).
11. M. Gell-Mann and K. A. Brueckner, *Phys. Rev.* **106**, 364 (1957).
12. D. Bohm and D. Pines, *Phys. Rev.* **92**, 609 (1953).
13. K. Sawada, *Phys. Rev.* **106**, 372 (1957).
14. D. Pines, Chap. XVI, this volume.
15. See Appendix [12].
16. K. Sawada, K. A. Brueckner, N. Fukuda, and R. Brout *Phys. Rev.* **108**, 507 (1957).
17. R. Brout, *Phys. Rev.* **108**, 515 (1957).
18. D. Pines, *Solid State Physics*, Academic, New York, 1955, Vol. I.

Part Two

CHAPTER VIII

Transitional Methods

JEROME K. PERCUS

We now consider a number of approaches to the many-body problem which are not best characterized as "individual" or "collective", and which may therefore be regarded as bridging the gap, in a sense which we carefully refrain from specifying. Perhaps one should simply say that these approaches are developed for more special situations than those of undesignated multiple scattering or collective behavior, and may thereby be more powerful for such situations.

1. The multiple boundary problem

If a wave, subject only to external boundary conditions (periodic, hard-wall, fixed-plane-wave plus outgoing-wave, etc.) is perturbed by (non-intersecting) small interior closed surfaces B_j, on and within which the wave must vanish, then the effectively infinite potential appears to bar the use of standard perturbation theory. As Eyges observes in Chap. IX, the multiple boundary problem includes the interaction problem for N impenetrable bodies; the space is then $3N$-dimensional, and the boundaries are the $\frac{1}{2}N(N-1)$ hypersurfaces (artificially separated at junctions) which represent two-body contact. Of course, the employment of reaction operators, as in Part One, solves the problem of infinite potentials in principle; on the other hand, since the effect has been to impose new boundaries, boundary perturbation methods have been developed for this class of problems. We shall here make contact to some extent between the various perturbation procedures.

Boundary Perturbation. The basic approach for bound states in usual boundary perturbation theory is this [1]. In addition to the wave equation to be solved

$$(E-T)\ \psi(\mathbf{r}) = 0 \qquad \text{outside all } B_j \tag{1a}$$

$$\psi(\mathbf{r}) = 0 \qquad \text{on and inside } B_j \tag{1b}$$

$\mathbf{r}$ being a multidimensional (e.g., $3N$) vector and T the corresponding kinetic energy operator $-(\hbar^2/2m)\ \nabla^2$ (although this is easily generalized), we introduce the Green's function for the unperturbed problem of waves not barred from the B_j:

$$(E-T)\ G_E(\mathbf{r},\mathbf{r}') = \delta(\mathbf{r}-\mathbf{r}') \tag{2a}$$

$$G_E(\mathbf{r}',\mathbf{r}) = G_E(\mathbf{r},\mathbf{r}'). \tag{2b}$$

Now, in customary fashion, multiplying eq. (1a) by G_E, eq. (2a) by ψ, integrating over the region outside the B_j, and applying the divergence theorem to the difference (assuming that ψ is such that the external surface terms vanish), we have

$$(\hbar^2/2m) \sum_j \int [\psi(\mathbf{r})\nabla G_E(\mathbf{r},\mathbf{r}') - G_E(\mathbf{r},\mathbf{r}')\nabla\psi(\mathbf{r}^+)] \cdot d\mathbf{S}_j = -\psi(\mathbf{r}') \tag{3}$$

for $\mathbf{r}'$ outside the B_j, zero otherwise. Here the surface element $d\mathbf{S}_j$ is directed along the *outward* normal to the closed surface B_j. The boundary conditions of eq. (1b) thereby yield [†]

$$\psi(\mathbf{r}') = (\hbar^2/2m) \sum_j \int G_E(\mathbf{r},\mathbf{r}')\nabla\psi(\mathbf{r}^+) \cdot d\mathbf{S}_j \tag{4}$$

where, since $\nabla\psi$ is discontinuous, $\mathbf{r}^+$ indicates evaluation at the outside surface when $\mathbf{r}$ is on B_j.

Since a bound state problem is being considered, E is not known, but must be determined. To achieve this, taking φ_n as the unperturbed state: $(\varepsilon_n - T)\varphi_n(\mathbf{r}) = 0$ with only external boundary conditions, and repeating the above process with φ_n^* replacing G_E, we find

$$E-\varepsilon_n = (\hbar^2/2m) \sum_j \int \varphi_n^*(\mathbf{r})\nabla\psi(\mathbf{r}^+) \cdot d\mathbf{S}_j / \int \varphi_n^*(\mathbf{r})\psi(\mathbf{r})\ d\tau \tag{5}$$

[†] For scattering states, if ψ represents the scattered wave, φ^{inc} the incoming wave, then eq. (1b) is replaced by $\psi(\mathbf{r}) + \varphi^{\text{inc}} = 0$ on B_j, and eq. (4) modified accordingly.

At times, G_E, required for (4), can only be obtained as a series expansion in unperturbed solutions φ_p,

$$G_E(\mathbf{r}, \mathbf{r}') = \sum_p \varphi_p^*(\mathbf{r})\varphi_p(\mathbf{r}')/(E-\varepsilon_p) \qquad (6)$$

We see then that if E is near ε_n, the term $\varphi_n^* \varphi_n$ has a very large co-efficient in (4). This difficulty is remedied by separating out the $p = n$ term in G_E from the remainder, which we may call $G'_{n,E}$, and eliminating the $E-\varepsilon_n$ denominator through eq. (5). Now eq. (4) becomes

$$\psi(\mathbf{r}') = \varphi_n(\mathbf{r}') \int \varphi_n^*(\mathbf{r})\psi(\mathbf{r})\, d\tau$$
$$+(\hbar^2/2m) \sum_j \int G'_{n,E}(\mathbf{r}, \mathbf{r}')\nabla\psi(\mathbf{r}^+) \cdot d\mathbf{S}_j \qquad (7)$$

with the unperturbed φ_n component of ψ literally separated; any value, say $\int \varphi_n^*(\mathbf{r})\psi(\mathbf{r})\, d\tau = 1$, chosen for this component will persist through the perturbation.

Effective Potential. The integral relation (4) may be converted to a differential relation by applying the operator $E-T'$:

$$(E-T')\psi(\mathbf{r}') = (\hbar^2/2m) \sum_j \int \delta(\mathbf{r}-\mathbf{r}')\nabla\psi(\mathbf{r}^+) \cdot d\mathbf{S}_j \qquad (8)$$

But, if $\mathcal{Z}_j(\mathbf{r})$ is defined as the characteristic function for B_j — unity inside and on B_j, and zero outside — we have $\int_{B_j} \delta(\mathbf{r}-\mathbf{r}')\nabla\psi(\mathbf{r}^+)$ $\cdot d\mathbf{S}_j = \int_{B_j} \nabla \cdot [\delta(\mathbf{r}-\mathbf{r}')\nabla\psi(\mathbf{r}^+)]\, d\tau = \int \mathcal{Z}_j(\mathbf{r})\nabla \cdot [\delta(\mathbf{r}-\mathbf{r}')\nabla\psi(\mathbf{r}^+)]\, d\tau =$ $-\int \delta(\mathbf{r}-\mathbf{r}')\nabla\mathcal{Z}_j(\mathbf{r}) \cdot \nabla\psi(\mathbf{r}^+)\, d\tau = -\nabla'\mathcal{Z}_j(\mathbf{r}') \cdot \nabla'\psi(\mathbf{r}'^+)$. Hence, the for-mulation (4), (8) corresponds merely to the addition of an effective potential:

$$V_{\text{eff}}\psi(\mathbf{r}) = -(\hbar^2/2m) \sum_j \nabla\mathcal{Z}_j(\mathbf{r}) \cdot \nabla\psi(\mathbf{r}^+) \qquad (9)$$

The fact that eq. (9) implies eq. (1) must be checked. In

$$(E-T)\psi(\mathbf{r}) = V_{\text{eff}}\psi(\mathbf{r}) \qquad (10)$$

the only problem is to show that $\psi(\mathbf{r}) = 0$ on each B_j; now integrating eq. (10) over a "pillbox" from $\mathbf{r}^-$, just inside the surface B_j, to $\mathbf{r}$ infinitesimally nearby and normally outward, we have for unit normal $\mathbf{n}$ at B_j,

$$\mathbf{n} \cdot [\nabla\psi(\mathbf{r})-\nabla\psi(\mathbf{r}^-)] = (-\mathcal{Z}_j(\mathbf{r})+1)\mathbf{n} \cdot \nabla\psi(\mathbf{r}^+) \qquad (11)$$

Hence, choosing $\mathbf{r} = \mathbf{r}^+$, (11) reduces to

$$\partial \psi(\mathbf{r}^-)/\partial n = 0 \qquad (12)$$

Considering $(E-T)\psi(\mathbf{r}) = 0$ inside B_j with boundary condition (12), we know that the solution of lowest energy is $\psi = $ constant, $E = 0$, and that for small B_j, the next lowest eigenvalue is very large. Hence an iteration or perturbation starting from a finite value of E will pick up only the trivial $\psi = 0$, E arbitrary, as initial solution. According to (11), $\mathbf{n} \cdot \nabla \psi$ is nonsingular and so ψ continuous; ψ will thus vanish as well on B_j, as desired.

It is not difficult to modify the effective potential so that the boundary condition $\psi = 0$ is obtained, irrespective of the mode of solution. We may write

$$V_{\text{eff}}\psi(\mathbf{r}) = (\hbar^2/2m) \sum_j \tfrac{1}{2}[\nabla^2[\mathcal{Z}_j(\mathbf{r})\psi(\mathbf{r})]+\mathcal{Z}_j(\mathbf{r})\nabla^2\psi(\mathbf{r})] \qquad (13)$$

The term $\mathcal{Z}\nabla^2\psi$ in (13) is included so that V_{eff} becomes Hermitian; it contributes to $(\mathcal{Z}_j-1)\nabla^2\psi$ in $(4m/\hbar^2)(T+V_{\text{eff}})\psi$, vanishing under a pillbox integration followed by a path integration, for ψ sufficiently nonsingular to be quadratically integrable. On the other hand, the first term in (13) contributes to $\nabla^2[(\mathcal{Z}_j(\mathbf{r})-1)\psi(\mathbf{r})]$ in $(4m/\hbar^2)(T+V_{\text{eff}})\psi$, which yields on a pillbox integration from $\mathbf{r}^-$ to $\mathbf{r}$, followed by a path integration from $\mathbf{r}^-$ to $\mathbf{r}$,

$$(\mathcal{Z}_j(\mathbf{r})-1)\psi(\mathbf{r}) = 0 \qquad (14)$$

so that $\psi(\mathbf{r}^+) = 0$. Further, since eq. (10) interior to B_j now becomes simply $E\psi(\mathbf{r}) = 0$, we have $\psi(\mathbf{r}) = 0$ throughout B_j, the spurious solution $E = 0$ always being recognized as such.

The corresponding problem with Neumann boundary condition $\partial \psi(\mathbf{r}^+)/\partial n = 0$ is similarly treated by imposing the Hermitian effective potential

$$V_{\text{eff}}\psi(\mathbf{r}) = (\hbar^2/2m) \sum_j \nabla \cdot [\mathcal{Z}_j(\mathbf{r})\nabla\psi(\mathbf{r})] \qquad (15)$$

and performing just a pillbox integration. In the classical case, both (13) and (15) reduce to

$$V_{\text{eff}} = - \sum \mathcal{Z}_j(\mathbf{r})p^2/2m \qquad (16)$$

Here, the fact that $H = p^2/2m+V_{\text{eff}}$ vanishes inside B_j excludes this volume from entry, due to energy conservation.

Pseudopotential. Returning to the orginal expression (9), the matrix elements (albeit not Hermitian)

$$\langle \varphi_1 | V_{\text{eff}} | \varphi_2 \rangle = \sum_j \int \varphi_1^*(\mathbf{r}) \nabla \varphi_2(\mathbf{r}) \cdot d\mathbf{S}_j \qquad (17)$$

do not decrease with momentum transfer ($\varphi_1 \sim \exp[i\mathbf{k} \cdot \mathbf{r}]$, $\varphi_2 \sim \exp[i\mathbf{l} \cdot \mathbf{r}]$) until $|\mathbf{k}-\mathbf{l}|$ exceeds $2\pi/d_j$, where d_j is the diameter of B_j, and then only slowly. This indicates that the convergence of a perturbation expansion depends crucially on wave lengths smaller than the size of B_j, i.e., on details of the scattering. Equally serious, if the unperturbed φ is a constant, then $V_{\text{eff}} \varphi = 0$, so that convergence is impossible, a phenomenon mirrored by eq. (4) itself. This defect appears intrinsic, resulting from the circumstance that although B_j may be small, the wave function, and more particularly its gradient, is greatly changed in the vicinity of B_j; this would be true even if B_j were to shrink to a point. To avoid the difficulty with constant φ, one may subtract from $V_{\text{eff}} \psi$ an appropriate term which would vanish if ψ had its correct surface value of zero, but which otherwise accelerates convergence. We shall consider two such modifications.

First, let us replace eq. (9) by

$$V_{\text{eff}} \psi(\mathbf{r}) = \sum V_{j,\text{eff}} \psi(\mathbf{r})$$
$$V_{j,\text{eff}} \psi(\mathbf{r}) = -(\hbar^2/2m)(1/a_j) \nabla \mathcal{Z}_j(\mathbf{r}) \cdot \nabla[R_j(\mathbf{r}^+) \psi(\mathbf{r}^+)] \qquad (18)$$

where the surface B_j corresponds (far from uniquely) to the equation $R_j(\mathbf{r}) = a_j$. Since only terms of the form $(1/a)(\nabla \mathcal{Z} \cdot \nabla R) \psi(\mathbf{r}^+)$ have been appended to eq. (9), one would expect (18) to be equivalent to (9); indeed, analyzing it in the same fashion as (9), eq. (12) is replaced by

$$\partial \psi(\mathbf{r}^-)/\partial n = [\partial \ln R_j(\mathbf{r}^+)/\partial n] \psi(\mathbf{r}^+) \qquad (19)$$

and continuity of ψ across B_j maintained, leading to the same conclusion. In the special case of a sphere of radius a,

$$V_{\text{eff}} \psi = (\hbar^2/2ma) \delta(r-a) \partial(r\psi)/\partial r^+ \qquad (20)$$

is a suitable choice. Clearly, the pseudopotential [2] of eq. (18) does not now vanish when acting on a constant.

To obtain a limiting class of effective potentials, suppose that the system is three-dimensional and that the volumes τ_j containing the surfaces B_j have small diameters d_j in the sense that $d_j k \ll 1$, where

$E = \hbar^2 k^2/2m$. Solving eq. (10) by eqs. (2) within a large container,

$$\psi(\mathbf{r}') = \sum_j \psi_j(\mathbf{r}')$$

where $\qquad \psi_j(\mathbf{r}') = \int G_E(\mathbf{r}', \mathbf{q}_j + \mathbf{r}) V_{j,\text{eff}} \psi(\mathbf{q}_j + \mathbf{r}) \, d\tau_j \qquad (21)$

and $\qquad G_E(\mathbf{r}', \mathbf{r}) = -(\hbar^2/8\pi m) \cos k|\mathbf{r}' - \mathbf{r}|/|\mathbf{r}' - \mathbf{r}|$

$\mathbf{q}_j$ is a fixed point within τ_j. Now let us specialize to spherical boundaries; the case of separable boundaries proceeds similarly and is spelled out in Chap. IX. From the well-known expansion

$$G_E(\mathbf{r}', \mathbf{r}) = (\hbar^2 k/8\pi m) \sum [(2l+1)(l-m)!/(l+m)!]e^{im(\varphi'-\varphi)}$$
$$P_l^m(\cos\theta')P_l^m(\cos\theta)n_l(kr')j_l(kr) \qquad (22)$$

for $r' > r$, coupled with the short-range dependence $j_l(kr) \to (kr)^l/1 \cdot 3 \cdot 5 \ldots (2l+1)$ and the assumption $d_j k \ll 1$, we see that only the s wave, $l = 0$, contributes to (21). Hence $\psi_j(\mathbf{r}')$ necessarily has the short-range dependence $n_0(k|\mathbf{r}' - \mathbf{q}_j|)$ $= -\cos k|\mathbf{r}' - \mathbf{q}_j|/k|\mathbf{r}' - \mathbf{q}_j|$. But only the integral $\int V_{j,\text{eff}} \psi(\mathbf{r}) \, d\tau_j$ is required in (21), and $\psi(\mathbf{r})$ either has leading term $|\mathbf{r} - \mathbf{q}_j|^{-1}$ (from ψ_j), or constant (from ψ_i, $i \neq j$). Any modification of $V_{j,\text{eff}}$ which leaves the integral unaltered under these conditions is permissible. Since $a^{-1} \int \delta(r-a)(\partial/\partial r)(r \cdot r^{-1}) \, d^3r = 0$, $a^{-1} \int \delta(r-a)(\partial/\partial r)(r \cdot 1) \, d^3r = 4\pi a$, it follows that if $D(\mathbf{r})$ is any narrow function of unit volume integral, e.g., $\delta(r-\varepsilon)/4\pi\varepsilon^2$ for arbitrarily small ε, then (20) is equivalent to

$$V_{j,\text{eff}} \psi(\mathbf{r}) = (\hbar^2/2m)4\pi a_j D_j(\mathbf{r} - \mathbf{q}_j)\mathbf{n} \cdot \nabla[|\mathbf{r} - \mathbf{q}_j|\psi(\mathbf{r}^+)] \qquad (23)$$

and under some circumstances to the extreme limit $V_{j,\text{eff}}$ $= (\hbar^2/2m)4\pi a_j \delta(|\mathbf{r} - \mathbf{q}_j|)$. To include p wave and higher, R_j requires higher powers $|\mathbf{r} - \mathbf{q}_j|^s$ and $D(\mathbf{r})$ is less arbitrary.

In the usual $3N$-dimensional many-body case, in which the boundaries are hypercylinders (defining equation for B_j involves only three relative coordinates) the above remains valid if $\mathbf{r}$ is simply the three-vector on which B_j does depend.

Multiple Scattering Expansion. If the eigensolutions can be obtained for each B_j separately, a second approach to the problem of the large local effect of a boundary perturbation is available (and, as Eyges shows in Chap. IX, considerable simplification is possible when, as is most often the case, the individual boundaries are of the separable type). Briefly, the trick is, at each boundary interaction B_j, to pre-liminarily subtract from any iterated solution that portion which is inconsistent with vanishing on B_j, or more graphically, that scattered by B_j.

Now suppose that the Green's function G_E^j in the presence of B_j alone is known,

$$(E-T)G_E^j(\mathbf{r}, \mathbf{r}') = \delta(\mathbf{r}-\mathbf{r}') \qquad \text{outside } B_j$$
$$G_E^j(\mathbf{r}, \mathbf{r}') = 0 \qquad \text{for } \mathbf{r} \text{ within } B_j \qquad (24)$$
$$G_E^j(\mathbf{r}, \mathbf{r}') = G_E^j(\mathbf{r}', \mathbf{r})$$

if necessary by use of (6) and the full set of eigensolutions for a wave vanishing on B_j. It is then easy to construct that solution of $(E-T)\varphi = 0$ outside of B_j which has any chosen set of values $\bar{\varphi}(\mathbf{r})$ on B_j; setting $G_E = 0$ and $\psi = \bar{\varphi}$ in the surface integral of eq. (3), taken for the single boundary B_j, we have

$$\varphi(\mathbf{r}) = Q_j\bar{\varphi}(\mathbf{r}) \equiv -(\hbar^2/2m) \int \bar{\varphi}(\mathbf{r}')\nabla'G_E^j(\mathbf{r}', \mathbf{r}) \cdot d\mathbf{S}_j' \qquad (25)$$

Although only the value of $\bar{\varphi}$ on B_j is required in eq. (12), Q_j can nonetheless be regarded as acting on a function which is everywhere defined; since $Q_j\bar{\varphi}$ preserves the value $\bar{\varphi}$ at the boundary, Q_j is clearly a projection:

$$(Q_j)^2 = Q_j \qquad (26)$$

Further, the specification of the wave function for the full set of boundaries is that $(E-T)\psi = 0$ exterior to all B_j and vanishes on each B_j; according to eq. (25), the latter becomes

$$Q_j\psi(\mathbf{r}) = 0, \qquad \text{all } j \qquad (27)$$

Equations (26), (27) may be fruitfully interpreted; consider a single boundary B_j and suppose that it is embedded in a wave function φ satisfying $(E-T)\varphi = 0$ but not vanishing on B_j. Since $Q_j\varphi$ has the same boundary values as φ on B_j, then if the boundary is regarded as reacting with (scattering) φ, producing $-Q_j\varphi$, the combination $\varphi' \equiv \varphi-Q_j\varphi$ does have the correct boundary conditions; formally, $Q_j\varphi' = (Q_j^2-Q_j)\varphi = 0$, as well as $(E-T)\varphi' = 0$ outside of B_j. Since $\varphi-Q_j\varphi$ is guaranteed to contain the direct effect of the bound-ary B_j, and coincides with φ when the latter already vanishes on B_j, the effective potential of eq. (9) can now be used for perturbation (and similarly for eq. (7)) if we choose the equivalent

$$V_{\mathrm{eff}}\psi(\mathbf{r}) = (\hbar^2/2m) \sum_j \nabla \mathcal{Z}_j(\mathbf{r}) \cdot \nabla[(Q_j - 1)\psi(\mathbf{r}^+)] \qquad (28)$$

Equation (28) for a small sphere reduces to the Fermi pseudopotential of eq. (23). Of course, the reaction to the "source" — the non-zero value of φ on B_j — while remedying the boundary conditions at B_j, also modifies the wave function at the other boundaries, but this at least appears as a perturbation effect, with inverse distance between boundaries as perturbation parameter. It should be observed that the foregoing also holds true if the boundaries B_j happen to intersect, a very useful characteristic.

The projection Q_j is helpful not only in forming an effective potential, but also in eliminating the need for one; that is, the fact that eq. (27) is based upon solutions to the elementary "scattering" process suggests that it is closely related to the multiple scattering perturbation formalism of Chap. I. To find the relation, we proceed by iteration. Adopting the classical Schwartz alternating process [3], we may find the wave function ψ by taking a corresponding φ which satisfies $(E-T)\varphi = 0$ in the full space, scattering it by the sequence $B_1, B_2, B_3, \ldots$ and then iterating the process:

$$\psi = \lim_{m \to \infty} [\prod_j (1 - Q_j)]^m \varphi \qquad (29)$$

Making use of eq. (26), this leads to

$$\psi = \varphi - \sum Q_j \varphi + \sum_{j' \neq j} Q_j Q_{j'} \varphi - \sum_{j' \neq j, j'' \neq j'} Q_j Q_{j'} Q_{j''} \varphi + \ldots \qquad (30)$$

The non-repetition or total scattering character of Q_j in eq. (30) is now a direct consequence of eq. (26), and the correspondance with multiple scattering bound state theory is given by $Q_j = -Gt_j$. Further, the fact that eq. (27) is satisfied stems at once from application of eq. (26) to ψ of (30) [also identifiable as $\psi = \delta(\sum Q_j)\varphi$].

Since a multiple boundary is here considered as little more than one big separated boundary, convergence in limiting cases, such as that of fixed large separation of boundaries, with the number of boundaries going to infinity, is scarcely guaranteed. For example, there certainly exists channeled or coherent scattering of the Bragg type.

As a further indication, $\mathcal{N}$ hard spheres, each of small volume τ in a volume V, see a volume in configuration space of V^N; the volume excluded by each interaction surface $|\mathbf{r}_i - \mathbf{r}_j| = a$ is $(8\tau/V)V^N$, but there are $\frac{1}{2}\mathcal{N}(\mathcal{N}-1)$ such volumes. Hence, the relative volume excluded appears to be $4\mathcal{N}\tau(\mathcal{N}/V)$; of course, we have neglected intersections of the excluded volumes, but the possible non-perturbative nature of multiple scattering as $\mathcal{N}\to\infty$ is indicated. The required developments and the influence of quantum statistics were considered to some extent in Part One; here they will be treated directly by Huang, Lee, and Yang (Chap. X) for the statistical mechanical case, and indirectly by Jastrow (Chap. XI) for the case of bound states.

2. Quantum statistical mechanics

Partition Function. We inquire as to appropriate methods for determining the Gibbs canonical partition function for a quantum mechanical $\mathcal{N}$-body system in equilibrium. With respect to the eigenstate problem, this question has the disadvantage of requiring all states, or at least their energies, but the advantage that only particular combinations are desired. Since the trace operation of quantum mechanics replaces the classical phase-space average (but see Wigner [4]), the canonical partition function for equilibrium at temperature T is given by

$$\mathcal{Z}_N = \mathrm{Tr}(e^{-\beta H_N}) \qquad \beta \equiv 1/\kappa T \tag{31}$$

where H_N is the $\mathcal{N}$-body Hamiltonian.

Now in eq. (31), the trace involves summation only over an independent complete set of states for the system. The unsymmetrized momentum eigenfunctions (periodic boundary conditions in a cubic volume $\Omega = L^3$ are assumed hereafter)

$$|\mathbf{k}_1, \mathbf{k}_2, \ldots, \mathbf{k}_N\rangle = \Omega^{-\frac{1}{2}N} \exp\left(i\hbar \sum \mathbf{k}_j \cdot \mathbf{x}_j\right) \tag{32}$$

must therefore give way to the set

$$\psi_\pm = (\mathcal{N}!C)^{-\frac{1}{2}} \sum_P (\pm 1)^P |\mathbf{k}_{P(1)}, \mathbf{k}_{P(2)}, \ldots, \mathbf{k}_{P(N)}\rangle \tag{33}$$

for Einstein-Bose or Fermi-Dirac statistics respectively, where P denotes any $\mathcal{N}$-body permutation, C is the number of permutations leaving $|\mathbf{k}_1 \ldots \mathbf{k}_N\rangle$ unaltered, and $\mathbf{k}_1 \geqq \mathbf{k}_2 \geqq \ldots \mathbf{k}_N$ or $\mathbf{k}_1 > \mathbf{k}_2 > \ldots \mathbf{k}_N$ respectively for some momentum ordering.

Expanding the trace in eq. (31) via the functions (33), and eliminating one of the permutation summations by the observation that $e^{-\beta H_N}$ is already symmetric, while the ordering restriction (and hence the Pauli principle in intermediate states) is dropped by simply dividing by $N!/C$, we obtain

$$\mathcal{Z}_N = (1/N!) \sum_{\{\mathbf{k}_j\}} \sum_P (\pm 1)^P \langle \mathbf{k}_{P(1)}, \ldots, \mathbf{k}_{P(N)} | e^{-\beta H_N} | \mathbf{k}_1, \ldots, \mathbf{k}_N \rangle \quad (34)$$

If the particles have spin J, but H_N contains no spin interaction, it is readily seen that one factor of $2J + 1$ must be included in $\mathcal{Z}_N$ for each cycle (including one-element cycles) of each permutation P.

On the other hand, $\mathcal{Z}_N$ of eq. (31) may also be written as an exponential energy sum. If for example, H_N is regarded as a perturbation of the free-particle Hamiltonian and the energy levels of H_N indexed by corresponding (assuming no qualitative change in the spectrum) free-particle momenta: $E(\mathbf{k}_1, \mathbf{k}_2, \ldots, \mathbf{k}_N)$, then

$$\mathcal{Z}_N = \sum_{\{\mathbf{k}_j\}}' \exp\left[-\beta E(\mathbf{k}_1, \ldots, \mathbf{k}_N)\right] \quad (35)$$

where the prime indicates the restriction $\mathbf{k}_1 > \mathbf{k}_2 \ldots > \mathbf{k}_N$ required for Fermi-Dirac statistics, $\mathbf{k}_1 \geqq \mathbf{k}_2 \ldots \geqq \mathbf{k}_N$ for Einstein-Bose. Even if the functional form of $E(\mathbf{k}_1, \ldots, \mathbf{k}_N)$ is assumed to be reasonably well known [5], one is left with a computation formally more difficult than that in the classical case, due to the generally complicated form of $E(\mathbf{k}_1, \ldots, \mathbf{k}_N)$. In practice, one may use an approximate formulation such as

$$\bar{\mathcal{Z}}_N = \sum_{\{\mathbf{k}_j\}}' \rho(\mathbf{k}_1, \ldots, \mathbf{k}_N)[1 - \beta E(\mathbf{k}_1, \ldots, \mathbf{k}_N) - \ln \rho(\mathbf{k}_1, \ldots, \mathbf{k}_N)] \quad (36a)$$

which, as ρ varies, has an absolute maximum at the correct value of eq. (35), and is thus suitable for evaluation with a variational form for ρ, or as

$$\bar{F}_N = \sum_{\{\mathbf{k}_j\}}' \rho(\mathbf{k}_1, \ldots, \mathbf{k}_N)[E(\mathbf{k}_1, \ldots, \mathbf{k}_N) + (1/\beta)\ln \rho(\mathbf{k}_1, \ldots, \mathbf{k}_N)]$$
$$\text{with} \quad \sum' \rho(\mathbf{k}_1, \ldots, \mathbf{k}_N) = 1 \quad (36b)$$

minimization of free energy $F = -(1/\beta) \ln \mathcal{Z}$, or finally by maximization of the entropy

$$\bar{S}_N = -\kappa \sum_{\{k_j\}}{}' \rho(\mathbf{k}_1, \ldots, \mathbf{k}_N) \ln \rho(\mathbf{k}_1, \ldots, \mathbf{k}_N) \qquad (36c)$$

with $\quad \sum{}' \rho(\mathbf{k}_1, \ldots, \mathbf{k}_N) = 1, \qquad \sum{}' \rho(\mathbf{k}_1, \ldots, \mathbf{k}_N) E(\mathbf{k}_1, \ldots, \mathbf{k}_N) = E$

For many purposes, it is more convenient to use the grand canonical partition function [6]

$$\mathcal{Z} = \sum_{N=0}^{\infty} z^N \mathcal{Z}_N \qquad (37)$$

in terms of which, e.g., the equation of state, or relation between mean density ρ and pressure p is found by eliminating the activity z from

$$\rho = (1/\Omega) \; \partial \ln \mathcal{Z} / \partial \ln z$$
$$p\Omega\beta = \ln \mathcal{Z} \qquad (38)$$

The difference between z/Ω and ρ mirrors the departure from an ideal gas; for example, (38) is seen to imply

$$\partial p / \partial \rho = (1/\beta) \; \partial \ln z / \partial \ln \rho \qquad (38')$$

thereby relating as well the activity and Gibbs potential: $G = (1/\beta) \ln z$. Assuming that $\mathcal{Z}$ of (37) is sharply peaked in N, (38) and (38') may now be regarded as representing the desired N-body problem.

For a condensed uncoupled Einstein-Bose system, particle number fluctuations in (37) are of the order of the number itself, so that the grand partition function serves only as a generating function for fixed-N systems. Now even weak coupling will lead to relative fluctuations vanishing as $N \to \infty$ and hence to the validity of the above usage for $\mathcal{Z}$, but one must be careful with perturbation procedures since there is clearly an analytic break at zero coupling. A modified perturbation method, generally consonant with a two-fluid picture of the condensed state, then becomes particularly appropriate, but will not be considered at this time.

If one switches to an occupation number representation: $E(\ldots, n_\mathbf{k}, \ldots)$, then the awkward limitation $\sum n_\mathbf{k} = N$ on the indices in (35) does not appear in (37), which may be written as

$$\mathcal{Z} = \sum_{\{n_\mathbf{k}\}} \exp \left[-\beta E(\ldots, n_\mathbf{k}, \ldots) + \sum n_\mathbf{k} \ln z \right] \qquad (35')$$

($n = 0,1$ in the Fermi-Dirac case) and treated in a fashion similar to that of eqs. (36).

Cluster Expansion. Returning to eqs. (34) and (37), our objective will be to obtain a cluster expansion analogous to that familiar from the classical case (see, e.g., Hill [6], Chap. V); restriction to the gaseous state is implied. We shall principally follow the developments of Montroll and Ward [7], and Huang, Lee, and Yang (Chap. X), working in a first quantized rather than second quantized formulation, for the identity of the two is manifested at an early stage. For a clear presentation of the latter approach to quantum statistics, see Bloch and de Dominicis [8].

A preliminary step in the evaluation of (34) is the series expansion in V_N of $e^{-\beta H_N}$, where H_N has been separated into kinetic (free) and potential contributions, $H_N = T_N + V_N$. This may be done in many ways [9]. For instance, using an imaginary shift of integration path if necessary, we have

$$e^{-\beta H_N} = (1/2\pi) \int_{-\infty}^{\infty} e^{i\beta s} (H_N + is)^{-1} \, ds \tag{39}$$

whose evident relation to the scattering problem has been exploited by Watson [10]. Expanding, eq. (39) becomes

$$(1/2\pi) \int_{-\infty}^{\infty} e^{i\beta s} (T_N + is)^{-1} [1 + V_N (T_N + is)^{-1}]^{-1} \, ds$$

$$= (1/2\pi) \int_{-\infty}^{\infty} e^{i\beta s} [(T_N + is)^{-1} - (T_N + is)^{-1} V_N (T_N + is)^{-1}$$

$$+ (T_N + is)^{-1} V_N (T_N + is)^{-1} V_N (T_N + is)^{-1} - \ldots] \, ds$$

$$= (1/2\pi) \int_{-\infty}^{\infty} e^{i\beta s} \left[\int_0^{\infty} e^{-\alpha_1 (T_N + is)} \, d\alpha_1 \right.$$

$$- \iint_0^{\infty} e^{-\alpha_2 (T_N + is)} V_N e^{-\alpha_1 (T_N + is)} \, d\alpha_1 \, d\alpha_2$$

$$+ \iiint_0^{\infty} e^{-\alpha_3 (T_N + is)} V_N e^{-\alpha_2 (T_N + is)} V_N e^{-\alpha_1 (T_N + is)} \, d\alpha_1 \, d\alpha_2 \, d\alpha_3$$

$$\left. + \ldots \right] \, ds$$

Finally, setting $\beta_1 = \alpha_1$, $\beta_2 = \alpha_1 + \alpha_2$, $\beta_3 = \alpha_1 + \alpha_2 + \alpha_3, \ldots$, and observing that integration over s creates a factor $\delta(\beta_n - \beta)$ in the nth term, there results

$$e^{-\beta(T_N + V_N)} = e^{-\beta T_N} - \int_0^{\beta} e^{-(\beta - \beta_1) T_N} V_N e^{-\beta_1 T_N} \, d\beta_1$$

$$+ \int_0^{\beta} \int_0^{\beta_2} e^{-(\beta - \beta_2) T_N} V_N e^{-(\beta_2 - \beta_1) T_N} V_N e^{-\beta_1 T_N} \, d\beta_1 \, d\beta_2 \tag{40}$$

$$- \int_0^{\beta} \int_0^{\beta_3} \int_0^{\beta_2} e^{-(\beta - \beta_3) T_N} V_N e^{-(\beta_3 - \beta_2) T_N} V_N e^{-(\beta_2 - \beta_1) T_N} V_N e^{-\beta_1 T_N} \, d\beta_1 \, d\beta_2 \, d\beta_3 + \ldots$$

Relating β to imaginary „time", a typical term in eq. (40) may be interpreted in familiar fashion (see, e.g., Bethe, Chap. II) as free-system propagation from 0 to β_1, interaction at β_1, free propagation until β_2, interaction at β_2, ..., and finally free propagation to β. However, as we shall see, the range of 0—β, rather than $-\infty$—t, complicates energy denominators resulting from β-integrations. It is to be observed that the classical case results from eq. (40) by commuting all $e^{-\beta T}$ factors through to the left; except for a normalization of $1/s!$ in the sth term and replacement of V by βV, the result of the integration is equivalent to setting each β_i equal to β, i.e., having all interactions at a common "time".

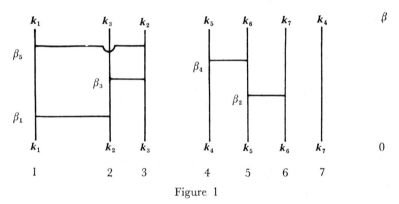

Figure 1

Now, we shall be interested in the case in which (at the cost of a slight inelegance of notation)

$$T_N = \sum_1^N T(j) \qquad V_N = \sum_{i<j\leqq N} V_{ij} \tag{41}$$

$$T(j) = p_j^2/2m = k_j^2\hbar^2/2m \qquad V_{ij} = V(\mathbf{x}_i-\mathbf{x}_j, \mathbf{p}_i, \mathbf{p}_j)$$

The interaction, being momentum-conserving, has matrix elements

$$\langle \mathbf{k}_i'\mathbf{k}_j'|V_{ij}|\mathbf{k}_i\mathbf{k}_j\rangle = \delta_{\mathbf{k}_j-\mathbf{k}_j',\mathbf{k}_i'-\mathbf{k}_i}V_{\mathbf{k}_j-\mathbf{k}_j'}(\hbar\mathbf{k}_i, \hbar\mathbf{k}_j) \tag{42}$$

which may be interpreted as the transfer of a quantum of wave number $\mathbf{k} = \mathbf{k}_j-\mathbf{k}_j' = \mathbf{k}_i'-\mathbf{k}_i$ from particle j to particle i; here $V_\mathbf{k}$ is the Fourier transform of V. A typical (5th-order) term in the full expansion of $\mathcal{Z}_N$ ($N = 7$ in Fig. 1) of eqs. (34), (40) may be represented diagrammatically as shown: the horizontal bars denote $(-V_{ij})$

interactions, the vertical lines free one-particle propagation; the matrix element between initial and final states is to be taken [here $P = (1)(23)(4567)$], and summation over the $\mathbf{k}$'s (this diagram exists only for $\mathbf{k}_4 = \mathbf{k}_7$) and properly ordered β's performed. One sees that, e.g., since the three intervening interactions V_{23}, V_{45}, V_{56} commute with $\mathbf{p}_1$, the parameters β_2, β_3, β_4 are not coupled to $\mathbf{p}_1$ (the products $\beta_2 p_1^2$ etc., in the exponents cancelling in pairs), and so $\mathbf{p}_1$ appears in eq. (40) only via exp $(\beta_1-\beta_5)p_1^2/2m$ for the region between β_1 and β_5. This remark may be extended at once to the statement that exp $\mp \beta_s T(i)$ appears only at ($\mp$ for before or after) an interaction of particle i at β_s. Hence, to the propagation line of particle i between β_s and β_t we associate the operator exp $(\beta_s-\beta_t)p_i^2/2m$; all exponentials are encompassed in this fashion.

Diagram Reduction. Two simplifications utilized in the analysis of classical statistical mechanics are the elimination of disconnected diagrams and the replacement of the interaction potential by a temperature-dependent smoothed interaction. Each has an analog in quantum statistics.

First, let us consider a diagram containing disconnected sets of particles. Connections are due either to interaction lines or to common initial and final momenta, e.g., $\mathbf{k}_2$ connects particles 2 and 3 in Fig. 1, $\mathbf{k}_7$ connects 6 and 7, etc. Now totally disconnected components of a diagram commute, as operators, and are independent under $\mathbf{k}$-summation; they are coupled only by virtue of the β-integration ordering in eq. (40): $0 < \beta_1 < \beta_2 \ldots < \beta$. However, accompanying any diagram with a given relative ordering between disconnected components will be diagrams with all other possible relative orderings; only the ordering within each component (e.g., $0 < \beta_1 < \beta_3 < \beta_5 < \beta$, $0 < \beta_2 < \beta_4 < \beta$ in Fig. 1) is maintained, and if all such diagrams are taken together and summed, there is no other restriction and no common integration region. Hence, the value of $\mathcal{Z}_N$ is unchanged if disconnected components are independently integrated, and if the contribution of an aggregate diagram is taken as the product of the disconnected contributions (as in the ground state problem, see Bethe, Chap. II).

To make use of this multiplicative decomposition, we observe that by permuting any diagram (i.e., by redesignating all particle indices and then rearranging in numerical order), we may arrange matters such that: (a) each disconnected component contains only consecutive indices (which need not, however, be ordered consecutively in a pictorial representation), (b) the lengths of the disconnected components are non-decreasing from left to right. The contribution of any diagram thus equals the contribution of some such canonical diagram, of which Fig. 1 is an example. Hence, taking only the canonical diagrams of order N and applying all $N!$ diagram permutations (numerically, just multiplying by $N!$), all Nth-order diagrams will be created. However, some diagrams will in this fashion be produced more than once, and their contributions must be appropriately divided. In particular, if under these permutations, a certain canonical diagram $\mathscr{D}$ gives rise to d other canonical diagrams, all diagrams emanating from $\mathscr{D}$ will appear d times in the full set of permuted diagrams, and so $\mathscr{D}$ must be divided by d. Now if a canonical diagram has n_l disconnected components of length l, the $n_l!$ permutations which permute these components also produce canonical diagrams, as do the $l!$ permutations within each component. From this remark and the multiplicative nature of disconnected diagrams, we conclude that if b_l is defined as $1/l!$ times the sum of contributions from all connected diagrams of length l, then

$$Z_N = 1/N! \sum_{\sum n_l = N} [N! \prod_l (b_l^{n_l}/n_l!)] \tag{43}$$

From eq. (37), the grand canonical partition function thus becomes

$$Z = \exp \left(\sum_1^\infty z^l b_l \right) \tag{44}$$

A second diagram reduction is occasioned by noting that eqs. (34), (40), as an expansion in the V_{ij}, are inappropriate for singular potentials, unlike the classical Mayer-Ursell expansion (See, e.g., Mayer and Mayer) [6], in $[\exp(-\beta V_{ij}) - 1]$. Now if, in the classical statistical case, one performs instead an expansion in the V_{ij}, the resulting cluster diagrams are altered by the appearance of any number of single links between each vertex pair i, j. Since we have observed that in the classical case, one contracts all values of the β_i to β, a quantum mechanical counterpart to the classical expansion in $[\exp(-\beta V_{ij}) - 1]$ will be obtained if we eliminate *successive* interactions between any pair i, j. Indeed it is clear that we may eliminate all diagrams involving successive interactions between pairs (and with no other intervening interactions, for these would introduce additional "time" ordering), if V_{ij} at β_s is replaced by the sum of all sequences of interactions of the pair i, j ending with an interaction at β_s.

Thus, denoting V_{ij}, $T_i + T_j$, and $\beta_s - \beta_{s-1}$ by V, T, α, we must make the replacement $Ve^{-\alpha T} \to Ve^{-\alpha T} - \int_0^\alpha Ve^{-\alpha' T} Ve^{-(\alpha-\alpha')T} d\alpha' + \int_0^\alpha \int_0^{\alpha-\alpha'} Ve^{-\alpha' T} Ve^{-\alpha'' T} Ve^{-(\alpha-\alpha'-\alpha'')T} d\alpha'' d\alpha' + \ldots = Ve^{-\alpha(T+V)}$, or

$$V_{ij} \exp[-(\beta_s - \beta_{s-1})(T_i + T_j)] \to$$
$$X_{ij}(\beta_s - \beta_{s-1}) = V_{ij} \exp[-(\beta_s - \beta_{s-1})(T_i + T_j + V_{ij})] \tag{45}$$

For the final interaction, one also requires the closing expression $U_{2ij}(\beta - \beta_n) = \exp[\beta - \beta_n)(T_i + T_j)]X_{ij}(\beta - \beta_n)$. The resulting expansion diagrams constitute what Huang, Lee, and Yang (Chap. X) refer to as the binary collision expansion. Eq. (45) may also be written as

$$V_{ij} \to K_{ij}(\beta_s - \beta_{s-1}) = V_{ij} \exp[-(\beta_s - \beta_{s-1})(T_i + T_j + V_{ij})]$$
$$\times \exp[(\beta_s - \beta_{s-1})(T_i + T_j)] \tag{45'}$$

V_{ij} being replaced by the statistical reaction operator K_{ij}, which satisfies the simple two-body equation $\partial K/\partial \alpha = -K(e^{-\alpha T} V e^{\alpha T})$. K_{ij} is momentum-conserving when V_{ij} is, but except for potentials of vanishingly short range (see Chap. X), it depends explicitly on $\alpha = \beta_s - \beta_{s-1}$ (similar to the energy dependence of t_{ij} in the eigenstate problem — see Chap. II). Since this β dependence will interfere with other reductions to be considered, and since the reaction operator can be introduced, with additional structure, after further reductions, we will not in general assume that the $V \to K$ transition has been made.

Toron Decomposition. A portion of a diagram which, in the absence of V_{ij} links, is still connected (e.g., 1, 23, or 4567 in Fig. 1) is called, in the terminology of Montroll and Ward [7], a toron; it represents a cycle in the cyclic decomposition. The terminology stems from assumed periodic boundary conditions in coordinate space, combined with the cyclic nature, e.g., $\mathbf{k}_4\mathbf{k}_5$, $\mathbf{k}_5\mathbf{k}_6$, $\mathbf{k}_6\mathbf{k}_7$, $\mathbf{k}_7\mathbf{k}_4$ of the columns constituting the toron (or the equivalent cyclic nature in a coordinate representation). A toron is the quantum mechanical extension of a vertex in classical cluster expansions; it collapses to a point when the β_s coalesce to β, and its identification with a single quantum mechanical entity is strengthened by the fact that, with spin, each toron acquires $2J+1$ new degrees of freedom. Thus, it should be possible to set up a formulation in which one can reasonably say that torons are in interaction, without delving into the internal structure of each toron.

Let us adopt an enumeration of connected diagrams which is appropriate to the toron concept. We define canonical connected diagrams of size n ($= n$ particles) as those in which each toron contains only consecutive indices presented in consecutive order, and in which the cyclic permutation carries each particle one step to the right. The $n!$ permutations required to construct all diagrams cancel the $1/n!$ in the definition of b_n if only canonical diagrams are retained in the definition, but in addition:

A connected diagram of q torons must be divided by $q!$ due to the possibility of toron reordering, maintaining canonical form, and the various cyclic permutations of component torons are not to be regarded as distinct. Further, a single toron with no external links is reduced by the number of cyclic permutations keeping it unchanged. Now torons are numbered, not particles.

The factor $q!$ is reminiscent of the classical normalization, if once more each toron is regarded as a single entity. To complete the description of a diagram, the full matrix element is of course analyzed in terms of one-body states, so that a distinct momentum $\mathbf{k}$ is associated with each particle line between interactions, with summation over all $\mathbf{k}$'s ultimately performed.

One superfluity which appears in the description of toron interactions is very easily removed. It is observed that a particle line, such as 7 in Fig. 1, may have no interactions at all, and be coupled only by virtue of the permutation between initial and final momenta; since $\mathbf{k}_7 = \mathbf{k}_4$, particle 7 simply contributes a factor of $\exp\left(-\beta \hbar^2 k_4^2/2m\right)$. In general, there are two possible situations. First, if a line of momentum $\mathbf{k}$ interacts at β_s, the next interaction β_t of this momentum line, following along the toron to another particle channel if necessary, may be later: $\beta_t > \beta_s$. In this case, the interactions may be: in the same particle column (e.g., particle 5 from β_2 to β_4 in Fig. 1), propagation yielding a factor of $\exp[-(\beta_t-\beta_s)\hbar^2 k^2/2m]$; in adjacent columns, yielding $\exp[-\beta_t+\beta-\beta_s)\hbar^2 k^2/2m]$, ...; l columns apart ($l = 2$ for $\mathbf{k}_7$ from β_2 to β_4 in Fig. 1), yielding $\exp[-(\beta_t+l\beta-\beta_s)\hbar^2 k^2/2m]$.

Further, each increase in the length of a cycle inserts a factor of $\pm z$ into $\ln \mathcal{Z} = \sum z^n b_n$. Hence, summing from $l = 0$ to ∞, the replacement of the propagation factor by

$$\beta_t > \beta_s: \qquad \exp[-(\beta_t-\beta_s)\hbar^2 k^2/2m][1/1\mp z \exp(-\beta\hbar^2 k^2/2m)] \quad (46a)$$

permits the elimination of all diagrams with interactionless segments of length $> \beta$ during a "forward" propagation in between interactions. On the other hand, there are the "backward" propagations for which $\beta_t < \beta_s$, e.g., $\mathbf{k}_2$ from β_5 to β_3 in Fig. 1 (if $\beta_t = \beta_s$, e.g., $\mathbf{k}_3$ from β_3 to β_3 in Fig. 1, an arbitrary order is set and retained).

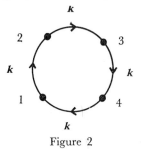

Figure 2

These are necessarily associated with a cross over from one particle channel to another, the shortest propagation thus contributing $\exp[-(\beta-\beta_s+\beta_t)\hbar^2 k^2/2m]$. Again, we sum over any number of intervening lines; it is also convenient to append a single factor z since, there now being one backward propagation per particle line, the complete z dependence of $\mathcal{Z}$ is thereby taken into account. Performing the summation, we have

$$\beta_t < \beta_s: \qquad [z \exp-(\beta\hbar^2 k^2/2m)/1\mp z \exp(-\beta\hbar^2 k^2/2m)]$$
$$\exp[-(\beta_t-\beta_s)\hbar^2 k^2/2m] \qquad (46b)$$

According to eqs. (46), we may write

$$\ln \mathcal{Z}(z) = \ln \mathcal{Z}^{(0)}(z) + \sum_1^\infty b_n(z) \qquad (47)$$

where $b_n(z)$ is computed with the propagation factors of (46) and with interactionless segments of length $> \beta$ omitted. The terms $b_0(z)$ corresponding to interactionless single torons have not been included in (47), for they are not of weight unity; that is, since a bare canonical toron of order l, shown "unfolded" in Fig. 2, is unchanged under l cyclic permutations, its contribution is to be divided by l. It follows at once that $\ln Z^{(0)} = \sum_k \sum_{l>0} (\pm)^{l-1} (z^l/l) \exp(-l\beta\hbar^2 k^2/2m)$ or

$$\ln Z^{(0)} = (\mp\Omega/2\pi^2) \int_0^\infty k^2 \ln[1 \mp z \exp(-\beta\hbar^2 k^2/2m)]\, dk$$
$$= \pm\Omega\lambda^{-3} g_{5/2}(\pm z) \tag{48}$$

where $\lambda \equiv (4\pi\beta\hbar^2/2m)^{\frac{1}{2}}$ is referred to as the thermal de Broglie wave length and $g_s(z) \equiv \sum_{l>0} l^{-s} z^l$.

Equations (46), (47), (48) effectively constitute the formulation of Bloch and de Dominicis [8]; it is only necessary to designate the forward propagations as particles, backward as holes (and draw them accordingly), to recover the field-theoretic form. Conversion of the β_s-integrations to energy denominators follows from the fact that the total propagation factor of an nth-order diagram depends on the β_s only through $\exp\{-[(\beta_2-\beta_1)E_1 + (\beta_3-\beta_2)E_2 + \ldots + (\beta_1-\beta_n)E_n]\}$, where E_s is the total kinetic energy after interaction at β_s (particle energy minus hole energy), coupled with the identity

$$\int \ldots\ldots\ldots \int_{0<\beta_1\cdots<\beta_n<\beta} \exp\{-[(\beta_2-\beta_1)E_1 + \ldots + (\beta_1-\beta_n)E_n]\}\, d\beta_1 \ldots d\beta_n$$
$$= \beta \sum_1^n [e^{-\beta(E_i-E_n)} \prod_{j\neq i} (1/E_j-E_i)] \tag{49}$$

Summation of successive interactions of two particles may be achieved as in (45′) either before or after this conversion; generally, a z-dependent (as well as β-dependent) reaction operator results, but again neither dependence occurs in K for strong short-range potentials.

The reasonableness of the particle-hole designation is attested to by the ground state or $\beta\to\infty$ limit for a Fermi-Dirac system. If one sets $ze^{-\beta\varepsilon} \to e^{-\beta(\varepsilon-\varepsilon_F)}$ in this limit, eq. (46) then allows only particles of energy $> \varepsilon_F$ and holes of energy $< \varepsilon_F$. Necessarily, E_n in eq. (49) is then the smallest of the E_i, and if $E_i = E_n$ only for $i = n$, only the term $i = n$ appears. Actually, ε_F is the energy of an added particle at fixed volume, disconnected terms corresponding to $E_i = E_n$ occur, and the internal energy $U = -\partial \ln Z/\partial\beta$ is obtained essentially in a Brillouin-Wigner expansion. However, dropping disconnected terms and choosing ε_F as the free Fermi energy, U reduces instead[†] to the Goldstone ground state expression (see Bethe, Chap. II).

[†] The reduction has recently been carried out explicitly by Kohn and Luttinger, and the realm of validity of Goldstone's result thus assessed. Phys. Rev. **118**, 41.

Toron Reduction. The replacement (46), while simplifying t**l**
structure of the cluster expansion, still does not exhibit the torons .
separate entities; let us then, following Montroll and Ward [7
reexamine the problem from the start. A typical toron (23 of Fig.
is here shown unwrapped. We know that in general, the propagatic
factor for a given particle momentum depends only on the distan**c**
in β between its interactions; thus if a line of kinetic ener**g**
$T(\mathbf{k}) = \hbar^2 k^2/2m$, in the toron numbered γ, starts at $\beta_{\gamma j}$ and ends
$\beta_{\gamma j+1}$, passing an initial-final state junction (shown here by a hea**v**
dot) $f_{\gamma j}$ times in the process, the associated factor is $\exp[-(\beta_{\gamma j}$
$+f_{\gamma j}\beta - \beta_{\gamma j})T(\mathbf{k})]$. This suggests that a generic toron with fix**e**
external links be obtained by integrating over the vario
$\alpha_{\gamma j} \equiv \beta_{\gamma j+1} + f_{\gamma j}\beta - \beta_{\gamma j}$ in toron γ. There are two difficulties.

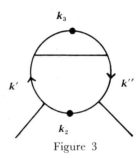

Figure 3

First, if the binary collision operator K_{ij} is used, there is a dependen**ce**
on the distance between an interaction and that interaction whi**ch**
follows in *any* toron; thus, summation over successive interactions
the same pair is to be deferred to a later stage. Second, even if a **V**
expansion is employed, the α's are still not independent, sinc**e**
(a) for a toron of length l, we must have $\sum_j \alpha_{\gamma j} = l\beta$; and (b) each
is simultaneously part of two or more torons (except for self-ener**gy**
parts — see below), so that there are many interrelations between t**l**
α's [e.g., $(\beta_5 - \beta_3) + (\beta_3 - \beta_1) = (\beta_5 - \beta_1)$ connects two torons
Fig. 1]. The first difficulty may be tackled after the fashion of (4**5**
the second requires a new concept.

Suppose that a $V_{\mathbf{k}}$ interaction links β' in one toron with β''
another (or perhaps the same one); to carry out the α-integrati**on**
suggested above, β' and β'' must be independent, but on the oth**er**

and, they must be set equal. These contradictory requirements may ffectively be met by associating a factor $e^{iu\beta'}$ with one side, $e^{-iu\beta''}$ ith the other, for if a summation with u running over integral mul- ples of $2\pi/\beta$ is made in the final evaluation, then

$$(1/\beta) \sum_u e^{iu(\beta'-\beta'')} = \delta(\beta'-\beta'') \tag{50}$$

stablishes the desired identity (note that $0 \leqq \beta', \beta'' < \beta$). Further, ιe condition $\sum \alpha_j = l\beta$ for a given n-interaction toron is simply btained by appending $\delta(l\beta - \sum_1^n \alpha_j) = (1/2\pi)\int_{-\infty}^{\infty} \exp[ir(l\beta - \sum_1^n \alpha_j)]\, dr$. Tow let us for convenience write the value of u entering at the jth ιteraction of a given toron as $u_j - u_{j-1}$ (with $u_0 \equiv 0$), and also rewrite ιe β_s in terms of β_1 and the α_s: $\beta_s = \beta_1 + \sum_1^{s-1}(\alpha_i - f_i\beta)$. Since $u_i f_i \beta = 1$, the complete propagation factor for an n-interaction toron f length l becomes

$$\pm (2\pi)^{-1}(\pm z)^l \int_{-\infty}^{\infty} \int_0^{\infty} \cdots \int_0^{\infty} \int_0^{\beta} e^{-\alpha_1 T(\mathbf{k}_1)} e^{-\alpha_2 T(\mathbf{k}_2)} \cdots e^{-\alpha_n T(\mathbf{k}_n)}$$

$$\times e^{iu_1\beta_1} e^{i(u_2-u_1)(\beta_1+\alpha_1)} \cdots e^{i(u_n-u_1)(\beta_1+\alpha_1\cdots+\alpha_{n-1})} \tag{51}$$

$$\times e^{ir(l\beta-\Sigma\alpha_j)}\, d\beta_1\, d\alpha_1 \ldots d\alpha_n\, dr$$

here k_s is the momentum following the sth interaction.

Carrying out the $\beta_1 \ldots \alpha_n$ integrations in eq. (51) and summing from 1 to ∞, the propagator for the geometrical toron γ is given by

$$\delta_{u_{\gamma n}, 0} (\beta/2\pi) \int_{-\infty}^{\infty} (z e^{ir_\gamma\beta})/(1 \mp z e^{ir_\gamma\beta})[1/(T(\mathbf{k}_{\gamma 1})+iu_{\gamma 1}+ir_\gamma)]$$

$$\times [1/(T(\mathbf{k}_{\gamma 2})+iu_{\gamma 2}+ir_\gamma)] \ldots [1/(T(\mathbf{k}_{\gamma n})+iu_{\gamma n}+ir_\gamma)]\, dr_\gamma \tag{52}$$

ιtegrations involving ordering of variables are no longer required. o interpret (52), we may imagine the toron as having a circulating air $(\mathbf{k}, u)$ with the value $(\mathbf{k}_{\gamma n}, 0)$; at the first interaction, quanta $_{\gamma 1} - \mathbf{k}_{\gamma n}, u_{\gamma 1})$ enter, giving the toron segment a complex energy *$(\mathbf{k}_{\gamma 1}, u_{\gamma 1}) \equiv T(\mathbf{k}_{\gamma 1})+iu_{\gamma 1}$; at the sth interaction, $(\mathbf{k}_{\gamma s}-\mathbf{k}_{\gamma s-1}, _s - u_{\gamma s-1})$ enters, producing $T^*(\mathbf{k}_{\gamma s}, u_{\gamma s})$; and after the nth inter- tion, the initial conditions have been regained. Both $\mathbf{k}$ and u are nserved in interactions, for if an interaction takes place from position of toron γ to t of toron γ', then both $\mathbf{k}_{\gamma s+1} - \mathbf{k}_{\gamma s} = -(\mathbf{k}_{\gamma' t+1} - \mathbf{k}_{\gamma' t})$ ιd $u_{\gamma s+1} - u_{\gamma s} = -(u_{\gamma' t+1} - u_{\gamma' t})$ [to obtain (50)] are necessary.

In order to evaluate a diagram, then, each interaction link transfers quantum $(\mathbf{k}, u)$, while inserting a factor $-(1/\beta) V_\mathbf{k}$ [to include the

$1/\beta$ in (50)], the total incoming and outgoing $(\mathbf{k}, u)$ for each tor being required to balance; the propagator for each toron is fou from (52) (which may be explicitly evaluated by residues) and $(\mathbf{k}, u)$ summations performed. A diagram of q torons must receiv weight of $1/q!$, while a single toron with only internal links (e.

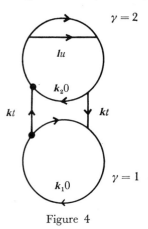

Figure 4

Fig. 3 with the two external links at the bottom removed) — a p self-energy diagram — is weighted as well by dividing by the num of permutations leaving it unaltered. For example, the left connec half of Fig. 1 becomes the geometrical diagram of Fig. 4, wh contribution (the black dots are taken as initial positions) is

$$\sum_{\mathbf{kl}} \sum_{\mathbf{k}_1 \mathbf{k}_2} (\beta/2\pi)^2 (z^2/2!) \sum_{tu} (1/\beta)^3$$
$$\times \iint_{-\infty}^{\infty} (e^{ir_1\beta}/1 \mp ze^{ir_1\beta})(e^{ir_2\beta}/1 \mp ze^{ir_2\beta})[-V_\mathbf{k}(\hbar\mathbf{k}_1, \hbar\mathbf{k}_2)]$$
$$\times [-V_l(\hbar(\mathbf{k}_2+\mathbf{k}), \hbar(\mathbf{k}_2+\mathbf{k}-1))][-V_\mathbf{k}(\hbar(\mathbf{k}_2+\mathbf{k}), \hbar\mathbf{k}_1)] \qquad ($$
$$\times \{[i(r_1-t)+\hbar^2(\mathbf{k}_1-\mathbf{k})^2/2m][ir_1+\hbar^2 k_1^2/2m]\}^{-1}$$
$$\times \{[i(r_2+t)+\hbar^2(\mathbf{k}_2+\mathbf{k})^2/2m][i(r_2+t-u)+\hbar^2(\mathbf{k}_2+\mathbf{k}-1)^2/2m]$$
$$\times [ir_2+\hbar^2 k_2^2/2m]\}^{-1} dr_1 \, dr_2$$

Partial Summations. There are a number of reductions comm in the classical cluster expansion approach for which one may s analogs in quantum theory. A grouping together of all interacti between two torons (as well as self-energy interactions withi toron) — a complete reaction operator analysis to mirror the classical picture — is quite complicated and will not be considered here.

The elimination of diagrams of single connectivity, which in the classical case facilitates the transformation from an activity to a density expansion, is, however, possible here. That is, suppose that the links to a toron can be divided into two classes which are not connected via any other toron, and that each class is grouped together along the toron. By momentum conservation, the total incoming momentum from each class vanishes, so that $\mathbf{k} = \mathbf{k}'$ for the toron momenta after each class has acted. Further, each β_s-ordering of the two sets of interactions with respect to each other comprises a possible diagram;

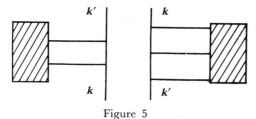

Figure 5

summing such possibilities, the β_s-integrations of the two sets become independent. The net effect then is that, appending the supplementary condition that the toron momenta after interaction are to be identified, $\mathbf{k} = \mathbf{k}'$, the two halves of the diagram may be summed and integrated separately.

Rather than attempt a general reduction along the above lines, let us restrict our attention to the simplest reducible diagrams, those for which any cut through a toron will break the diagram into two.

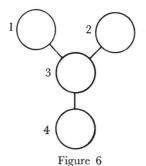

Figure 6

Such diagrams must appear as "trees", connected n-toron configurations with $n-1$ intervening links; there are n^{n-2} numbered trees possible (not distinguishing order of links around each toron) for each n. Since there are no closed loops at all, conservation guarantees that each link transfers $\mathbf{k} = 0, u = 0$; thus if $V(\mathbf{x}_i - \mathbf{x}_j)$ is independent of $\mathbf{p}_i, \mathbf{p}_j$, only interaction factors $-V_0/\beta$ are required. Further, observing eq. (52), we see that addition of a $\mathbf{k} = 0, u = 0$ link at an arbitrary position of a given toron simply repeats each factor $[T(\mathbf{k}_s) + iu_s + ir]^{-1}$ in sequence, thereby applying the operation $i\,\partial/\partial r$ to the product of denominators. Integrating by parts, this is equivalent to applying $\beta z\,\partial/\partial z$ to the complete toron propagator, and is seen to be valid for interactionless torons as well. Now let $g(z)$ be the propagation factor for an isolated toron with a single $\mathbf{k} = 0, u = 0$ link; thus $g(z) = \beta\Omega\lambda^{-3}z$ for a toron of one vertex, $g(z) = \beta z(\partial/\partial z)\ln \mathcal{Z}^{(0)} = \pm\beta\Omega\lambda^{-3}g_{3/2}(\pm z)$ for a generic interactionless toron [see (48)], while $g(z)$ is considerably more complicated for a generic toron including arbitrary internal self-energy links. It is clear that all n-toron trees may then be obtained by spreading the remaining $n-2$ $\mathbf{k} = 0, u = 0$ vertices among the torons already armed with one $\mathbf{k} = 0, u = 0$ vertex apiece: $(\beta z\,\partial/\partial z)^{n-2}g(z)^n$. Hence the total contribution due to trees is given by

$$\ln \mathcal{Z}(z) = \ln \mathcal{Z}^{(0)}(z) - (V_0/\beta)\sum_{n>1}(-V_0 z\,\partial/\partial z)^{n-2}g(z)^n/n! \qquad (54)$$

To utilize eq. (54), let us choose $g(z) = \beta\,\partial \ln \mathcal{Z}^{(0)}/\partial \ln z$ and recall that $\Omega\rho = \partial \ln \mathcal{Z}/\partial \ln z$; then applying $-\beta V_0\,\partial/\partial \ln z$ to (54) yield

$$-\beta V_0\Omega\rho = \sum_{n>0}(\partial/\partial \ln z)^{n-1}[-V_0 g(\exp \ln z)]^n/n! \qquad (54')$$

which, according to the Lagrange inversion formula [11], is equivalent to the implicit relation

$$\beta\Omega\rho = g(ze^{-\beta V_0\Omega\rho}) \qquad (55)$$

Solving (55) for $z : z = \exp(\beta V_0\Omega\rho)[g^{-1}(\beta\Omega\rho)]$ and substituting into (38'), one has the equation of state; on the other hand, the internal energy per particle $U = (\partial/\partial\beta)\beta F = (\partial/\partial\beta)\beta(1/\rho)\int G\,d\rho = (1/\rho)(\partial/\partial\beta)\int \ln z\,d\rho$, or

$$U = \tfrac{1}{2}V_0\Omega\rho + (1/\rho)\int(\rho/\beta)\,d\ln g^{-1}(\beta\Omega\rho) \qquad (56)$$

The energy increment is simply the weak-interaction correlation energy: since the free system is uniform, only the constant component V_0 of the $\frac{1}{2}N^2$ pair interactions is required, yielding an energy per particle of $(\frac{1}{2}N^2V_0)/N = \frac{1}{2}V_0\Omega\rho$. For weak singular potentials (i.e. short-range interaction at low temperature), since no diagrams are disallowed when a link, V_0, of a tree is replaced by the sum, K_0, of successive interactions, this replacement may be made in (54), and in (56) as well, for K_0 is then independent of β and z.

A second level of reduction may be arranged to eliminate diagrams which decompose on cutting through two torons. Once more, let us consider the simplest possibility, in which *any* two cuts accomplish

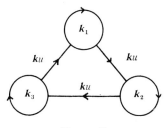

Figure 7

this; if the potential is supposed normalized so that $V_0 = 0$, the remaining diagrams are rings of torons. By momentum and u conservation, the same quantum $(\mathbf{k}u)$ is passed from toron to toron. Now assuming no internal lines, the propagator for a single toron in this situation is clearly

$$\beta\Gamma_{\mathbf{k}u} = (\beta/2\pi) \iint [ze^{ir\beta}/(1\mp ze^{ir\beta})][1/(T(\mathbf{k}'+\mathbf{k})+iu+ir)]$$
$$\times [1/(T(\mathbf{k}')+ir)]\, d^3k'\, dr \tag{57}$$

since there are $(n-1)!$ distinct rings of n torons which have the same value (all index permutations in which one toron is held fixed), the weight of a diagram is $(n-1)!/n! = 1/n$; an exception is the isolated toron with internal link, $n = 1$, having weight $\frac{1}{2}$ [see paragraph preceding (46a)]. Hence $\ln Z = \ln Z^{(0)} + \frac{1}{2}\sum V_{\mathbf{k}}\Gamma_{\mathbf{k}u} + \sum\sum_{n>0}(-V_{\mathbf{k}}\Gamma_{\mathbf{k}u})^n/n$, or converting $\mathbf{k}$-summation to integration and performing the sum over n,

$$\ln \mathcal{Z} = \ln \mathcal{Z}^{(0)} + \tfrac{1}{2}(\Omega/8\pi^3) \sum_u \int V_{\mathbf{k}} \Gamma_{\mathbf{k}u} \, d^3k$$

$$+ (\Omega/8\pi^3) \sum_u \int \ln \left[1 + V_{\mathbf{k}} \Gamma_{\mathbf{k}u}\right] d^3k \tag{58}$$

Again V_{ij} is assumed to be a function of $\mathbf{x}_i - \mathbf{x}_j$ alone, so that only $V_{\mathbf{k}}$ appears. The remaining summations and integrations in (58) are readily carried out only in principle; approximations for special cases are discussed by Montroll and Ward [7]; the Gell-Mann and Brueckner [12] results for an electron gas are obtained in this fashion.

The closed forms (55) and (58) appear to be the beginning of a hierarchy, for if one considers a connected diagram of n torons, the smallest possible number of interaction links is $n-1$, giving rise to (55); the next-to-the-smallest number of $V_{\mathbf{k}}$ links is n, and if $V_0 = 0$, such diagrams are rings (responsible for the classical Debye-Huckel expression [13] for an electrolyte, as well), comprising (58). Thus, for each toron number, a power series expansion in the interaction potential (or reaction operator) is being developed. However, the appropriate dimensionless expansion parameter depends upon the nature of both potential and thermodynamic conditions (there being for example a dimensionless quantity $\lambda^3\rho$ available independently of V) and must be decided in individual cases.

3. *Pair coordinate methods*

Transformation to Pair Space. In Chap. XI, R. Jastrow treats the ground state of an Einstein-Bose many-body system with pair interactions by a variational ansatz of the form $\psi = \prod_{i>j} f(\mathbf{x}_i - \mathbf{x}_j)$. O. Penrose has pointed out [14] that both low-density and "collective" limits may be obtained by requiring the Schrödinger equation itself to be satisfied, in an appropriate sense, by such an ansatz. These approaches are to some extent subsumed as special cases of a procedure known mainly through the work of Bogoliubov and Zubarev [15]. Consider the $\mathcal{N}$-body Schrödinger equation

$$[-(\hbar^2/2m) \sum_j \nabla_j^2 + \sum_{i<j} V(\mathbf{x}_i - \mathbf{x}_j) - E]\psi(\mathbf{x}_1 \ldots \mathbf{x}_N) = 0 \tag{59}$$

and suppose that $\psi(\mathbf{x}_1 \ldots \mathbf{x}_n)$ is rewritten in terms of the center of mass and relative coordinates

$$\mathbf{X} = \sum \mathbf{x}_i/\mathcal{N} \qquad \mathbf{x}_{ij} = \mathbf{x}_i - \mathbf{x}_j \qquad i < j$$
$$\psi(\mathbf{x}_1 \ldots \mathbf{x}_N) = \bar{\psi}(\mathbf{X}, \ldots \mathbf{x}_{ij}, \ldots) \tag{60}$$

Since the $\mathcal{N}$ vectors $\mathbf{x}_i$ can be expressed in many ways in terms of the $\frac{1}{2}\mathcal{N}(\mathcal{N}-1)+1$ vectors $\mathbf{X}, \mathbf{x}_{ij}$, the form of $\bar{\psi}$ is scarcely unique, but whatever its form, we may use the obvious ($\nabla = \mathbf{X}$- gradient, $\nabla_{ij} = \mathbf{x}_{ij}$ gradient)

$$\nabla_j = \nabla/\mathcal{N} + \sum_{i<j} \nabla_{ij} - \sum_{k>j} \nabla_{jk} \tag{61}$$

to convert eq. (59) to an equation for $\bar{\psi}$. Defining $\mathbf{x}_{ij} = -\mathbf{x}_{ji}$, $\nabla_{ij} = -\nabla_{ji}$ for $i > j$ and $\nabla_{ii} = 0$, eq. (59) may then be written as

$$[(-\hbar^2/2m)(\nabla^2/\mathcal{N} + \sum_{ijk} \nabla_{ij} \cdot \nabla_{ik}) + \tfrac{1}{2} \sum_{i \neq j} V(\mathbf{x}_{ij}) - E]\bar{\psi}(\mathbf{X} \ldots \mathbf{x}_{ij} \ldots) = 0 \tag{62}$$

If desired, the center of mass motion may be completely separated out.

Now the meaning of eq. (62) is simply this. If $\bar{\psi}$ is a function satisfying eq. (62), then making the replacement of (60) and applying the identity (61), eq. (59) is satisfied as well. Thus to every eigenstate $\bar{\psi}$, there corresponds either a true eigenstate ψ or the trivial function zero. However, $\bar{\psi}$, containing so many variables, may be expected to have a high anomalous degeneracy — that is, there will be many $\bar{\psi}$ which reduce to the same ψ *if* there is at least one.

To show that any solution ψ of (59) emanates from some $\bar{\psi}$ of (62), we shall try to solve (62). For this purpose transform to variables $\mathbf{y}_i$, which reduce to the $\mathbf{x}_i$, and $\mathbf{y}_{ij}$ which vanish, on identification (60):

$$\mathbf{y}_i = \mathbf{X} - \sum \mathbf{x}_{k1}/\mathcal{N} + \mathbf{x}_{i1} \qquad \mathbf{y}_{ij} = \mathbf{x}_{ij} + \mathbf{x}_{j1} - \mathbf{x}_{i1} \tag{63}$$

If we require $1 < i < j$ and set $\mathbf{y}_{ji} = -\mathbf{y}_{ij}$, $\mathbf{y}_{il} = 0$, these are independent; however, the succeeding comments are unaltered if, e.g., the symmetric but non-independent variables $\mathbf{y}_i = \mathbf{X} - \sum \mathbf{x}_{ki}/\mathcal{N}$, $\mathbf{y}_{ij} = \mathbf{x}_{ij} + \sum (\mathbf{x}_{ki} - \mathbf{x}_{kj})/\mathcal{N}$ are employed instead. The $\mathbf{y}_{ij}$ commute with the operators (61) and hence are constants of the motion; indeed, eq. (62) reverts under this transformation to

$$(-\hbar^2/2m) \sum \nabla^2_{\mathbf{y}_j} + \tfrac{1}{2} \sum_{i \neq j} V(\mathbf{y}_i - \mathbf{y}_j + \mathbf{y}_{ij}) - E]\bar{\psi}(\ldots \mathbf{y}_i \ldots \mathbf{y}_{ij} \ldots) = 0 \tag{64}$$

It is easy to replace $\mathbf{x}_{ij}$ in $V(\mathbf{x}_{ij})$ of (62) by a combination of $\mathbf{x}_{ij}$

such that (64) reduces exactly to (59), but the principal advantages of the form (62) would then be lost.) Certainly if $\psi_s(\ldots \mathbf{x}_i \ldots)$ is a solution of eq. (59) with eigenvalue E_s, then

$$\bar{\psi}(\ldots \mathbf{y}_i \ldots \mathbf{y}_{ij} \ldots) = [\prod_{1 < i < j} \delta(\mathbf{y}_{ij})]\psi_s(\ldots \mathbf{y}_i \ldots) \tag{65}$$

satisfies (64), with $E = E_s$. Here the $\{\mathbf{y}_{ij}\}$ are fixed at $\{0\}$. More generally, a solution $\bar{\psi}_s(\ldots \mathbf{y}_i \ldots \mathbf{y}_{ij} \ldots)$ to (64) will exist when the $\{\mathbf{y}_{ij}\}$ are fixed at some values $\{\mathbf{y}'_{ij}\}$ in the vicinity of zero; if the corresponding energy is $E_s(\ldots \mathbf{y}'_{ij} \ldots)$, it follows that the general solution of (64) and hence of (62) with eigenvalue E is

$$\bar{\psi}(\ldots \mathbf{y}_i \ldots \mathbf{y}_{ij} \ldots) = F(\ldots \mathbf{y}_{ij} \ldots)\delta[E_s(\ldots \mathbf{y}_{ij} \ldots) - E]\bar{\psi}_s(\ldots \mathbf{y}_i \ldots \mathbf{y}_{ij} \ldots) \tag{66}$$

for arbitrary F. Under the identification (60), eq. (66) does then reduce as desired to a multiple of $\psi_s(\ldots \mathbf{x}_i \ldots)$ if $E = E_s$, an eigenvalue of (59); it must vanish upon this identification if E is not an eigenvalue of (59).

We have thus established the correspondence between the wave functions in coordinate space and those in pair space; not only are all energies and wave functions of (59) obtainable from eq. (62) but they are obtainable from more than one solution of the latter which unfortunately will have solutions for other energy values as well. If the extraneous levels can be eliminated, e.g., by reducing back to coordinate space to see if the wave function vanishes, then (62) may be usefully regarded in its own right as a physical system whose eigenvalues also happen to include those of (59). From (66), the correct pair-space wave function may be expected to have a singular factor [except in the case mentioned in the parenthetical remark following (64)] which is thereby to be regarded as the square root of a Dirac δ function. On the other hand, (62) may be used by at once transcribing back to coordinate space, in which case a Kronecker δ function is to be employed.

The relation between ψ and $\bar{\psi}$ of course depends upon the explicit system and upon the state considered. It is only when the singular factor is enlarged to the form of (65) that the relation becomes universal; for this purpose, one rewrites (65) as

$$\bar{\psi}(\mathbf{X}, \ldots \mathbf{x}_{ij} \ldots)$$

$$= \int \ldots \int \delta(\sum_i \mathbf{x}_i - N\mathbf{X}) \prod_{i<j} \delta(\mathbf{x}_j - \mathbf{x}_i + \mathbf{x}_{ij}) \psi_s(\mathbf{x}_1 \ldots \mathbf{x}_N) dx^{3N} \quad (65')$$

which clearly contains the factors $\delta(\mathbf{y}_{ij})$ or equivalently the factors $\delta(\mathbf{x}_{ij} + \mathbf{x}_{jk} + \mathbf{x}_{ki})$. Another aspect of the universality is that (65') is also an eigenfunction of the transcription to pair space of any coordinate space operator of which ψ is an eigenfunction. Finally, since (65') corresponds to all $\mathbf{y}_{ij} = 0$ in (64), a change of any $\mathbf{y}_{ij}$ yields a perturbation energy of $\nabla_{\mathbf{y}_{ij}} E_s(0 \ldots 0) = \langle \bar{\psi} | \nabla V(\mathbf{y}_i - \mathbf{y}_j) | \bar{\psi} \rangle$, which vanishes for any $\bar{\psi}$ corresponding to a symmetric or antisymmetric state; thus, there is a predisposition towards the correct energy if enough factors $\delta(\mathbf{y}_{ij})$ are retained in ansatz for $\bar{\psi}$ to assure being in the vicinity of $\{\mathbf{y}_{ij}\} = 0$.

The solution of (62) is not complete until we specify boundary conditions. For periodic boundary conditions in $\mathbf{x}_j$ space, one would use periodic δ functions in (65'), and the corresponding boundary condition in the enlarged space is thus periodicity in $N\mathbf{X}$ and the $\mathbf{x}_{ij}$. Another possible boundary condition in configuration space, applying to large uniform systems and producing normalization to within $1/N$, is that the pair distribution function $\sigma(\mathbf{x}_1 \mathbf{x}_2)$ $\equiv \Omega^2 \int \psi^*(\ldots \mathbf{x}_i \ldots) \psi(\ldots \mathbf{x}_i \ldots) d^3 x_3 \ldots d^3 x_N$, for volume Ω, be unity for large $|\mathbf{x}_1 - \mathbf{x}_2|$ ("on and near the boundary"). This might correspond to the same condition on $\Omega \int \psi^*(\mathbf{X} \ldots \mathbf{x}_{ij} \ldots) \psi(\mathbf{X} \ldots \mathbf{x}_{ij} \ldots)$ $d\tau/d^3 x_{12}$ in the enlarged space. For use in a variational principle for $\int \psi^* H \psi \, d\tau^N$, such a condition may be applied in various ways; maintaining the constancy of $\int [\sigma(\mathbf{x}_1 \mathbf{x}_2) - 1] \, d^3 x_1 \, d^3 x_2$ is equivalent to the usual quadratic normalization. A different possibility, used to advantage by Jastrow in Chap. XI, is to fix $\int [\sigma^{1/2}(\mathbf{x}_1, \mathbf{x}_2) - 1]^2 \, d^3 x_1 \, d^3 x_2$. If $\int \psi^* H \psi d\tau^N - (\lambda/\Omega^2) \int (\sigma^{1/2} - 1)^2 \, d\tau^2$ is varied with respect to ψ, one finds

$$\{H + [\lambda/N(N-1)] \sum_{i \neq j} \sigma^{-1/2}(\mathbf{x}_i \mathbf{x}_j)\} \psi = \lambda \psi \quad (67)$$

Thus a Schrödinger equation results in which the potential $V(\mathbf{x}_i - \mathbf{x}_j)$ is replaced by $V(\mathbf{x}_i - \mathbf{x}_j) + (2/N)(E/N) \sigma^{-1/2}(\mathbf{x}_i \mathbf{x}_j)$, which is adequate as $N \to \infty$. The same approach is applicable in the larger space.

Variation and Perturbation Techniques. In order to obtain the system ground state (or the lowest state subject to some compatible requirement such as fixed total momentum), one may try to solve eq. (62) by a variational principle on the space $\{\mathbf{X} \ldots \mathbf{x}_{ij} \ldots\}$, on which the Hamiltonian of (62) remains Hermitian. Since the ground state energy of (62) may very well be below that of (59), obvious difficulties arise. However, we know that a spurious energy is characterized by a wave function which vanishes on the identification (60); hence, if a reasonable variational ansatz has the property that, in the notation of (63), $\bar{\psi}(\ldots \mathbf{y}_i \ldots 0 \ldots)/\bar{\psi}(\ldots \mathbf{y}_i \ldots \mathbf{y}_{ij} \ldots)$ remains of order unity, the danger of an anomalously low ground state energy should not be serious.

For example, for the Einstein-Bose ground state, a reasonable trial function to include two-body effects is

$$\bar{\psi} = \prod_{i<j} f(\mathbf{x}_{ij}) \tag{68}$$

The variation of $\langle H - E \rangle$ in (62), f being chosen as even, then yields the fully separated

$$(-\hbar^2/2m)\nabla^2 f(\mathbf{x}) + V(\mathbf{x})f(\mathbf{x}) = \varepsilon f(\mathbf{x}) \tag{69}$$

$\bar{\psi}$ is simply the product of independent two-body interactions with potential $V(\mathbf{x})$, and the total energy $\frac{1}{2}N(N-1)$ times the two-body energy, with no contributions from mixing. This is of course strictly a low-density approximation, with collective effects of propagation and interaction in the medium totally absent.

The solution (68), (69) may be extended by perturbation; for this purpose, the Hamiltonian in $\{\mathbf{X} \ldots \mathbf{x}_{ij} \ldots\}$ space is decomposed as

$$H_0 = P^2/2mN + \sum_{i<j} [p_{ij}^2/m + V(\mathbf{x}_{ij})]$$
$$\Delta H = \sum_{j \neq k} \mathbf{p}_{ij} \cdot \mathbf{p}_{ik}/2m \tag{70}$$

where we have written $(\hbar/i)\ \partial/\partial x$ as p, for all coordinates. In this form, ordinary perturbation theory corresponds roughly to a multiple scattering expansion in the particle configuration space, with solution to the two-body problem required as preliminary; the sequence and form of the pair interactions is however distinct from the multiple scattering expansion (see Chap. I). For the ground state energy perturbation, one readily finds no first-order contribution, and

$$(1/N)\Delta E = [-1/(2\pi)^6][(N-1)(N-2)/\Omega^2]$$

$$\iint |\Omega^2\langle 0|\mathbf{p}|n\rangle \cdot \langle 0|\mathbf{p}|n'\rangle|^2/[(2m)^2(\varepsilon_n+\varepsilon_{n'}-2\varepsilon_0)]\,dn\,dn' \qquad (71)$$

to second order. Here the system volume is Ω and the pair states are indexed by n, denoting wave number of the (not localized) state in the $V=0$ limit; it is to be noted that for a potential of finite range, $\langle 0|\mathbf{p}|n\rangle \propto 1/\Omega$. Higher order terms introduce problems of N dependence discussed in Chap. I.

The possibility of eliminating successive interactions of the same pair of pairs, in analogy with the effect of the reaction operator of Chap. I, also suggests itself. This requires determining the scattering operator for a pure (ij, ik) interaction, and so for

$$H_{i,jk} \equiv p_{ij}^2/m+p_{ik}^2/m+\mathbf{p}_{ij}\cdot\mathbf{p}_{ik}/m+V(\mathbf{x}_{ij})+V(\mathbf{x}_{ik}) \qquad (72)$$

While simpler than the three-body problem, (72) does not appear to be of great analytic value.

Now all of the foregoing is subject to doubt, for the necessary restriction to the surface $E_s(\ldots \mathbf{x}_{ij}\ldots) = E_s$ [see (66)] has not been made. Indeed, since this surface is not known until the problem is solved, one is driven to adopt the much more stringent requirements $\mathbf{x}_{ij}+\mathbf{x}_{jk}+\mathbf{x}_{ki} = 0$ [see (65)]. In a variational procedure, one may tend towards this direction by gradually restricting the variational ansatz. Thus, (68) already satisfies the condition $\langle \mathbf{x}_{ij}+\mathbf{x}_{jk}+\mathbf{x}_{ki}\rangle = 0$. Further steps introduce kinematical correlations. Perhaps the simplest is included in

$$\bar{\psi} = [\sum \delta(\mathbf{x}_{ij}+\mathbf{x}_{jk}+\mathbf{x}_{ki})]^{1/2} \prod_{i<j} f(\mathbf{x}_{ij}) \qquad (73)$$

Equation (69) is then modified by the appearance of a weight function $\int f^2(\mathbf{y})f^2(\mathbf{x}+\mathbf{y})\,d^3x$ and effective potentials $\int V(\mathbf{y})f^2(\mathbf{y})f^2(\mathbf{x}+\mathbf{y})\,d^3x$, $\int f(\mathbf{y})f(\mathbf{x}+\mathbf{y})(\hbar^2/m)\nabla^2[f(\mathbf{y})f(\mathbf{x}+\mathbf{y})]\,d^3x$. Going all the way, we may try

$$\bar{\psi} = \prod \delta(\mathbf{x}_{ij}+\mathbf{x}_{jk}+\mathbf{x}_{ki}) \prod_{i<j} f(\mathbf{x}_{ij}) \qquad (74)$$

As is readily verified, (74) is equivalent to using the trial function $\psi = \prod_{i<j} f(\mathbf{x}_i-\mathbf{x}_j)$ in $\langle H-E\rangle$ for the space $\{\ldots \mathbf{x}_j \ldots\}$. The greater reliability of (74), thus corresponding to Jastrow's choice (Chap. XI), is balanced by the greater complication of the resulting equations, which are ingeniously handled by Jastrow.

The ease with which one obtains the variational equations for (73) and (74) is a consequence of the fact that the various factors of $\prod \delta(\mathbf{x}_{ij}+\mathbf{x}_{jk}+\mathbf{x}_{ki})$ all commute with the pair coordinate Hamiltonian (62); effectively, then, these factors just change the volume element for the space integral of $\langle H-E\rangle$. The change is one which restricts the integration to a subspace, all such subspaces having the property of including that one which may be parametrized by $\mathbf{x}_{ij} = \mathbf{x}_i-\mathbf{x}_j$; hopefully, one of the spaces before the smallest will also satisfy $E_s(\ldots \mathbf{y}_{ij}\ldots) = E_s$. An equivalent sequence is suggested for the perturbation approach; that is, one evaluates scalar products (matrix elements) via an integral restricted to a smaller space, which might just as well be that satisfying $\mathbf{x}_{ij} = \mathbf{x}_i-\mathbf{x}_j$. Since the pair-space eigenfunctions are then neither orthogonal nor independent, results such as (71) must be rewritten in terms of perturbation theory for non-orthogonal functions (see, e.g., [1], p. 1034), and then the eigenvalues will still have an anomalous degeneracy; however, this degeneracy will not in practice interfere with the perturbation computation, and convergence will be towards a real rather than a spurious energy level.

Another method of approaching the desired restriction to $\mathbf{x}_{ij} = \mathbf{x}_i-\mathbf{x}_j$ is to modify the Hamiltonian. For instance, noting that $\sum_{i\neq j\neq k}(\mathbf{x}_{ij}+\mathbf{x}_{jk}+\mathbf{x}_{ki})^2 = 6[\frac{1}{2}(N-2)\sum_{i\neq j}x_{ij}^2 - \sum \mathbf{x}_{ij}\cdot\mathbf{x}_{ik}]$, one may approximate to the ground state wave function for the Hamiltonian

$$H+\lambda[\tfrac{1}{2}(N-2)\sum_{i\neq j}x_{ij}^2 - \sum_{i\neq j\neq k}\mathbf{x}_{ij}\cdot\mathbf{x}_{ik}] \tag{75}$$

allowing λ to increase as the approximation improves, and compute $E = \langle H\rangle$ with this wave function.

Further Developments. The preceding considerations lead to the dynamic approach of Penrose [14] for the Boson ground state problem, although they are scarcely necessary for the purpose. Substituting the ansatz (68) directly into eq. (62), and setting $f = \exp \varphi$, we have at once

$$-(\hbar^2/2m)\sum_{j<k}\nabla^2\varphi(\mathbf{x}_{jk}) - (\hbar^2/2m)\sum \nabla\varphi(\mathbf{x}_{ij})\cdot\nabla\varphi(\mathbf{x}_{ik}) + \sum_{j<k}V(\mathbf{x}_{jk}) = E \tag{76}$$

First, knowing that the true wave function may be regarded as having the factor $\delta(\mathbf{x}_{ij}+\mathbf{x}_{jk}+\mathbf{x}_{ki})$, we make the replacement

$$\sum_i \nabla\varphi(\mathbf{x}_{ij})\cdot\nabla\varphi(\mathbf{x}_{ik}) \to \sum_i \nabla\varphi(\mathbf{x}_{ij})\cdot\nabla\varphi(\mathbf{x}_{ij}+\mathbf{x}_{jk}) \tag{77}$$

The trick is then to average the unmalleable terms over the state of the system [16]; since, for most of its range, $\mathbf{x}_{ij}$ for fixed j is equi-distributed, this occasions the further replacement of (77) by $(\mathcal{N}/\Omega)\int\nabla\varphi(\mathbf{y})\cdot\nabla\varphi(\mathbf{y}+\mathbf{x}_{jk})\,d^3y$. Equation (76) now separates into the set ($\mathbf{x}$ denoting any $\mathbf{x}_{jk}$)

$$-(\hbar^2/m)\nabla^2\varphi(\mathbf{x})-(\mathcal{N}\hbar^2/m\Omega)\int\nabla\varphi(\mathbf{y})\cdot\nabla\varphi(\mathbf{y}+\mathbf{x})\,d^3y+V(\mathbf{x})=\varepsilon \quad (78)$$

which, introducing the Fourier transform $\varphi(\mathbf{x})=\sum\varphi_{\mathbf{k}}e^{i\mathbf{k}\cdot\mathbf{x}}$, $\varphi_{\mathbf{k}}=\varphi_{-\mathbf{k}}$, may be solved at once, for $\mathbf{k}\neq0$ (i.e., except for normalization of e^{φ}) as

$$\varphi_{\mathbf{k}}=(1/2\mathcal{N})[1-(1+(2m/\hbar^2k^2)\,2\mathcal{N}V_{\mathbf{k}})^{1/2}] \quad (79)$$

identical with the familiar result of Bogoliubov [17]. The inadequacy of (79) for singular potentials is, in this formulation, due in part to the assumed equidistribution for $\mathbf{x}_{ij}$ rather than the more accurate $e^{2\varphi}$; inserting this factor instead into (77), the result (78) is altered to

$$-(\hbar^2/m)\nabla^2 f(\mathbf{x})+(\hbar^2/m)[\nabla f(\mathbf{x})\cdot\nabla f(\mathbf{x})/f(\mathbf{x})]-(\mathcal{N}/\Omega)\int f(\mathbf{y})\nabla f(\mathbf{y}) \\ \cdot\nabla f(\mathbf{y}+\mathbf{x})/f(\mathbf{y}+\mathbf{x})\,d^3y+mV(\mathbf{x})/\hbar^2]f(\mathbf{x})=\varepsilon f(\mathbf{x}) \quad (80)$$

whose superiority stops short of the computational phase.

Due principally to the form of the prototype wave function (68), attention thus far has been mainly restricted to the Einstein-Bose ground state. Properly symmetrized products may be used for Fermi-Dirac and excited Einstein-Bose systems, but are somewhat involved. In these cases, as well as those for potentials with both one- and two-body forces, one solution is to enlarge the space to include both the $\mathbf{x}_i$ and the $\mathbf{x}_{ij}$; for a Fermi-Dirac system, the $\mathbf{x}_i$ can then be used to account for the omnipresent antisymmetric factor, while in the case of one-body potentials, the $\mathbf{x}_i$ are appropriate for representing the non-uniform system density. The detailed treatment is similar to that given above, but appreciably more complex in form; it is of some advantage to reduce the superfluity of coordinates by using only the lengths $|\mathbf{x}_{ij}|$, and this has been done by Levinson and Gold [18] for the case of a finite nucleus, in which of course the density is non-uniform without the imposition of one-body forces.

In the case of a spinless one-dimensional Fermi-Dirac ground state, the above is not necessary, for if f_{ij} is required to be an odd function,

ψ is automatically antisymmetric, while the symmetry of the pair distribution function about the origin is not altered (indeed, for highly singular potentials, it is well known that one-dimensional Einstein-Bose and Fermi-Dirac systems without spin are indistinguishable, in their coordinate space behavior). From another viewpoint, the antisymmetric determinental factor (see Jastrow, Chap. XI) is itself expressible as $\prod \sin \frac{1}{2}k_0(x_i-x_j)$. There appears to be no simple extension of this technique to real three-dimensional systems.

4. *Low-lying nuclear energy levels*

Abstract

The rotational levels ot an even-even nucleus are obtained from the ground state by introducing a flow pattern into the wave function. One- to N-body modifications — fluid flow to rigid rotation — are considered. The intrinsic state concept is developed to simplify interpretation and calculation; relevant projection operators are derived. The "cranking model" is treated as a special case and the domain of validity of the perturbational moment of inertia assessed. Several subcases are examined in detail. Intrinsic states are generalized through the generator coordinate approach and application made to vibrational levels.

Notes and References

1. P. Morse and H. Feshbach, *Methods of Theoretical Physics*, McGraw-Hill, New York, 1954, p. 806.
2. See, e.g., J. M. Blatt and V. F. Weisskopf, *Theoretical Nuclear Physics*, Wiley, New York, 1952, p. 76.
3. See, e.g., W. R. Smythe, *Static and Dynamic Elasticity*, McGraw-Hill, New York, 1939, p. 116.
4. E. P. Wigner, *Phys. Rev.* **40**, 479, (1932); see also J. E. Moyal, *Proc. Cambridge Phil. Soc.* **45**, 99 (1949).
5. W. B. Riesenfeld and K. M. Watson, *Phys. Rev.* **108**, 518 (1957).
6. T. L. Hill, *Statistical Mechanics*, McGraw-Hill, New York, 1956, p. 45, J. E. Mayer and M. G. Mayer, *Statistical Mechanics*, Wiley, New York, 1940, Chap.13.
7. E. Montroll and J. C. Ward, Phys. of Fluids **1**, 55 (1958).
8. C. Bloch and C. de Dominicis, *Nuclear Phys.* 7, 459 (1958).
9. See, e.g., R. P. Feynman, *Phys. Rev.* **84**, 108 (1951); M. L. Goldberger and E. N. Adams, *J. Chem. Phys*, **20**, 240 (1952); S. T. Butler and M. H. Friedman, *Phys. Rev.* **98**, 287 (1955); S. Golden, *Phys. Rev.* **107**, 1283 (1957).

10. K. M. Watson, *Phys. Rev.* **103**, 489 (1956).
11. See, e.g., E. Goursat and E. R. Hedrick, *Mathematical Analysis*, Ginn, Boston, 1904, p. 404.
12. M. Gell-Mann and K. A. Brueckner, *Phys. Rev.* **106**, 364 (1957).
13. P. Debye and E. Hückel, *Z. Physik* **24**, 185 (1923); J. E. Mayer, *J. Chem. Phys.* **18**, 1426 (1950).
14. O. Penrose, private communication.
15. N. N. Bogoliubov and D. N. Zubarev, *ZETF* **28**, 129 (1955); [translation: *JETP*, **1**, 83 (1955)].
16. See also J. K. Percus and G. J. Yevick, *Nuovo cimento* **5**, 65 (1957).
17. N. N. Bogoliubov, *J. Phys, (U. S. S. R.)* **11**, 23 (1947).
18. C. A. Levinson and E. Gold, private communication.

CHAPTER IX

Non-Separable Boundary Value Problems and the Many-Body Problem[†]

Leonard Eyges

1. Introduction

A large class of interesting and important quantum mechanical problems concerns systems which move freely within boundaries for which the Schrödinger (or multi-dimensional Helmholtz) equation is not separable. For example, a system of N hard spheres of diameter a inside a spherical enclosure of diameter $2R+a$ may be regarded as a point in $3N$-dimensional space bounded by the N $(3N-1)$-dimensional surfaces $|\mathbf{r}_j| = R$ and the $N(N-1)/2$ $(3N-1)$-dimensional surfaces $|\mathbf{r}_i - \mathbf{r}_j| = a$. Thus the system is to be treated not as one of moving spheres in three-space, but as that of stationary boundaries in $3N$-space. Although such non-separable boundary value problems are deemed virtually intractable, analytically, we shall show that when the boundary happens to be a sum of separable boundaries, considerable progress may be made; the N-body hard sphere problem is clearly an instance of this type.

The properties of separable boundaries, with respect to the Helmholtz equation

$$(\nabla^2 + k^2)\psi(\mathbf{r}) = 0 \tag{1}$$

($\mathbf{r}$ being an s-dimensional vector and ∇^2 the corresponding Laplacian) which facilitate our analysis are readily described. If separability obtains, then we may choose a coordinate system composed of a

[†] As summarized and interpreted by the editor. For a complete exposition, see Ref. (1).

157

single normal variable r, and a set of $s-1$ transverse variables symbolized by $\mathbf{r}_T$, such that:

a. The boundary is given by $r = c$, for some constant c.

b. The volume element may be written as $d\tau_r\, d\tau_{r_T}$, where $d\tau_r$ is independent of $\mathbf{r}_T$, $d\tau_{r_T}$ of r.

c. The solutions of the Helmholtz equation are generated by those of the form

$$\varphi(\mathbf{r}) = R_{kl}(r) Y_1(\mathbf{r}_T) \tag{2}$$

for some index set $\mathbf{l}$. In (2), the $Y_1(\mathbf{r}_T)$ may be assumed to be a complete orthonormal set over the boundary (in cases other than those we investigate, the set Y_1 may depend on k as well).

The particular $R_{kl}(r)$ employed are determined by boundary conditions, but our interest will center rather on the factors J_{kl}, K_{kl} occurring in Green's function expansions for (1) at fixed k, which are available in the form

$$g_k(\mathbf{r}, \mathbf{r}') = \sum_{\mathbf{l}} J_{kl}(r) K_{kl}(r') Y_1(\mathbf{r}_T) Y_1^*(\mathbf{r}'_T). \tag{3}$$

2. Exact solutions

We first consider an approach which, in principle, can yield exact results, and which in practice is readily amenable to meaningful approximation. Suppose that a system obeying (1) is confined to the volume interior to a closed separable surface A: $r^A = c^A$ and exterior to a similar surface B: $r^B = c^B$; extension to more than two surfaces and to open systems with travelling wave boundary conditions proceeds directly. Then if $g_k(\mathbf{r}, \mathbf{r}')$ is an appropriate boundary-independent Green's function:

$$(\nabla^2 + k^2) g_k(\mathbf{r}, \mathbf{r}') = \delta(\mathbf{r} - \mathbf{r}') \tag{4}$$

it follows by use of Green's theorem in the usual fashion [2] that if ψ is constrained to vanish at the surfaces A and B, then

$$\psi(\mathbf{r}) = -\int_A g_k(\mathbf{r}, \mathbf{r}') \nabla' \psi(\mathbf{r}') \cdot d\mathbf{S}' - \int_B g_k(\mathbf{r}, \mathbf{r}') \nabla' \psi(\mathbf{r}') \cdot d\mathbf{S}'$$
$$\equiv \psi_A(\mathbf{r}) + \psi_B(\mathbf{r}) \tag{5}$$

In (5), the function ψ is represented as being produced by a set of sources $\nabla' \psi(\mathbf{r}')$ on the surface A by the wave from B, and a similar set on B; the determination of these sources would solve our problem. Equivalently, from (3) and (5), we have

$$\psi_A(\mathbf{r}) = \sum_1 A_{k1} J_{k1}^A(r^A)\, Y_1^A(\mathbf{r}_T^A)$$
$$\psi_B(\mathbf{r}) = \sum_1 B_{k1} J_{k1}^B(r^B)\, Y_1^B(\mathbf{r}_T^B) \tag{6}$$

for uniquely determined sets of constants A_{kl}, B_{kl}, which are found from the conditions

$$\psi_A(\mathbf{r}) + \psi_B(\mathbf{r}) = 0 \qquad \text{on } A \text{ and } B \tag{7}$$

We can extract the $Y_1^A(\mathbf{r}_T^A)$ component of (7) on A if $J_{k1}^B(r^B)\, Y_1^B(\mathbf{r}_T^B)$ is easily expandable in a series of $Y_1^A(\mathbf{r}_T^A)$, or certainly by multiplying (7) by $Y_1^{A*}(\mathbf{r}_T^A)$ and integrating over A; similarly for the $Y_1^B(\mathbf{r}_T^B)$ component on B. In either event, inserting (6) yields relations of the form

$$J_{k1}^A(c^A)\, A_{k1} + \sum C_{k11'} B_{k1'} = 0$$
$$J_{k1}^B(c^B)\, B_{k1} + \sum D_{k11'} A_{k1'} = 0 \tag{8}$$

thereby determining the A_{k1}, B_{k1}, and eigenvalue k.

Finally, it should be noted that if boundaries A and B intersect, the integrals in (5) are to be taken only over the non-intersecting parts A' and B'. In solving, it is preferable to regard $\partial/\partial n\psi(\mathbf{r}_T^A) = \sum \alpha_{k1} Y_1^A(\mathbf{r}_T^A)$ on A' and $\partial/\partial n\psi(\mathbf{r}_T^B) = \sum \beta_{k1} Y_1^B(\mathbf{r}_T^B)$ on B' as unknowns, integrate to find ψ_A, ψ_B, and perform the final integration only over A' and B' to obtain the analog to (8), which is now considerably more complicated.

3. An example

Let A be a sphere of radius R with coordinate system (r^A, θ^A, φ), B a smaller sphere of radius a, wholly contained in A, with center a distance d along the z axis from that of A, and with coordinate system (r^B, θ^B, φ) based at its center. As Green's function, we may choose

$$g_k(\mathbf{r}, \mathbf{r}') = -\cos k|\mathbf{r} - \mathbf{r}'|/4\pi|\mathbf{r} - \mathbf{r}'| \tag{9}$$

which may be expanded as

$$g_k(\mathbf{r}, \mathbf{r}') = \frac{(k/2\pi) \sum\limits^{|m| \le l} j_l(kr^A)\, n_l(kr'^A)\, Y_l^m(\theta^A, \varphi)\, Y_l^{m*}(\theta'^A, \varphi')}{(k/2\pi) \sum n_l(kr^B) j_l(kr'^B)\, Y_l^m(\theta^B, \varphi)\, Y_l^{m*}(\theta'^B, \varphi')} \tag{10}$$

where $r'^A > r^A > 0$, $r^B > r'^B > 0$, Y_l^m is a normalized spherical harmonic, and j_l and n_l spherical Bessel and Neumann functions. We thus have

$$\psi_A = \sum A_{klm} j_l(kr^A)\, Y_l^m(\theta^A, \varphi)$$
$$\psi_B = \sum B_{klm} n_l(kr^B)\, Y_l^m(\theta^B, \varphi) \tag{11}$$

To reduce (7) to (8), we may use the known addition formulas for spherical harmonics [3] and spherical Bessel functions [4]. Equations (6) and (7) thus yield

$$0 = \sum A_{klm} j_l(kR)\, Y_l^m(\theta^A, \varphi) + \sum (-1)^{l-s} F_{lmns} B_{klm} j_{l+n}(kd)(kR)^{-l} n_{l+n}(kR)$$
$$\times\, (R/d)^s C_n^{l+\frac{1}{2}}(\cos\theta^A)\, Y_s^m(\theta^A, \varphi)$$
$$0 = \sum B_{klm} n_l(ka)\, Y_l^m(\theta^B, \varphi) + \sum (-1)^n F_{lmns} A_{klm} j_{l+n}(kd)(ka)^{-l} j_{l+n}(kA)$$
$$\times\, (R/d)^s C_n^{l+\frac{1}{2}}(\cos\theta^B)\, Y_s^m(\theta^B, \varphi) \tag{12}$$

where C_n^v is a Gegenbauer Polynomial [5], and

$$F_{lmns} \equiv \sqrt{(2/\pi)}\, 2^{l+\frac{1}{2}} [(2l+1)/(2s+1)]^{\frac{1}{2}} [\Gamma(l+\tfrac{1}{2})/(l-s!)]$$
$$\times\, [(l+m!\, l-m!)/(s+m!\, s-m!)]^{\frac{1}{2}} \tag{13}$$

The form (8) is then readily obtained.

The complexity of (12) and (13) demands an approximate treatment. We need merely realize, e.g., that only a finite number of values of l of a wave incident from a source at B can effectively be "scattered" by A, so that an expansion of ψ_B in A eigenfunctions must cut off, in practice. Formally, one simply notes that, k having been roughly guessed, $j_{l+n}(kd) \approx 0$ if $l+n > kd$, thereby limiting l (hence m and s) and n; further limitation is afforded by the remaining Bessel functions and power ratios. We conclude that in practice, only a finite number of equations for a finite number of coefficients A_{klm}, B_{klm} remain, a comment which is not restricted to the particular example under consideration.

4. Perturbation methods

If there is in some sense one principal boundary, the remaining ones being smaller in size and effect, one might expect a perturbation method to be feasible. Of course, standard quantum mechanical perturbation theory fails because of the infinite potential required to keep the system from crossing the boundary, and the usual boundary perturbation theory [6] is notably non-convergent. However, if all perturbing boundaries are separable, the previous approach may be employed to construct a practical and even convergent perturbation formalism.

We consider a system bounded by a surface A, for which all eigenfunctions have been obtained:

$$(\nabla^2 + k_l^2)\,\varphi_l = 0 \qquad \varphi_l = 0 \text{ on } A \qquad (14)$$

as well as the Green's function $g_k^A(\mathbf{r}, \mathbf{r}')$ for solutions vanishing on A. The volume is then further restricted by a set of separable boundaries B_j, and we wish to solve

$$(\nabla^2 + k^2)\,\psi = 0 \qquad \psi = 0 \qquad \text{on } A \text{ and the } B_j \qquad (15)$$

Using Green's theorem, and the fact that ψ vanishes on A and the B_j, φ_l on A, we find as usual [6]

$$k^2 = k_l^2 + \sum_j \int_{B_j} \varphi_l^* \, \nabla \psi \cdot d\mathbf{S} \Big/ \int \varphi_l^* \, \psi \, d\tau \qquad (16)$$

Further, expanding g_k^A in unperturbed eigenfunctions and substituting in the many-boundary extension of (5) yields [6] (for a nondegenerate unperturbed state φ_l)

$$\psi = \varphi_l \int \varphi_l^* \, \psi \, d\tau + \sum_{p \neq l}^{j} \varphi_p \, (k_p^2 - k^2)^{-1} \int_{B_j} \varphi_p^* \, \nabla \psi \cdot d\mathbf{S} \qquad (17)$$

So far, all is standard. The trouble arises when we try to iterate (17). Thus, for the first approximation, we would take ψ in the full volume integral on the left-hand side of (17) as φ_l. However, we cannot take $\nabla \psi$ as $\nabla \varphi_l$, for, although $\nabla \psi$ differs from $\nabla \varphi_l$ only in a small region, B_j is situated right in the middle of this region; for example, perturbation of a large sphere by a small concentric sphere introduces spherical Neumann functions which, with their gradients, are singular at the origin of the small sphere and large at its boundary.

Now we observe that if ψ is decomposed according to its sources, as in (5),

$$\psi = \psi_A + \sum_j \psi_{B_j} \qquad (18)$$

the singularity in ψ near B_j will be due to ψ_{B_j} alone. Thus, given an approximant to ψ_A, we may solve for the ψ_B, (using the process leading to (8) and the fact that $\psi = 0$ on B_j) then compute $\nabla\psi$ on B_j; insert in (16) and (17), and iterate.

5. *An example*

Two hard spheres of diameter a are situated in an enclosure A; if a is small compared to the enclosure (which is $a/2$ larger in all directions than the unperturbed enclosure) there is a single boundary B: $|\mathbf{r}_1 - \mathbf{r}_2| = a$, which may be regarded as a perturbation. We can easily obtain the first-order energy.

Using, for convenience, relative and center of mass coordinates $\mathbf{r} = \mathbf{r}_1 - \mathbf{r}_2$, $\mathbf{R} = (\mathbf{r}_1 + \mathbf{r}_2)/2$, the expansion functions associated with B may clearly be taken as

$$\varphi_{\sigma l m}(\mathbf{R}, \mathbf{r}) = e^{i\boldsymbol{\sigma}\cdot\mathbf{R}} n_l(\kappa r) Y_l^m(\theta, \varphi) \tag{19}$$

where $2\kappa^2 + \sigma^2/2 = k^2$. Now if $\psi^{(0)}(\mathbf{R}, \mathbf{r})$ is the unperturbed solution, this may be identified with ψ_A to first order. Furthermore, unless $\psi^{(0)}(\mathbf{R}, 0)$ vanishes, then ψ_A may, to the same order, be taken as $\psi^{(0)}(\mathbf{R}, 0)$ in the vicinity of B, leading to pure s-wave scattering.

Since ψ_B is s-wave in r-space, we now have

$$\psi_B(\mathbf{R}, \mathbf{r}) = \int g(\boldsymbol{\sigma}) e^{i\boldsymbol{\sigma}\cdot\mathbf{R}} n_0[\kappa(\sigma) r] d^3\sigma$$
$$\simeq \int g(\boldsymbol{\sigma}) e^{i\boldsymbol{\sigma}\cdot\mathbf{R}} \sqrt{(2/\pi)}[1/\kappa(\sigma) r] d^3\sigma \tag{20}$$

for small r. But then since

$$\psi_B(\mathbf{R}, a) = -\psi^{(0)}(\mathbf{R}, 0) = \int g(\boldsymbol{\sigma}) e^{i\boldsymbol{\sigma}\cdot\mathbf{R}}/\kappa(\sigma) a \, d^3\sigma \tag{21}$$

we conclude that

$$\partial\psi_B/\partial r \simeq (a/r^2) \psi^{(0)}(\mathbf{R}, 0) \tag{22}$$

and inserting into (16), we obtain at once

$$k^2 = k_0^2 + 4\pi a \int |\psi^{(0)}(\mathbf{R}, 0)|^2 d^3 R \tag{23}$$

equivalent to using a pseudopotential [7] $4\pi a \, \delta(\mathbf{r}_1 - \mathbf{r}_2)$.

If $\psi^{(0)}(\mathbf{R}, 0) = 0$, as in a Fermi-Dirac system, p-wave scattering is the lowest order present, and the energy increment proportional to a^3 is easily found.

6. The many-body problem

To the same order in a, the problem of N hard spheres perturbed from identical free states is readily solved by the observation that since $N(N-1)/2$ pairs interact, the energy perturbation must be correspondingly multiplied. Thus for particles of mass m, and a cubical enclosure of volume V, we find for the Einstein-Bose or Maxwell-Boltzmann ground state

$$E = E_0 + [N(N-1)/2][27\pi a/4][\hbar^2/mV] \tag{24}$$

The result differs from that of Brueckner and Sawada [8] and Lee, Huang, and Yang [9]:

$$E = E_0 + [N(N-1)/2] 4\pi a [\hbar^2/mV] \tag{25}$$

for these authors use periodic boundary conditions, which are unphysical except at high density, where perturbation results are invalid. However, we may just as easily insert the periodic boundary condition ground state wave function ($\psi^{(0)} = 1/V$) into (23), and then of course (25) is reproduced.

To go to the next highest order, the intersections of the $\frac{1}{2}N(N-1)$ boundaries and the rescattering from A may be neglected, but the full treatment of the discussion following (18) is required. Further, it appears that extension, by our method, to still higher orders in a is not at all an insuperable task.

Notes and references

1. L. Eyges, *Annals of Physics* **2**, 101 (1957).
2. P. Morse and H. Feshbach, *Methods of Theoretical Physics*, McGraw-Hill, New York, 1954, p. 806.
3. P. Morse and H. Feshbach, *Methods of Theoretical Physics*, McGraw-Hill, New York, 1954, p. 1271.
4. A. Erdelyi et al, *Higher Transcendental Functions*, McGraw-Hill, 1953, Vol. 11, p. 101.
5. W. Magnus and F. Oberhettinger, *Special Functions of Mathematical Physics*, Chelsea Publishing Co., New York, 1949, p. 76.
6. P. Morse and H. Feshbach, *Methods of Theoretical Physics*, McGraw-Hill, New York, 1954, Chap. 9.2.
7. K. Huang and C. N. Yang, *Phys. Rev.* **105**, 767 (1957).
8. K. A. Brueckner and K. Sawada, *Phys. Rev.* **106**, 1117 (1957).
9. T. D. Lee, K. Huang, and C. N. Yang, *Phys. Rev.* **106**, 1135 (1957).

CHAPTER X

Quantum Mechanical Many-Body Problem and the Low Temperature Properties of a Bose System of Hard Spheres[†]

KERSON HUANG, T. D. LEE, and C. N. YANG

I wish to discuss some recent work with Drs. Kerson Huang and T. D. Lee on the quantum statistical many-body problem.

1. *Binary collision expansion method*

First we shall describe a binary collision expansion method [1] developed by Lee and myself. We recall that Ursell [2] and Kahn and Uhlenbeck [3] had discussed a long time ago a method of decomposition of the propagation function W_N^s for an N-particle Bose system into functions U^s:

$$W_N^s(\mathbf{x}_1', \mathbf{x}_2' \ldots; \mathbf{x}_1, \mathbf{x}_2 \ldots) \equiv N! \sum_{\mathrm{Sym}\,\psi} \psi_i(\mathbf{x}_1', \mathbf{x}_2', \ldots)\,\psi_i^*(\mathbf{x}_1, \mathbf{x}_2, \ldots)\,e^{-\beta E_i}$$

$$W_1^s(1', 1) \equiv U_1^s(1', 1)$$

$$W_2^s(1', 2'; 1, 2) \equiv U_1^s(1', 1)U_1^s(2', 2) + U_2^s(1', 2'; 1, 2) \tag{1}$$

$$W_3^s(1', 2', 3'; 1, 2, 3) \equiv U_1^s(1', 1)U_1^s(2', 2)U_1^s(3', 3)$$

$$+ U_1^s(1', 1)U_2^s(2', 3'; 2, 3) + U_1^s(2', 2)U_2^s(1', 3'; 1, 3)$$

$$+ U_1^s(3', 3)U_2^s(1', 2'; 1, 2) + U_3^s(1', 2', 3'; 1, 2, 3) \qquad \text{etc.}$$

where $1' \equiv \mathbf{x}_1'$, $2' \equiv \mathbf{x}_2'$, etc., and $\beta \equiv 1/kT$. The superscript s in the propagation functions W^s, and in the U^s functions in these equations, all refer to the symmetry of the Bose system. If one had treated a system with Boltzmann statistics, one could easily write down the corresponding decompositions

---

[†] As presented by C. N. Yang.

$W_1(1', 1) \equiv U_1(1', 1)$

$W_2(1', 2'; 1, 2) \equiv U_1(1', 1)U_1(2', 2) + U_2(1', 2'; 1, 2)$

$$W_3(1', 2', 3'; 1, 2, 3) \equiv U_1(1', 1)U_1(2', 2)U_1(3', 3) \qquad (2)$$

$$+ U_1(1', 1)U_2(2', 3'; 2, 3) + U_1(2', 2)U_2(1', 3'; 1, 3)$$

$$+ U_1(3', 3)U_2(1', 2'; 1, 2) + U_3(1', 2', 3'; 1, 2, 3) \qquad \text{etc.}$$

$$W_N(\mathbf{x}_1', \mathbf{x}_2', \ldots; \mathbf{x}_1, \mathbf{x}_2, \ldots) \equiv \sum_{\text{all } \psi} \psi_i(\mathbf{x}_1', \mathbf{x}_2', \ldots)\psi_i^*(\mathbf{x}_1, \mathbf{x}_2, \ldots) e^{-\beta E_i}$$

The reason for the introduction of the U functions and the U^s functions is that they are related simply to the fugacity expansion [4] coefficients b_l:

$$\Omega b_l = (1/l!) \int_{\Omega^l} d^{3l}x \, U_l(\mathbf{x}, \mathbf{x}) \qquad (\mathbf{x} \equiv \mathbf{x}_1, \ldots, \mathbf{x}_l)$$

$$\Omega b_l^s = (1/l!) \int_{\Omega^l} d^{3l}x \, U_l^s(\mathbf{x}, \mathbf{x}) \qquad (3)$$

where Ω is the volume of the box. One recalls [5] that the equations of state are expressible in terms of b_l by

$$p/kT = \sum_1^\infty b_l z^l$$

$$\rho \equiv N/\Omega = \sum_1^\infty l b_l z^l \qquad (4)$$

The first step in the binary collision expansion method is to express the propagation function with Bose statistics in terms of the U functions for Boltzmann statistics. (This is desirable because, as one recalls, for non-interacting particles $U_2 = U_3 = \ldots = 0$. To express everything in terms of this Boltzmann U therefore allows an easier treatment for expansions near the non-interacting system.) To complete this step, one needs the following equation, which can be easily proved:

$$W_N^s(\mathbf{x}', \mathbf{x}) = \sum_{p'} P'\{W_N(\mathbf{x}', \mathbf{x})\} \qquad (5)$$

where the sum extends over the $N!$ permutations P' of the coordinates $\mathbf{x}_i'$. Starting from the U functions, one constructs W from (2) and then W^s from (5). Substituting this W^s into eq. (1), one can solve for the functions U^s. The fugacity coefficients b_l^s can then be easily computed from (3).

The second step in the binary collision expansion method is to express the functions $U_3, U_4, \ldots$ in terms of U_2. This is accomplished by an expansion method that can be derived in the following way. One writes

$$W_N(\mathbf{x}', \mathbf{x}) = \langle \mathbf{x}'|e^{-\beta H}|\mathbf{x}\rangle \equiv \langle \mathbf{x}'|e^{-\beta(T+V)}|\mathbf{x}\rangle \qquad V = \sum_{i \neq j} V_{ij}$$

Now [6]

$$e^{-\beta(T+V)} = e^{-\beta T} + \int_0^\beta e^{-\beta' T}(-V)e^{-(\beta-\beta')T}\,d\beta'$$

$$+ \iint_0^{\beta'+\beta'' \leq \beta} e^{-\beta' T}(-V)e^{-\beta'' T}(-V)e^{-(\beta-\beta'-\beta'')T}\,d\beta'\,d\beta'' + \cdots$$

(6)

The individual terms in this sum can be graphically represented as follows: (for $N = 3$)

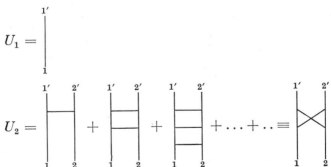

etc., where vertical lines represent $\langle \mathbf{x}'|e^{-\beta T}|\mathbf{x}\rangle$ for individual particles and horizontal lines represent the potential $(-V)$ between two particles. In terms of these graphs, the first two equations of (2) yield immediately, on solving for the U_l,

If one applies the idea of these graphs to the third equation of (2), one sees that the decomposition of W into U is just a sorting out of graphs with different connectedness. One obtains

$$U_3 = \quad + \quad + \quad + \quad + \quad + \quad$$

+ terms with 3 or more horizontal lines

Graphs in which the points 1, 2, or 3 are isolated from each other are not included in the sum.

It is obvious that if one introduces the sum

$$X \equiv \quad + \quad + \quad + \ldots + \ldots \equiv \quad = V_{12} W_2 \quad (7)$$

one can express U_3 in the following way

$$U_3 = \quad + \text{ five other terms obtained by switching the crosses around}$$

$$\quad (8)$$

$$+ \quad + \text{ etc.}$$

To be explicit we write out the algebraic meaning of the first graph:

$$= \int_0^\beta \left\{ \int [U_2(1', 2'; 1'', 2'') U_1(3', 3'')|_{\beta'} \right.$$
$$\left. U_1(1'', 1') X(2'', 3''; 2, 3)]|_{\beta - \beta'} \, d^9 x'' \right\} d\beta' \quad (8')$$

It is easy to prove that X is related to U_2 through the equation

$$X(1', 2'; 1, 2) = -\partial U_2(1', 2'; 1, 2)/\partial \beta + (\nabla_{1'}^2 + \nabla_{2'}^2) U_2 \quad (9)$$

in units defined by $2m = 1$, $\hbar = 1$. Equations (8), (8′) and (9) together allow one to calculate U_3 in terms of U_2. [It can be seen without difficulty that for hard sphere interactions of diameter a, the function U_2 is of first order in a. By (9), X is also of the same order. Equation (8) therefore expresses U_3 in powers of a, beginning with the order a^2.] For the calculation of U_4, U_5, ... the procedure is exactly similar to that for U_3; in each case, an expansion in X is possible, except for the final interaction, which requires U_2.

Using the two steps described above, one can compute the fugacity coefficients b_l^s starting from the function U_2, which can be obtained because the solution of the two-body problem is known. The procedure described above can obviously also be applied to a system with Fermi statistics. Only minor changes of sign are necessary in the formulae.

The introduction of the sum X, it appears, corresponds to Professor Bethe's summation of diagrams in his discussion [7] of the Brueckner method.

2. Application

Lee and I have applied [1] this binary collision expansion method to a system of hard spheres with diameter a. Two types of singularities may be expected in such a problem. The first, because of the severe singularity of the hard sphere potential, has been eliminated by our expansion in X rather than in the potential V. The second is associated with the non-convergence of typical expansions at transition temperatures. To illustrate the treatment that is required in such cases, we consider the ground state ($T = 0°$ K) energy per particle for a hard sphere Bose gas at finite density and infinite volume. The following notation and units will be used:

$\hbar = 1$, $m = $ mass of particles $= 1/2$, $\mathcal{N} = $ number of particles, $\Omega = $ volume of box, $\rho = \mathcal{N}/\Omega$, $\lambda = (4\pi/kT)^{\frac{1}{2}}$.

Now since Bose and Boltzmann systems have the same ground state, we confine our attention to a Boltzmann system. The method described above leads to expressions for b_l of the following form:

$$b_l = (1/\lambda^3)(a/\lambda)^{l-1}\{\alpha_l + (a/\lambda)\,\beta_l + O[(a/\lambda)^2]\} \tag{10}$$

The coefficients α_l and β_l in this equation can be explicitly computed, but the form of the equation is obvious without a detailed calculation (U_l contains an integral over a product of one U_2 and at least $l-2$ X's. Hence b_l is of order a^{l-1}). We now try to approach the limit $T \to 0$, i.e., $\lambda = \infty$. Writing

$$\sum_1^\infty \alpha_l x^l \equiv f(x) \qquad \sum_1^\infty l\alpha_l x^l \equiv f_1(x) = df(x)/d\ln(x)$$

$$\sum_1^\infty \beta_l x^l \equiv g(x) \qquad \sum_1^\infty l\beta_l x^l \equiv g_1(x) = dg(x)/d\ln(x) \tag{11}$$

and

$$x \equiv az/\lambda \tag{12}$$

one therefore has from (4):

$$p/4\pi = (1/a\lambda^4)[f(x)+(a/\lambda)g(x)+\ldots]$$
$$\rho = (1/a\lambda^2)[f_1(x)+(a/\lambda)g_1(x)+\ldots] \tag{13}$$

Taking only the first term on the right-hand side of (13), one sees that at a finite ρ, as $\lambda \to \infty$, one obtains a finite pressure p if and only if

$$f_1(x) \to \text{constant} \ (\lambda^2) \qquad \text{and} f(x) \to \text{constant} \ [f_1(x)]^2$$

This is possible only if

$$f(x) \to \text{constant} \ (\ln x)^2 \qquad \text{and } x \to \infty$$

A detailed computation of the coefficients α_l explicitly bears out this conjecture.

One obtains consequently, as $T \to 0$

$$p \propto (\ln x)^2/a\lambda^4 \qquad \rho \propto \ln x/a\lambda^2 \tag{14}$$

Hence

$$p \propto a\rho^2 \tag{15}$$

Now the pressure at $T \to 0$ is related to the ground state energy E_0 in the following way

$$p = \rho^2 \, d(E_0/N)/d\rho \tag{16}$$

Equations (15) and (16) together yield

$$E_0/N \propto a\rho \tag{17}$$

The coefficient in (17), on detailed computation, turns out to be 4π.

Now we can include the second term in the right-hand side of (13). Remembering that

$$\lambda \to (\ln x)^{1/2} \, (a\rho)^{-1/2}$$

one easily sees that these terms contribute a finite correction to p if and only if

$$g(x) \to (\ln x)^{5/2} \qquad (18)$$

which is also borne out by a detailed computation of the coefficients. The correction term $(a/\lambda)\,g(x)$ compared with $f(x)$ is thus of order $(a/\lambda)(\ln x)^{1/2} \propto (\rho a^3)^{1/2}$.

We indicate briefly the considerations involved in determining the explicit coefficients α_l. To first order in $a \ll \lambda$, U_2 and X are very easily obtained in momentum space:

$$\langle \mathbf{p}' | U_1 | \mathbf{p} \rangle = \delta^3(\mathbf{p} - \mathbf{p}') e^{-\beta p^2}$$

$$\langle \mathbf{p}_1' \, \mathbf{p}_2' | U_2 | \mathbf{p}_1 \mathbf{p}_2 \rangle = -(a\beta/\pi^2)\, \delta^3(\mathbf{p}_1 + \mathbf{p}_2 - \mathbf{p}_1' - \mathbf{p}_2')\, e^{-\beta(p_1^2 + p_2^2)} \qquad (19)$$

$$\langle \mathbf{p}_1' \mathbf{p}_2' | X | \mathbf{p}_1 \mathbf{p}_2 \rangle = -(1/\beta) \langle \mathbf{p}_1' \mathbf{p}_2' | U_2 | \mathbf{p}_1 \mathbf{p}_2 \rangle$$

Now all diagrams representing U_l must be connected and contain one U_2; the lowest order, required for f, will then have one U_2 and $l-1$ X's. The integrations, as in (3) and (6), are readily performed and, given l, are independent of the diagram chosen. Hence, we need merely the number of $(l-1)$-branch, connected diagrams with l vertices (i.e., trees), and this may be determined by use of a generating function.

The higher order terms, representing β_l, etc., are found by a similar process, but here several types of diagram must be distinguished. For the ground state energy of a Bose (or Boltzmann) gas, one finds [8]

a. $$E/N = 4\pi a\rho[1 + 128(\rho a^3)^{1/2}/15\sqrt{\pi} + O(\rho a^3)] \qquad (20)$$

in agreement with the prediction of (17) and (18). Further, the following results [8] are similarly obtained (particles of spin J are considered, where $J = 0$ for Bose and Boltzmann gases, and is arbitrary for a Fermi gas; P_F denotes the maximum Fermi momentum $[6\pi^2\rho/(2J+1)]^{1/3}$):

b.   The ground state energy per particle for a Fermi gas at a finite density ρ and infinite volume is given by

$$E/N = (3P_F^2/5) + 8\pi a \rho J (2J+1)^{-1}[1+6(11-2\ln 2) P_F a/35\pi + O(P_F^2 a^2)]$$
$$(21)$$

c.   For the Fermi gas the fugacity expansion is

$$\lambda^3 p/kT = \lambda^3 \sum_1^\infty b_l z^l$$

$$\begin{aligned}
= & -(2J+1)g_{5/2}(-z) - 2J(2J+1)[g_{3/2}(-z)]^2(a/\lambda) \\
& -8J^2(2J+1)\, g_{1/2}(-z)[g_{3/2}(-z)]^2(a/\lambda)^2 \\
& +8J(2J+1)\, F(-z)(a/\lambda)^2 + O(a^3/\lambda^3)
\end{aligned}$$
$$(22)$$

where

$$g_n(z) = \sum_1^\infty l^{-n} z^l \tag{23}$$

and
$$F(z) = \sum_{r,s,t=1}^\infty (rst)^{-1/2}(r+s)^{-1}(r+t)^{-1} z^{r+s+t} \tag{24}$$

d.   For the Bose gas the fugacity expansion is

$$\begin{aligned}
\lambda^3 p/kT = & \; g_{5/2}(z) - 2[g_{3/2}(z)]^2(a/\lambda) + 8g_{1/2}(z)[g_{3/2}(z)]^2(a/\lambda)^2 \\
& + 8F(z)(a/\lambda)^2 + O(a^3/\lambda^3)
\end{aligned}$$
$$(25)$$

e.   For the Bose gas the pressure and density at the transition point are given by

$$\begin{aligned}
\lambda^3 p/kT &= 1.34 + (2.61)^2\, 2(a/\lambda) + O[(a/\lambda)_{3/2}] \\
\lambda^3 \rho &= 2.61 + O(a/\lambda)
\end{aligned}$$
$$(26)$$

To obtain this expression it was necessary to sum the dominant terms in the fugacity expansion to all orders of a/λ near $z = 1$.

3. *Pseudopotential method*

The pseudopotential method was discussed long ago by many people. It was very clearly discussed in the book of Blatt and Weiss-kopf [9]. Using the pseudopotential to simulate the hard sphere potential, the energy per particle, E/N, of a system of hard sphere Bosons has been previously computed [10] in powers of a up to a^3. Because in this computation the coefficient of a^2 was 0; that of a^3 being ∞, a comparison with the result we just discussed, which conains fractional powers of a, was very illuminating. Huang, Lee, and I were led [11] by such a comparison to a new use of the pseudopotential method consisting essentially of calculating to all integral powers of the terms that have a maximum dependence on N. The sum of such terms yields exactly eq. (20), which is discussed above.

A natural generalization is to a calculation of the energies and wave functions of the low-lying excited states [11]. The results confirm the usual notion of phonon waves [with velocity corresponding to that calculated from the energy expression (20)] as the *only* low-lying excitations, and the idea of *momentum-space ordering*. Due to the low energy-level density associated with phonon states, one concludes [12] from the calculation that a dilute system of hard sphere Bose particles shows superfluidity and exhibits the two-fluid behavior at low temperatures. A similar computation for a Fermi-Dirac system reveals an infinitely greater energy-level density, and so superfluidity, e.g., in He^3, is not to be expected. One also concludes that a correlation length $8\pi a\rho)^{-1/2}$ can be defined within which London's idea [13] of an ordering in momentum space is effective; residual spatial correlations vary as $1/r$ well within this length, and as $1/r^4$ outside it. It is interesting to observe that if the volume is restricted to this region of superfluidity and high correlation, then even the unmodified approach of Huang and Yang [10] yields the correct form for the mean particle energy. It is also suggestive that the superfluid flow for the hard sphere system is irrotational, as was pointed out by Onsager [14] and Feynman [12].

4. *Further remarks*

I shall make two more remarks. The first has to do with what happens when the system becomes very dense. One can conclude from a different kind of reasoning that when the system is so dense as to be near "jamming", the qualitative properties of the energy-level density near the ground state are very different from the case of low density — they resemble rather a collection of Fermions. What happens between the two extremes of high and low density is very interesting, but seems difficult to study.

The other remark has to do with the motivation underlying the study of a system of hard spheres. One would like, of course, to study the general many-body problem with any interaction potential between the particles. Such a program can be formalistically carried out. It is, however, generally recognized that to draw any definite physical conclusions from such a general program is very difficult. If one makes approximations on the general problem to arrive at concrete results, one usually encounters the great difficulty of defining and justifying the validity of the approximation made. We therefore start instead from the concrete model of hard sphere interactions, which is sufficientlly simple so that one can discuss the validity of the method of approach. The interaction between real He atoms contains, besides a hard repulsive core, an attractive interaction outside the core. This attractive interaction is responsible for many properties of the He liquid. For example, the ground state of a system of He atoms is known to have a negative energy corresponding to a binding energy per He atom of $(k \times 7° \text{K})$, as determined from the experimental vapor pressure curve near the absolute zero of temperature. Such a bound system owes its origin, of course, to the attractive force. The strength of the attractive force also determines the density of the He atoms in the ground state. Now at this density the total attractive potential that a He atom experiences from its neighbors is expected not to fluctuate very much. This fact suggests the following approximate picture: One replaces the attractive interparticle forces by a constant uniform negative external potential that acts on the individual particles, the repulsive core is retained, and the system is kept by an external pressure at a density equal to that of the ground state of He. Many qualitative characteristics of this hypothetical model may then be expected to resemble those of real He. Since the uniform external potential does not influence the system except to give it a negative total energy, *one may consider simply a system of hard spheres at a given density* and in the end add the external potential separately. I should add that this kind of reasoning is essentially contained in the work of London on the density and the energy of liquid He in the ground state.

NOTE ADDED IN PROOF (Jan. 1962). The considerations outlined in this report and further developments were subsequently reported in full in the following publications: *Phys. Rev.* **106,** 1135 (1957); **112,** 1419 (1958); **113,** 1406 (1959); **113,** 1165 (1959); **116,** 25 (1959); **117,** 12, 22, 897 (1959). See also *Physica Suppl.* **26,** S49 (1960).

Notes and references

1. Reported at the International Conference on Theoretical Physics, Seattle, Wash., Sept. 1956, see also T. D. Lee and C. N. Yang, *Phys. Rev.* **105**, 1119 (1957).
2. H. D. Ursell, *Proc. Cambridge Phil. Soc.* **23**, 685 (1927).
3. B. Kahn and G. E. Uhlenbeck, *Physica* **5**, 399 (1938).
4. See, e.g., ter Haar, *Elements of Statistical Mechanics*, (Rinehart, New York, 1954, Chap. 8.
5. J. E. Mayer and M. G. Mayer, *Statistical Mechanics*, Wiley, New York, 1940, Chap. 13.
6. See, e.g., R. P. Feynman, *Phys. Rev.* **84**, 108 (1951).
7. H. A. Bethe, Chap. II, this volume.
8. T. D. Lee and C. N. Yang, *Phys. Rev.* **105**, 1119 (1957).
9. J. M. Blatt and V. F. Weisskopf, *Theoretical Nuclear Physics*, Wiley, New York, 1952, p. 76.
0. K. Huang and C. N. Yang, *Phys. Rev.* **105**, 767 (1957).
1. Lee, Huang, and Yang, *Phys. Rev.* **106**, 1135 (1957).
2. R. P. Feynman, in *Progress in Low Temperature Physics*, C. J. Gorter, ed., Interscience, New York, 1955, Vol. I.
3. F. London, *Superfluids*, Wiley, New York, 1954, Vol. II, Chap. B.
4. L. Onsager, *Nuovo cimento* **6**; *Suppl.*, 249 (1949).

CHAPTER XI

The Many-Body Problem with Strong Forces

R. Jastrow

1. Introduction

I should like to discuss with you the simplest possible extension of the Hartree method which will still be adequate for systems of particles interacting through very strong, short-range, two-body forces; we shall always have in mind the typical case of the hard sphere interaction. The method consists of a variational procedure, using a trial function in which two-body correlations have been explicitly included. That is [1],

$$\psi(\mathbf{r}_1, \mathbf{r}_2, \ldots, \mathbf{r}_N) = \prod_{i<j} f(\mathbf{r}_{ij}) \, S(\mathbf{r}_1, \mathbf{r}_2, \ldots, \mathbf{r}_N) \tag{1}$$

where the function $f(\mathbf{r}_{ij})$ is a correlation function, and S describes single-particle orbitals, which may be complicated, e.g., for the finite nucleus, but are very simple for the infinite nuclear medium.

Before continuing with the detailed evaluation of the energy, I should like to make a few additional remarks. The method I have been discussing is really intended for the ground state, but if we wish to describe the low-lying spectrum, we can attempt to do so by introducing excited states for the one-particle orbital functions. For an ordinary Fermi system, for example, the single-particle function is antisymmetric and represents a completely filled Fermi sea, but if we wish to describe excited states of the system, we can place some of the particles entering into the function S in excited orbitals. An example of a system of this sort is the ferromagnetic state of the Fermion gas, in which not all the spins are paired, and similar remarks hold for the Boson case, for which we employ a symmetric S. In any case, the strong, short-range interaction which we wish to describe is always allowed for by the correlation functions $f(\mathbf{r}_{ij})$. It is clear that for the ground state of a system of uniform density, we must take the single-particle function S, with suitable normalization, to be unity for Bosons and a Slater determinant for Fermions.

Let me also remark that the function $f(r)$ must approach unity, or some constant close to unity, at values of the argument large compared to the range of the forces, since in this region the pair correlations disappear (except in the solid state) and the particles are independent of each other. Within the range of the forces, and for low density, we expect the behavior of the correlation function f to resemble the solution to the two-body Schrödinger equation with the same potential, and we will see later to what extent this is true.

2. Bose systems

Assume now that we are dealing with a set of $\mathcal{N}$ Bosons in an enclosure of volume Ω large enough for the surface effects to be neglected. The expectation value of the energy of such a system is given by:

$$\bar{H} = \int B[- \sum_k \hbar^2/2m \, \nabla_k^2 + \sum_{s<t} V(\mathbf{r}_{st})] B \, d\tau / \int B^2 \, d\tau$$

$$B \equiv \prod_{i<j} f(\mathbf{r}_{ij}) \qquad d\tau = d\mathbf{r}_1 \ldots d\mathbf{r}_N \tag{2}$$

where, with no loss of generality, B has been chosen real.
Using the identity

$$B\nabla^2 B = \tfrac{1}{2} B^2 \nabla^2 \ln B + \tfrac{1}{4}\nabla^2 B^2 \tag{3}$$

eq. (2) may be transformed to

$$\bar{H}/\mathcal{N} = \tfrac{1}{2}\rho \int d\mathbf{r}\{(\hbar^2/2m)[-f(\mathbf{r})\nabla^2 f(\mathbf{r})+\nabla f(\mathbf{r})\cdot\nabla f(\mathbf{r})]+V(\mathbf{r})f^2(\mathbf{r})\}G(\mathbf{r})$$

$$G(\mathbf{r}_{12}) \equiv [\Omega^2/f^2(\mathbf{r}_{12})][\int B^2 \, d\mathbf{r}_3 \ldots d\mathbf{r}_N/\int B^2 \, d\mathbf{r}_1 \ldots d\mathbf{r}_N], \quad \rho \equiv \mathcal{N}-1/\Omega \tag{4}$$

This result is strikingly similar to the expectation value of the two-body Hamiltonian, except for the presence here of the function $G(\mathbf{r})$. Now we can apply the methods used in the classical theory of the imperfect gas to this distribution function $G(\mathbf{r})$; that is, we can use the cluster development [2] of Ursell, Mayer, Kahn, and Uhlenbeck.

It is then found that

$$G(\mathbf{r}) = 1 + \rho \int d\mathbf{r}_3 \left[f^2(\mathbf{r}_{13}) - 1 \right] \left[f^2(\mathbf{r}_{23}) - 1 \right] + O(\rho^2) \qquad (5)$$

The direct linking of particles 1 and 2 is through the interaction and appears in the first term of $G(\mathbf{r})$. The first cluster correction to the leading term of $G(\mathbf{r})$ represents the correlations in the wave function that come from the presence of a third particle in the vicinity of 1 and 2, and is represented by the cluster diagram. This is an extra linking of the two particles.

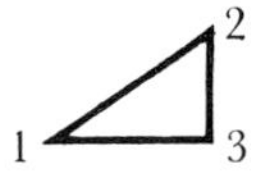

Figure 1

Then we have other terms of order ρ^2 and higher, which represent linkings of 4 or more particles. These higher-order cluster terms generally involve complicated integrals, so in what follows I will restrict my remarks to moderate densities.

We may now insert various forms [3] for the function $f(\mathbf{r})$ and try to minimize the energy. A more elegant and less arbitrary procedure is to minimize the energy analytically against variations in the form of the function $f(\mathbf{r})$. In this minimization, it is convenient to define a new function $\chi(\mathbf{r}) \equiv G^{\frac{1}{2}} f$, whose square is the pair distribution function. Now to ensure that the boundary condition at $r \to \infty$, which I mentioned before, is satisfied, we include the subsidiary condition

$$\int \left[\chi(\mathbf{r}) - 1 \right]^2 d\mathbf{r} = \text{constant} \qquad (6)$$

(This seems to be the simplest form of subsidiary condition that gives the desired results.) The writing eq. (4) in terms of $\chi(\mathbf{r})$, the extremum condition may be written:

$$\delta \left\{ \int \left[(-\hbar^2/2m) \chi \nabla^2 \chi + \tfrac{1}{2}(V + \bar{V}) \chi^2 \right] d\mathbf{r} + \lambda^2 \int (\chi - 1)^2 \, d\mathbf{r} \right\} = 0$$
$$\bar{V} \equiv (\hbar^2/4m)[(\nabla^2 G/G) - (\nabla G \cdot \nabla G/G^2)] \qquad (7)$$

and this yields the equation:

$$-(\hbar^2/2m)\nabla^2\chi + \tfrac{1}{2}(V + \bar{V})\chi + \lambda^2(\chi - 1) + \tfrac{1}{2}\chi^2(\delta\bar{V}/\delta\chi) = 0 \qquad (8)$$

which is to be solved for $\chi(\mathbf{r})$.

3. *Hard sphere gas*

The form of eq. (8) is of some interest: although it is inhomogeneous, it bears a strong resemblance to the two-body Schrödinger equation, plus additional terms which represent the effective interaction of the pair of particles in question with all the other particles in the system. In the low-density limit, these extra terms are negligible, as we expect; the remaining equation can be solved for the hard sphere gas, giving the result:

$$\chi = f(r) = 1 - (a/r) e^{-\lambda(r-a)} \qquad r \geqq a$$
$$= 0 \qquad r < a \tag{9}$$

which is the solution which goes to zero at $r = a$, the hard sphere diameter. The form $\chi^2(r) = (1-a/r)^2$ for the radial distribution function at $r \sim a$ coincides with that of Lee, Huang, and Yang [4] although the asymptotic forms differ, to the present order of approximation.

Now if we insert $\chi(r)$ of eq. (9) into the expression for the energy and minimize with respect to the parameter λ, we obtain the following result: The energy of the Bose hard sphere gas appears as an expansion in integral powers of the density, corresponding to the successive terms in the cluster series. But it turns out, in the low-density limit at least, that when we vary the energy, λ itself depends on the density, i.e.,

$$\lambda = (8\pi\rho a)^{1/2} \tag{10}$$

and hence the coefficients of the cluster series also depend on the density. The form of the energy is now modified to

$$E/N = 4\pi\rho a[1 + (2\sqrt{2})(\pi\rho a^3)^{1/2} + O(\rho a^3)] \tag{11}$$

where units have been chosen such that $\hbar^2/2m = 1$. Here the coefficient of the second term has been evaluated approximately, since it involves complicated integrals, and agrees quite well with the result of Huang et al. [5]. They obtain $128/15\pi = 2.716$ instead of $2\sqrt{2} = 2.828$ for this coefficient.

4. *Fermi systems*

A similar program can be carried out for a spin 1/2 Fermi system where one has antisymmetrized plane waves in the wave function

The leading term in the energy is the Fermi energy: $(3/5)\hbar^2 K_F^2/2m$, which goes as $\rho^{2/3}$, but there are additional terms T_c which come from the presence of the correlation functions $f(r)$ in the wave function; then there is the mean value of the potential energy, and finally there are terms T_{cf} which come from the scalar product of the gradient of the Slater determinant and the gradient of the correlation functions. We can manipulate these expressions so that they take the form:

$$\bar{H} = \int d\tau[-(\hbar^2/2m) \sum_k (S^*S\,B\nabla_k^2 B + 2S^*\nabla_k S\cdot B\nabla_k B$$
$$+B^2 S^*\nabla_k^2 S) + \sum_{s<t} V_{st} S^*SB^2]/\int B^2 S^*S\,d\tau \tag{12}$$

Except for some modification of the cluster development due to the determinants present, the calculation closely follows that of the Bose case. That is, the leading cluster term, unity for the Bose gas, is replaced by a two-by-two determinant — the customary result for the free Fermi gas. Again taking $\hbar^2/2m = 1$, the net result for a hard sphere gas is

$$E/\mathcal{N} = (3/5)K_F^2 + \rho \int d\mathbf{r}\ (\nabla f)^2[1 - \tfrac{1}{2}l^2(K_F r)] + \dots$$
$$l(r) \equiv (3/r^3)(\sin r - r\cos r) \tag{13}$$

The same trial function is used as in the Bose case, but with a different form for the variation parameter: $\lambda = K_F/\sqrt{2}$. If we retain only the first two terms of the expansion for $l^2(r)$, we obtain the series

$$E/\mathcal{N} = E_{\text{Fermi}} + 2\pi\rho a(1 + K_F a/\sqrt{2} + \dots) \tag{14}$$

while if we keep more terms, the coefficient $1/\sqrt{2}$ is lowered by perhaps 10 %. This is to be compared with the exact numerical value of this coefficient, given as $6(11-\ln 4)/35\pi = 0.525$ by Huang et al [5]. The agreement is fairly good, but the method has the advantage of not being limited by this type of expansion; the integral appearing in the energy can be evaluated exactly, and then the cluster development is the only type of approximation which remains, beyond the basic variational approximation. It has been estimated that the higher cluster terms are fairly small for $K_F a \lesssim 1.5$, and so the method should be quite useful for the spin $1/2$ Fermi gas.

R. JASTROW

Notes and references

1. See also R. B. Dingle, *Phil. Mag.* **40**, 573 (1947).
2. J. De Boer, *Repts. Progr. Phys.* **12**, 305 (1948).
3. R. Jastrow, *Phys. Rev.* **98**, 1479 (1955).
4. T. D. Lee, K. Huang, and C. N. Yang, *Phys. Rev.* **106**, 1135 (1957).
5. K. Huang, T. D. Lee, and C. N. Yang, Chap. X, this volume.

CHAPTER XII

Collective Variables Without Subsidiary Conditions

C. A. LEVINSON and M. K. BANERJEE

1. *Introduction*

The collective variables I should like to discuss are the ones first introduced in the work of Bohr and Mottelson [1]. These variables, nine in number, are those associated with the surface motion of a nucleus.

First of all, there are three center of mass coordinates R^1, R^2, R^3 — of course, these were not introduced by Bohr. If there are A nucleons, all of equal mass (a convenient restriction, but not a necessary one), at positions r_p^x, $p = 1, \ldots, A$, $x = 1, 2, 3$, the coordinates relative to the center of mass are then determined by

$$r_p^x = R^x + r_p^x (\text{C.M.}) \tag{1}$$

with the three constraints

$$\sum_p^{p} r_p^x (\text{C.M.}) = 0 \tag{2}$$

balancing the introduction of three new variables R^x.

Secondly, one may describe the Euler angles θ, φ, ψ, of the transformation required to rotate to the principal axis system of the nucleus; the corresponding orthogonal rotation matrix [2], denoted by $R_{xx'}^3 (\theta, \varphi, \psi)$, satisfies

$$\sum_x^{x} R_{xx'}^3 (\theta, \varphi, \psi) R_{xx''}^3 (\theta, \varphi, \psi) = \delta_{x'x''} \tag{3}$$

The nine $R_{xx'}^3$ with the six restrictions of eq. (3) thus leave θ, φ, ψ as independent defining parameters. Then, the coordinates in the principal axis system, determined by

183

$$r_p^x(\text{C.M.}) = \sum^{x'} R_{xx'}^3(\theta, \varphi, \psi)\, r_p^{x'}(\text{P.A.}) \qquad (4)$$

are restricted by the vanishing of the cross products of inertia, that is, by the constraints

$$\sum^p r_p^x(\text{P.A.})\, r_p^{x'}(\text{P.A.}) = (\alpha_x)^2 \delta_{xx'} \qquad (5)$$

for $x \neq x'$

The third set of collective variables will be the α_x of eq. (5) which are, linear combinations of the principal radii of inertia for the nuclear system; the corresponding constraints are simply the defining relations, given by $x' = x$ in eq. (5).

To the extent that the three sets of collective variables just described can be decoupled, the R_x represent merely translational motion of the nucleus and θ, φ, ψ rotation, and thus responsibility for the $I(I+1)$ excitation spectrum [3] of non-spherical nuclei. The α_x account for volume and surface vibrations prominent in spherical nuclei whose configurations are not near closed shell configurations. Bohr's β and γ collective variables [1] are related to the α_x; a third variable is lacking because of his assumption of constant volume, or neglect of "breathing modes". Now not only are rotational and vibrational modes coupled, but they are coupled as well to the individual particle motions. When collective motion truly obtains, the individual particle motions determine the adiabatic parameters of the nucleus, whereas, for nearly closed shells, they interfere strongly with the character of the collective states, and ultimately appear in the form of pair excitations.

2. Internal variables

The individual particle coordinates cannot, together with the nine collective variables, form a legitimate coordinate system, for they overdetermine the system. A possible solution is simply to impose the nine interrelations, eqs. (2) and (5), as subsidiary conditions [4]. More satisfactory would be the choice of $3A-9$ internal variables — combinations of individual coordinates — to describe the residual motions in a physically meaningful way. In particular, although the choice may not be completely symmetric in all nucleons, an interchange of particles should result at most in a trivial transformation of the internal variables, and one can then formulate the theory proposed by Bohr in a much neater fashion. This is the problem to which I now address myself.

The problem then is that of constructing a transformation to $3A-9$ internal variables, such that the subsidiary conditions are automatically encompassed; this is done in two stages. We first treat the transition to relative coordinates from this point of view. In general, the kinetic properties of our system will be unaltered by an orthogonal transformation among the A vectors $\mathbf{r}_p$ (origin and orientation of the coordinate system unspecified, for the time being). A transformation of particular value to us is generated (see Fig. 1) by taking $\bar{\boldsymbol{\rho}}_1$ as the vector

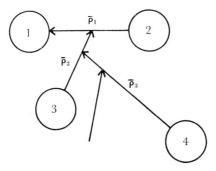

Figure 1

from $\mathbf{r}_2$ to $\mathbf{r}_1$, $\bar{\boldsymbol{\rho}}_2$ from $\mathbf{r}_3$ to the center of mass of $\mathbf{r}_2$ and $\mathbf{r}_1$ (midway along $\bar{\boldsymbol{\rho}}_1$), $\bar{\boldsymbol{\rho}}_3$ from $\mathbf{r}_4$ to the center of mass of $\mathbf{r}_1$,$\mathbf{r}_2$, $\mathbf{r}_3$ (2/3 way along $\bar{\boldsymbol{\rho}}_2$), . . ., and finally $\bar{\boldsymbol{\rho}}_A$ from the origin to the center of the system. With the normalization $\boldsymbol{\rho}_n = (n/n+1)^{1/2}\,\bar{\boldsymbol{\rho}}_n$, we then have

$$\boldsymbol{\rho}_n = [n(n+1)]^{-1/2}(\mathbf{r}_1+\mathbf{r}_2+\ldots\mathbf{r}_n)-(n/n+1)^{1/2}\mathbf{r}_{n+1} \tag{6}$$

which is readily verified to be an orthogonal transformation; here $\mathbf{r}_{A+1}\equiv 0$.

The important point now is that one of the transformed vectors, $\boldsymbol{\rho}_A$, is proportional to the position of the center of mass. This means that if the center of mass is at the origin, inverting eq. (6) to obtain the $\mathbf{r}_p$, we may simply omit $\boldsymbol{\rho}_A$. Hence, in the principal axis system, we have

$$\mathbf{r}_p(\text{P.A.}) = \{[A(A-1)]^{-1/2}\boldsymbol{\rho}_{A-1}+[(A-1)(A-2)]^{-1/2}\boldsymbol{\rho}_{A-2}$$
$$+ \ldots +[p(p-1)]^{-1/2}\boldsymbol{\rho}_p\}-(p-1/p)^{1/2}\boldsymbol{\rho}_{p-1} \tag{7}$$

which will be abbreviated as

$$r_p^x(\text{P.A.}) = \sum_{n=1}^{A-1} \varepsilon_p^n \boldsymbol{\rho}_n \tag{8}$$

The constraint, eq. (2), (or its analog for the principal axis system) is then automatically satisfied by the observation that

$$\sum^p \varepsilon_p^n = 0 \tag{9}$$

and we are left with only $A-1$ vectors $\boldsymbol{\rho}_n$. Further, although ε_p^n, being a rectangular matrix, cannot be orthogonal, it is very nearly so, as evidenced by

$$\sum_{p=1}^A \varepsilon_p^n \varepsilon_p^m = \delta_{nm} \tag{10a}$$

$$\sum_{n=1}^{A-1} \varepsilon_p^n \varepsilon_q^n = \delta_{pq}^{-1/A} \tag{10b}$$

Indeed, eqs. (9), (10) comprise all of the properties of ε_p^n which we require.

Applying eq. (8) to eq. (5), we have, by virtue of the orthogonality condition (10a)

$$\sum_{n=1}^{A-1} \rho_n^x \rho_n^{x'} = (\alpha_x)^2 \delta_{xx'} \tag{11}$$

Thus, the $\boldsymbol{\rho}_n$ encompass the center of mass condition and maintain the form of eq. (5). To make things clearer, let us turn our notation around a bit, and regard the ρ_n^x as being a set of three vectors of dimension $A-1$; then eq. (11) says nothing more than that the vectors ρ^x are mutually orthogonal, with lengths α_x. Since the α_x are themselves to be collective variables, the second stage of our transformation starts by normalizing the vectors ρ^x

$$\rho_n^x = \alpha_x U_n^x \tag{12}$$

(or equivalently, by converting to a spherical moment ellipsoid for the ordinary three-vectors). Equation (11) then reduces to

$$\sum_{n=1}^{A-1} U_n^{x'} U_n^x = \delta_{xx'} \tag{13}$$

Our task now is simply to parametrize the three orthonormal vectors U^x in $(A-1)$-dimensional space, and these parameters will be our internal variables. Such a description clearly requires $3A-9$ parameters: $A-2$ for the first unit vector U^1, $A-3$ for the second one orthogonal to it, and $A-4$ for the third one orthogonal to both. To explicitly represent the U_n^x, we may take any fixed orthogonal triad of vectors in $(A-1)$-dimensional space and apply $3A-9$ rotations, e.g., of the type

$$R_{13}(\zeta) = \begin{pmatrix} \cos\zeta & 0 & \sin\zeta & \cdots \\ 0 & 1 & 0 & \cdots \\ -\sin\zeta & 0 & \cos\zeta & \cdots \\ \cdots & \cdots & \cdots & \cdots \end{pmatrix} \tag{14}$$

required to rotate it to U_n^x. The corresponding rotation angles ζ^{xn}, $x < n \leq A-1$ may be defined in more than one way, but for example, generalizing the Euler angles, the form

$$U_n^1 = a_n^{(1)}(\zeta^1)$$
$$U_n^2 = \sum^{s} b_n^{(s)}(\zeta^1) a_{s+1}^{(2)}(\zeta^2) \tag{15}$$
$$U_n^3 = \sum^{st} b_n^{(s)}(\zeta^1) b_{s+1}^{(t)}(\zeta^2) a_{t+1}^{(3)}(\zeta^3)$$

(which is readily extended to a full orthogonal transformation) is appropriate. Here $0 < s, t < A-1$, and

$$a_n^{(s)}(\zeta^x) = \cos\zeta^{x\,n+1} \prod_{j=s}^{n-1} \sin\zeta^{x\,j+1}$$
$$b_n^{(s)}(\zeta^x) = \partial a_n^{(s)}(\zeta^x)/\partial\zeta^{x\,s+1} \qquad \zeta^{xA} \equiv 0 \tag{16}$$

Now, what have we accomplished? By transforming away successively, and explicitly, the center of mass, principal axis orientation, and non-sphericity of the moment ellipsoid, we have obtained, combining eqs. (1), (4), (8), (12) and (15),

$$r_p^x = R^x + \sum^{yn} R_{xy}^3(\theta, \varphi, \psi) \alpha_y \varepsilon_p^n U_n^y(\ldots \zeta^{xs} \ldots) \tag{17}$$

a description of the A nucleon system directly in terms of nine collective and $3A-9$ internal variables. Further, the angles ζ^{xs} constitute a physically symmetric set in the particle positions. To see this, we recognize that all particle permutations may be generated by transpositions or particle interchanges of the form $\mathbf{r}_p \rightarrow \mathbf{r}_{p+1}$, $\mathbf{r}_{p+1} \rightarrow \mathbf{r}_p$, but from eq. (6), such a transposition results in

$$\begin{pmatrix} \mathbf{\rho}_{p-1} \\ \mathbf{\rho}_p \end{pmatrix} \rightarrow \begin{pmatrix} 1/p & (p^2-1)^{\frac{1}{2}}/p \\ (p^2-1)^{\frac{1}{2}}/p & -1/p \end{pmatrix} \begin{pmatrix} \mathbf{\rho}_{p-1} \\ \mathbf{\rho}_p \end{pmatrix} \tag{18}$$

merely a set of three geometric reflections in the $(A-1)$-dimensional ρ space, and so a reflection in ζ space as well. The explicit form of the ζ-space reflection is however not very simple.

3. Transformation of momenta

We are not quite yet in a position to do some physics with our new set of collective and internal variables, for it is still necessary to express the particle momenta in terms of the new conjugate momenta. To accomplish this, we suppose for convenience that the wave function for the system is first written as a function of $\{R^x, \alpha_x, R_{xx'}, U_n^x\}$, and that $\{R_{xx'}, U_n^x\}$ will then be expressed in terms of $\{\theta, \varphi, \psi, \zeta^{xs}\}$. Thus (dropping the superscript in $R_{xx'}^3$), we wish to obtain the explicit form of

$$\partial/\partial r_p^y = \sum (\partial R^x/\partial r_p^y)(\partial/\partial R^x) + \sum (\partial \alpha_x/\partial r_p^y)(\partial/\partial \alpha_x)$$
$$+ \sum (\partial R_{xx'}/\partial r_p^y)(\partial/\partial R_{xx'}) + \sum (\partial U_n^x/\partial r_p^y)(\partial/\partial U_n^x) \tag{19}$$

This procedure, it develops, is considerably more effective, e.g., in determining the kinetic energy operator, than an attempt at direct substitution into a formula for the transformed Hamiltonian [5].

To find the coefficients in eq. (19), we differentiate the defining relation

$$r_q^x = R^x + \overset{x'n'}{\sum} \varepsilon_q^{n'} U_n^{x'} \alpha_{x'} R_{xx'} \tag{17'}$$

with respect to r_p^y, which yields

$$\delta_{xy}\delta_{pq} = (\partial R^x/\partial r_p^y) + \overset{x'm}{\sum} \varepsilon_q^m (\partial U_m^{x'}/\partial r_p^y) \alpha_{x'} R_{xx'}$$
$$+ \overset{x'm}{\sum} \varepsilon_q^n U_m^{x'} (\partial \alpha_{x'}/\partial r_p^y) R_{xx'} + \overset{x'm}{\sum} \varepsilon_q^m U_m^{x'} \alpha_{x'} (\partial R_{xx'}/\partial r_p^y) \tag{20}$$

Knowing that $\partial R^x/\partial r_p^y = \delta_{xy}/A$, we have, on performing the operation $\sum^{qx} \varepsilon_q^n R_{xy'}$, using eqs. (3), (9), (10a),

$$R_{yy'}\,\varepsilon_p^n = (\partial U_n^{y'}/\partial r_p^y)\alpha_{y'} + U_n^{y'}(\partial \alpha_{y'}/\partial r_p^y) + \sum^{xx'} U_n^{x'}\alpha_x(\partial R_{xx'}/\partial r_p^y)R_{xy'} \quad (21)$$

and then, applying $\sum^n U_n^z$, using eq. (13),

$$R_{yy'}\sum^n \varepsilon_p^n U_n^z = \alpha_{y'}\sum^n U_n^z(\partial U_n^{y'}/\partial r_p^y) + (\partial \alpha_{y'}/\partial r_p^y)\delta_{y'z} + \alpha_z\sum^x (\partial R_{xz}/\partial r_p^y)R_{xy'}$$
$$(22)$$

Now, taking $y' = z$ in eq. (22), there results

$$(\partial \alpha_z/\partial r_p^y) = R_{yz}\sum^n \varepsilon_p^n U_n^z \quad (23)$$

Substituting back into eq. (22), symmetrizing with respect to y' and z, and using the relations

$$\sum^x (\partial R_{xy'}/\partial r_p^y)R_{xz} + \sum^x (\partial R_{xz}/\partial r_p^y)R_{xy'} = (\partial/\partial r_p^y)\sum^x R_{xy'}R_{xz} = 0 \quad (24)$$

yields an expression for $\sum^x R_{xy'}(\partial R_{xz}/\partial r_p^y)$, which may be solved by virtue of eq. (3). Thus

$$(\partial R_{xz}/\partial r_p^y) = \sum_n^{z'\neq z} \varepsilon_p^n[R_{xz'}/(\alpha_z^2-\alpha_{z'}^2)](R_{yz'}\,\alpha_z U_n^z + R_{yz}\,\alpha_{z'}U_n^{z'}) \quad (25)$$

Finally, from eqs. (21), (23), (25),

$$(\partial U_m^z/\partial r_p^y) = (R_{yz}/\alpha_z)[\varepsilon_p^m - \sum^n \varepsilon_p^n U_m^z U_n^z]$$
$$+ (1/\alpha_z)\sum_n^{z'\neq z} \varepsilon_p^n U_m^{z'}(\alpha_{z'}/\alpha_z^2 - \alpha_{z'}^2)(R_{yz'}\,\alpha_z U_n^z + R_{yz}\,\alpha_{z'}U_n^{z'}) \quad (26)$$

Equations (23), (25), (26) enable us to cast $\partial/\partial r_p^y$ in eq. (19) explicitly as an operator on the $\{R^x, \alpha_x, R_{xx'}, U_n^x\}$. However, there are of course relations among the $R_{xx'}$ and among the U_n^x, whose elimination yields the independent θ, φ, ψ, and ζ^{xs}, of which the $R_{xx'}$ and U_n^x are functions. We wish ultimately to write $\partial/\partial r_p^y$ as an operator on these independent variables, but it is easier to use the $R_{xx'}$ and U_n^x in intermediate stages. The trouble is that relations among differential operators on, say, the $R_{xx'}$ are not necessarily maintained when these operators are written in terms of θ, φ, ψ, a consequence of the fact that when differentiations are involved, it matters whether the identities of eq. (3) are employed before or after differentiation. If, on the other hand, we make use only of first order differential operators in the $R_{xx'}$ which vanish on any identities among the $R_{xx'}$, then we

are assured that any operator relations will be maintained on trans-
forming to θ, φ, ψ, irrespective in fact of the precise definition of the
new independent coordinates.

The form of the elementary operators which leave identities among
the $R_{xx'}$ unchanged is clear physically. We know that an infinitesimal
change in r_p^y can result only in conversion of the orthogonal matrix
$R_{xx'}$ into another orthogonal matrix, i.e., in post- (or pre-)multi-
plication by an infinitesimal orthogonal matrix. But, applied to the
matrix $R_{xv'}$, post-multiplication by an infinitesimal rotation can be
written as a pure differential operator. e.g.,

$$\begin{pmatrix} R_{11} R_{12} R_{13} \\ R_{21} R_{22} R_{23} \\ R_{31} R_{32} R_{33} \end{pmatrix} \begin{pmatrix} 0 & 1 & 0 \\ -1 & 0 & 0 \\ 0 & 0 & 0 \end{pmatrix} = \sum^{y} (R_{y1}(\partial/\partial R_{y2}) - R_{y2}(\partial/\partial R_{y1})) \begin{pmatrix} R_{11} R_{12} R_{13} \\ R_{21} R_{22} R_{23} \\ R_{31} R_{32} R_{33} \end{pmatrix}$$

(27)

Thus, setting

$$L_{xz} = (\hbar/i) \sum^{y'} [R_{y'x}(\partial/\partial R_{y'z}) - R_{y'z}(\partial/\partial R_{y'x})]$$ (28)

the L_{xz} maintain the orthogonality of the $R_{xx'}$ and generate all variations of $R_{xx'}$ produced by any $\partial/\partial r_p^y$. A consequence is that the
characteristic commutation relations

$$(i/\hbar)[L_{xz}, R_{x'z'}] = R_{x'x}\delta_{z'z} - R_{x'z}\delta_{xz'}$$

$$(i/\hbar)[L_{xz}, L_{x'z'}] = L_{xz'}\delta_{zx'} + L_{zx'}\delta_{xz'} - L_{zz'}\delta_{xx'} - L_{xx'}\delta_{zz'}$$

(29)

are equally true for the infinitesimal matrices, the operators on $R_{xx'}$,
or the corresponding operators on θ, φ, ψ. One may summarize eqs.
(29) by observing that the L_{xy} behave like $\eta_x (\partial/\partial\eta_y) - \eta_y(\partial/\partial\eta_x)$, R_{xz}
like the row vector with components R_z.

Similarly, the (post-)rotations specified by

$$\Lambda_{xz} = (\hbar/i) \sum^{n} [U_n^x(\partial/\partial U_n^z) - U_n^z(\partial/\partial U_n^x)]$$ (30)

maintain the orthogonality of the U_m^x; they obey the commutation
relations analogous to eq. (29), which may be translated at once to
ζ^{xs} space. The remaining $3A-12$ independent rotations may be
constructed if we first extend the three orthonormal vectors U^x to a full

set of orthonormal vectors U^s, $s = 1, 2, \ldots, A-1$:

$$\sum_{n}^{s} U_m^s U_n^s = \delta_{mn} \tag{31}$$

this may be done, e.g., by the Schmidt process [6] or by a simple extension of eq. (15). We then introduce

$$\Lambda_{sx} = (\hbar/i) \sum_{n}^{n} U_n^s(\partial/\partial U_n^x) \qquad s > 3 \tag{32}$$

The Λ_{sx} again maintain the orthogonality of the U_m^x. But the Λ_{sx} cannot possibly satisfy the full set of relations analogous to eqs. (29), for they would then be identical in their action on the full matrix U_n^s as the corresponding elementary rotator matrices, and these generate the complete $[(A-1)(A-2)/2]$-parameter rotation group, which would endow the U_n^s with too many parameters. We leave in abeyance the Λ_{sx} commutation rules.

We have thus succeeded in showing that $(\partial/\partial r_p^y)$ in eq. (19) can be expressed in terms of the L_{xy}, Λ_{xy}, Λ_{sx}, and in elucidating the reasons for doing so. There remains the task of accomplishing this, but it is quickly established by direct substitution that eq. (19), with the identities of eqs. (23), (25), (26), is equivalent to

$$\partial/\partial r_p^y = (1/A)(\partial/\partial R^y) + \sum_{n}^{n} \varepsilon_p^n \{ \sum^{x} R_{yx} U_n^x (\partial/\partial \alpha_x)$$

$$+ (i/\hbar) \sum^{xz} [\alpha_z/(\alpha_z^2 - \alpha_x^2)] R_{yx} U_n^z L_{xz}$$

$$+ (i/\hbar) \sum^{xz} [\alpha_x/(\alpha_z^2 - \alpha_x^2)] R_{yx} U_n^z \Lambda_{xz} + (i/\hbar) \sum_{s>3}^{x} R_{yx} U_n^s \Lambda_{sx} \} \tag{33}$$

If the potential of the system is not velocity-dependent, then eq. (33) is required only for the Laplacian or kinetic energy operator; using eqs. (29) as needed, we arrive at the quite simple expression

$$\sum^{py} (\partial/\partial r_p^y)^2 = \sum^{x} (\partial/\partial \alpha_x)^2 + \sum^{x} \{(A-4)/\alpha_x) + \sum^{z} [2\alpha_x/(\alpha^2 - \alpha_z^2)] \}(\partial/\partial \alpha_x)$$

$$- (1/\hbar^2) \sum^{xz} [\alpha_z^2/(\alpha_z^2 - \alpha_x^2)^2][(L_{xz})^2 + (\Lambda_{xz})^2] + \sum^{x} (\partial/\partial R^x)^2$$

$$- (2/\hbar^2) \sum^{xz} [\alpha_x \alpha_z/(\alpha_z^2 - \alpha_x^2)^2] L_{xz} \Lambda_{xz} - (1/\hbar^2) \sum_{st>3}^{xn} (1/\alpha_x^2) U_n^s \Lambda_{sx} U_n^t \Lambda_{tx} \tag{34}$$

If we choose the U_n^s to satisfy, for $s > 3$,

$$\sum_{n}^{n} \partial U_n^s / \partial U_n^x = 0 \tag{35}$$

then Λ_{sx} and U_n^s may be interchanged in eq. (34), with corresponding simplification. Finally, one can express the L_{xz} in terms of θ, φ, ψ in the standard fashion [7], and obtain an analogous but more complicated expression for the Λ_{sx} in terms of the ζ^{xs}.

4. Description of the Hamiltonian

For a potential V, the complete Hamiltonian for the system may now be written as

$$H = -(\hbar^2/2mA) \sum (\partial/\partial R^x)^2 \tag{36a}$$

$$+ (1/2m)\{[(\alpha_2^2 + \alpha_3^2)/(\alpha_2^2 - \alpha_3^2)^2](L_{23}^2 + \Lambda_{23}^2) + \text{cyclic permutations}\} \tag{36b}$$

$$+ (2/m)\{[(\alpha_2\alpha_3/(\alpha_2^2 - \alpha_3^2)^2]L_{23}\Lambda_{23} + \text{cyclic permutations}\} \tag{36c}$$

$$- (\hbar^2/2m)\, g^{-1/2} \sum^x (\partial/\partial\alpha_x)\, g^{1/2}\,(\partial/\partial\alpha_x) + V \tag{36d}$$

$$+ (1/2m) \sum_{s=4}^{A-1} (\Lambda_{sx^2}/\alpha_x^2) \tag{36e}$$

$$g^{1/2} = (\alpha_1^2 - \alpha_2^2)(\alpha_2^2 - \alpha_3^2)(\alpha_3^2 - \alpha_1^2)(\alpha_1\alpha_2\alpha_3)^{A-4} \tag{37}$$

Let us investigate the various contributions to eq. (36). First of all, the center of mass kinetic energy (36a) of course separates completely from the remainder.

Next are the separated energies in (36a), (36b), due to the external angular momentum L_{xy} and the internal angular momentum Λ_{xy} (which commute, being in different spaces). The former, by our construction (also obtained in this form by Bohr [8]), is a consequence of the rotation of the principal axis system of the nucleus. The latter does not change the moment of inertia ellipsoid at all, and thus corresponds roughly to a particle flow along the nuclear surface; it is distinguished from the rotation of the geometric surface by virtue of the surface being non-spherical, and should thereby be associated with a relatively small moment of inertia. However, the cross terms (36c), or Coriolis contribution to the kinetic energy, prevent a sharp separation between the internal and external rotations; these are the terms which change the irrotational moments of inertia to solid-body moments of inertia in the cranking model [9]. Note that even for a rigid body — no internal motion — the Λ_{xy} will not vanish, for a slight movement of the ζ^{xs} (or of the U_n^x consistent with the constraints) will contribute in first order to the kinetic energy. A crude idea of the angular momentum associated with the internal motion is obtained by observing that in (36b), (36c)

$$[(\alpha_2^2+\alpha_3^2)/(\alpha_2^2-\alpha_3^2)^2](L_{23}^2+\Lambda_{23}^2)+[4\alpha_2\alpha_3/(\alpha_2^2-\alpha_3^2)^2]L_{23}\Lambda_{23}$$
$$= (L_{23}+\Lambda_{23})^2/2(\alpha_2-\alpha_3)^2+(L_{23}-\Lambda_{23})^2/2(\alpha_2+\alpha_3)^2 \tag{38}$$

so that $L_{23}+\Lambda_{23}$ corresponds to a low moment of inertia.

The vibrational contribution to the kinetic energy in (36d) has been written in a form which indicates that it may be regarded as that of a simple three-dimensional particle with a change of metric. It is easy to find the connection between the α_x and Bohr's β and γ collective variables; one can then verify that this term is just the vibrational contribution to the kinetic energy that Bohr gave in his first paper [1], if we expand to lowest order in β.

A possible potential energy arises as follows. Suppose that one wants to investigate a deformed nucleus which is looked at from the viewpoint of the shell model, that is, in some sense the particles are in harmonic wells, but the harmonic well is rotating with the nucleus. The potential energy thus becomes

$$V = \tfrac{1}{2}\omega_x^2 \sum^p x_p^2 + \tfrac{1}{2}\omega_y^2 \sum^p y_p^2 + \tfrac{1}{2}\omega_z^2 \sum^p z_p^2 \tag{39}$$

where the coordinates are to be taken in a principal axis system; note that the particles can not quite oscillate independently, because of the implicit center of mass condition (and of course because of the complicated kinetic energy coupling). If the harmonic well axes are identified with the principal axes, then by eq. (5), we have simply

$$V = \tfrac{1}{2} \sum^x \omega_x^2 \alpha_x^2 \tag{40}$$

the α_x take over the burden of the potential energy for the rotating shell model picture.

Finally, there are the completely internal kinetic energy terms of

(36e); the motions represented occur only in these terms and we shall not discuss them further.

5. *Discussion of solutions*

The collective potential of eq. (40) may be determined by the Born-Oppenheimer approach [10]. That is, working in the principal axis system, the collective α_x are fairly sluggish compared to the particle variables ζ^{xs}, something like the nuclei in a molecule compared to the molecules running around them. Thus, the potential seen by the α_x will be the true potential averaged over the state of the rapidly fluctuating ζ^{xs}:

$$V(\alpha) = \int \psi^*(\alpha, \zeta) \sum V_{ij}(\alpha, \zeta) \psi(\alpha, \zeta) \, d\zeta / \int \psi^*(\alpha, \zeta) \psi(\alpha, \zeta) \, d\zeta \quad (41)$$

where the actual two-body potentials V_{ij}, $i > j$, have been written in terms of the α_x and ζ^{xs}. Alternatively, the small mass associated with the ζ^{xs} insists on a large energy for their excitation; if we consider a vibrational (α) state well below this energy, no excited ζ states appear in the wave function, so that matrix elements of V may be taken to be diagonal with respect to the ζ. In computing eq. (41), one may use the shell-model wave functions for the potential of eq. (39); if the quadratic part of $V(\alpha)$ is compared with eq. (40), a self-consistent formulation for the ω_x is thus obtained.

If the purely internal term of (36e) is included with $\sum V_{ij}$ in computing $V(\alpha)$ in eq. (41), the resulting Hamiltonian of eq. (36) is, aside from the trivial center of mass terms, a function of the commuting L's, Λ's, and α's alone. However, even if the vibrational portion were averaged à la Born-Oppenheimer, reducing consideration to the low-energy rotational levels, the Coriolis term (36c) would still keep the internal and overall external motion coupled. Now the Bohr model conceives of the rotating distorted nucleus having internal motion independent of the external motion; in the different bands 0, 2, 4, 6, the internal motion is considered to be constant, and the only thing that is changing is the rotational motion. This cannot be the case here, for as L changes, the coupled internal motion must change as well.

Since empirical data indicates the validity of Bohr's picture [3], one is led to seek a unitary transformation on this Hamiltonian which eliminates (36c) or at least minimizes it. In the case of the cranking model [9], one has a similar problem; there is a similar coupling term, with L however being a c number, the cranking velocity. If this can be done, we will be in what one may call Bohr's model space, the new coefficients of the L^2 terms will be the proper reciprocal moments of inertia, and we will be in a position to proceed to the vibrational motion. In particular, it will be possible to determine to what extent the vibrations associated with the α_x are slower than those associated with the ζ^{xs}, as well as to check on the mass parameter and indeed on the general validity of the rotating shell model as a starting point.

Notes and references

1. A. Bohr, *Kgl. Danske Videnskab. Selskab, Mat.-fys. Medd.* **26**, No. 14 (1952); A. Bohr and B. R. Mottelson, *Kgl. Danske Videnskab. Selskab, Mat.-fys. Medd.* **27** No. 16 (1953).

2. H. Goldstein, *Classical Mechanics*, Addison-Wesley, Reading, Massachusetts, 1950, p. 109.

3. Alder, Bohr, Huus, Mottelson, and Winther, *Revs. Modern Phys.* **28**, 432 (1956).

4. F. Villars, *Ann. Rev. Nuclear Sc.* **7**, 185 (1957).

5. E. C. Kemble, *Fundamentals of Quantum Mechanics*, McGraw-Hill, New York, 1937, p. 238.

6. P. M. Morse and H. Feshbach, *Methods of Theoretical Physics*, McGraw-Hill, New York, 1953, p. 930.

7. A. Sommerfeld, *Mechanics*, Academic, New York, 1952, p. 227.

8. A. Bohr, *Rotational States of Atomic Nuclei*, Munksgaard, Copenhagen, 1954, Appendix.

9. D. R. Inglis, *Phys. Rev.* **96**, 1059 (1954).

10. N. F. Mott and I. N. Sneddon, *Wave Mechanics and its Applications*, Oxford, New York, 1948, p. 162.

Part Three

CHAPTER XIII

Collective Methods

JEROME K. PERCUS

1. *Introduction*

Classical System. If a strongly coupled system is subjected to a localized perturbation, its response is not localized, but rather system-wide or collective. Indeed, a system obeying linear homogeneous equations of motion decomposes completely into independent system-wide normal modes [1]. In the case of a non-linear classical many-body system of $3N$ degrees of freedom which is spatially bounded, the analogous decomposition is into real (as opposed to complex) action-angle variables [2] $(J_1, \ldots, J_{3N}; \varphi_1, \ldots, \varphi_{3N})$. This canonical set, in the sense of momenta and conjugate coordinates, is specified by the conditions that the J_i be single-valued constants of the motion and the φ_i have the multivaluedness $\Delta \varphi_i = 2\pi n$ of angles. There is not in general a single analytic expression for the $\{J, \varphi\}$ as functions on phase space, since different independent classes of motions or regions in phase space correspond to different $\{J, \varphi\}$ sets; but in each region the $\{J, \varphi\}$ are a legitimate coordinate system, uniquely specifying each phase point. The existence of $3N$ single-valued constants of motion, the action variables, is not to be construed as a violation of Fermi's "theorem" [3] on quasi-ergodicity, which merely shows that these constants will not generally have the same analytic form throughout an isoenergetic surface, and exhibits the singular degenerate solutions for this purpose. Other grounds for disbelief exist, if the use of pathological functions is to be avoided, but we shall uncritically assume the above action-angle structure without further delineating the required functional generality of $\{J, \varphi\}$ for a given system, or the extent to which a "nearby" system is acceptably described in this manner. We adopt the philosophy that the intrinsically

199

complicated systems under consideration can only be solved approx-imately, and if reasonable restrictions on the regularity of the action-angle set then produce no internal inconsistencies — they will still mirror as much physical structure as one could possibly desire.

For time-independent systems, to which we henceforth restrict our attention, the Hamiltonian is a function of the J_i alone, $H(J_1, \ldots, J_{3N})$, and the angular frequencies of the cyclic coordinates φ_i thereby given by $\dot{\varphi}_i = \omega_i$, where $\omega_i = \{\varphi_i, H\} = \partial H/\partial J_i$; here $\{A, B\}$ denotes the classical Poisson bracket $\sum [(\partial A/\partial x_i)(\partial B/\partial p_i) - (\partial A/\partial p_i)(\partial B/\partial x_i)]$. The motion is said to be non-degenerate when the set of ω_i is incommensu-rable — no linear combinations with integer coefficients vanish. Degeneracy due to invariance is omnipresent, but if the invariance is maintained at all stages it causes no trouble, for one is effectively operating in a non-degenerate subspace; we henceforth assume non-degeneracy. When this is the case, the set of J_i is uniquely determined, for continuous changes, to within arbitrary additive constants, $J_i \to J_i + C_i$; the angles are determined to within a gauge trans-formation $\varphi_i' \to \varphi_i + \partial \Lambda(\ldots J_j \ldots)/\partial J_i$. There are, further, the possibilities of discrete changes, these being encompassed by the simultaneous linear transformations $J_i \to \sum a_{ij} J_j$, $\varphi_i \to \sum (a^{-1})_{ij} \varphi_j$, where the a_{ij} are integers of either sign and Det $a = \pm 1$ so that the $(a^{-1})_{ij}$ are also integers. A consequence is that the frequencies are unique to within $\omega_i \to \sum (a^{-1})_{ij} \omega_j$, or more cogently that the set $\{\sum n_i \omega_i\}$ for integers n_i is unique; this set comprises the frequencies present in a multiply periodic Fourier expansion in time of any observable of the system.

Many properties of linear systems have simple analogues. Thus, for any path from an origin in action space, we have

$$H(\ldots J_j \ldots) = H_0 + \int_0^{\{J_i\}} \sum_i \omega_i(\ldots J_j' \ldots) \, dJ_i' \qquad (1)$$

replacing the expression $H = H_0 + \sum \omega_i J_i$ which is valid for a linear system, in which all ω_i are constant. Finally, and importantly, com-plex oscillating variables and momenta may be introduced:

$$q_i = e^{-i\partial \Lambda/\partial J_i} e^{-i\varphi_i} \qquad \pi_i = (J_i - C_i) e^{i\partial \Lambda/\partial J_i} e^{i\varphi_i}$$
$$\{q_i, \pi_j\} = -i\delta_{ij} \qquad \{q_i, q_j\} = \{\pi_i, \pi_j\} = 0 \qquad (2)$$

an i being inserted for convenience into the bracket relations. These quantities satisfy the first-order equations of motion $\dot{q}_i = -i\omega_i q_i$, $\dot{\pi}_i = i\omega_i \pi_i$; Λ and the constants C_i, permitted to be complex, merely mirror the slight non-uniqueness of $\{J, \varphi\}$. If $J_i > 0$, one can also switch to real conjugate oscillating variables: choosing $\xi_i = (\beta_i)^{-1}(2J_i)^{\frac{1}{2}} \sin \varphi_i$, $\eta_i = \beta_i (2J_i)^{\frac{1}{2}} \cos \varphi_i$, β_i a constant, then $\ddot{\xi}_i + \omega_i^2 \xi_i = 0$, $\eta_i = (\beta_i^2/\omega_i)\dot{\xi}_i$, and the Hamiltonian is converted to $H(\ldots, \frac{1}{2}\beta_i^{-2}\eta^2 + \frac{1}{2}\beta_i^2\omega_i^2\xi^2, \ldots)$.

As we have noted, each class of motions has its own action-angle set. An explicit categorization of the types of motion for a dynamical system of many degrees of freedom will not be attempted, but some general remarks are in order. Let us fix the energy, $H = E$. Then, confining our attention to configuration space $(x_1, \ldots, x_{3N})$, it being easier to visualize than phase space, only a certain portion of this space may be reached by the system, e.g., for $H = \sum p_i^2/2m + V(\ldots x_j \ldots)$ a natural bound occurs due to the condition $V(\ldots x_j \ldots) \leq E$. The space then generally decomposes into portions which cannot be connected by trajectories. Further, in each connected component, one can divide up the trajectories into families, no two of which have trajectories infinitesimally near each other (in two dimensions, one family might contain paths, each surrounding a certain point, another family surrounding a different point). Enumeration of a typical member from each family determines the topology (which can be defined quantitatively) and there will be a distinct analytical expression for the $\{J, \varphi\}$ set corresponding to each family. Some visualization is possible if it is realized that, for $H = \sum p_i^2/2m + V = E$, the trajectories are geodesics for a "distance" function $ds^2 = (E-V)\sum dx_i^2$, or equivalently are paths of multidimensional light rays for an index of refraction $n(\ldots x_j \ldots) = (E-V)^{\frac{1}{2}}$; the various families of trajectories are then bounded by caustic surfaces. Now as E is allowed to vary, the action-angle structure of the system can persist only as long as the topological structure of each component is maintained; if, e.g., a prohibited region inside a component disappears as the energy is raised, the analytic form of some (J_i, φ_i) will change, as well as when two previously disconnected regions join up.

Action-Angle Structure. One special circumstance bears elaboration. Many of the systems one wishes to treat are bounded only by virtue of explicit boundary conditions, particularly periodic boundary conditions, which are the mildest form. When the periodic boundaries are identified, configuration space becomes cylindrical for each dimension — a generalized torus; there is then a necessary distinction between those trajectories which continually rotate about a cylinder (the equivalent of unbounded or translational motion) and those which remain localized without such rotation (librational motion), a distinction evidenced in the prototype of a simple pendulum.

In a complicated system, appropriate vehicles for the above characterization are the frequencies ω_i. Let us henceforth restrict our consideration to systems invariant under time reversal: if $\{x_i(t)\}$ is a solution of the equations of motion, then $\{x_i'(t) \equiv x_i(-t)\}$ is too; since $\dot{x}_i'(t) = -\dot{x}_i(-t)$, this will be true if the Lagrangian is invariant under $x \to x$, $\dot{x} \to -\dot{x}$, and consequently if the Hamiltonian is invariant under $T: x \to x, p \to -p$, which we assume. If the $\omega_i[\mathbf{x}(t), \mathbf{p}(t)]$ are the frequencies for a complete connected set of trajectories, $x_i(t) = \sum c_{in_1 \cdots n_{3N}} \exp i \sum n_j \omega_j t$ with suitably limited $c_{in_1 \cdots n_{3N}}$, and the $\bar{\omega}_i[\mathbf{x}'(t), \mathbf{p}'(t)]$ are those for the possibly different set $x_i'(t) = x_i(-t)$, then clearly $\bar{\omega}_i[\mathbf{x}'(t), \mathbf{p}'(t)] = \sum a_{ij}\omega_j[\mathbf{x}(t), \mathbf{p}(t)]$, a linear combination with integral coefficients and Det $a = \pm 1$ so that the inverse has the same form. If the ω_i and $\bar{\omega}_j$ are unrelated, then the ω_i may be redefined so that $\bar{\omega}_i[\mathbf{x}'(t), \mathbf{p}'(t)] = \omega_i[\mathbf{x}(t), \mathbf{p}(t)]$, or, since $\mathbf{p}'(t) = -\mathbf{p}(-t)$ follows from $\dot{\mathbf{x}}'(t) = -\dot{\mathbf{x}}'(-t)$, so that $T\bar{\omega}_i[\mathbf{x}(-t), \mathbf{p}(-t)] = \omega_i[\mathbf{x}(t), \mathbf{p}(t)]$. On the other hand, if each class of trajectories is unchanged under time reversal, then one may select $\bar{\omega}_i[\mathbf{x}(-t), \mathbf{p}(-t)] = \omega_i[\mathbf{x}(t), \mathbf{p}(t)]$; hence $T\omega_i = \sum a_{ij}\omega_j$, but since $T^2 = 1$, one can diagonalize with integral coefficients and so choose the ω_i such that $T\omega = \pm\omega$ for each one. Observing that $TH = H$ and $T\{A, B\} = \{TB, TA\}$, and normalizing the $\{J_i, \varphi_i\}$, it follows that only the two possibilities

$$T\omega_i = -\omega_i \qquad T\varphi_i = \varphi_i \qquad TJ_i = -J_i \qquad (3a)$$

$$T\bar{\omega}_i = \omega_i \qquad T\bar{\varphi}_i = -\varphi_i \qquad TJ_i = J_i \qquad (3b)$$

exist for a given i. In the first case, (3a), including translation or scattering in a periodic system as well as a real rotation, time reversal produces an intrinsically different situation. Since J_i changes sign, the real oscillating pair following (2) cannot be constructed; taking $C_i = A = 0$, the complex oscillating pair (2) consists of individual eigenfunctions of T, with opposite eigenvalues. In the second case, (3b), time reversal conceptually picks up the system at a later time (different for each i) but on the same trajectory as far as J_i is concerned — this includes the case of oscillation or libration. There is here no restriction on the range of J_i, which may be normalized with $J_i \geqq 0$, or if required be split at $J_i = 0$ into two ranges of $J_i \geqq 0$; hence a real oscillating pair may be constructed, or of equal value, the oscillating pair (2) taken as complex conjugates: $q_i = J_i^{\frac{1}{2}} e^{-i\varphi_i}$, $\pi_i = J_i^{\frac{1}{2}} e^{i\varphi_i}$.

To gain some insight into the action-angle structure of a many-body system, we may start with limiting cases and travel inward towards the state desired. Since topological changes must be encountered in the process, this travel can be via a perturbation expansion only if some of the expansion can be summed up in closed form. An obvious limit is that of a free particle system, $H = \sum p_i^2/2m$, bounded by periodic boundary conditions on a cube of side L. The space of constants of motion is generated by $\{\ldots, \mathbf{p}_i, \ldots, x_{i\alpha}/p_{i\alpha}-x_{j\beta}/p_{j\beta}, \ldots\}$, where $\mathbf{x}_i = (x_{i1}\, x_{i2}\, x_{i3})$; sets of $3N$ commuting quantities (in the sense of Poisson brackets) may be chosen in many ways, e.g., $\{\ldots p_i \ldots\}$, or $\{H, \ldots, x_{11}/p_{11}-x_{i\alpha}/p_{i\alpha}, \ldots\}$, but for single-valued action variables, and proper multiplicity of angle variables, only $J_{i\alpha} = (L/2\pi)p_{i\alpha}$, $\varphi_{i\alpha} = (2\pi/L)x_{i\alpha}$ will do. The J_i are unbounded from above and below, the periodic translational motion taking the typical form of an oriented motion or rotation, and J_i changes sign on reversal of orientation or time.

An opposite limiting case is that of strong coupling in a periodic box, very strong two-body interactions producing a deep and narrow N-body potential minimum, or rather $N-1!$ minima, one for each equilibrium particle ordering. The motion in each of the $N-1!$ components consists of small harmonic vibrations, except for free translation of the center of mass which we shall set aside. Now the full set of constants is generated by the $3 \times (N-1)$ individual oscillator energies (single-valued) and their normalized phase differences (infinitely multi-valued in the absence of degeneracy), while the proper action-angle variables are simply the individual energies (divided by frequency) and phases, all librational in constitution. Each J is here non-negative, for the motions are to and fro, not oriented.

Let us create an initial free-particle state for a system with repulsive pair interactions (normalized to zero at large separation) by starting at very high total energy, and then letting the energy drop; as this happens, the possibilities of provisional localization in configuration space increase. An energy interval during which topological changes proliferate rapidly would appear to correspond to a phase transition. For a pure hard sphere system (see Chap. XXIX), there are no topological changes with energy, but rather with mean density, and here too a coalescence of localized structure is evident at a density distinct from that of close packing. With further energy decrease, the species of translational motion are lessened, until at a very low total energy, of the order of the maximum interaction potential (if non-singular), strong coupling sets in for the one-dimensional case, but even later for two or three dimensions. If the same procedure is applied to the case of attractive forces, the large class of provisional two-, and more body bound states, including qualitatively new rotational states in two or three dimensions, enters rapidly as the energy rops or the density increases. The variations with density of attractive and repulsive systems are to a large extent complementary: The interparticle holes of the latter behave much like the particles of the former — another qualitative suggestion of a hard sphere condensation.

A notable characteristic of both limits in the classical many-body problem is the absence of permutation symmetry for the normal modes. One cannot expect total symmetry for each action and angle, since the coordinates and momenta would then not be uniquely determined by the action-angle set. In fact, since the angles are defined only to within a gauge transformation, they need not themselves be symmetric to produce a symmetric formulation. The least symmetric situation is that in strong coupling, where the phase space domains produced by the $N-1$! effectively independent permutations are not even connected to each other. The next level is the free-particle end, in which the phase space domain is unchanged by permutations so that the action-angle set is at least invariant to permutations, although not the individual members. In between, it appears reasonable that, barring singular cases, a sort of ergodicity with respect to permutation is typical, the individual actions being symmetric; this will not hold for the angles, and indeed for either dilute gas or imperfect solid, it will take a very long time for an arbitrary permuted situation to approximately occur.

Quantum System, Classical Statistics. Consider a time-independent quantum mechanical N-body system which is spatially bounded; the form $H = \sum p_i^2/2m + V(x_1 \ldots x_{3N})$ is typical. If all eigenvalues exceed zero, the strongest singularity of the Green's function (kernel of the integral operator representing H^{-1}) will be $G(\mathbf{x}, \mathbf{x}') \sim [\sum_1^{3N} (x_i - x_i')^2]^{-\frac{1}{2}(3N-2)}$; performing the sth iterated convolution, where $s \geq \frac{3}{2}N - 1$, eliminates this singularity. Hence $\int G(\mathbf{x}^{(1)}, \mathbf{x}^{(2)}) G(\mathbf{x}^{(2)}, \mathbf{x}^{(3)}) \ldots G(\mathbf{x}^{(s)}, \mathbf{x}^{(1)}) \, d^{3N} x^{(1)} \ldots d^{3N} x^{(s)} = Tr(H^{-s}) = \sum E^{-s}$ is finite. It follows that the energy spectrum is discrete and cannot even have a point of accumulation. In each region of states which are qualitatively comparable, the energy eigenvalue will then depend upon a number of identifiable discrete indices, $E = E(j_1, \ldots, j_n)$, where matters may be so arranged that each j_i runs over integral multiples of $\hbar$. The Hermitian operators J_i defined by their matrix elements: $\langle j_1 \ldots j_n | J_i | j_1'' \ldots j_n'' \rangle = j_i \, \delta_{j_1 j_1'} \ldots \delta_{j_n j_n'}$ are thus the quantum mechanical analogues of the action variables.

Although the angle variables do not exist in any energy representation, U_i, an analog to $e^{-i\varphi_i}$, may be defined by $\langle j_i | U_i | j_i'' \rangle = \delta_{j_i + \hbar, j_i'}$, with diagonality in the remaining j's; we then find that $[J_i, U_i] = -\hbar U_i$, consistent with the formal relation $U = e^{-i\varphi}$. The U_i are undetermined to within the continuous unitary transformation $U_i \to [\exp iA(\ldots J_j \ldots)/\hbar] U_i$, where $[\exp -iA(\ldots J_j \ldots)/\hbar]$ is the quantum analog of the gauge transformation $\varphi_i \to \varphi_i + \partial A/\partial J_i$, corresponding to a c-number phase change for each wave function. The remaining non-uniqueness includes that of the classical case, although the discrete nature of the spectrum means that the set of frequencies cannot be reduced beyond energy differences, i.e., $\sum n_i \omega_i \to \hbar^{-1}[H(\ldots J_i \ldots) - H(\ldots J_i - n_i \hbar \ldots)]$. There are also many other available discontinuous transformations due to the manifold possibilities for the phrase "region of similar states".

U_i and U_i^* are essentially annihilation and creation operators, generating displacements in the J_i: $U_i|j_i\rangle = |j_i - \hbar\rangle$, $U_i^*|j_i\rangle = |j_i + \hbar\rangle$; they are nearly unitary, for $U_i^* U_i = 1$ except where j_i is at its lowest bound, $U_i U_i^* = 1$ except at an upper bound. It is then easy to construct complex oscillating variables

$$q_i = e^{i\Delta\Lambda/\Delta J_i} U_i \qquad \pi_i = U_i^*(J_i - C_i) e^{-i\Delta\Lambda/\Delta J_i} \qquad (4)$$

where $\quad \Delta\Lambda/\Delta J_i = \hbar^{-1}[\Lambda(\ldots J_j \ldots) - \Lambda(\ldots J_j - \hbar\delta_{ij} \ldots)]$

These satisfy $[q_i, \pi_i] = \hbar$ if either the range of j_i is unbounded from above and below, or unbounded above and bounded by C_i below; in the latter case, they may be chosen as Hermitian conjugates: $q_i = (J_i - C_i)^{\frac{1}{2}} U_i$, $\pi_i = q_i^* = U_i^*(J_i - C_i)^{\frac{1}{2}}$, and Hermitian oscillating coordinates and momenta also constructed, although these are not as useful. q_i and π_i of eq. (4) are appropriate as Bose-type creators and annihilators: $[q_i, \pi_i] = \hbar$, only if j_i has at least a large finite range, which is not always the case in quantum mechanics; it may be noted that if J_i is dichotomic, possessing only the values $j_i = 0, \hbar$, then choosing $C_i = -\hbar$, one has instead $q_i\pi_i + \pi_i q_i = \hbar$. In any event, it follows from (4) and the relation $d/dt = i/\hbar \, [H, \;]$ that $(d/dt)q_i = -iq_i\omega_i$, $(d/dt)\pi_i = i\omega_i\pi_i$, where $\omega_i = \Delta H(\ldots J_j \ldots)/\Delta J_i$ is just the excitation energy operator for an excitation of type i. Now, since all $\Delta j = \hbar$, we have

$$E(j_1 \ldots j_n) = E_0 + \sum_{\{j^0\}}^{\{j\}} \sum_i \omega_i(j_1' \ldots j_n') \Delta j_i' \qquad (5)$$

the summations being over any discrete path from a single excitation above $\{j_k^0\}$ to $\{j_k\}$.

The quantum mechanical division into regions of states of similar structure is not as clear-cut as that in the classical case. In principle, since the number of states is countable, they could be enumerated by a single J, but this is clearly artificial; rather, it often seems reasonable to introduce more than $3N$ action indices for a region of similar states. From the semiclassical point of view, at least two effects contribute. The first is the tunneling effect, which causes two regions of space which are disconnected classically at a given energy to simultaneously contribute to a quantum mechanical state. Hence the semiclassical quantum numbers from both regions are required, and this generalizes at once to classically disconnected sets of trajectories; the effective degrees of freedom may considerably exceed $3N$ in a given region. The second effect is the lack of sharpness of a transition. For instance, the low-energy states of a classical simple pendulum are librational, with a finite range for the action; at a critical energy, a branching takes place into rotational motion with doubly infinite range for the new action variable. Quantum mechanically, the "fuzziness" of the wave function allows no critical energy in the corresponding Mathieu equation; the odd and even nearly degenerate scattering-type wave functions arise smoothly from the low-energy oscillator wave functions, with parity as a most appropriate index. The high-energy wave functions, still sampling the low-energy situation, are in all rigor non-degenerate and cannot be formed into travelling waves; however the energy pairs do coalesce extremely rapidly with greater excitation.

In order to classify the states, or equivalently to pick out suitable action variables, some J_i may be known directly from invariance considerations. A special case of importance is again that of time reversal, now regarded as transforming $x \rightarrow x$, $p \rightarrow -p$ and reversing the order of factors; the behavior of ω_i under this transformation may be defined to produce the same characterization as in (3). Recognition may also be achieved by comparing with various limiting situations. For example, letting $\hbar \rightarrow 0$, the quantum numbers of semiclassical theory [4] may be taken over, or a correspondence may be obtained from a nearly separable system, using a conceptual perturbation process. On the other hand, the many-body problem for $N \rightarrow \infty$ at fixed density is already a limiting situation (with volume as well going to infinity); if one imposes sufficient restrictions on the portion of the bound spectrum (oscillation and real rotation both included) being considered, it remains unchanged in this limit, in contrast to the increasingly dense energy spectrum of the scattering states. In the continuous limit, the scattering states involve factors $(E-H+i\varepsilon)^{-1}$ and are often identifiable as such [5]. Moreover, the range of J is generally either infinite, as is the energy range, for a scattering sequence as $N \rightarrow \infty$, or of very small range, while the various bound motions evince moderate finite ranges of J and merge into each other, being separated with some degree of arbitrariness. For very long-range binding (Coulomb, harmonic oscillator), a finite range is not present. A point J_i^{max} of branching or demarcation for J_i will usually be a function of the other J's and not a fixed constant; it is then often convenient to use oscillating variables which are not canonically conjugate, but which express the action simply and whose commutation rules do not break down at special states, e.g., in the elementary case of rotation, if $L_\pm = L_x \pm L_y$, then $[L_+, L_-]_+ = 2(L^2 - L_z^2)$ while $[L_+, L_-] = 2\hbar L_z$.

For quantum mechanical systems involving non-classical observables such as internal spin, the energy E must utilize additional discrete indices of finite range, whose identification is generally straightforward. When the index is dichotomic, as we have seen, anti-commutation relations are suitable; a realization of the motion of the oscillating variables is that of $\sigma_x \pm i\sigma_y$ for a spin $\frac{1}{2}$ rotator: $\dot{\boldsymbol{\sigma}} = \boldsymbol{\sigma} \times \mathbf{F}$. Of course, indices for spin waves will not be restricted to spin $\frac{1}{2}$.

Quantum Statistics. The full set of eigenfunctions of a symmetric Hamiltonian may be chosen to belong to irreducible representations of the permutation group. The physically significant symmetric (Einstein-Bose) and antisymmetric (Fermi-Dirac) wave functions (expectations being unchanged by particle permutation) belong to the two one-dimensional representations. Since symmetrization then annihilates all wave functions but the symmetric ones, and similarly for antisymmetrization, very few of the full set of wave functions, and correspondingly of the energy eigenvalues, appear in Einstein-Bose or Fermi-Dirac systems. This means that an energy parametrization $H(\ldots J_i \ldots)$ valid for arbitrary (Maxwell-Boltzmann) statistics will be inappropriate for quantum statistics, since the allowed values of the J's will have large gaps. There is however a simple characterization of the relevant J_i, U_i for quantum statistics: they may be chosen as completely symmetric; the reason of course is that if $J\psi_j = j\psi_j$, $U\psi_j = \psi_{j-h}$, where ψ_j is either symmetric or anti-symmetric, then if J and U are symmetrized, precisely the same relations obtain. U will also produce chains of non-symmetric states, but we are not concerned with these, only with sequences arising from a symmetric or antisymmetric ground state.

To indicate typical forms for the action variables, we again spe-

ialize to the zero coupling and strong coupling limits. Consider a
ree spinless Einstein-Bose system. In this case, classically described
by the pure translational motion associated with individual momenta,
ndistinguishability of particles compels the use of a different sequence
or enumerating states on the Maxwell-Boltzmann grid and produces
he effect of successive excitations of an oscillator. Since there are at
most $3N$ distinct one-body momenta present in any given state, say
he $\{\mathbf{k}_\alpha\}$, one possibility is to list the $\{\mathbf{k}_\alpha\}$ together with the occupation
numbers $\{n_{\mathbf{k}_\alpha}\}$, with the restriction $\sum n_{\mathbf{k}_\alpha} = 3N$; the different sets
$\{\mathbf{k}_\alpha\}$ are here all topologically disconnected. The use of an infinite
number of action variables is far more convenient: consider all $\mathbf{k}$
except $\mathbf{k} = 0$ and choose the set $\{n_\mathbf{k}\}$ of occupation numbers as
actions; they are infinite in number and satisfy only $\sum n_\mathbf{k} \leqq 3N$.
The interpretation is that of excitation from the ground state particle
sea in which all particles are at $\mathbf{k} = 0$ and is appropriate principally
below the Einstein-Bose condensation. Explicitly, one then has
$J_\mathbf{k} = \hbar \sum \delta(\mathbf{p}_i - \hbar\mathbf{k})$, using Kronecker δ functions, and $U_\mathbf{k}^*$
$= J_\mathbf{k}^{-\frac{1}{2}} \sum e^{i\mathbf{k} \cdot \mathbf{x}_i} \delta(\mathbf{p}_i) J_0^{-\frac{1}{2}}$; conjugate canonical oscillating variables $q_\mathbf{k}^* = \sum e^{i\mathbf{k} \cdot \mathbf{x}_i} \delta(\mathbf{p}_i) J_0^{-\frac{1}{2}}$ and $q_\mathbf{k}$ can also be defined, but to
avoid denominators, it may be better to employ $\bar{q}_\mathbf{k}^* = \sum e^{i\mathbf{k} \cdot \mathbf{x}_i} \delta(\mathbf{p}_i)$
which still oscillates with $\hbar\omega_k = \hbar^2 k^2/2m$ but whose non-zero com-
mutators are given by $[\bar{q}_\mathbf{k}, \bar{q}_\mathbf{k}^*] = J_0 - J_\mathbf{k}$. The foregoing (which is
also applicable to classical states) simplifies materially in the notation
of second quantization:
$$J_\mathbf{k} = \hbar a_\mathbf{k}^* a_\mathbf{k}, \quad U_\mathbf{k}^* = (a_\mathbf{k}^* a_\mathbf{k})^{-\frac{1}{2}} a_\mathbf{k}^* a_0 (a_0^* a_0)^{-\frac{1}{2}}, \quad q_\mathbf{k}^* = a_\mathbf{k}^* a_0 (a_0^* a_0)^{-\frac{1}{2}}, \quad \bar{q}_\mathbf{k}^* = a_\mathbf{k}^* a_0.$$
Of course, one can then take advantage of indefinite particle number
and choose the non-particle-conserving $J_\mathbf{k} = \hbar a_\mathbf{k}^* a_\mathbf{k}$, $U_\mathbf{k}^* = (a_\mathbf{k}^* a_\mathbf{k})^{-\frac{1}{2}} a_\mathbf{k}^*$,
$\dot{}_\mathbf{k}^* = a_\mathbf{k}^*$ for all $\mathbf{k}$. In general, the restriction on the $n_\mathbf{k}$ need not be
specifically applied, for any wave function to which the $U_\mathbf{k}^*$ are
applied too many times simply vanishes.

At the other extreme, in strong coupling, a first quantized symmetric state is fully characterized by symmetrization of a localized
state in which each particle is near its equilibrium point (or more
accurately, each interparticle distance near its equilibrium value).
At fixed wave number and longitudinal or transverse character, the
symmetrized mode energy (divided by frequency) is here a suitable
action, but its explicit operator form is complicated. One notes that

there are now $3\mathcal{N}$ action variables of semi-infinite range (although only in the limit can the strong coupling harmonic oscillator wall rise to infinity to permit this), vastly different from the infinite number of finite ranges in the zero coupling case. There are nonetheless at least two obvious connections between the two ends. First, one cannot in strong coupling distinguish a wave vector $\mathbf{k}$ from the set of $\mathbf{k}$'s which may be reached from it by an Umklapp process (i.e., are the same modulo reciprocal vectors for a unit cell in the lattice of strong coupling equilibrium positions). Thus, the semi-infinite range of action is distributed among infinitely many $\mathbf{k}$'s, and infinitely many combinations may be produced as the coupling is weakened, each responsible for only a finite range of action. Second, the longitudinal modes for strong coupling with a long-range force may be written as $\sum e^{i\mathbf{k}\cdot\mathbf{x}_i}$, but in second quantization this becomes $\sum a_{\mathbf{k}+1}^{*}\, a_1$, and restricting to a (condensed) system with most particles at $\mathbf{k} = 0$, reduces to $a_{\mathbf{k}}^{*}\, a_0 + a_0^{*}\, a_{-\mathbf{k}}$. Due to the degeneracy of $\mathbf{k}$ and $-\mathbf{k}$, this is indeed an oscillating coordinate in the weak coupling limit.

For a Fermi-Dirac system, the problem of spin arises, but we shall imagine this as subsumed in the momentum index. Moreover, the very low density of states ($k_1 < k_2 < \ldots$ for free particles compared to $k_1 \leqq k_2 \leqq k_3 \ldots$ in the Einstein-Bose case) produces involved boundary relations among the J's, resulting in a complicated explicit form for the U's. An extended approach which becomes valuable and feasible is then to work with "angles" which are not fully independent. Now all excitations may be described by complex oscillating variables; conversely, suppose that a commuting (even this is not crucial) set $\{q_\alpha^{*}\}$ has been determined, satisfying

$$dq_\alpha^{*}/dt = iq_\alpha^{*}\,\omega_\alpha \tag{6}$$

where the ω_α are non-vanishing constants of the motion. Thus $(i/\hbar)[H, q_\alpha^{*}] = iq_\alpha^{*}\omega_\alpha$, or $Hq_\alpha^{*} = q_\alpha^{*}(H+\hbar\omega_\alpha)$; assuming non-degeneracy and applying this to an eigenfunction ψ, $H(q_\alpha^{*}\,\psi) = [E+\hbar\omega_\alpha(E)]q_\alpha^{*}\,\psi$, so that q_α acts as a creator, producing a new eigenfunction with excitation energy $\hbar\omega_\alpha(E)$. (With degeneracy, the state sequence must be chosen to diagonalize each ω_α.) Further, since $dq_\alpha/dt = -i\omega_\alpha q_\alpha$, we see that $q_\alpha^{*}q_\alpha$ is a constant of the motion — measuring the strength of excitation of q_α^{*} — and hence that $q_\alpha^{*}(q_\alpha\,\psi) = \lambda\psi$, informing us that q_α is an annihilator as well. The set $\{q_\alpha, q_\alpha^*\}$, q_α commuting with q_β, q_α^* with q_β^*, but not necessarily q_α with q_β^*, may be termed complete if it is so extensive that only c numbers commute with all of its members. Under this condition, it is possible to get from an arbitrary state to any other via the q_α, q_α^*, and the action of the $\{q_\alpha, q_\alpha^*\}$ completely determines a state. This information is sufficient for many purposes.

To obtain further detail, the nearly unitary $U_\alpha^* = q_\alpha^*(q_\alpha q_\alpha^*)^{-\frac{1}{2}}$ and U_α may be constructed, U_α^* not necessarily commuting with U_β for $\beta \neq \alpha$ (as with "quasi coordinates" [6] in classical mechanics), and these joined by a complete but not necessarily independent commuting set of constants of the motion J_i; since $[U_\alpha, J_i]$ satisfies the same equation of motion as U_α, then $[U_\alpha, J_i] = d_{i\alpha} U$ for some constants of the motion $d_{i\alpha}$. If this has been done, the relation $U_\alpha \omega_\alpha = (i/\hbar)[U_\alpha, H(\ldots J_i \ldots)] = (i/\hbar)U_\alpha[H(\ldots J_i \ldots) - H(\ldots J_i - d_{i\alpha} \ldots)]$ or $H(\ldots J_i \ldots) = H(\ldots J_i - d_{i\alpha} \ldots) + \hbar\omega_\alpha$ both determines say, $H(\ldots J_i \ldots) - H(\ldots 0 \ldots)$ as a function of the J's and, by consistency, picks out the connections between the J_i. To find the ground state energy $E_0 = H(\ldots 0 \ldots)$, a c number, it is only necessary to compute $H - [H(\ldots J_i \ldots) - E_0]$ by transcribing back to phase and spin space $(\ldots \mathbf{x}_i \, \mathbf{p}_i \, s_i \ldots)$. Finally, in the special case that a subset of the q_α has the property that U_α does commute with all other U_β^*, but that no U_α can be expanded as a product of other U_β, U_β^*, then the subset may be termed independent, and its creators $\prod U_\alpha^{*n_\alpha}$ produce a wide swath of states which may be indexed by $n_\alpha = j_\alpha/\hbar$. In fact, a number of independent sets can be found which convert one given state to another.

The above extension has clearly been guided by the example of a free Fermi-Dirac system, to which application is now immediate. If $\mathbf{k}$ denotes a one-body state outside the ground state Fermi sea, $\mathbf{l}$ inside, and $M_{\mathbf{kl}}$ takes the spin state of $\mathbf{l}$ into that of $\mathbf{k}$, then the $q_{\mathbf{kl}} = \sum e^{i(\mathbf{k}-\mathbf{l}) \cdot \mathbf{x}_i} \delta(\mathbf{p}_i - \hbar\mathbf{l}) M_{\mathbf{kl}}(i)$, or $a_{\mathbf{k}}^* a_{\mathbf{l}}$ in second quantized notation, represent particle-hole excitations and oscillate with $\omega_{\mathbf{kl}} = (\hbar/2m)(l^2 - k^2)$. Here indeed $U_{\mathbf{kl}} = q_{\mathbf{kl}}$, and these are complete, the $U_{\mathbf{kl}}^*$ alone generating any state from the ground state. If one defines $J_{\mathbf{m}} = \hbar a_{\mathbf{m}}^* a_{\mathbf{m}} = \hbar \sum \delta(\mathbf{p}_i - \hbar\mathbf{m}) M_{\mathbf{mm}}(i)$, then $[U_{\mathbf{kl}}, J_{\mathbf{m}}] = \hbar(\delta_{\mathbf{lm}} - \delta_{\mathbf{km}})U_{\mathbf{kl}}$, while $H - E_0 = \sum (\hbar^2 k^2/2m) J_{\mathbf{k}}$. Further, the largest independent subsets of $\{q_{kl}, q_{kl}^*\}$ are readily characterized: each $\mathbf{k}$ and each $\mathbf{l}$ occurs in precisely one q_{kl}. The difficulty of using a "standard" action-angle formulation is clear: Independent sets can be constructed so as to produce disjoint state sequences only in a non-symmetric fashion, and the resulting decomposition has no physical basis; for any index $\mathbf{k}, \mathbf{l}$, the combinations of U_{kl} and U_{kl}^* can act only on four states, all of which are on the boundary and must be treated specially. Very similar comments apply to the highly excited or non-condensed Einstein-Bose systems, in which the absence of $\mathbf{l} = 0$ states causes the independent oscillating set $\{a_k^* a_0 (a_0^* a_0)^{-\frac{1}{2}}, (a_0^* a_0)^{-\frac{1}{2}} a_k^* a_0\}$ to hit the boundary too often. The extended action-angle formulation is appropriate here as well, as it is indeed whenever the relevant states should properly be described as free translation or scattering rather than collective or bound. The condensed Einstein-Bose system, it is noted, fits into the latter category, for the $\mathbf{k} = 0$ sea extracts and amplifies any long-range variation.

Of course, it is possible to utilize the high degeneracy of the free-particle Fermi-Dirac system and construct oscillating variables such as $q_{k\mu\lambda} = \sum e^{i\lambda \cdot \mathbf{l}} a_{k+l}^* a_l$ summed over all $\mathbf{l}$ satisfying $\mathbf{l} \cdot \mathbf{k} = \mu$, which may be highly excited. But in the absence of more direct motivation, this seems artificial. On the other hand, one may again take advantage of the indefinite particle number in second quantization to choose a_k and a_k^* as oscillating coordinates as well as annihilators and creators and $J_k = \hbar a_k^* a_k$; the canonical commutation relations now employ anti-commutators, but this introduces no essential difficulties and produces a superior description in many respects.

The comments on Einstein-Bose strong coupling have direct analogues in the Fermi-Dirac case. However, the (nearly) indefinitely excitable modes $\sum e^{i\mathbf{k} \cdot \mathbf{x}_i}$ bear little relation to the zero coupling particle-hole excitations and it is not clear that they can be extended that far. This suggests that both types of excitation are required in the intermediate domain, a matter which will be examined more closely in Sec. 2.

Summary. There exist then in a very real sense oscillating variables, travelling wave in form, which completely describe classical and quantum mechanical systems in each region of qualitatively similar states. Intrinsically collective states may be represented by independent pairs of real or complex conjugate oscillating coordinates. Scattering states may, by virtue of quantum statistics, also be described collectively and oscillating coordinates introduced in the event of periodic boundary conditions; especially in Fermi-Dirac systems, they may be far from independent. Unlike linear systems with pure coordinate potentials, in which the real oscillating variables (as distinguished from the canonical momenta) may be taken as functions of the original configuration coordinates (i.e., only a point transformation is required), the real oscillating coordinates for a general system will be complicated functions of coordinates, momenta, spin variables, etc. The computation of any of these but trivial ones, in the absence of physical motivation, is of the same order of difficulty as the solution of the complete problem.

However, if one has physical (if need be, only empirical) evidence as to the approximate form of the independent oscillations of a system, a transformation to these modes as generalized coordinates should exhibit the residual behavior in a fashion suitable for standard approximation procedures. Alternatively, if only some of the modes are predicted, then it should be possible to extract or subtract their nearly independent behavior in some rational manner. Part Three of this book deals with problems of this nature. It will be noted that, concomitant with the practical limits on detailed physical intuition, the approximate collective variables will, despite the ultimate inadequacy of the form, very often be functions of the original configuration coordinates alone.

2. Transformation to collective variables

Mode Analysis. Let us consider a domain of states for which a single analytic form of symmetric action-angle variables $(J_1, \ldots, J_n; U_1, \ldots, U_n)$ is valid. There may be many more than $3N$ allowed modes (since the characteristic J, U commutation relations, unlike the classical J, φ relations, can hold even on a discrete space of as few points as the number of pairs), but most of these belong to the intrinsically non-collective scattering states and will be deemphasized. If interest is centered upon a single pair, say $J_1 U_1$, at a time, the now separable Hamiltonian $H = H(J_1, \ldots, J_n)$ may be written in the form

$$H = H(0, J_2, \ldots, J_n) + \{[H(J_1, \ldots, J_n) - H(0, J_2, \ldots, J_n)]/J_1\}J_1 \quad (7)$$

a J_1-independent constant of the motion plus $\Omega_1 J_1$ where Ω_1 is a state-dependent frequency. If a separation into components allocated to all non-scattering pairs is desired, there is no unique form, as indicated by the path-dependent eq. (5). A convenient possibility is

$$H = [H(J_1, \ldots, J_n) - \sum_1^s \omega_i J_i] + \sum_1^s \omega_i J_i \quad (8)$$

in which the first term would be independent of $J_1, \ldots, J_s$ if the ω_i were as well; approximational methods will in general choose their own preferred decompositions. There is, as we have seen, no compelling reason to seek a similar form for scattering modes (which of course can contribute significantly to total energy even when unexcited); these should rather be treated on a more dynamical basis.

For large-scale atomic, ionic, or molecular fluids, one is interested to a considerable extent in systems for which the Hamiltonian commutes with the total momentum $\mathbf{P} = \sum \mathbf{p}_i$. It may then be assumed without loss of generality that all states are eigenstates of $\mathbf{P}$: $\mathbf{P}\psi_{j_1 \cdots j_n} = \mathbf{P}(j_1 \cdots j_n)\psi_{j_1 \cdots j_n}$, and it follows that, with the notation of (4),

$$\begin{aligned} \mathbf{P}U_i^* - U_i^*\mathbf{P} &= \hbar(\Delta\mathbf{P}/\Delta J_i)\,U_i^* \\ \mathbf{P}J_i - J_i\mathbf{P} &= 0 \end{aligned} \quad (9)$$

where $\Delta\mathbf{P}/\Delta J$ is necessarily a wave vector for the periodic box the system is assumed to reside in. Since the chains of states defining the U_i^* are not infinite anyway, they may certainly be chosen such that for each U_i^*, $\Delta\mathbf{P}/\Delta J = \mathbf{k}$ is fixed. Thus, each U^* is characterized by an excitation wave vector $\mathbf{k}$, and eq. (9) becomes

$$(\hbar/i) \sum_s \partial U^*/\partial x_{s\alpha} = \hbar k_\alpha U^* \quad (10)$$

solved at once in the form (if it converges)

$$\begin{aligned} U^* &= \sum_s e^{i\mathbf{k}\cdot\mathbf{x}_s} f_{\mathbf{k}s}(\cdots \mathbf{p}_i \cdots) \\ &\quad + \sum_{s_1, s_2, \mathbf{k}_1 + \mathbf{k}_2 = \mathbf{k}} e^{i\mathbf{k}_1\cdot\mathbf{x}_{s1}} e^{i\mathbf{k}_2\cdot\mathbf{x}_{s2}} f_{\mathbf{k}_1 \mathbf{k}_2 s_1 s_2}(\cdots \mathbf{p}_i \cdots) + \cdots \end{aligned} \quad (11)$$

On the other hand, each J_i commutes with $\mathbf{P}$, so that J satisfies (11) with $\mathbf{k} = 0$; an oscillating variable q_i of eq. (4) is clearly of the form (11), while π_i is characterized by $-\mathbf{k}$.

Generalization of (11) to second quantized form is direct. One obtains two types of creators, $a_{\mathbf{k}}^* + \sum f_{\mathbf{lm}} a_{\mathbf{k+l+m}}^* a_l a_m + \ldots$ and $\sum f_l a_{\mathbf{k+l}}^* a_l + \sum f_{\mathbf{lmns}} a_{\mathbf{k+n+s}}^* a_{\mathbf{l-n}}^* a_{\mathbf{m-s}}^* a_l a_m + \ldots$, which may be allocated to scattering and collective modes. We shall not however at this time take advantage of such an approach.

Without attempting extreme generality, we shall consider the spin-independent quantum mechanical Hamiltonian

$$H = \sum_1^N p_i^2/2m + V(\mathbf{x}_1, \ldots, \mathbf{x}_N) \tag{12}$$

where, for (11) to be valid, V is translation-invariant. Further, since the collective modes which then occur are little affected in form by slight vagaries of the potential, V will be taken as nonsingular and generally well-behaved. Possible treatments include: simultaneous determination of a few action-angle pairs, with constants evaluated on the basis of some knowledge of the residual Hamiltonian; determination of the complete set of oscillating variables directly from the equations of motion, with absolute energies obtained by indirection; point transformation to $6N$ collective oscillating coordinates and momenta, with state-dependent coefficients accounting for any additional indices; and direct dynamical determination of individual action-angle pairs, with absolute energies again obtained by indirection.

Single Oscillating Mode. We first investigate the possible existence of approximate momentum-independent oscillating variables. Equation (11) informs us of what to expect: functions of the $\sum_s e^{i\mathbf{l}\cdot\mathbf{x}_s}$, with each term having the same fixed total wave vector $\mathbf{k}$. If consideration is limited at this time to a single pair of oscillating variables q, π, they will perforce be real, and hence a relation such as $J = \pi q$ emanating from (4) is replaced by one of the form $J = (\pi + i\gamma q)(\pi - i\gamma q)/2\gamma = (\pi^2 + \gamma^2 q^2 - \hbar\gamma)/2\gamma$ for some c number γ; q and π, being real, are now taken to satisfy $[\pi, q] = \hbar/i$. Thus, with respect to the pair q, π, the Hamiltonian (7) appears as

$$H = H_0 + (1/2M)\pi^2 + (K/2)q^2 \tag{13}$$

where H_0, M and K are constants of the motion with the property that MK is a c number; the analogue of eq. (11) in this case contains terms of both $\pm$ **k**. Let us not at first make use of periodic boundary conditions or translation invariance and simply require, following Tomonaga [7], that

$$q = q(\mathbf{x}_1, \ldots, \mathbf{x}_N) \tag{14}$$

a pure coordinate function; the conjugate momentum must then have the form (dropping any additive coordinate function)

$$\pi = \tfrac{1}{2} \sum [\mathbf{g}_j(\ldots \mathbf{x}_i \ldots) \cdot \mathbf{p}_j + \mathbf{p}_j \cdot \mathbf{g}_j(\ldots \mathbf{x}_i \ldots)] \tag{15a}$$

$$\text{where} \quad \sum \mathbf{g}_j \cdot \nabla_j q = 1 \tag{15b}$$

If the Hamiltonian indeed decomposes as in eq. (13), our task is to determine the coefficients M, K. Of course, the limited form of (14), (15) is insufficient for an exact decomposition of the type desired: q and π may enter in other terms, and the coefficients may not be constants of the motion. An optimal representation is obtained by rewriting the Hamiltonian so that it has the form (13), plus some undesirable terms; q and the $\mathbf{g}_i$ are then chosen to annul the undesirable terms, while the remaining coefficients are converted to constants of the motion by averaging over the state of the system. Such a rewriting is far from unique; roughly, the more terms which can be annulled, the closer the remaining coefficients are to true constants of the motion. Since a large number of terms can be annulled only approximately or on the average, one must strike a balance between the averaging required to convert such terms to zero and the coefficients M^{-1}, K to constants.

If all oscillating coordinates were of the form (14), we would have a general point transformation, under which of course the quadratic kinetic energy would remain quadratic in the full set of momenta. Thus, we cannot reasonably avoid both π and π^2 terms in H; on the other hand, we shall insist that only q^2 occur. Hence the form (13) is replaced by

$$H = H_0 + \tfrac{1}{2}(\pi\alpha + \alpha^* \pi) + \tfrac{1}{2}\pi M^{-1}\pi + \tfrac{1}{2}qKq \tag{16}$$

and we must assure the vanishing of α and constancy of H_0, M, K.

To determine these coefficients, we employ the identity

$$H(q, \pi) = [H - \tfrac{1}{2}\pi H'_\pi - \tfrac{1}{2}H'_\pi \pi + \tfrac{1}{2}\pi H''_{\pi\pi}\pi - \tfrac{1}{2}qH''_{qq}q]$$
$$+ \tfrac{1}{2}\pi[H'_\pi - H''_{\pi\pi}\pi] + \tfrac{1}{2}[H'_\pi - \pi H''_{\pi\pi}] + \tfrac{1}{2}\pi[H''_{\pi\pi}]\pi + \tfrac{1}{2}q[H''_{qq}]q \quad (17)$$

the bracketed quantities being Taylor series for $H(0, 0)$, $H'_\pi(0, 0)$, . . .
when the complete q, π dependence of H is truly given by (16), in
which case they would reduce to constants with respect to q, π.
Since $H'_\pi = (i/\hbar)[H, q]$, $H''_{\pi\pi} = (i/\hbar)^2[q, [q, H]]$, $H''_{qq} = (i/\hbar)^2[\pi, [\pi, H]]$,
we see on inserting (12) into (17) that the form (15) is achieved by
choosing

$$\alpha = \tfrac{1}{2}\sum[(\nabla_i q/m - \mathbf{g}_i/M)\cdot\mathbf{p}_i + \mathbf{p}_i\cdot(\nabla_i q/m - \mathbf{g}_i/M) + \tfrac{1}{2}(\hbar/i)\mathbf{g}_i\cdot\nabla_i(1/M)]$$
$$m/M = \sum\nabla_i q\cdot\nabla_i q$$
$$K = \sum(\mathbf{g}_i\cdot\nabla_i)(\mathbf{g}_j\cdot\nabla_j)V(\mathbf{x}_1, \ldots, \mathbf{x}_N) + (i/\hbar)^2[\pi, [\pi, \sum p_j^2/2m]] \quad (18)$$
$$H_0 = H - \tfrac{1}{2}(\pi\alpha + \alpha^*\pi) - \tfrac{1}{2}\pi M^{-1}\pi - \tfrac{1}{2}qKq$$

Now we wish to arrange matters, by choice of the functions $q, \mathbf{g}_i$,
such that $\alpha = 0$ and K, M, H_0 are diagonal on the eigenstates as
closely as possible, as well as satisfying eq. (15b). Physical considerations dictate a possible form for the $\mathbf{g}_i$. Suppose in particular
that there exists a macroscopic standing wave material velocity
distribution $K(t)\,\mathbf{u}(\mathbf{x})$; conservation of matter then implies $\partial\rho(\mathbf{x}, t)/\partial t$
$= -K(t)\nabla\cdot[\mathbf{u}(\mathbf{x})\rho(\mathbf{x}, t)]$, or using the microscopic representation
$\rho = m\sum\delta(\mathbf{x} - \mathbf{x}_i)$, one has

$$\partial\rho/\partial t = K(t)\sum\mathbf{u}(\mathbf{x}_i)\cdot\nabla_i\rho \quad (19)$$

On the other hand, if the motion of ρ is due to the independent
oscillation of the collective variable $q(t)$, then (without regard to
order of factors) $\partial\rho/\partial t = \dot{q}(\partial\rho/\partial q) = (i/\hbar)\dot{q}[\pi, \rho]$, or

$$\partial\rho/\partial t = \dot{q}\sum\mathbf{g}_i\cdot\nabla_i\rho \quad (20)$$

Thus, a collective momentum π corresponding to excitation of the
velocity distribution $\mathbf{u}(\mathbf{x})$ may be defined by choosing

$$\mathbf{g}_i = \mathbf{u}(\mathbf{x}_i) \quad (21)$$

If α, of eq. (18), is to vanish, we must then certainly have $\nabla_i q$
$= (m/M)\,\mathbf{u}(\mathbf{x}_i)$. But M, a coordinate function alone, can be a constant

of the motion only if it is a pure constant. We conclude at once that $\mathbf{u}$ has a velocity potential, and that q is a simple sum:

$$\mathbf{u}(\mathbf{x}) = \nabla\varphi(\mathbf{x})$$
$$q = (m/M) \sum \varphi(\mathbf{x}_i) \tag{22}$$

By virtue of (22), relations (18) for (m/M), and (15b) are identical:

$$M = m \sum \nabla\varphi(\mathbf{x}_i) \cdot \nabla\varphi(\mathbf{x}_i)$$

Clearly M is not a constant, but nonetheless, to the extent that the $\mathbf{x}_i$ are not highly correlated (the excitation amplitude is not very large), the deviation of M from its expectation $mN\langle\nabla\varphi(x_i) \cdot \nabla\varphi(x_i)\rangle$ will have relative order $N^{-\frac{1}{2}}$ and may be neglected. Note that since even the approximate vanishing of α depends on the velocity $\mathbf{u}$ being irrotational, a rotational collective coordinate will generally have non-vanishing α (and so non-vanishing mean momentum $\langle\pi\rangle$); this is to be expected, for J is not positive in such a case and H cannot be put in the form of (13).

Conditions for the near diagonality of K and H_0 are not readily established, but if q, π does represent an independent physical oscillation(individual particle modes being, e.g., of high enough energy for them to stay unexcited), we may justifiably take mean values; thus the q, π (collective) part of the Hamiltonian now becomes

$$H_{\text{coll}} = \pi^2/(2mN\langle\nabla_i\varphi_i \cdot \nabla_i\varphi_i\rangle) + \tfrac{1}{2}\langle(\sum \nabla_i\varphi_i \cdot \nabla_i)^2 V$$
$$- [\pi,[\pi, \sum p_i^2/2m\hbar^2]]\rangle q^2 \tag{24}$$

For example, a fluid of compressibility κ, density ρ_0, will support a small amplitude velocity potential determined by $\nabla^2\varphi - (\kappa\rho_0)\partial^2\varphi/\partial t^2 = 0$ (κ, ρ_0 are assumed to vary slowly compared to any relevant wave length); hence for a uniform system, dropping the time factor, we may investigate the excitation $\varphi = (2^{\frac{1}{2}}/Nk^2) \sin \mathbf{k} \cdot \mathbf{x}$ for some $\mathbf{k}$. Specializing to the case $V = \sum_{i>j} V(\mathbf{x}_i - \mathbf{x}_j)$, and inserting it into (24), regarding the $\mathbf{x}_i$ as independent and uniformly distributed (valid for sufficiently small $\mathbf{k}$), so that summations over $\mathbf{x}_i$ may be replaced by integrations over $\mathbf{x}$, we have $\langle(\sum \nabla\varphi_i \cdot \nabla_i)^2 V\rangle = \langle V \sum \nabla_i \cdot (\nabla\varphi_i\nabla_j \cdot \nabla\varphi_j)\rangle = \tfrac{1}{2}\langle \sum_{r\neq s} V_{rs}[\sum \nabla \cdot (\nabla\varphi_i\nabla^2\varphi_i) + \sum_{i\neq j} \nabla^2\varphi_i\nabla^2\varphi_j]\rangle = N(N-1)$ $\langle V(\mathbf{x}_i - \mathbf{x}_j)\nabla^2\varphi_i\nabla^2\varphi_j\rangle$; similarly, computing $[\pi,[\pi, p_i^2]]$ by using

$\langle \exp\left(\pm\ 2i\mathbf{k}\cdot\mathbf{x}_i\right)f(\mathbf{p}_i)\rangle = 0$, we readily obtain

$$q = 2^{\frac{1}{2}}\sum\sin\mathbf{k}\cdot\mathbf{x}_i$$

$$H_{\mathrm{coll}} = (Nk^2/2m)\pi^2 + \tfrac{1}{2}[V_{\mathbf{k}} + (\hbar^2 k^2/4mN) + (3/mNk^2)\langle(\mathbf{k}\cdot\mathbf{p}_i)^2\rangle]q^2 \tag{25}$$

$$\omega = [(Nk^2 V_{\mathbf{k}}/m) + (\hbar k^2/2m)^2 + (3/m^2)\langle(\mathbf{k}\cdot\mathbf{p}_i)^2\rangle]^{\frac{1}{2}}$$

which conforms with the prediction of (11) and is in agreement, at low $\mathbf{k}$ with the familiar result of Bogoliubov [8]. Here $V_{\mathbf{k}} = (1/\Omega)\int V(\mathbf{x})\exp i\mathbf{k}\cdot\mathbf{x}\,d^3x$ is the kth Fourier component of V. In the special case of Coulomb forces in a neutral system, $V(\mathbf{x}) = e^2/r - (e^2/r)_{\mathrm{av}}$, $\Omega V_{\mathbf{k}} = 4\pi e^2/k^2$, and $\omega = (4\pi ne^2/m)^{\frac{1}{2}}$ at low $\mathbf{k}$ is the usual plasma frequency.

Multiple Mode Decomposition. The above procedure may be used with only slight modification to simultaneously extract a number of normal modes. Indeed one may hope at least to approximately obtain the complete action-angle structure in this fashion if one has some idea of what it looks like. As we have mentioned, a complete independent mode decomposition is inherently unsuitable for scattering states, as in a Fermi-Dirac system; this suggests the use of the equations of motion to determine the oscillating modes, a strategy which we now pursue. The major task is still to secure a sufficiently general form for the oscillating variables.

Now the result (25) is not appropriate for high $\mathbf{k}$, formally because its "constant" coefficients fluctuate too much, and physically because density oscillations cannot propagate in the vicinity of interparticle wave numbers. Thus, only a fraction of $3N$ of the coordinates can literally oscillate independently; the remaining modes vary descriptively from transverse in the strong coupling limit to scattering in weak coupling. While the construction of a transverse coordinate function is difficult precisely because fine details of local behavior must be sampled [9], transverse momenta are readily found, e.g., $\sum e^{i\mathbf{k}\cdot\mathbf{x}_i}\mathbf{k}\times\mathbf{p}_i$ performs a transverse displacement at wave vector $\mathbf{k}$. On the other hand, we have already observed that the free translation or scattering modes at zero coupling have the form $\sum e^{i\mathbf{k}\cdot\mathbf{x}_i}\delta(\mathbf{p}_i - \hbar\mathbf{l})$. The common denominator is clear. The pure coordinate functions (22) must be generalized for translation-invariant systems to the form

$$\zeta^* = \sum_i e^{i\mathbf{k}\cdot\mathbf{x}_i} f(\mathbf{p}_i) \tag{26}$$

Equation (26) also includes the momenta of (15), (21) and in fact according to (11) is the most general possible one-body sum; it will be taken as the canonical form for the oscillating variables. In general, for spin $\frac{1}{2}$ particles but spin-independent Hamiltonian, $f(\mathbf{p}_i)$ could have the spin dependence $S_i = 1$ or $\sigma_x(i)$ — that is, either no spin change or spin flip. However, the two classes have identical dynamical properties, and to obtain the characteristics of ground state and single excitations, we may restrict our attention to spin-conserving modes, being careful to include spin doubling in momentum summations. Another specific omission will be that of the set of $\mathbf{k} = 0$ modes, for these include the actions which, with the exception of the total momentum, are poorly represented by one-body sums.

The problem is to choose the $f(\mathbf{p}_i)$ in a Fermi-Dirac system so that

$$d\zeta^*/dt = i\zeta^*\omega \tag{27}$$

for some constants of the motion ω. We shall limit ourselves once more to the Hamiltonian

$$H = \sum p_i^2/2m + \frac{1}{2}\sum_{i\neq j} V(\mathbf{x}_i-\mathbf{x}_j) \tag{28}$$

although the replacement of $p^2/2m$ by an arbitrary $\mathscr{E}(\mathbf{p})$ occasions no essential change in what follows. Making use of the relation $g(\mathbf{p})\,e^{i\mathbf{k}\cdot\mathbf{x}} = e^{i\mathbf{k}\cdot\mathbf{x}}g(\mathbf{p}+\hbar\mathbf{k})$, then $d\zeta^*/dt = (i/\hbar)[H, \zeta^*]$ is readily computed and the condition for oscillation of ζ^* expressed as

$$0 = \sum_i e^{i\mathbf{k}\cdot\mathbf{x}_i}\{f(\mathbf{p}_i)\,\hbar[\omega-\omega_{\mathbf{k}}(\mathbf{p}_i)]$$

$$-\sum_{\mathbf{l},\,j\neq i} V_{\mathbf{l}}[\exp i(\mathbf{k}-\mathbf{l})\cdot(\mathbf{x}_j-\mathbf{x}_i)][f(\mathbf{p}_j)-f(\mathbf{p}_j-\hbar\mathbf{l})] \tag{29}$$

$$\text{where}\qquad \omega_{\mathbf{k}}(\mathbf{p}) = [(\mathbf{p}+\hbar\mathbf{k})^2-p^2]/2m$$

and $V_{\mathbf{k}}$ is again the Fourier coefficient of V. There remains the operation of averaging suitable coefficients over the system motion — if they are sufficiently tightly distributed; the form and legitimacy of the averaging depends upon the system under investigation. Suppose that the correlation of $\mathbf{x}_j$ with $\mathbf{x}_i$ is weak except at distances short compared to $1/|\mathbf{l}-\mathbf{k}|$ and the correlation with $\mathbf{p}_j$ is also weak; then in the coefficient $[\exp i(\mathbf{k}-\mathbf{l})\cdot(\mathbf{x}_j-\mathbf{x}_i)][f(\mathbf{p}_j)-f(\mathbf{p}_j-\hbar\mathbf{l})]$ of $V_{\mathbf{l}}\,e^{i\mathbf{k}\cdot\mathbf{x}_i}$

in (29), the summation over x_j may be taken independently and converted to integration, yielding $\delta_{\mathbf{kl}}$ — the random phase approximation [10] Hence (29) reduces to

$$\sum_i e^{i\mathbf{k}\cdot\mathbf{x}_i}\{f(\mathbf{p}_i)[\hbar\omega-\hbar\omega_{\mathbf{k}}(\mathbf{p}_i)+V_{\mathbf{k}}]-f(\mathbf{p}_i-\hbar\mathbf{k})V_{\mathbf{k}}$$
$$-V_{\mathbf{k}}\sum_j [f(\mathbf{p}_j)-f(\mathbf{p}_j-\hbar\mathbf{k})]\} = 0 \tag{30}$$

Even a pure quantum statistical correlation may connect $\mathbf{x}_j$ and $\mathbf{x}_i$ more closely than assumed above; we shall return to this point.

To effect further reduction, let us here make the apparently drastic assumption that the coupling is weak, in that the mean potential energy (exchange energy) and correlation energy are small compared to the kinetic energy; if true, this means that in secondary evaluations, the momentum distribution may be replaced by the corresponding free-particle distribution. But consider a Fermi-Dirac system. The free kinetic energy per particle goes as $n^{2/3}$ where n is the particle density; hence if the potential is not too singular (Coulomb forces will do, hard spheres will not), and finite correlation length assumed, subject to later verification, weak coupling is a consequence of high density and represents a situation worth inspecting. Now if the excitation is not too high, the sum of the $\mathbf{p}_j$ in (30) becomes a static sum over the unperturbed Fermi sea, bounded by k_f (where $\frac{1}{2}\mathcal{N}=\sum_{k\leq k_f}1$ $=(2\pi)^{-3}\Omega\int_0^{k_f}4\pi k^2\,dk$ or $k_f^3=3\pi^2 n$); further, as the system volume Ω becomes infinite, $V_{\mathbf{k}}\propto\Omega^{-1}\to 0$, so that single terms in $V_{\mathbf{k}}$ will be dropped. Equating coefficients of $e^{i\mathbf{k}\cdot\mathbf{x}_i}$, (30) is then valid if

$$\hbar[\omega-\omega_{\mathbf{k}}(\mathbf{p})]f(\mathbf{p}) = 2V_{\mathbf{k}}\sum_{s\leq k_f}\{f[\hbar\mathbf{s}]-f[\hbar(\mathbf{s}-\mathbf{k})]\} \tag{31}$$

an eigenvalue problem for ω, a c number. Dividing through by $\omega-\omega_{\mathbf{k}}(\mathbf{p})$ to obtain $f(\mathbf{p})$ and summing to compute $\sum_{s\leq k_f}\{f(\hbar\mathbf{s})$ $-f[\hbar(\mathbf{s}-\mathbf{k})]\}$, this sum drops out and there remains the implicit equation for the eigenvalue

$$1 = (2V_{\mathbf{k}}/\hbar)\sum_{s\leq k_f}\{[\omega-\omega_{\mathbf{k}}(\hbar\mathbf{s})]^{-1}-[\omega-\omega_{\mathbf{k}}(\hbar(\mathbf{s}-\mathbf{k}))]^{-1}\} \tag{32a}$$

$$1 = (2V_{\mathbf{k}}/\hbar)\sum'\{[\omega-\omega_{\mathbf{k}}(\hbar\mathbf{s})]^{-1}-[\omega+\omega_{\mathbf{k}}(\hbar\mathbf{s})]^{-1}\} \tag{32b}$$

$$\text{or}\quad (\hbar/4V_{\mathbf{k}}) = \sum'_s \omega_{\mathbf{k}}(\hbar\mathbf{s})/[\omega^2-\omega_{\mathbf{k}}(\hbar\mathbf{s})^2] \tag{32c}$$

where $\sum'$ denotes $s\leq k_f$, $|\mathbf{s}+\mathbf{k}| > k_f$

To obtain (32b), one uses $\omega_{\mathbf{k}}(\hbar(\mathbf{s}-\mathbf{k})) = -\omega_{\mathbf{k}}(-\hbar\mathbf{s})$ and changes the sign of $\mathbf{s}$; since the terms with $|\mathbf{s}-\mathbf{k}| < k_f$ cancel in the sums, the restriction $|\mathbf{s}+\mathbf{k}| > k_f$ may be included or deleted as desired.

In the foregoing, the possibility $\sum \{f(\hbar\mathbf{s}) - f[\hbar(\mathbf{s}-\mathbf{k})]\} = 0$ also occurs, and implies that higher-order terms should be considered. These appear to lead to modes of transverse character, the ones on page 212 serving as prototype. If however the system is slightly modified, anisotropically and asymmetrically, so that the $\omega_{\mathbf{k}}(\hbar\mathbf{s})$ are all distinct, the above factor cannot vanish. This assumption — clearly in the nature of a holding action — will be made, and will aid considerably in the ensuing calculations.

The nature of the eigenfrequencies of (32c) is readily established. Note first that the conditions $s \leqq k_f$, $|\mathbf{s}+\mathbf{k}| > k_f$, i.e. that $\mathbf{s}$ be within, $\mathbf{s}+\mathbf{k}$ outside of the unperturbed Fermi sea, are precisely those under which $\omega_{\mathbf{k}}(\hbar\mathbf{s}) = (\hbar/2m)[(\mathbf{s}+\mathbf{k})^2 - s^2]$ is guaranteed positive. Now there are $\mathcal{N}'_{\mathbf{k}}$ $[= (\Omega/24\pi^2) k(3k_f^2 - \frac{1}{4}k^2)$ or $(\Omega/6\pi^2)k_f^3$ as $k \lessgtr 2k_f]$ terms represented by $\sum'$, and correspondingly the equation (32c) written in polynomial form has exactly $\mathcal{N}'_{\mathbf{k}}$ roots. As ω^2 varies from $-\infty$ to the lowest value of $\omega_{\mathbf{k}}(\hbar\mathbf{s})^2$, the right-hand side $\sum'$ of (32c) drops from 0 to $-\infty$; as ω^2 sweeps across the values of $\omega_{\mathbf{k}}(\hbar\mathbf{s})^2$, $\sum'$ descends from ∞ to $-\infty$ $\mathcal{N}'_{\mathbf{k}}-1$ times; finally, as ω^2 varies from the peak value $[(\hbar/2m)(k^2+2kk_f)]^2$ of $\omega_{\mathbf{k}}(\hbar\mathbf{s})$ to ∞, $\sum'$ falls from ∞ to 0. All values are assumed $\mathcal{N}'_{\mathbf{k}}-1$ times and hence we have located all roots. If $V_{\mathbf{k}} < 0$, there may conceivably be a root $\omega^2 < 0$, but as long as

$$V_{\mathbf{k}} + [\sum' 4/\hbar\omega_{\mathbf{k}}(\hbar\mathbf{s})]^{-1} > 0 \qquad (33)$$

this cannot happen. Condition (33) fails only for very long-range or highly singular attractive forces, and we henceforth assume that all roots $\omega^2 > 0$; in fact, let us limit our attention to the case $\omega > 0$, the reverse corresponding to the annihilator ζ which we are not yet considering.

There is then one frequency ω following each value of $\omega_{\mathbf{k}}(\hbar\mathbf{s})$. If $\omega \sim \omega_{\mathbf{k}}(\hbar\mathbf{1})$, then according to (31), $f(\mathbf{p})$ is sharply peaked at $\mathbf{p} = \hbar\mathbf{1}$ and hence has contributions from only a small number of particles. If only this term were present, then ζ^* of (26) would denote a free propagation; the remaining terms clearly convert ζ^* into a scattering mode, and as the $\omega_{\mathbf{k}}(\hbar\mathbf{1})$ spectrum fills with increase of

Ω, ω approaches its non-interaction value. An exception occurs with the largest frequency; it may be close to Max $\omega_{\mathbf{k}}(\hbar\mathbf{s}) = (\hbar/2m)(k^2 + 2kk_f)$, or may be isolated, somewhere between this value and ∞. To more sharply distinguish the two cases, we observe that if ω is an isolated root, none of the denominators in (32c) become small, and we may evaluate by integration; doing so yields

$$(\hbar/4V_{\mathbf{k}}) = (m\Omega/16\pi\hbar k)[(K^2 - k_f^2) \ln |(K + k_f)/(K - k_f)|$$
$$- (K'^2 - k_f^2) \ln|(K' + k_f)/(K' - k_f)| - 2kk_f] \qquad (34)$$

$$\text{where} \qquad K, K' = (m\omega/\hbar k) \pm \tfrac{1}{2}k$$

which may be written in several alternate forms [11]. For large $V_{\mathbf{k}}$ (and hence large ω) an approximate solution is available at once,

$$\omega^2 = (Nk^2 V_{\mathbf{k}}/m) + (\hbar k^2/2m)^2 + \tfrac{3}{5}(\hbar kk_f/m)^2 + \ldots \qquad (35)$$

which coincides with (25); this represents a true collective (longitudinal) motion.

If $V_{\mathbf{k}}$ is too small, (34) does not have a solution $\omega > (\hbar/2m)(k^2 + 2kk_f)$; solving, we find that the collective mode will exist only if

$$V_{\mathbf{k}} > (4\pi\hbar^2/m\Omega)[(k + 2k_f) \ln((k + 2k_f)/k) - 2k_f]^{-1} \qquad (36)$$

which, e.g., in the Coulomb case imposes a high wave number cutoff for k. On the other hand, if ω of (34) is exceeded by $(\hbar/2m)(k^2 + 2kk_f)$, which cannot of course actually be the case, we return to the region of vanishing denominators in (32) and so to the scattering modes. Although (34) is no longer valid, it becomes so providing we separately add the relevant resonance term; that is, (32c) may be solved to first order as

$$\omega^2 - \omega_{\mathbf{k}}(\hbar\mathbf{l})^2 = (4V_{\mathbf{k}}\omega_{\mathbf{k}}(\hbar\mathbf{l})/\hbar)/(1 + 4V_{\mathbf{k}}C_{\mathbf{k}}(\mathbf{l})/\hbar) \qquad (37)$$

$$\text{where} \qquad C_{\mathbf{k}}(\mathbf{l}) = \sum_{\mathbf{s} \neq \mathbf{l}}' \omega_{\mathbf{k}}(\hbar\mathbf{s})/(\omega_k(\hbar\mathbf{s})^2 - \omega_{\mathbf{k}}(\hbar\mathbf{l})^2)$$

and the integration of (34) applied. Not only does $\omega - \omega_{\mathbf{k}}(\hbar\mathbf{l}) \to 0$ as $\Omega \to \infty$, but the relative error in the deviation (37), important, e.g., for the evaluation of $f(\hbar\mathbf{l})$, is readily shown to approach zero as well. This suggests an alternative expression for the collective frequency. Since, according to (32c) expressed in polynomial form, the sum of all ω^2 is known to be $\sum' \omega_{\mathbf{k}}(\hbar\mathbf{s})(\omega_{\mathbf{k}}(\hbar\mathbf{s})+4V_{\mathbf{k}}\hbar)$, the collective frequency is found by inserting (37):

$$\omega^2 = (4V_{\mathbf{k}}/\hbar) \sum' \omega_{\mathbf{k}}(\hbar\mathbf{1})(4V_{\mathbf{k}} C_{\mathbf{k}}(\mathbf{1})/\hbar)/(1+4V_{\mathbf{k}} C_{\mathbf{k}}(\mathbf{1})/\hbar) \qquad (38)$$

Equation (38) is equivalent to a contour integral determination of ω^2 from the dispersion relation (32), based upon the fact that ω^2 necessarily lies between $\omega^2_{\max}$ and ∞.

Now let us solve eq. (30) for the $f(\mathbf{p})$. It is useful to observe that, referring to (26), ζ has the same form as ζ^*, with momentum $\mathbf{k}$ reversed and the coefficient of $e^{i\mathbf{k}\cdot\mathbf{x}}$ given by

$$\bar{f}(\mathbf{p}) = f^*(\mathbf{p}-\hbar\mathbf{k}) \qquad (39)$$

If we then adopt the convenient normalization $[\zeta, \zeta^*] = 1$ on the ground state Fermi sea, an easy computation shows that (extracting spin index summation)

$$2 \sum' (|f(\hbar\mathbf{s})|^2-|\bar{f}(\hbar\mathbf{s})|^2) = 1 \qquad (40)$$

Equations (30) then solve at once to yield

$$\zeta^*_{\mathbf{k}\omega} = D_{\mathbf{k}\omega} \sum e^{i\mathbf{k}\cdot\mathbf{x}_i}[\omega-\omega_{\mathbf{k}}(\mathbf{p}_i)]^{-1}$$
$$\zeta_{\mathbf{k}\omega} = D_{\mathbf{k}\omega} \sum e^{-i\mathbf{k}\cdot\mathbf{x}_i}[\omega+\omega_{-\mathbf{k}}(\mathbf{p}_i)]^{-1} \qquad (41)$$

where $\qquad D_{\mathbf{k}\omega}^{-2} = \sum' 8\omega \, \omega_{\mathbf{k}}(\hbar\mathbf{s})[\omega^2-\omega_{\mathbf{k}}(\hbar\mathbf{s})^2]^{-2}$

The existence of the normalizing square root in (41) stems from both ω and $\omega_{\mathbf{k}}(\hbar\mathbf{s})$ being positive; of course, for φ^* to really be a creator, $[\zeta, \zeta^*] = 1$, not -1, must hold.

It is important to realize that (41) need be considered only for the range $p_i \leq k_f\hbar$, $|\mathbf{p}_i-\hbar\mathbf{k}| > \hbar k_f$, according to our approximation that the momentum distribution is essentially unaffected by the interaction; only this range of course is required for (31). If the domain of $\mathbf{p}$ is so restricted, then rewriting (31) as

$$\omega_{\mathbf{k}}(\mathbf{p})f(\mathbf{p})+(2V_{\mathbf{k}}/\hbar) \sum' f(\hbar\mathbf{s})-(2V_{\mathbf{k}}/\hbar) \sum' \bar{f}(-\hbar\mathbf{s}) = \omega f(\mathbf{p})$$
$$\omega_{\mathbf{k}}(\mathbf{p})\bar{f}(-\mathbf{p})+(2V_{\mathbf{k}}/\hbar) \sum' \bar{f}(-\hbar\mathbf{s})-(2V_{\mathbf{k}}/\hbar) \sum' f(\hbar\mathbf{s}) = -\omega\bar{f}(-\mathbf{p}) \qquad (42)$$

the combined vector $\{f(\mathbf{p}), \bar{f}(-\mathbf{p})\}$ is an eigenvector of a Hermitian operator with weight function $\{1, -1\}$. The complete set of eigenvectors corresponding to (41) is then orthogonal (again assuming the $\omega_{\mathbf{k}}(\hbar\mathbf{s})$ to be distinct, there are sufficiently many vectors to span the space) and, according to (40), normalized to $\frac{1}{2}$. An immediate consequence is that $[\zeta, \zeta^*] = 1$ extends to

$$[\zeta_{\mathbf{k}\omega}, \zeta^*_{\mathbf{k}\omega'}] = \delta_{\omega\omega'} \qquad [\zeta_{\mathbf{k}\omega}, \zeta_{\mathbf{k}'\omega'}] = 0 \qquad (43)$$

the second relation resulting merely from the reduced domain of $\mathbf{p}$.

Knowing the excitation energies and normal annihilators and creators, we would still like to determine, if not a full action expansion of H, at least the ground state energy with which to normalize the energy sequence. A simple but effective method is to compute the ground state energy expectation, using the fact that with each $\omega > 0$, the ground state is annihilated by all $\zeta_{\mathbf{k}\omega}$. The Hamiltonian (28) must therefore be written in terms of the $\zeta_{\mathbf{k}\omega}$ and $\zeta^*_{\mathbf{k}\omega}$; for the potential energy, $V = \frac{1}{2}\sum_{i \neq j} V(\mathbf{x}_i - \mathbf{x}_j) = \frac{1}{2}\sum V_{\mathbf{k}}(\sum_{ij} e^{i\mathbf{k}\cdot\mathbf{x}_i} e^{-i\mathbf{k}\cdot\mathbf{x}_j} - N)$ and $\sum e^{i\mathbf{k}\cdot\mathbf{x}_i}$ alone is required. But all one-body sums may be obtained by inverting (41). From completeness, we have $\sum f_{\mathbf{k}\omega}(\hbar\mathbf{s}) f_{\mathbf{k}\omega}(\mathbf{p}) = \frac{1}{2}\delta(\mathbf{p} - \hbar\mathbf{s})$ and also $\sum \bar{f}_{-\mathbf{k}\omega}(\hbar\mathbf{s}) f_{\mathbf{k}\omega}(\mathbf{p}) = 0$. The ω resulting from (42) are clearly both positive and negative; however, we may certainly choose $f_{\mathbf{k}, -\omega}(\mathbf{p}) = f_{-\mathbf{k}, \omega}(\mathbf{p})$, noting that these are normalized to $-\frac{1}{2}$. It follows then that

$$\sum_{\omega > 0} [f_{\mathbf{k}\omega}(\hbar\mathbf{s}) - \bar{f}_{-\mathbf{k}\omega}(\hbar\mathbf{s})][f_{\mathbf{k}\omega}(\mathbf{p}_i) + \bar{f}_{-\mathbf{k}\omega}(\mathbf{p}_i)] = \frac{1}{2}\delta(\mathbf{p}_i - \hbar\mathbf{s}) \qquad (44)$$

Consequently, multiplying (44) by $e^{i\mathbf{k}\cdot\mathbf{x}_i}$, summing over i, and then over $\mathbf{s}$,

$$\sum e^{i\mathbf{k}\cdot\mathbf{x}_i} = 2 \sum_{\omega > 0} \sum{}' [f_{\mathbf{k}\omega}(\hbar\mathbf{s}) - \bar{f}_{-\mathbf{k}\omega}(\hbar\mathbf{s})](\zeta_{\mathbf{k}\omega} + \zeta^*_{-\mathbf{k}\omega}) \qquad (45)$$

Inserting this into the potential energy and averaging over the ground state, using (43), we have at once

$$\langle V \rangle_0 = \frac{1}{2} \sum_{\mathbf{k}} V_{\mathbf{k}} \{ \sum_{\omega > 0} [2 \sum{}' f_{\mathbf{k}\omega}(\hbar\mathbf{s}) - \bar{f}_{-\mathbf{k}\omega}(\hbar\mathbf{s})]^2 - N \} \qquad (46)$$

which by virtue of (41) and (32b) may be rewritten as

$$\langle V \rangle_0 = \frac{1}{2} \sum_{\mathbf{k}} V_{\mathbf{k}} [\sum_{\omega > 0} (\hbar D_{\mathbf{k}\omega} / V_{\mathbf{k}})^2 - N] \qquad (47)$$

Now the mean kinetic energy, corresponding to $\mathbf{k} = 0$, involves more suble considerations. Nonetheless, (47) will suffice, for there are several ways of obtaining the total energy from the potential energy. One need only observe that if the potential energy is varied infinitesimally, then the variation of the ground state energy is given by first-order perturbation theory as $\delta E_0 = \langle \delta V \rangle_0$. Hence if V is turned on from zero and there is no energy branching in the process,

$$E_0(V) = E_f + \int_0^V \langle \delta V \rangle_0 \qquad (48)$$

where E_f is the unperturbed Fermi energy. Let us make use of the special circumstance [11] that from differentiating the dispersion relation (32c) with respect to $V_{\mathbf{k}}$ there results simply $\partial \omega / \partial V_{\mathbf{k}} = (\hbar/V_{\mathbf{k}}^2) D_{\mathbf{k}\omega}^2$, so that following (47), $\langle \delta V \rangle_0 = \frac{1}{2} \sum_{\mathbf{k}} \delta V_{\mathbf{k}} [\sum_{\omega > 0} \hbar \, \partial \omega / \partial V_{\mathbf{k}} - \mathcal{N}]$. Hence (48) integrates to

$$E_0(V) = E_f + \frac{1}{2} \sum_{\mathbf{k}} \{ \sum_{\omega > 0} [\hbar \omega(V) - \hbar \omega(0)] - \mathcal{N} V_{\mathbf{k}} \} \qquad (49)$$

our principal result, which of course a most naive action expansion would have predicted: the zero-point energy is composed of the zero-point energies of the oscillators.

The evaluation of (49) may proceed in various ways. For example, the sum of oscillation frequencies at fixed $\mathbf{k}$ may be found directly by a contour integral. Alternatively, one may consider scattering and collective contributions separately; thus, employing (37) for the scattering modes (noting that $\omega^2 - \omega_{\mathbf{k}}(\hbar 1)^2 = 2\omega_{\mathbf{k}}(\hbar 1)[\omega - \omega_{\mathbf{k}}(\hbar 1)]$), eq. (49) is converted to

$$E_0(V) = E_f + \frac{1}{2}\mathcal{N}(\mathcal{N}-1) \sum_{\mathbf{k}} \sigma_{\mathbf{k}} V_{\mathbf{k}} + \frac{1}{2} \sum_{\mathbf{k}} [\hbar \omega_{\mathbf{k}}(V) - \hbar \omega(0)]$$

$$- \sum_{\mathbf{k}} \sum_{1}' (4 V_{\mathbf{k}} C_{\mathbf{k}}(1)/\hbar)/(1 + 4 V_{\mathbf{k}} C_{\mathbf{k}}(1)/\hbar) \qquad (50)$$

where $\omega_{\mathbf{k}}$ is the collective frequency at wave vector $\mathbf{k}$, and $\mathcal{N}(\mathcal{N}-1)\sigma_{\mathbf{k}} = 2\mathcal{N}_{\mathbf{k}}' - \mathcal{N}$ is the unperturbed ground state expectation $\langle \psi_0(V=0)|\sum_{i \neq j} \exp i\mathbf{k} \cdot (\mathbf{x}_i - \mathbf{x}_j)|\psi_0(V=0)\rangle$. Hence (50) represents zeroth-order kinetic energy, first-order exchange energy, collective contributions to ground state energy, and scattering contributions. For detailed computations in the case of Coulomb interaction, see [11] and [12].

One point glossed over was the neglect of interparticle correlations in the transition from (29) to (30), a neglect which eventually has the effect of making (50) a sum of terms each due to a single $V_{\mathbf{k}}$. Thus, the second-order exchange energy in $\langle \psi_0(V{=}0)|V(E_F{-}T)^{-1}P_F V|\psi_0(V{=}0)\rangle$ has been omitted; it may in general be easily computed and appended [11], [12]. More satisfactory is the realization that the mean unperturbed correlation effect may be included in (30) by replacing exp $i(\mathbf{k}{-}\mathbf{l}) \cdot (\mathbf{x}_i{-}\mathbf{x}_j)$ in (29) by $\sigma_{\mathbf{k}{-}\mathbf{l}}$, most ensuing steps being only trivially modified in the process. A further improvement might utilize coordinate and momentum distributions and correlations defined self-consistently. In a more straightforward fashion, the computation of ζ, ζ^* may be refined by including higher than one-body terms — at least one new aspect is expected to arise. The collective modes that we have found, while higher in energy than any single scattering excitation, are in the continuum (as $\Omega \to \infty$) for multiple excitations, which with their sensitive dependence on exact frequency, may be regarded as the repositories of randomness. The single scattering excitations are similarly part of large, nearly degenerate sets. There must then be a great deal of delicate mixing in the exact normal modes. But one does not have to consider these combinations, which certainly must depend as well upon slight modifications of boundary conditions. Physically, it is known that if any reasonably regular initial wave function is set up, then approximately normal modes will decay in time and that fine details do not disturb the form of the decay. Hence, an expansion in decaying modes, with complex ω familiar from the theory of alpha decay [13], is more appropriate, and if one attempts to construct smoothly varying normal modes, these are precisely the modes which may be expected to result.

Direct Collective Transcription. Consider a condensed Boson system. It then becomes meaningful to ask for a complete decomposition into independent normal modes. These may be determined by making a refined guess, e.g., on the style of (26), and using either the Hamiltonian (Tomonaga) or the equation of motion technique to fix the available parameters. It is also possible, and in some ways easier, to take advantage of simple but very approximate oscillating variables, but either to devote major attention to optimal determination of the effective oscillator coefficients, employing a self-consistent process if required, or to make use of perturbation methods to treat the residual terms. The interpretation of the resulting oscillator Hamiltonian may become somewhat obscure. For example, if one restricts the collective coordinates to those obtainable by a point transformation, one can be sure that some of them will be quite poor representations of independent collective modes. (Even this may nevertheless be preferable to utilizing only those coordinate functions which are bona fide oscillators, and regarding the residual Hamiltonian as containing non-collective or scattering-type behavior, whose solution then permits determination of the mean oscillator coefficients for the collective part of the Hamiltonian; the trouble is that the non-collective part of the Hamiltonian no longer contains $3N$ degrees of freedom. See however Sec. 4 and Levinson and Banerjee, Chap. XII). One must at least be certain that, for a given state, collective variables appropriate to that state are included, as well as universally collective variables, and perhaps a sampling [14] by further collective variables to complete the description of the system.

Let us see what happens to the Hamiltonian (12) under a general point transformation to $3N$ new variables $\{q_s\}$. If we merely wish to change variables to the q "picture," retaining the x space volume element for expectations, scalar products, etc., then the kinetic energy transforms directly as [15]

$$(-\hbar^2/2m) \sum \nabla_i^2 = -(\hbar^2/2m) \sum (\nabla_i q_s \cdot \nabla_i q_t)(\partial/\partial q_s)(\partial/\partial q_t)$$
$$-(\hbar^2/2m) \sum (\nabla_i^2 q_s)(\partial/\partial q_s) \quad (51)$$

However, if we wish to operate in the q representation, and we do, then since the point transformation is completed to a canonical transformation by $\pi \to J^{\frac{1}{2}}\pi J^{-\frac{1}{2}}$, J being the transformation Jacobian, or by

$$p_i \to \tfrac{1}{2} \sum_s (\nabla_i q_s \pi_s + \pi_s \nabla_i q_s) \quad (52)$$

where π_s is canonically conjugate to q_s, a computation of a few steps enables us to write

$$\sum p_i^2/2m \to (1/4m) \sum (\nabla_i q_s^* \cdot \nabla_i q_t \pi_s^* \pi_t + \pi_s^* \pi_t \nabla_i q_s^* \cdot \nabla_i q_t)$$
$$+ (\hbar^2/8m)[\sum (\nabla_i q_s \cdot \nabla_i q_t)(\nabla_j \cdot \partial \mathbf{x}_j/\partial q_s^*)(\nabla_k \cdot \partial \mathbf{x}_k/\partial q_t)$$
$$+ 2 \sum \partial \nabla_i^2 q_s/\partial q_s] \quad (53)$$

The complex conjugate variables q_s^*, assumed to be members of the coordinate family themselves, are here used for notational convenience. If (53) is to be relevant for an independent set of oscillators, the cross terms, $\pi_s^* \pi_t$ for $t \neq s$, must vanish. To establish the vanishing at least on the average (employing somewhat of a Hartree treatment on q space) of the coefficient of such a term, invariance considerations often suffice. Thus, we may write

$$\sum_i \nabla_i q_s^* \cdot \nabla_i q_t = \tfrac{1}{2} \sum_i [\nabla_i^2 (q_s^* q_t) - (\nabla_i^2 q_s^*) q_t - q_s^* (\nabla_i^2 q_t)] \qquad (54)$$

and consider a group of transformations G under which kinetic energy (hence $\sum \nabla_i^2$) and potential energy are separately invariant, as is the density matrix of the state being observed. In this event, it follows from (54) that the expectation $\sum_i \nabla_i q_s^* \cdot \nabla_i q_t$ necessarily vanishes if q_s and q_t belong to different irreducible unitary representations of the group G. Common examples are the full translation group, rotation group, lattice translation and symmetry groups.

On the other hand, invariance properties are not required for the separation of the kinetic energy. In particular, for an idealized macroscopic fluid of density $\rho_0(\mathbf{x})$, we know that small density oscillations occur, governed by $(\partial^2/\partial t^2)\delta\rho = \nabla \cdot [(\partial p/\partial \rho)_0 \nabla \delta\rho]$, where the relation of the pressure p to ρ depends upon the type of process (adiabatic, isothermal, etc.) which is effective. The normal modes are determined by $\omega^2 \varphi_\omega + \nabla \cdot [(\partial p/\partial \rho)_0 \nabla \varphi_\omega] = 0$; it follows that, with suitable boundary conditions, $(\partial^2/\partial t^2) \int \varphi_\omega \delta\rho d^3x + \omega^2 \int \varphi_\omega \delta\rho d^3x = 0$. Switching to the microscopic density $\rho(\mathbf{x}) = m \sum \delta(\mathbf{x} - \mathbf{x}_i)$, this suggests that the

$$q_s = a_s + \sum_i \varphi_s(\mathbf{x}_i) \qquad (55)$$

where $\qquad \nabla \cdot [d(\mathbf{x}) \nabla \varphi_s(\mathbf{x})] + \lambda_s \varphi_s(\mathbf{x}) = 0$

are possible normal modes, for some appropriate $d(\mathbf{x}), a_s$. It may be noted that the particle symmetry of q_s precludes any simple application to other than Einstein-Bose systems. Now if one chooses $d(\mathbf{x})$ to be the mean particle density $\rho_0(\mathbf{x})/m$ (implying a rather special macroscopic equation of state) and the φ_s to be orthonormal, then not only is $\langle \sum_i \nabla_i q_s^* \cdot \nabla_i q_t \rangle = \langle \sum_i \nabla \varphi_s^*(\mathbf{x}_i) \cdot \nabla \varphi_t(\mathbf{x}_i) \rangle = m^{-1} \int \rho_0(\mathbf{x}) \nabla \varphi_s^*(\mathbf{x}) \cdot \nabla \varphi_t(\mathbf{x}) \, d^3x = -\int \varphi_s^*(\mathbf{x}) \nabla \cdot [d(\mathbf{x}) \nabla \varphi_t(\mathbf{x})] \, d^3x = \lambda_s \delta_{st}$, as desired, but also the dispersion is small if no q_s is highly excited.

Although the ensuing comments apply without substantial (but tedious) changes to the general case, let us restrict our attention to a uniform fluid with two-body potential, (28); thus the replacements $a_s = 0$, $d(\mathbf{x}) = 1$ may be made in (55). φ_s will now be normalized to unit volume. To compute the transformation of the kinetic energy, we observe to the extent that $\sum_i \nabla_i q_s^* \cdot \nabla_i q_t \sim N\lambda_s \delta_{st}$, that, -1 denoting matrix inverse, $\partial \mathbf{x}_i/\partial q_s^* = \sum_t [\sum_s (\partial \mathbf{x}_j/\partial q_s^*) \cdot (\partial \mathbf{x}_j/\partial q_t)] \nabla_i q_t = \sum_t [\sum_j (\nabla_j q_t \cdot \nabla_j q_s^*)]^{-1} \nabla_i q_t$ yields

$$
\begin{aligned}
\partial \mathbf{x}_i/\partial q_s^* &\sim (1/N\lambda_s) \nabla_i q_s \\
\sum \nabla_i q_s^* \cdot \nabla_i q_t &\sim N\lambda_s \delta_{st}
\end{aligned}
\tag{56}
$$

Inserting this into (53), we have at once

$$
\sum p_i^2/2m \to (N/2m) \sum \lambda_s \pi_s^* \pi_s + (\hbar^2/8mN) \sum \lambda_s (q_s^* q_s - 2N)
\tag{57}
$$

It is also possible, and indeed not difficult, to literally expand (51) and then (53) as power series in the q_s.

There remains the task of diagonalizing V. Now in obtaining (55), we have made the implicit assumption that only modes which alter the macroscopic density need be considered, and have thus totally omitted transverse waves. In fact, for a fluid, which does not support shear (although viscosity and ensuing turbulence do occur), this neglect appears justifiable until wavelengths of the order of inter-particle spacing are reached, and then the transverse and longitudinal modes are so closely coupled that neither may be regarded as in-dependent; thus either may be used. On the other hand, one might not expect a description of the central potential terms to require close consideration of the transverse, or equivalently of the highest $2N$ longitudinal modes — to the extent that either can be defined in configuration space alone. For such a description [16], we expand the two-body potential in a double series of φ's

$$
V(\mathbf{x}-\mathbf{y}) = \sum' v_{st} \varphi_s^*(\mathbf{x}) \varphi_t(\mathbf{y})
\tag{58}
$$

the $\sum'$ indicating that only a predetermined N of the $3N$ φ_s are chosen. Of course, eq. (58) cannot be exact, but we may, in the sense of interpolation, require that it hold whenever $\mathbf{x}$, $\mathbf{y}$ reduces to a pair $\mathbf{x}_i$, $\mathbf{x}_j$. This is sufficient for our purposes, and the resulting v_{st} will be uniquely determined as functions of the x_j; introducing the matrices $\boldsymbol{\varphi} = (\varphi_{sj}) \equiv [\varphi_s(\mathbf{x}_j)]$, $\mathbf{V} = (V_{ij}) \equiv [V(\mathbf{x}_i - \mathbf{x}_j)]$, we have

$$\nu_{st} = [(\boldsymbol{\varphi}\boldsymbol{\varphi}^*)^{-1}\boldsymbol{\varphi}\mathbf{V}\boldsymbol{\varphi}^*(\boldsymbol{\varphi}\boldsymbol{\varphi}^*)^{-1}]_{st} \tag{59}$$

Equation (59) is reduced through $(\boldsymbol{\varphi}\boldsymbol{\varphi}^*)_{st} = \sum \varphi_s(\mathbf{x}_i)\,\varphi_t^*(\mathbf{x}_i)$ $\sim (N/\Omega)\int \varphi_s(\mathbf{x})\varphi_t^*(\mathbf{x})\,d^3x = N\delta_{st}$, while $(\boldsymbol{\varphi}\mathbf{V}\boldsymbol{\varphi}^*)_{st} = \sum \varphi_s(\mathbf{x}_i)V(\mathbf{x}_i - \mathbf{x}_j)$ $\varphi_t^*(\mathbf{x}_j) \sim (N/\Omega)^2 \int \varphi_s(\mathbf{x})V(\mathbf{x} - \mathbf{y})\,\sigma(\mathbf{x}, \mathbf{y})\varphi_t^*(\mathbf{y})\,d^3x\,d^3y$, σ being the pair distribution function normalized to Ω^2. In the event of translation invariance, or any other sufficiently extensive symmetry, only $s = t$ contributes and we obtain

$$\tfrac{1}{2}\sum_{i \neq j} V(\mathbf{x}_i - \mathbf{x}_j) = \tfrac{1}{2}\sum{}' \nu_{ss}(q_s^* q_s - N) \tag{60}$$

where $\quad \nu_{ss} = (1/\Omega^2)\int \varphi_s(\mathbf{x})\varphi_s^*(\mathbf{y})V(\mathbf{x} - \mathbf{y})\,\sigma(\mathbf{x}, \mathbf{y})\,d^3x\,d^3y$

If the dispersion of ν_{ss} about its mean is small, we have completed a harmonic oscillator decomposition of the Hamiltonian. It is, to be sure, a self-consistent formulation, since $\sigma(\mathbf{x}, \mathbf{y})$ is not known until the state has been found; when this has been done, the relations

$$(1/\Omega^2)\int \sigma(\mathbf{x} - \mathbf{y})\,e^{i\mathbf{k}\cdot(\mathbf{x} - \mathbf{y})}\,d^3x\,d^3y = \langle q_\mathbf{k}^* q_\mathbf{k} - N\rangle \tag{61}$$

suffice to determine σ in translation invariant systems, for here $\varphi_\mathbf{k} = e^{i\mathbf{k}\cdot\mathbf{x}}$ and only the terms (61) — but for all $\mathbf{k}$ — are needed in (60). Similar simplifications are available with other invariances. The complete set of coefficients of σ must here be derived from analytically continuing the set of $\mathbf{k}$ represented by the chosen "sampling" of $q_\mathbf{k}$.

Dynamic Mode Analysis. The validity of the forced decomposition (57), (60) depends upon the uses to which it is put. Oscillator masses and frequencies, being independent of the "sampling", cause least concern. But these are also obtainable by dynamic or equation of motion methods which are certainly most suitable if we wish to treat Fermion systems in a similar fashion. The effective potential coefficient ν_s is presented in a different form through such considerations, and it may be shown that this form has certain advantages when dealing with singular potentials, aside from the question of the greater intrinsic merit of the dynamic approach.

Restricting our attention to translation invariant systems, with

$$q_{\mathbf{k}} = \sum_i e^{i\mathbf{k}\cdot\mathbf{x}_i} \tag{62}$$

we use $\dot{F} = (i/\hbar)[H, F]$ to find the equations of motion for $q_{\mathbf{k}}$, obtaining

$$\dot{q}_{\mathbf{k}} = (i/m) \sum_i e^{i\mathbf{k}\cdot\mathbf{x}_i} (\mathbf{k}\cdot\mathbf{p}_i + \tfrac{1}{2}\hbar k^2) \tag{63}$$

$$\ddot{q}_{\mathbf{k}} = (-1/m^2) \sum_i e^{i\mathbf{k}\cdot\mathbf{x}_i} (\mathbf{k}\cdot\mathbf{p}_i + \tfrac{1}{2}\hbar k^2)^2$$
$$- (i/m) \sum_{i,j\neq i} e^{i\mathbf{k}\cdot\mathbf{x}_i} \mathbf{k}\cdot\nabla V(\mathbf{x}_i - \mathbf{x}_j) \tag{64}$$

If $\sigma(\mathbf{x}|\mathbf{x}_j)$ is the instantaneous conditional probability (normalized to Ω) for a particle other than the jth being at $\mathbf{x}$ when it is known that the jth is at $\mathbf{x}_j$, then

$$\sum_{i\neq j} f(\mathbf{x}_i, \mathbf{x}_j) = (\mathcal{N}-1/\Omega) \int \sigma(\mathbf{x}|\mathbf{x}_j) f(\mathbf{x}, \mathbf{x}_j)\, d^3x \tag{65}$$

so that the potential term of (64) becomes

$$\sum_{i,j\neq i} e^{i\mathbf{k}\cdot\mathbf{x}_i} \mathbf{k}\cdot\nabla V(\mathbf{x}_i - \mathbf{x}_j) = n \sum_j \int \sigma(\mathbf{x}+\mathbf{x}_j|\mathbf{x}_j)\mathbf{k}\cdot\nabla V(\mathbf{x})\, e^{i\mathbf{k}\cdot\mathbf{x}}\, d^3x\, e^{i\mathbf{k}\cdot\mathbf{x}_j} \tag{66}$$

where $n \equiv \mathcal{N}-1/\Omega$, or equally well,

$$(n/\Omega) \sum_{\mathbf{l}} \iint \sigma(\mathbf{x}+\mathbf{y}|\mathbf{y})\mathbf{k}\cdot\nabla V(\mathbf{x})\, e^{i\mathbf{k}\cdot\mathbf{x}} e^{-i\mathbf{l}\cdot\mathbf{y}}\, d^3x\, d^3y\, q_{\mathbf{k}-\mathbf{l}} \tag{67}$$

summed over all $\mathbf{l}$.

This is exact. But if $\mathbf{k}$ is low enough, an average over a few mean collisions will not change $q_{\mathbf{k}}$ and will convert $\sigma(\mathbf{x}+\mathbf{y}|\mathbf{y})$ to its uniform mean fluid value $\sigma(\mathbf{x})$; thus (67) becomes

$$n q_{\mathbf{k}} \int \sigma(\mathbf{x})\mathbf{k}\cdot\nabla V(\mathbf{x})\, e^{i\mathbf{k}\cdot\mathbf{x}}\, d^3x \tag{68}$$

An integration by parts converts (68) to

$$i n q_{\mathbf{k}} \int e^{i\mathbf{k}\cdot\mathbf{x}} \nabla\cdot[\sigma(\mathbf{x})\nabla V(\mathbf{x})]\, d^3x \tag{69}$$

and so, using a crude average for the residual kinetic force, we have for the equation of motion

$$0 = \ddot{q}_{\mathbf{k}} + [(\mathcal{N}-1)(k^2/m)V_{\mathbf{k}}^* + \langle(\mathbf{k}\cdot\mathbf{p}/m)^2\rangle + (\hbar k^2/2m)^2 + (\hbar k^2/m^2)\langle\mathbf{k}\cdot\mathbf{p}\rangle]q_{\mathbf{k}} \tag{70}$$

where the effective potential $V^*(\mathbf{x})$ is now determined by

$$\nabla^2 V^*(\mathbf{x}) = \nabla \cdot [\sigma(\mathbf{x})\nabla V(\mathbf{x})] \tag{71}$$

and is more properly to be regarded as an effective force: $\mathbf{F}^*(\mathbf{x})$ $= \sigma(\mathbf{x})\mathbf{F}(\mathbf{x})$. In (70), there is no restriction to just $3\mathcal{N}\mathbf{k}$'s.

Based on (70), $\sigma_{\mathbf{k}}$ may be redetermined, and so a self-consistent formulation for $\sigma(\mathbf{x})$ is available in principle. Explicitly, from $[\dot{q}_{\mathbf{k}}^*, q_{\mathbf{k}}] = (\hbar/i)(\mathcal{N}k^2/m)$, the effective oscillator mass is again $m/\mathcal{N}k^2$; since the energy of the $n_{\mathbf{k}}$th oscillator level is $(n_{\mathbf{k}}+\frac{1}{2})\hbar\omega_{\mathbf{k}}$, then $\frac{1}{2}(n_{\mathbf{k}}+n_{-\mathbf{k}}+1)\hbar\omega_{\mathbf{k}} = (m/\mathcal{N}k^2)\omega_{\mathbf{k}}^2\langle q_{\mathbf{k}}^* q_{\mathbf{k}}\rangle$ and $\sigma_{\mathbf{k}}$ is secured by application of (61). Summing up, we may write

$$\mathcal{N}\sigma_{\mathbf{k}} = \tfrac{1}{2}(n_{\mathbf{k}}+n_{-\mathbf{k}}+1)(\hbar k^2/m\omega_{\mathbf{k}})-1 \qquad \mathbf{k} \neq 0$$

$$\omega_{\mathbf{k}}^2 = (\mathcal{N}k^2/m)\,V_{\mathbf{k}}^*+(2k^2/3m\mathcal{N})\langle T\rangle+(\hbar k^2/2m)^2 \qquad \mathbf{k} \neq 0 \tag{72}$$

$$k^2 V_{\mathbf{k}}^* = \sum \mathbf{k} \cdot \mathbf{l}\,\sigma_{\mathbf{k}-\mathbf{l}}V_{\mathbf{l}} \qquad \sigma_0 = 1$$

$\langle T\rangle$ being the mean kinetic energy, the state assumed isotropic, and 1 neglected compared with $\mathcal{N}$. One may justifiably object to the fact that the higher $\sigma_{\mathbf{k}}$'s, necessary for (72), will be obtained with poor accuracy, since the corresponding $q_{\mathbf{k}}$'s are poor normal coordinates. But the major duty of the higher $\sigma_{\mathbf{k}}$ is to supply a short-range cutoff for V in (71), and if this is achieved, their mission is accomplished.

Now what can be done with (72), aside from computing collective excitation energies and two-body correlations? For either Fermi-Dirac or Einstein-Bose systems with Hamiltonian (28), knowledge of the $q_{\mathbf{k}}$ is also sufficient to determine ground state energy, with the potential variation technique of (48) or density variation approach of Chap. XVII both being applicable. A slight modification is necessitated by the appearance of $\langle T\rangle$ itself in (72). Knowing that $\langle V\rangle_0 = \frac{1}{2}\mathcal{N}^2 \sum V_{\mathbf{k}}\sigma_{\mathbf{k}}$, one calculates $\delta\langle T\rangle_0 = \delta E_0 - \delta\langle V\rangle_0$ by the above methods, leading to the combined form

$$\delta(\mathcal{N}^{-2/3}\langle T\rangle_0/\mathcal{N}) = \tfrac{1}{2}\mathcal{N}^{-2/3}[-\sum V_{\mathbf{l}}\delta(\mathcal{N}\sigma_{\mathbf{l}})+V_0^*\,\delta\mathcal{N}] \tag{73}$$

$\delta\sigma_{\mathbf{l}}$ and $\delta\langle T\rangle_0$ may then in principle be obtained from (73) and the variation of (72). Integrating to find $\langle T\rangle_0$, $E_0 = \langle T\rangle_0 + \langle V\rangle_0$ may then be found as well; the details of the process depend very much on the form of the potential and will not be considered further.

Finally, it should be stressed that the assumption of pure oscillation for $q_{\mathbf{k}}$, being inexact, implies the existence of a large number of distinct and inequivalent expressions for the frequency $\omega_{\mathbf{k}}$, e.g., the identity $\langle T \rangle = (m^2/2\hbar^2 k^4) \langle [[\dot{q}_{\mathbf{k}}, T], \dot{q}_{\mathbf{k}}^*] \rangle - N\hbar^2 k^2/2m$ together with $[[\dot{q}_{\mathbf{k}}, H], \dot{q}_{\mathbf{k}}^*] = i\hbar[\ddot{q}_{\mathbf{k}}, \dot{q}_{\mathbf{k}}^*] = -i\hbar\omega_k^2[q_{\mathbf{k}}, \dot{q}_{\mathbf{k}}^*] = -N\hbar^2 k^2\omega_{\mathbf{k}}^2/m$ is readily applied in this fashion, but the only selective criterion seems to be that of simplicity.

3. *Subsidiary conditions*

If one adopts a restricted form, such as that of momentum independence, for the mode variables, it is nonetheless possible to describe dynamically independent, large-scale or collective motions in a fashion which is adequate for many purposes. Suppose that our major interest lies in these modes. There is still the problem of designating the remaining degrees of freedom, not necessarily in the sense of a normal mode analysis if we are not concerned with the corresponding excitations, but at least to complete the description of the system. If the regular behavior of the system has been extracted, the remaining degrees of freedom represent rather haphazard uncorrelated motions, and average values may be computed on this basis with a minimum of additional sophistication.

Now on the one hand, the individual particle behavior of the residual motion suggests that we simply append the $3N$ particle coordinates. But, on the other hand, $3N$ additional coordinates are not available, and it is not possible to set up those which are available to correspond to fine-grained motion while at the same time are unchanged as a set under particle permutation which is clearly desirable in the presence of quantum statistics (see however Levinson and Banerjee, Chap. XII). A conceivable formal alternative is to employ a full $3N$ individual coordinates, but to fix them, in a sense, relative to the collective motions by including those relations existing between the complete set of coordinates as subsidiary conditions.

Subsidiary conditions appear in innumerable guises and represent a wide range of information which is to be taken in conjunction with the nominal Schrödinger equation, from infinitely many equalities and inequalities (see Chap. XVIII), through a circumscribed set as above, down to a single condition on particle number (see Sec. 5).

Many important aspects appear in transparent form in the theory of Bohm, Pines [10], [17] which we shall examine first.

Auxiliary Fields. Consider a system interacting through repulsive Coulomb forces (but kept neutral by a background of uniform charge density). These forces may be described *either* by direct pair interactions *or* by interaction with the electromagnetic field, say the longitudinal vector potential **A**. The field is a true collective entity; however, only Fourier components of sufficiently low wave number $k < k_c$ can propagate (via density oscillations) apparently independently and freely through the medium. If the interaction could sensibly be decomposed into long-range field and short-range direct interaction, a collective-individual description of the desired form would be obtained; indeed by virtue of $\nabla \times \mathbf{E} = 0$, $\nabla \cdot \mathbf{E} = 4\pi\rho$, the quantities $\mathbf{E_k} \propto (\mathbf{k}/k^2) q_\mathbf{k}$, with $q_\mathbf{k}$ Fourier coefficients of matter density, are the type of collective coordinates that one would thus introduce in such a system.

To set up a Hamiltonian to yield the correct equations of motion for the particles and the long-range field, Bohm and Pines [17] first write down the usual Hamiltonian [18] for particles in a field with kinetic reaction; the necessary subsidiary condition $\nabla \cdot \mathbf{E} - 4\pi\rho = 0$ is appended. Then a canonical transformation is made, with new momenta satisfying $\nabla \cdot \mathbf{\Pi} = \nabla \cdot \mathbf{E} - 4\pi\rho$; the momenta being longitudinal, the subsidiary condition $\mathbf{\Pi} = 0$ results. Moreover, the transformed Hamiltonian becomes a simple pair (Coulomb) interaction Hamiltonian with additional particle-field interaction and field kinetic energy which would vanish on application of the subsidiary condition. If the undesirable high wave number components, $k < k_c$, of $\mathbf{\Pi}$ are simply dropped from the Hamiltonian together with the associated subsidiary conditions, the formulation is then still valid. But now, as a final and crucial step, the remaining low wave number components of $\mathbf{\Pi}$ are transformed back to the corresponding components of $\mathbf{E}$, using precisely the original transformation. There then results an intermediate Hamiltonian, with subsidiary conditions, which describes the motion of the individual coordinates and of the low wave number components of $\mathbf{E}$.

The physical significance of the foregoing is clear. Without a subsidiary condition, the equations of motion for the particle-field Hamiltonian imply only $d/dt\,(\nabla\cdot\mathbf{E}-4\pi\rho)=0$. Thus a solution exists in which the field $\mathbf{E}$ differs from the true field by what may be regarded as a time-independent externally applied field: $\nabla\cdot\mathbf{E}(t)$ $=\nabla\cdot\bar{\mathbf{E}}+4\pi\rho(t)$; equivalently, one may insert a fixed source charge distribution which produces this external field: $\nabla\cdot\mathbf{E}(t)=4\pi\rho(t)+4\pi\bar{\rho}$. If the true field is then eliminated in favor of two-body interactions, those fixed charge components that were introduced remain attached to the true charge density. Then if the low wave vector fixed charge components, being at our disposal, are regarded as dynamical variables, a canonical redefinition can be made to attribute both true and fixed fictitious charge low wave vector components to new dynamical collective variables,

This process generalizes at once to non-Coulombic interaction [10], [19]. Thus, writing $H=\sum p_i^2/2m+\frac{1}{2}\sum_{i\neq j}V(\mathbf{x}_i-\mathbf{x}_j)$ in a periodic box Ω as

$$H=\sum p_i^2/2m+\tfrac{1}{2}\sum_k V_k\,(q_k q_k^*-\mathcal{N})\tag{74}$$

where $q_k=\sum_i e^{i\mathbf{k}\cdot\mathbf{x}_i}$ and V_k are the Fourier coefficients of $\Omega\rho(\mathbf{x})$ and $V(\mathbf{x})$, the q_k are the collective coordinates of eq. (62). (Since a complete description by the q_k alone is not attempted, there is no restriction here to Einstein-Bose statistics.) In order to make contact with the collective behavior for $k<k_c$, comprising say n' wave vectors, an external source density $V_k^{-\frac{1}{2}}\Pi_k$ is introduced, (henceforth assuming $V_k>0$), converting eq. (74) to

$$H'=\sum p_i^2/2m+\tfrac{1}{2}\sum_{k>k_c}V_k(q_k q_k^*-\mathcal{N})$$
$$+\tfrac{1}{2}\sum_{k<k_c}[(\Pi_k+V_k^{\frac{1}{2}}q_k)(\Pi_k^*+V_k^{\frac{1}{2}}q_k^*)-\mathcal{N}V_k]\tag{75}$$

As quantum mechanical subsidiary condition, we must choose $\Pi_k\psi=0$, consistent with H'; if Π_k is a momentum and ζ_k the conjugate coordiante, then $\partial\psi/\partial\zeta_k=0$, so that while $3\mathcal{N}+n'$ coordinates are used, the coordinates ζ_k are absent from ψ. Finally, the canonical transformation

$$\Pi_k+V_k^{\frac{1}{2}}q_k\to\Pi_k$$
$$\mathbf{p}_i\to\mathbf{p}_i+i\sum_{k<k_c}V_k^{\frac{1}{2}}\zeta_k\,\mathbf{k}\,e^{i\mathbf{k}\cdot\mathbf{x}_i}\tag{76}$$

transfers the complete collective behavior to $\Pi_{\mathbf{k}}$, ζ_k — the $\mathbf{x}_i$ and $\mathbf{p}_i$ remain as individual coordinates. The significance and consequences of the transformed Hamiltonian, which indeed breaks up into well separated collective and individual parts, are discussed in detail (with slightly different notation) by Pines in Chap. XVI.

If one wishes to determine the ground state of the above system, a variational calculation is recommended. Now, the variation must be carried out with the subsidiary conditions as constraints, and this is quite difficult to do in practice [20]. One can readily show [21] that if the ground state of the system without constraints is non-degenerate, then it will be identical with that of the constrained system. To see whether such a situation is to be expected, it is simplest to investigate the untransformed Hamiltonian H' of eq. (75). For a translation invariant state, with respect to the configuration coordinate $\mathbf{x}_i$ (of which the $q_{\mathbf{k}}$ are functions), the particle-"field" interaction $\Pi_{\mathbf{k}}^* q_{\mathbf{k}}$ has vanishing mean value, and the lowest energy does occur at vanishing field: $\Pi_{\mathbf{k}} \psi = 0$. However, for states that are not translation invariant, $\Pi_{\mathbf{k}} \psi = 0$ does not in general yield the minimum energy, so that one would like to show that the unconstrained ground state is not of this form; no a priori reason exists for the uniform system to be stable against insertion of sources, and any non-uniformity is difficult to recognize after transformation (76) has been made. Note that spatial translation of a stationary state that is not translation invariant produces a distinct state of the same energy, so that the condition of non-degeneracy is understood.

Ground State Energy of Collective Hamiltonian. In order to see whether the subsidiary conditions can be dropped for a ground state energy determination, we first observe that H' of (75) contains the $\Pi_{\mathbf{k}}$, but not the conjugate $\zeta_{\mathbf{k}}$, so that in a representation in which the $\Pi_{\mathbf{k}}$ are diagonal, only c numbers $\Pi_{\mathbf{k}}$ may be regarded as entering. Since the omission of required conditions on a wave function results in a *lower* bound to ground state energy, we now ask whether numbers $\Pi_{\mathbf{k}}$ exist such that the lowest eigenvalue of H' of eq. (75) is lower than that of H of eq. (74). More generally, suppose that a Hamiltonian H has ground state ψ and ground state energy E_0; we consider

$$H' = H + \Delta \tag{77}$$

and investigate its ground state energy E_0'. To do this, a φ as yet unspecified is introduced, and $\psi+\lambda\varphi$ employed as a variational trial function; hence

$$E_0' \leqq \langle\psi+\lambda\varphi|H+\Delta|\psi+\lambda\varphi\rangle/\langle\psi+\lambda\varphi|\psi+\lambda\varphi\rangle \tag{78}$$

or using the fact that $H\psi = E_0\psi$,

$$E_0'-E_0 \leqq \frac{\langle\psi|\Delta|\psi\rangle+\lambda\langle\psi|\Delta|\varphi\rangle+\lambda^*\langle\varphi|\Delta|\psi\rangle+\lambda\lambda^*\langle\varphi|H+\Delta-E_0|\varphi\rangle}{1+\lambda\langle\psi|\varphi\rangle+\lambda^*\langle\varphi|\psi\rangle+\lambda\lambda^*\langle\varphi|\varphi\rangle} \tag{79}$$

Now we shall certainly have $E_0' < E_0$ if $\langle\varphi|H+\Delta|\varphi\rangle < E_0\langle\varphi|\varphi\rangle$; let us therefore assume that $\langle\varphi|H+\Delta-E_0|\varphi\rangle \geqq 0$. Then, since the numerator of (79) has a minimum value of $\langle\varphi|H+\Delta-E_0|\varphi\rangle^{-1}$ · $[\langle\psi|\Delta|\psi\rangle\langle\varphi|H+\Delta-E_0|\varphi\rangle-\langle\varphi|\Delta|\psi\rangle\langle\psi|\Delta|\varphi\rangle]$, $E_0' < E_0$ will result if

$$\langle\varphi|H+\Delta-E_0|\varphi\rangle < \langle\varphi|\Delta|\psi\rangle\langle\psi|\Delta|\varphi\rangle/\langle\psi|\Delta|\psi\rangle \tag{80}$$

which also includes the possibility $\langle\varphi|H+\Delta|\varphi\rangle < E_0\langle\varphi|\varphi\rangle$. The case $\langle\psi|\Delta|\psi\rangle < 0$ need not be considered, for that obviously implies $E_0' < E_0$.

For a perturbation Δ, one would expect ψ to receive a considerable component in the $\Delta\psi$ direction; let us therefore choose $\varphi = \Delta\psi$ (More appropriate for Δ dividing naturally as $\sum \Delta_j$ would be the replacement of $\lambda\varphi$ by $\sum \lambda_j \Delta_j \psi$, but we shall not examine such nuances.) Observing that $(H-E_0)\psi = 0$ establishes the identity of $\langle\psi|\Delta(H-E_0)\Delta|\psi\rangle$ and $\frac{1}{2}\langle|[\Delta, [H, \Delta]]|\psi\rangle$, condition (80) then becomes, employing averages in the state ψ,

$$\tfrac{1}{2}\langle[\Delta, [H, \Delta]]\rangle < (\langle\Delta^2\rangle^2/\langle\Delta\rangle)-\langle\Delta^3\rangle \tag{81}$$

We may apply this at once to the comparison of H and H' of (74) and (75); restricting ourselves to one real field component Π for wave numbers $\mathbf{k}, -\mathbf{k}$, we therefore set

$$\begin{aligned} H &= \sum p_i^2/2m+\tfrac{1}{2}\sum V_1(q_1q_1^*-\mathcal{N}) \\ \Delta &= \Pi^2-\Pi V_\mathbf{k}^{\frac{1}{2}}(q_\mathbf{k}+q_\mathbf{k}^*) \end{aligned} \tag{82}$$

Since ψ is translation invariant, $\langle q_\mathbf{k}\rangle = \langle q_\mathbf{k}^* q_{-\mathbf{k}}\rangle = \langle q_\mathbf{k}^3\rangle = 0$, and, efining $\mathscr{E}_{\mathbf{k}} = \hbar^2 k^2/2m$, condition (81) thereby reduces to

$$2\mathscr{N}\Pi^2 V_{\mathbf{k}} \mathscr{E}_{\mathbf{k}} < 2\Pi^2 V_{\mathbf{k}} \langle q_{\mathbf{k}} q_{\mathbf{k}}^* \rangle (2V_{\mathbf{k}} \langle q_{\mathbf{k}} q_{\mathbf{k}}^* \rangle - \Pi^2) \qquad (83)$$

But $V_{\mathbf{k}} > 0$ and we are interested of course in $\Pi \neq 0$; we conclude that the undesirable result that E_0' is lower than E_0 arises if

$$\mathscr{N}\mathscr{E}_{\mathbf{k}} < 2V_{\mathbf{k}} \langle q_{\mathbf{k}} q_{\mathbf{k}}^* \rangle^2 \qquad (84)$$

Example and Counterexample. To investigate the possibility of eq. (84) being true, we find that in the zeroth approximation in the Bohm-Pines theory, $\langle q_{\mathbf{k}} q_{\mathbf{k}}^* \rangle = (\mathscr{E}_{\mathbf{k}}/2\mathscr{N}V_{\mathbf{k}})^{\frac{1}{2}}$. On this basis, (84) is an equality, not an inequality, and we would say that the energy E_0' with subsidiary conditions omitted, if lower than E_0, can be so only through a higher order effect. On the other hand, any improvement of the variational expression (79) will cause $E_0' < E_0$, even with an equality in (84); but then, the improved Bohm-Pines theory [16] and Chap. XVI) generally reduces the value of $\langle q_{\mathbf{k}} q_{\mathbf{k}}^* \rangle$.

It seems then that although it is possible in special cases to have $E_0' < E_0$, the deviation will generally be small. That such special cases do exist is verified by choosing the highly non-physical spinless Fermi gas with δ function interactions. The interaction does not change the wave function at all, so that the ground state is the simple independent particle ground state, for which one verifies that, for low $\mathbf{k}$ (with $\Omega = 1$),

$$\langle q_{\mathbf{k}} q_{\mathbf{k}}^* \rangle = (3\mathscr{N}/4\pi)^{2/3} k \qquad (85)$$

The Fourier component of the interaction is now simply a constant V, so that criterion (84) is satisfied if

$$V > (4\pi/3)^{4/3} (\hbar^2/4m) \mathscr{N}^{-1/3} \qquad (86)$$

To see that the order of magnitude is not unreasonable, we note that the Bohm-Pines criterion for collective behavior at wave number k, which here becomes $(2/m) k^2 E_F \ll \mathscr{N}k^2 V/m$, E_F being the Fermi energy, yields

$$(6\pi^2)^{2/3} (\hbar^2/2m) \mathscr{N}^{-1/3} \ll V \qquad (87)$$

which is certainly consistent with (86).

The above counterexample was, strangely enough, essentially used by Bohm, Huang, and Pines [21] for $\mathscr{N} = 2$ and one-dimensional space [(86) thereby changing to $V > 4\pi^2 \mathcal{N}(\hbar^2/4m)$] as an example to indicate that the situation $E_0' < E_0$ does not arise. They took advantage of the fact that the Schrödinger equation could be solved explicitly in this case by Mathieu functions (indeed a simple strong coupling solution exists for any $\mathcal{N}$). Aside from a non-trivial but non-crucial error in the asymptotic Mathieu energy, the trouble in this example resided in the convenient normalization which was used for the particle-field coupling, equivalent to choosing $V = \hbar^2/4m$ and thus incapable of evoking the $E_0' < E_0$ situation.

4. Individual and collective variables

We now return to the problem of delineating the residual degrees of freedom, after an approximate set of collective modes has been constructed. If we are willing to accept the necessity of using relatively innocuous subsidiary conditions, then a rather general solution is available. Attention will be specifically restricted to the study of momentum-independent variables, since any extension leads to substantial complications; it is true however that a corresponding analysis in quantum mechanical phase space (e.g., via the Wigner distribution [22]) proceeds along closely analogous lines.

Residual Variables. Suppose that $n' < 3\mathcal{N}$ collective coordinates $\{q_s\} = \{g_s(\mathbf{x}_1, \ldots, \mathbf{x}_N)\}$ have been introduced to describe gross collective features of a system of $3\mathcal{N}$ configurational coordinates $\mathbf{x}_1, \ldots, \mathbf{x}_N$. We now define $3\mathcal{N}$ individual coordinates $\mathbf{y}_1, \ldots, \mathbf{y}_N$ *with respect to* the collective motions by the following conditions: (1) the $\mathbf{y}_j$ must coincide with the $\mathbf{x}_j$ when there is no collective motion; (2) there is no collective motion associated with $\mathbf{y}_j$ themselves. Thus if we write

$$\mathbf{y}_j = \mathbf{r}_j(\mathbf{x}_1, \ldots, \mathbf{x}_N; q_1, \ldots, q_{n'}) \qquad (88)$$

the $3\mathcal{N}$ functions ($\mathcal{N}$ vectors) $\mathbf{r}_j$ must satisfy

$$\mathbf{r}_j(\mathbf{x}_1, \ldots, \mathbf{x}_N; 0, \ldots, 0) = \mathbf{x}_j \qquad (89a)$$

$$g_s(\mathbf{r}_1[\mathbf{x}; \mathbf{g}(\mathbf{x})], \ldots, \mathbf{r}_N[\mathbf{x}; \mathbf{g}(\mathbf{x})]) = 0 \qquad (89b)$$

Here $\mathbf{x}$ and $\mathbf{g}$ refer to the full set of $\mathbf{x}_i$ and g_s. The consistency of the $3\mathcal{N}+n'$ relations (89) is established by noting that if the $g_s(\mathbf{x}) = 0$, then the relations $g_s(\mathbf{x}) = 0$ are regained by substituting (89a) into (89b). Although the $\mathbf{r}_j$ are not uniquely determined by (89), their form in any physical situation will admit of little uncertainty; in particular, in many cases of interest, $\mathbf{r}_j$ will depend explicitly only upon $\mathbf{x}_j$: $\mathbf{y}_j = \mathbf{r}(\mathbf{x}_j; q_1, \ldots, q_{n'})$.

As an elementary example, essentially the prototype, one may extract the center of mass motion as sole collective entity:

$$\mathbf{q} = (1/N) \sum_i \mathbf{x}_i \tag{90}$$

The $\mathbf{y}_j$ will then of course be the relative coordinates

$$\mathbf{y}_j = \mathbf{x}_j - \mathbf{q} \tag{91}$$

which indeed satisfy both of the conditions (89). For more extensive sets of collective coordinates, the determination of the $\mathbf{y}_j$ may be less than obvious; however, if the collective amplitudes can be regarded as small, the general form for $\mathbf{y}_j$ may be replaced by

$$\mathbf{y}_j = \mathbf{x}_j - \sum \mathbf{f}_j^{(s)}(\mathbf{x}) q_s \tag{92}$$

which automatically satisfies (89a), while (89b) is valid to second order in the q_s if

$$q_s - \sum_{ju} q_u \mathbf{f}_j^{(u)}(\mathbf{x}) \cdot \nabla_j g_s = O(q^2) \tag{93}$$

Suppose for example that

$$q_\mathbf{s} = \sum_i \exp\left(i\mathbf{s} \cdot \mathbf{x}_i\right) \tag{94}$$

are a set of density fluctuation Fourier components; then we may employ, with Brenig [23],

$$\mathbf{f}_j^{(\mathbf{u})}(\mathbf{x}) = (-i\mathbf{u}/Nu^2) \exp\left(-i\mathbf{u} \cdot \mathbf{x}_j\right) \tag{95}$$

for it is clear that $\sum_j \mathbf{f}_j^{(\mathbf{u})}(\mathbf{x}) \cdot \nabla_j g_\mathbf{s} = (1/N) q_{\mathbf{s}-\mathbf{u}} = \delta_{\mathbf{su}} + O(q)$.

Condition (93) can be extended to a solution to all orders of (89). To do so, we observe that (93) is certainly satisfied if the $(n')^2$ relations

$$\sum \mathbf{f}_j^{(s)}(\mathbf{x}) \cdot \nabla_j g_t(\mathbf{x}) = \delta_{st} \tag{96}$$

hold true; furthermore, these $(n')^2$ algebraic relations for $3Nn'$ quantities $\mathbf{f}_j^{(s)}(\mathbf{x})$ have infinitely many solutions; if $\mathbf{f}_j^{(s)} = \nabla_j f^{(s)}$, (96) says that the coordinate system $\{f^{(s)}\}$ is orthogonal to $\{g_t\}$. Now define the operators

$$F^{(s)} = \sum \mathbf{f}_j^{(s)} \cdot \nabla_j \tag{97}$$

Since $F^{(s)}g_t = \delta_{st}$, the $F^{(s)}$ act like partial derivatives with respect to the q_s; they do not commute unless

$$\sum \mathbf{f}_j^{(s)} \cdot \nabla_j \mathbf{f}_i^{(t)} = \sum \mathbf{f}_j^{(t)} \cdot \nabla_j \mathbf{f}_i^{(s)} \tag{98}$$

but these conditions will not prove necessary. Having the "q_s derivatives", an obvious suggestion is that the residual $\mathbf{r}_j$ be obtained by "translating" each q_s back be precisely q_s. In other words, consider

$$\mathbf{r}_j(\mathbf{x}, \mathbf{q}) = \exp(-\sum q_s F^{(s)}) \mathbf{x}_j \tag{99}$$

Clearly $\mathbf{r}_j(\mathbf{x}_1, \ldots, \mathbf{x}_N; 0, \ldots, 0) = \mathbf{x}_j$; furthermore $g_s(\mathbf{r}_1, \ldots, \mathbf{r}_N)$ $= \exp(-\sum q_t F^{(t)}) g_s(\mathbf{x}) = g_s(\mathbf{x}) - \sum q_t F^{(t)} g_s + \frac{1}{2} \sum q_t q_u \, F^{(t)} F^{(u)} g_s$ $+ \ldots = g_s(\mathbf{x}) - q_s$, vanishing for $q_s = q_s(\mathbf{x})$. Thus, both of (89) are verified.

Floating Coordinates. Although we have set up a physically meaningful criterion for the residual coordinates associated with a set of collective coordinates, the $3N+n'$ $\{q_s\}$ and $\{\mathbf{y}_i\}$ are far from constituting an independent set, as evidenced by the explicit restriction $g_s(\ldots \mathbf{y}_i \ldots) = 0$. There then arises the problem of transforming the Hamiltonian to the new overdetermined set of variables. This will be done by direct transcription in Sec. 5. Here however we shall examine the consequences of introducing initial supplementary variables, in the manner of Bohm and Pines, allocating one to each subsidiary condition and thus making the transformation one-to-one. Indeed, one can arrange matters such that the subsidiary Hamiltonian is identical with the physical one, and thus overcome the type of difficulty associated with the Bohm-Pines treatment.

Let us now introduce [24], [25], [26] a "floating" set of individual coordinates $\{\mathbf{x}_i'\}$ possessing the same residual coordinates $\mathbf{r}_j[\mathbf{x}'; \mathbf{g}(\mathbf{x}')] = \mathbf{y}_j$ as the original $\{\mathbf{x}_i\}$, but with the $q_s' = g_s(\mathbf{x}')$ which are required to fix the definition of the $\mathbf{x}_i$ (the values of the $\mathbf{r}_j$ alone, being dependent, are insufficient) left unspecified. The $\{\mathbf{x}_i'\}$ are rigidly tied to the collective background, but that is left floating.

Then the two coordinate sets $\{\mathbf{x}_i, q'_s\}$ and $\{\mathbf{x}'_i, q_s\}$ defined by

$$q_s = g_s(\mathbf{x}_1, \ldots, \mathbf{x}_N) \qquad q'_s = g_s(\mathbf{x}'_1, \ldots, \mathbf{x}'_N) \qquad (100a)$$

$$\mathbf{r}_j(\mathbf{x}'_1, \ldots, \mathbf{x}'_N; q'_1, \ldots, q'_{n'}) = \mathbf{r}_j(\mathbf{x}_1, \ldots, \mathbf{x}_N; q_1, \ldots, q_{n'}) \quad (100b)$$

with conditions (89) again applying, are formally equivalent. Each coordinate system is an independent one, for by virtue of the identities $g_s[\mathbf{r}(\mathbf{x}; \mathbf{q})] = g_s[\mathbf{r}(\mathbf{x}'; \mathbf{q}')]$, (100) consists only of $3N + n'$ independent relations. It is only when we append subsidiary conditions

$$q'_s = 0 \qquad \text{or} \qquad g_s(\mathbf{x}'_1, \ldots, \mathbf{x}'_N) = 0 \qquad (101)$$

that, using (89a), the $\{\mathbf{x}'_i, q_s\}$ system reduces to the physically significant but algebraically overdetermined $\{\mathbf{y}_i, q_s\}$ system.

The advantages of this formalism are twofold. First of course is that the subsidiary conditions are automatically consistent with the Schrödinger equation, which like the Hamiltonian, does not contain the redundant variables $\{q'_s\}$ at all, and thus may be applied to the wave function at any stage of the calculation In fact, since a non-degenerate eigenstate of $H\psi(\mathbf{x}) = E\psi(\mathbf{x})$ on $\mathbf{x}$ space corresponds to the (very highly degenerate) set $\psi = f(\mathbf{q}')\psi(\mathbf{x})$ for arbitrarily normalized $f(\mathbf{q}')$ on $\{\mathbf{x}, \mathbf{q}'\}$ space many restrictions have the same effect, from evaluating at any set of $\{q'_s\}$ values to imposing the conditions $(\partial/\partial q'_s)\psi = 0$. Now although the conditions in (101) are needed to recover the original significance of the collective variables, (100) by itself is a perfectly good coordinate transformation from the expanded configuration space. The second advantage then is that the subsidiary conditions may be completely dropped, for not only do they fail to affect the energy levels, but q'_s commutes with all $\mathbf{x}$ space operators, so that expectation values will also be unchanged.

The infinite degeneracy of the unrestricted wave functions, in conformity with the availability of $> 3N$ quantum numbers, does provide an embarrassment of riches in carrying out approximate computations. The point is that in such theories as perturbation theory, the "unperturbed" Hamiltonian is generally chosen to have an essentially non-degenerate set of states, and it may not always be clear which of the perturbed states are really to be identified and which apparently distinct energies will ultimately coalesce. In a ground state energy variational computation, no restriction at all need be placed on the ansatz. In a variational calculation for other than the ground state energy, one can readily avoid the above difficulty by applying the restriction (101), e.g., by multiplying the ansatz by $\Pi\delta[g_s(\mathbf{x}')]^{\frac{1}{2}}$, which is completely equivalent to inserting a factor $\Pi\delta[g(\mathbf{x}')]$ into the volume element. On the other hand, for a state of surmised collective character $F(\mathbf{q})$, with residual coordinates unexcited, a variational computation of the lowest state using $\psi = \varphi(\mathbf{x}')F(\mathbf{q})$ is as physically unambiguous as the separation of collective states; this ansatz can be further improved by including the factor $\Pi\delta[g_s(\mathbf{x}')]^{\frac{1}{2}}$ and then indeed, with only $3N-n'$ functional parameters remaining, the full sequence of approximate states is guaranteed to be non-degenerate.

As a simple example of the foregoing, consider once more the case in which the collective coordinates are the components of the center of mass position. The coordinate transformation (100), with $\mathbf{r}$ given as before by $\mathbf{r}_i(\mathbf{x}, \mathbf{q}) = \mathbf{x}_i - \mathbf{q}$, may be solved at once to yield

$$\mathbf{x}_i = \mathbf{x}'_i + \mathbf{q} - (1/N) \sum \mathbf{x}'_j \qquad \mathbf{q}' = (1/N) \sum \mathbf{x}'_j$$
$$\text{or} \qquad \mathbf{x}'_i = \mathbf{x}_i + \mathbf{q}' - (1/N) \sum \mathbf{x}_j \qquad \mathbf{q} = (1/N) \sum \mathbf{x}_j \tag{102}$$

and the subsidiary condition $\sum \mathbf{x}'_j = 0$. The kinetic enegy $T = \sum p_i^2/2m$ becomes on transforming to the $(\mathbf{x}', \mathbf{q})$ representation,

$$T = P^2/2mN + \sum (p'_i)^2/2m - (\sum \mathbf{p}'_i)^2/2mN \tag{103}$$

where $\mathbf{P}$ and $\mathbf{p}'_i$ are conjugate to $\mathbf{q}$ and $\mathbf{x}'_i$. Now a state of total momentum $\overline{\mathbf{P}}$ yields an $F(\mathbf{q}) = \Omega^{-\frac{1}{2}}\exp(i\overline{\mathbf{P}} \cdot \mathbf{q}/\hbar)$, so that for such a collective motion, we may choose, e.g., for variational purposes

$$\psi = \varphi(\mathbf{x}')[\delta(\sum \mathbf{x}'_j)]^{\frac{1}{2}} \Omega^{-\frac{1}{2}} \exp(i\overline{\mathbf{P}} \cdot \mathbf{q}/\hbar) \tag{104}$$

yielding a kinetic energy expectation

$$\langle T \rangle = \overline{\mathbf{P}}^2/2mN + \int (dx')^{3N} \delta(\sum \mathbf{x}'_j) \varphi^*(\mathbf{x}')$$
$$[\sum (p'_i)^2/2m - (\sum \mathbf{p}'_i)^2/2mN] \varphi(\mathbf{x}') \tag{105}$$

separated exactly into collective and individual parts in this case

A less trivial situation, considered for simplicity in two dimensions is that in which q is the angle of the principal axis, and the residual coordinates are those in the principal axis frame. Hence

$$q = \tfrac{1}{2}\tan^{-1}[2\sum x_i y_i / \sum (x_i^2 - y_i^2)] \qquad q' = \tfrac{1}{2}\tan^{-1}[2\sum x_i' y_i' / \sum (x_i'^2 - y_i'^2)]$$

$$x_i \cos q + y_i \sin q = x_i' \cos q' + y_i' \sin q'$$

$$y_i \cos q - x_i \sin q = y_i' \cos q' - x_i' \sin q' \tag{106}$$

(and supplementary condition $\sum x_i' y_i' = 0$), solvable as

$$x_i = x_i' \cos [g(\mathbf{x}') - q] + y_i' \sin [g(\mathbf{x}') - q]$$

$$y_i = y_i' \cos [g(\mathbf{x}') - q] - x_i' \sin [g(\mathbf{x}') - q] \tag{107}$$

$$q' = \tfrac{1}{2}\tan^{-1} [2\sum x_i' y_i' / \sum (x_i'^2 - y_i'^2)]$$

and the reverse. Let us just look at the π^2 (π conjugate to q) or un-mixed collective part of the Hamiltonian, in either $\{\mathbf{x}', \mathbf{q}\}$ picture or representation [see (51), (53)]. Since $\sum [(\partial q/\partial x_j)^2 + (\partial q/\partial y_j)^2]$ $= \sum (x_j^2 + y_j^2)/[(\sum x_j^2 - y_j^2)^2 + 4(\sum x_j y_j)^2] = \sum (x_j'^2 + y_j'^2)/[(\sum x_j'^2 - y_j'^2)^2 + 4(\sum x_j' y_j')^2]$, it is

$$T_{\text{coll}} = \pi(\tfrac{1}{2}/\mathscr{I})\,\pi \tag{108}$$

where $\quad \mathscr{I} = m\{[\sum (x_j'^2 - y_j'^2)]^2 + 4(\sum x_j' y_j')^2\}/\sum (x_j'^2 + y_j'^2)$

$\mathscr{I}$ is the fluid moment of inertia, vanishing for an axially symmetric distribution, and is of consequence for nuclear rotational levels.

Finally, if the q_s are not really too large, a power series expansion is appropriate. In principle, it is only necessary to solve for the $\mathbf{x}_j$. But using (99)

$$\mathbf{x}_j - \sum \mathbf{f}_j^{(s)}(\mathbf{x})q_s + \tfrac{1}{2}\sum \mathbf{f}_i^{(s)}(\mathbf{x}) \cdot \nabla_i \mathbf{f}_j^{(t)}(\mathbf{x})q_s q_t + \cdots$$

$$= \mathbf{x}_j' - \sum \mathbf{f}_j^{(s)}(\mathbf{x}')q_s' + \tfrac{1}{2}\sum \mathbf{f}_i^{(s)}(\mathbf{x}') \cdot \nabla_i \mathbf{f}_j^{(t)}(\mathbf{x}')q_s' q_t' + \cdots \tag{109}$$

which is readily solved as a power series in q and q', yielding

$$\mathbf{x}_j = \mathbf{x}_j' + \sum \mathbf{f}_j^{(s)}(\mathbf{x}')[q_s - g_s(\mathbf{x}')] +$$

$$\tfrac{1}{2}\sum \mathbf{f}_k^{(t)}(\mathbf{x}') \cdot \nabla_k \mathbf{f}_j^{(s)}(\mathbf{x}')[q_s q_t - 2q_s g_t(\mathbf{x}') + g_s(\mathbf{x}')g_t(\mathbf{x}') + \cdots] \tag{110}$$

5. Enlargement of configuration space

The introduction of collective coordinates q_s' corresponding to "floating" coordinates $\mathbf{x}_j'$ in (100) has made it possible to transform from configuration space to a larger set of collective and residual coordinates. The question arises as to whether a transformation to a superfluously large coordinate set can be performed directly, and without availing ourselves of the concept — elegant in principle but complicated in practice — of residual coordinates. Such an approach has appeared in the work of A. Bohr [27], and more extensively in that of Zubarev [28] and collaborators [29]. A special case was examined in Chap. VIII, Sec. 3.

Extended Hamiltonian. To be reasonably general, we shall consider the transformation from $3\mathcal{N}\{\mathbf{x}_i\}$ — omitting internal degrees of freedom — to a larger set of $\{q_s\}$. The q_s may be all collective, collective plus the original configuration coordinates, collective plus residual individual coordinates, or any other appropriate possibility, but they will be functions (explicit or implicit) of the original $3\mathcal{N}\{\mathbf{x}_i\}$ and of no other coordinates. Clearly, an x space wave function $\psi(\ldots\mathbf{x}_i\ldots)$ can be written in many ways as a wave function $\bar{\psi}(\ldots q_s\ldots)$ on q space; if the functional form of the q_s is $q_s = g_s(\ldots\mathbf{x}_i\ldots)$, the relation is simply that

$$\psi(\ldots\mathbf{x}_i\ldots) = \bar{\psi}(\ldots g_s(\ldots\mathbf{x}_i\ldots)\ldots) \qquad (111)$$

The interpretation of $\bar{\psi}$ is of course that of a q picture but x representation, i.e., evaluations (such as integrations required for expectations) are to be performed in x space, with all quantities transformed back to x space for this purpose.

The Schrödinger equation may also be transcribed, again non-uniquely, to q space. Momentum transformation is effected by the observation that $\partial\psi[\ldots g_s(\ldots\mathbf{x}_i\ldots)\ldots]/\partial x_{i\alpha} = \sum (\partial g_s/\partial x_{i\alpha})(\partial\psi/\partial q_s)$, or if $\pi_s \equiv (\hbar/i)\,\partial/\partial q_s$ is the formal momentum conjugate to q_s, then

$$\mathbf{p}_i \to \sum_s (\nabla_i g_s)\pi_s \qquad (112)$$

There remains the transformation of coordinates, and a balance must be struck between simplicity and utility. First, the technique of the previous section may be described by saying that the q_s are really functions $q_s = G_s(\ldots\mathbf{x}_i\ldots f_\alpha\ldots)$ of $n'-3\mathcal{N}$ new variables as well, say the $\{f_\alpha\}$, but in such a fashion that

$$G_s(\ldots\mathbf{x}_i,\ldots 0\ldots) = g_s(\ldots\mathbf{x}_i\ldots) \qquad (113)$$

Thus the f_α are specified as functions which vanish when the q_s are given their desired functional form $g_s(\mathbf{x})$. In this case, the transformation (112) is unchanged ($\nabla_i q_s$ as defined coincides with $\nabla_i q_s$ at fixed f_α), but in addition one can solve explicitly for the $\mathbf{x}_i$ in terms of the q_s. Thus, the transformation of the Schrödinger equation $H(\mathbf{x}, \mathbf{p})\psi(\mathbf{x}) = E\psi(\mathbf{x})$ is unique, yielding

$$\bar{H}(\mathbf{q}, \boldsymbol{\pi})\,\bar{\psi}(\mathbf{q}) = E\bar{\psi}(\mathbf{q}) \tag{114}$$

in n'-dimensional space; the solutions of the two Schrödinger equations are identical, except that $\bar{\psi}(\mathbf{q})$ may have any factor $F[\dots f_\alpha(\dots q_s\dots)\dots]$ and is thus infinitely degenerate. Finally, since there are neither f_α nor $\partial/\partial f_\alpha$ in the Hamiltonian, the subsidiary conditions $f_\alpha = 0$ can be inserted at any time.

A second approach which is less rigid but still maintains the ever present availability of the subsidiary conditions is set up so that the transformed Hamiltonian $\bar{H}$ is a legitimate operation on the space for which all $f_\alpha(\dots q_s\dots) = 0$. To do this, suppose only that each $\nabla_i g_s$ in (112) is written (in any of a large variety of ways) as a fixed function of the q_t, while other coordinate terms are written in any fashion as q functions. $\bar{H}(\mathbf{q}, \boldsymbol{\pi})$ as given by (112) then has the desired properties. Indeed we may show that given $\psi(\mathbf{x})$ there is a corresponding $\bar{\psi}(\mathbf{q})$ which vanishes unless all $f_\alpha(\mathbf{q}) = 0$. It is

$$\bar{\psi}(\mathbf{q}) = Q[\psi(\mathbf{x})] \equiv \int \Pi_s \delta(q_s - g_s(\mathbf{x})) J^{-1}(\mathbf{x})\,\psi(\mathbf{x})\,dx^{3N} \tag{115}$$

where $J(\mathbf{x})$ is a generalization of the one-to-one transformation Jacobian $J(\mathbf{x}/\mathbf{q})$ and satisfies

$$\nabla_i J + J \sum_s \delta(\nabla_i g_s)/\partial q_s = 0 \tag{116}$$

(thereby implying integrability relations for the $\nabla_i g_s$). Then

$$q_s \bar{\psi}(\mathbf{q}) = Q[g_s(\mathbf{x})\,\psi(\mathbf{x})] \tag{117a}$$

$$\sum (\nabla_i g_s)\,\partial\bar{\psi}(\mathbf{q})/\partial q_s = Q[\nabla_i \psi(\mathbf{x})] \tag{117b}$$

Equation (117a) is obvious. To prove (117b), we see that

$$\sum \nabla_i q_s(\partial/\partial q_s) \int \Pi[q_s - g_s(\mathbf{x})] J^{-1}(\mathbf{x})\,\psi(\mathbf{x})\,dx^{3N} = \sum [(\partial/\partial q_s)\nabla_i q_s$$
$$-\partial\nabla_i q_s/\partial q_s] \int \Pi[q_s - g_s(\mathbf{x})] J^{-1}(\mathbf{x})\,\psi(x)\,dx^{3N} = \int \sum [\nabla_i g_s(\mathbf{x})\,\partial/\partial q_s$$
$$-\partial\nabla_i q_s/\partial q_s(\mathbf{x})] \Pi[q_s - g_s(\mathbf{x})] J^{-1}(\mathbf{x})\,\psi(\mathbf{x})\,dx^{3N} = \int J^{-1}(\mathbf{x})\,\psi(\mathbf{x})[-\nabla_i$$
$$-\sum \partial\nabla_i q_s/\partial q_s(\mathbf{x})]\Pi[q_s - g_s(\mathbf{x})]\,dx^{3N} = \int \Pi[q_s - g_s(\mathbf{x})][\nabla_i$$
$$-\sum \partial\nabla_i q_s/\partial q_s(\mathbf{x})] J^{-1}(\mathbf{x})\,\psi(\mathbf{x})\,dx^{3N} = \int \Pi[q_s - g_s(\mathbf{x})] J^{-1}(\mathbf{x})\nabla_i \psi(\mathbf{x})\,dx^{3N}$$

It follows now that if $H\psi(\mathbf{x}) = E\psi(\mathbf{x})$, then $\bar{H}\bar{\psi}(\mathbf{q}) = E\bar{\psi}(\mathbf{q})$, as desired. On the other hand, by our construction of $\bar{H}$, we are guaranteed that for any $\bar{\psi}(\mathbf{q})$ satisfying $\bar{H}\bar{\psi}(\mathbf{q}) = E\bar{\psi}(\mathbf{q})$, then defining $\psi(\mathbf{x})$ as in (111), $H\psi(\mathbf{x}) = E\psi(\mathbf{x})$. Thus every $\psi(\mathbf{x})$ emanates from at least one $\bar{\psi}(\mathbf{q})$, while all $\bar{\psi}(\mathbf{q})$ reduce either to $\psi(\mathbf{x})$ *or to zero*; the equivalence of the two sets is not guaranteed. It may be remarked that a considerably wider class of $\bar{H}(\mathbf{q}, \boldsymbol{\pi})$ exists satisfying the above conditions, for if we add to $\bar{H}(\mathbf{q}, \boldsymbol{\pi})$ any q space expression $\sum F_n'(\mathbf{q}) O_n(\mathbf{q}, \boldsymbol{\pi}) F_n(\mathbf{q})$ where F_n, F_n' vanish for $q_s = g_s(\mathbf{x})$, then $\bar{H}\bar{\psi}(\mathbf{q})$ of (116) and consequent conclusions are unaltered.

As a third and more general q-space transcription, one dispenses with the possibility of a consistent subsidiary condition, that is of obtaining a solution on the subspace $f_\alpha(\mathbf{q}) = 0$. For this purpose, $H(\mathbf{x}, \mathbf{p})$ is written in ordered form, with $\mathbf{x}_i$ to the left, $\mathbf{p}_i$ to the right, and the $\mathbf{p}_i$ transformed in a manner which is independent of the final transcription of x to q space; thus π_s is allowed to act only on the wave function and not, e.g., on $\nabla_i g$ whose q space form is not predetermined. The process is easy. $\mathbf{p}_i$ appears as in (112), with $\nabla_i g_s$ in x space. Then $\mathbf{p}_i \mathbf{p}_j \to \mathbf{p}_i \sum_t (\nabla_j g_t)\pi_t = \sum_t \nabla_j g_t) \mathbf{p}_i \pi_t + (\hbar/i)\sum_t (\nabla_i \nabla_j g_t)\pi_t$, or

$$\mathbf{p}_i \mathbf{p}_j \to \sum_{st} (\nabla_i g_s)(\nabla_j g_t)\pi_s \pi_t + (\hbar/i) \sum_t (\nabla_i \nabla_j g_t)\pi_t \qquad (118)$$

and similarly for higher order terms. The final step is to write each x-space coefficient in any fashion as a q space function; again, however, one may add to the resulting $\bar{H}(\mathbf{q}, \boldsymbol{\pi})$ an operator, this time of the form $\sum F_n(\mathbf{q}) O_n(\mathbf{q}, \boldsymbol{\pi})$. It is clear that if (114) holds, then on returning to x space, $H(\mathbf{x}, \mathbf{p}) \psi(\mathbf{x}) = E\psi(\mathbf{x})$ is valid as well, so that if $\psi(\mathbf{x})$ does not vanish, it is an eigenfunction and hence E of (114) a correct eigenvalue. It is also true in the general situation that every eigenfunction $\psi(\mathbf{x})$ may be obtained (at fixed $\bar{H}$) by reduction of some $\bar{\psi}(\mathbf{q})$. Let us suppose, after a suggestion of B. Zumino [30], that $\bar{H}$ and its associated boundary conditions are such that the $\bar{\psi}(\mathbf{q})$ of (114) constitute a complete set ($\bar{H}$ not compelled to be Hermitian). Then from the fact that any $f(\mathbf{x})$ is expandable in terms of the $\bar{\psi}(\mathbf{q})$, we see on identifying $q_s = g_s(\mathbf{x})$ that any $f(\mathbf{x})$ is likewise expandable in terms of the $\psi(\mathbf{x}) = \bar{\psi}[g(\mathbf{x})]$; hence the $\bar{\psi}[g(\mathbf{x})]$ include all eigenfunctions of H.

Examples. To illustrate the first type of configuration space extension, we may again consider appending the center of mass, $\mathbf{q} = \sum \mathbf{x}_i/\mathcal{N}$ to the $3\mathcal{N}$ relative coordinates $\mathbf{q}_j = \mathbf{x}_j - \sum \mathbf{x}_i/\mathcal{N}$. If $\mathbf{P}$ is conjugate to $\mathbf{q}$, $\mathbf{p}'_j$ to $\mathbf{q}_j$, then

$$\mathbf{p}_i = (1/\mathcal{N})\mathbf{P} + \mathbf{p}'_i - \sum \mathbf{p}'_i/\mathcal{N} \qquad (119)$$

Now as vanishing combinations, choose $f(\ldots \mathbf{q} \ldots) = \sum_j \mathbf{q}_j/\mathcal{N}$. With the corresponding modifications: $\mathbf{q} = \sum \mathbf{x}_i/\mathcal{N}$, $\mathbf{q}_j = \mathbf{x}_j - \sum \mathbf{x}_i/\mathcal{N} + \mathbf{f}$, one can solve uniquely as $\mathbf{x}_j = \mathbf{q}_j - \sum \mathbf{q}_i/\mathcal{N} + \mathbf{q}$, and the "standard" Hamiltonian (28) becomes

$$\bar{H} = P^2/2m\mathcal{N} + \sum (p'_i)^2/2m - (\sum \mathbf{p}'_i)^2/2m\mathcal{N} + \tfrac{1}{2} \sum V(\mathbf{q}_i - \mathbf{q}_j) \quad (120)$$

precisely as in Sec. 4, eq. (103). On the other hand, we may just as easily select the $\mathbf{q}_j$ as absolute coordinates: $\mathbf{q}_j = \mathbf{x}_j + \mathbf{f}$, with $\mathbf{f} = \sum \mathbf{q}_j \mathcal{N} - \mathbf{q}$; hence

$$\bar{H} = \mathbf{P} \cdot (\mathbf{P} + 2 \sum \mathbf{p}'_i)/2m\mathcal{N} + \sum (p'_i)^2/2m + \tfrac{1}{2} \sum V(\mathbf{q}_i - \mathbf{q}_j) \quad (121)$$

An important difference is that the collective kinetic energy separates in the relative coordinate case (120), but not in (121), consistent with the fact that the total momentum $\sum \mathbf{p}_i = \mathbf{P}$ in the former case, but $\sum \mathbf{p}_i = \mathbf{P} + \sum \mathbf{p}'_i$ in the latter. This suggests that the use of absolute coordinates is appropriate mainly when the corresponding part of the wave function — the medium on which the collective motion rides — is regarded as well-known, and so can be fixed, e.g., in a variational process.

The pair coordinate transformation $\mathbf{q}_{ij} = \mathbf{x}_i - \mathbf{x}_j$, $\mathbf{q}_0 = \sum \mathbf{x}_i/\mathcal{N}$, is an example of the second type of conpguration space extension; it has been discussed in detail in Chap. VIII, Sec. 3. This type is appropriate and easy to apply when the extended coordinates consist of the original $\mathbf{x}_j$ together with an additional collective set. If the $\nabla_i g_s$ are taken as functions of the $\mathbf{x}_i$, the integrability conditions required for (116) are automatically satisfied; however the incomplete separation of individual and collective motions generally necessitates a further canonical transformation. Suppose we are interested in the collective levels of a uniform system (e.g., condensed Einstein-Bose) in which individual motions are not readily excited. Following the path of Tomonaga, we then append two collective variables

$q_+ = \sum_j e^{i\mathbf{k}\cdot\mathbf{x}_j}$, $q_- = \sum_j e^{-i\mathbf{k}\cdot\mathbf{x}_j}$ to the original $\mathbf{x}_1, \ldots, \mathbf{x}_N$; thus

$$\mathbf{p}_i \to i\mathbf{k}\, e^{i\mathbf{k}\cdot\mathbf{x}_i}\, \pi_+ - i\mathbf{k}\, e^{-i\mathbf{k}\cdot\mathbf{x}_i}\, \pi_- + \mathbf{p}_i \qquad (122)$$

and the Hamiltonian (28) may be written as

$$\bar{H} = \{(Nk^2/m)\pi_+\pi_- + V_k(q_+q_- - N)\} - (k^2/2m)(q_{2\mathbf{k}}\pi_+^2 - q_{-2\mathbf{k}}\pi_-^2)$$
$$+ (i/2m)\sum[(e^{i\mathbf{k}\cdot\mathbf{x}_i}\mathbf{k}\cdot\mathbf{p}_i + \mathbf{k}\cdot\mathbf{p}_i\, e^{i\mathbf{k}\cdot\mathbf{x}_i})\pi_+ - (e^{-i\mathbf{k}\cdot\mathbf{x}_i}\mathbf{k}\cdot\mathbf{p}_i$$
$$+ \mathbf{k}\cdot\mathbf{p}_i e^{-i\mathbf{k}\cdot\mathbf{x}_i})\pi_-] + \{\sum p_i^2/2m + \tfrac{1}{2}\sum_{\mathbf{l}\neq\pm\mathbf{k}} V_\mathbf{l}\sum_{i\neq j} e^{i\mathbf{k}\cdot(\mathbf{x}_i-\mathbf{x}_j)}\} \qquad (123)$$

where $q_\mathbf{s} \equiv \sum e^{i\mathbf{s}\cdot\mathbf{x}_i}$. Equation (123) will be recognized as the single wave-vector form of the Bohm-Pines Hamiltonian; indeed the canonical transformation obtained by reversing (122) and letting $q_\pm \to q_\pm + \sum e^{\pm i\mathbf{k}\cdot\mathbf{x}_i}$ recovers the extended Bohm-Pines Hamiltonian (see Chap. XVI). Of course, the pure collective portion of $\bar{H}$, namely $(Nk^2/m)\,\pi_+\pi_- + V_\mathbf{k} q_+q_-$, is quite primitive. To further decouple the individual and collective motions one may: (1) use a canonical transformation; (2) find the x space self-energy due to the "sources" $\pi_\pm$, neglecting $q_\pm$ recoil and then diagonalize in q, π space; or (3) directly apply perturbation theory.

By choosing as new coordinates center of mass, Euler angles to principal axis frame, and principal radii of inertia, in addition to the $\mathbf{x}_i$, Gold and Levinson [31] easily reproduce the formulation of Levinson and Banerjee (Chap. XII).

Proceeding to the more powerful extension of (118), the complete collective transformation (55) for a Boson system may be generalized, since the onerous restriction to $3N$ coordinates does not apply. In fact, in the treatment of Bogoliubov and Zubarev [29], reviewed by Bogoliubov, Tolmachev, Tyablikov, and Zubarev in Chap. XIV, all $q_\mathbf{k} = \sum_j e^{i\mathbf{k}\cdot\mathbf{x}_j}$ for $\mathbf{k} \neq 0$ are employed; applying (118) yields at once

$$\bar{H}_B = \sum \mathbf{k}\cdot\mathbf{l}\, q_{\mathbf{k}-\mathbf{l}}\pi_\mathbf{k}\pi_\mathbf{l}^*/2m + \sum (i\hbar k^2/2m)\, q_\mathbf{k}\pi_\mathbf{k}$$
$$+ \tfrac{1}{2}\sum_{\mathbf{k}\neq 0} V_\mathbf{k}(q_\mathbf{k} q_\mathbf{k}^* - N) + \tfrac{1}{2}N(N-1)V_0 \qquad (124)$$

On the other hand, for a Fermion system, with antisymmetric wave function, it is difficult to make use of a full set of symmetric coordinates, and since the zeros are not known except in one-dimensional systems, one cannot rigorously remove a basic antisymmetric factor. This is due to the physical necessity of both collective and scattering-type modes, and a corresponding artifice is to include the absolute coordinates; $\mathbf{p}_i$ transforms as in (122), and we obtain

$$\bar{H}_F = \bar{H}_B + \sum p_i^2/2m + \sum (i/m) e^{i\mathbf{k}\cdot\mathbf{x}_i} \mathbf{k} \cdot \mathbf{p}_i \pi_\mathbf{k} \qquad (125)$$

in a sense particles embedded in a self-consistent field. For an initial variational solution, one may for example take a product of a q space function and an appropriate Slater determinant (including spin). In a non-uniform system, not only the external potential but also the mean (self-consistent) one-body part of the two-body potential should be written in x space and used to construct the Slater determinant, the residual potential expressed in q space. If only a finite number of $q_\mathbf{k}$ are employed [32], the major modification in (124), (125) is that the Fourier components of V corresponding to the missing $q_\mathbf{k}$ leave a residual short-range x space potential, leading quickly to the form and conclusions of the Bohm-Pines approach.

Even for a uniform system, the Slater determinant described above may be altered in Born-Oppenheimer fashion to encompass $q_\mathbf{k}$ fluctuations, and the particle solution then fed back to produce an additional collective potential. Without going into details, the simplest technique is merely to recognize that for a slowly varying density, the ground state kinetic energy of a Fermi-Dirac system will be given as

$$W = \tfrac{3}{5}(3\pi^2)^{2/3} (\hbar^2/2m) \int \rho(\mathbf{x})^{5/3} d^3x \qquad (126)$$

while the energy of the third term in (125) will vanish. Thus for the ground state with respect to particle-like excitations, it is only necessary to replace (125) by $\bar{H}_F = \bar{H}_B + W$, writing $\rho(\mathbf{x})$ explicitly as $\sum q_\mathbf{k} e^{-i\mathbf{k}\cdot\mathbf{x}}$. This extended Thomas-Fermi viewpoint has been used to advantage by E. P. Gross [33] in analyzing the problem of superconductivity.

Approximation Methods. The above configuration space extensions are in ascending order of inclusiveness, but descending order of guaranteed accuracy. The more elegant second and third types [(115)–(118)] suffer from the notable disadvantage that a solution

$\bar{\psi}(\mathbf{q})$ to (114) may reduce not only to a true eigenstate $\psi(\mathbf{x})$ but also to a spurious state which vanishes on transcription to x space. Thus E may not be an eigenvalue at all and in particular the lowest eigenvalue of (114) may be below the true E_0 (although in a variational approximation, an upper bound to an energy less than E_0 may be quite close to E_0). To examine this situation somewhat more carefully, let us again replace the n' q_s's by $3N$ combinations $\mathbf{x}_i(\ldots q_s \ldots)$ which reduce to the $\mathbf{x}_i$ under $q_s \to g_s(\mathbf{x})$, and $n'-3N$ expressions f_α which then vanish. The extended Hamiltonian thus has the form $\bar{H}(\ldots, \mathbf{x}_i, \ldots, f_\alpha, \ldots, \nabla_i, \ldots, \partial/\partial f_\alpha, \ldots)$, and by the mechanism of its construction we must have

$$\bar{H}(\ldots, \mathbf{x}_i, \ldots, 0, \ldots, \nabla_i, \ldots, \partial/\partial f_\alpha, \ldots) = H(\ldots, \mathbf{x}_i, \ldots, \nabla_i, \ldots) \quad (127)$$

For (115)–(117) to apply, (127) must also be true if $\bar{H}$ is ordered with the $\partial/\partial f_\alpha$ to the left and f_α to the right, or equivalently, taking the formal adjoint,

$$\bar{H}^+(\ldots, \mathbf{x}_i, \ldots, 0, \ldots, \nabla_i, \ldots, \partial/\partial f_\alpha, \ldots) = H(\ldots, \mathbf{x}_i, \ldots, \nabla_i, \ldots) \quad (128)$$

For (113)–(114) to apply, $\bar{H}$ can contain neither f_α nor $\partial/\partial f_\alpha$. But except in this (type 1) case, since there are no a priori restrictions on the eigenvalues of $\bar{H}(\mathbf{x}, \mathbf{f}, \nabla, \partial/\partial \mathbf{f}) \bar{\psi}(\mathbf{x}, \mathbf{f}) = E\bar{\psi}(\mathbf{x}, \mathbf{f})$, from which $H(\mathbf{x}, \nabla) \psi(\mathbf{x}) = E\psi(\mathbf{x})$ follows, then "most" $\bar{\psi}$ choose spurious eigenvalues and so correspond to vanishing wave functions in x space. Hence the subsidiary relations $f_\alpha = 0$ cannot simply be dropped; they serve to distinguish true from trivial wave functions and true from false eigenvalues. One can assess the validity of an approximate $\bar{\psi}$ only by converting to ψ in x space and convincing oneself that ψ is not an approximation to zero.

In special cases, the situation may be brighter. Thus, $\bar{H}-H$ may be higher order in the f's, so that eigenfunctions and eigenvalues will tend to cluster about the correct values, or $\bar{H}-H$ may be a nonnegative operator which produces an energy gap to the lowest spurious level so that at least the ground state energies coincide; these matters may be verified in the fashion of (77)–(81). Further, although the extent to which this is helpful is not easy to check, an $\bar{H}$ which is not Hermitian may have a substantially reduced space of eigenfunctions. In general however, the more detailed a solution required, the more one must insist on the restrictions $f_\alpha = 0$ being taken into account. For the most general (type 3) extended Hamiltonian, in which these restrictions are not consistent with the Schrödinger equation, but can only be applied at the end of the computation, every case is a special case. If the subsidiary conditions are at least consistent (type 2), a number of general techniques are available, from adding potentials to "center" the system about $f_\alpha = 0$ to achieving this by careful choice of variational ansatz; they are considered in greater detail in Chap. VIII, Sec. 3.

Assuming that these difficulties have been satisfactorily resolved, another may arise. It is that the extended Hamiltonian $\bar{H}$ is not necessarily Hermitian. This simply requires a little more effort in a perturbation calculation, but is more serious in a variational approximation, for only the Hermitian part of $\bar{H}$ appears (in $\langle \psi | \bar{H} | \psi \rangle$) in such an approach. For a one-to-one transformation, a non-Hermitian $\bar{H}$ is a consequence of using a q picture rather than a q representation [see (51), (53)], and the inclusion of a weight function adjusts matters properly. Let us then see if a similar adjustment

$$\psi(\mathbf{q}) = J(\mathbf{q})^{\frac{1}{2}} \, \bar{\psi}(\mathbf{q})$$
$$H(\mathbf{q}, \boldsymbol{\pi}) = J(\mathbf{q})^{\frac{1}{2}} \bar{H}(\mathbf{q}, \boldsymbol{\pi}) \, J(\mathbf{q})^{-\frac{1}{2}} \tag{129}$$

for suitable $J(\mathbf{q})$ is appropriate; in the one-to-one case, $J(\mathbf{q}) = |J(\mathbf{x}/\mathbf{q})|$ is the absolute Jacobian from x to q space (henceforth assumed to be real), a conclusion which follows at once from the fact that $\int \varphi^*(\mathbf{q}) H(\mathbf{q}, \boldsymbol{\pi}) \psi(\mathbf{q}) \, dq^{3N} = \int J(\mathbf{q}) \bar{\varphi}^*(\mathbf{q}) \bar{H}(\mathbf{q}, \boldsymbol{\pi}) \bar{\psi}(\mathbf{q}) \, dq^{3N} = \int \varphi^*(\mathbf{x}) H(\mathbf{x}, \mathbf{p}) \psi(\mathbf{x}) \, dx^{3N}$.

In general, if $H(\mathbf{q}, \boldsymbol{\pi})$ of (129) is to be Hermitian, we must have $J^{\frac{1}{2}} \bar{H} J^{-\frac{1}{2}} = J^{-\frac{1}{2}} \bar{H}^+ J^{\frac{1}{2}}$, or $J\bar{H} = \bar{H}^+ J$. If A is a real pure coordinate function it follows that $J(i/\hbar)[\bar{H}, A] = \{(i/\hbar)[\bar{H}, A]\}^+ J$. But all π derivatives are obtainable through such commutators; there results the criterion

$$J(\mathbf{q})[\prod_s (\partial/\partial \pi_s)^{n_s} \bar{H}(\mathbf{q}, \boldsymbol{\pi})] = [\prod_s (\partial/\partial \pi_s)^{n_s} \bar{H}(\mathbf{q}, \boldsymbol{\pi})]^+ J(\mathbf{q}) \tag{130}$$

for all derivatives, and this is readily applied by starting with the highest non-vanishing derivatives and working downwards. For a randomly constructed $\bar{H}$, one would scarcely expect (130) to be satisfied; one may require a non-diagonal $J(\mathbf{q}, \boldsymbol{\pi})$, or it may also be necessary to modify $\bar{H}$ by a "vanishing" $\sum F_n(\mathbf{q}) O_n(\mathbf{q}, \boldsymbol{\pi})$, but we shall not consider such modifications.

For an extended Hamiltonian (type 2) generated by (112) with fixed q space form for the $\nabla_i g_s$ and no further modifications, the required non-negative $J(\mathbf{q})$ is readily found; it is determined by

$$\sum_s \nabla_i g_s \, \partial J/\partial q_s + J \sum_s \partial(\nabla_i g_s)/\partial q_s = 0 \qquad (131)$$

and goes over on transcription to $J(\mathbf{x})$ of (116). To prove the adequacy of (131) we notice that now $\mathbf{p}_i \to J^{\frac{1}{2}} \sum_s (\nabla_i g_s) \pi_s J^{-\frac{1}{2}} = \sum_s (\nabla_i q_s \pi_s - \frac{1}{2} J^{-1} \nabla_i g_s \, \partial J/\partial q_s)$, or, from (131),

$$\mathbf{p}_i \to \frac{1}{2} \sum_s [(\nabla_i g_s) \pi_s + \pi_s (\nabla_i g_s)] \qquad (132)$$

which is Hermitian in q space, as will be $H(\mathbf{q}, \boldsymbol{\pi})$ constructed from it; (132) then induces a "q representation". Of course, we can now add to $H(\mathbf{q}, \boldsymbol{\pi})$ any Hermitian quantity of the form $\sum F'_n(\mathbf{q}) O_n(\mathbf{q}, \boldsymbol{\pi}) F_n(\mathbf{q})$, where F_n and F'_n vanish at $f_\alpha = 0$.

If one is willing to employ a Schrödinger equation with explicit weight function, an alternative formulation is available. That is, if $J^{\frac{1}{2}} \bar{H} J^{-\frac{1}{2}}$ is Hermitian, then so is $J\bar{H}$, but then $\bar{H}\bar{\psi} = E\bar{\psi}$ may be written as the Schrödinger equation with Hermitian Hamiltonian and non-negative weight

$$(J\bar{H})\bar{\psi} = (EJ)\bar{\psi} \qquad (129')$$

The advantage of (129') is that it remains meaningful even if J^{-1} does not exist. For example, a "universal" but highly singular solution to (131) is readily shown to be

$$J = \int \Pi_s \delta[q_s - g_s(\mathbf{x})] \, dx^{3N} \qquad (131')$$

(131') is then a singular equation with the property that all calculations may be carried out on the $3N$-dimensional subspace $\{q_s = g_s(\mathbf{x})\}$ or $\{f_\alpha = 0\}$. In fact, the combination (129'), (131') is not unfamiliar. If a complete set on the full $\{q_s\}$ space is selected, written in x space (in which it is overcomplete: non-orthonormal and non-independent), and used with undetermined coefficients in a secular determinant, perturbation, or Rayleigh-Ritz approach, one finds without difficulty that the q space equation to be solved is precisely (129′); the attendant drawbacks are also those of (129′).

Finally, let us note two special cases of (129)–(132). If the q_s include the $\mathbf{x}_i$, in terms of which all $\nabla_i g_s$ are expressed, then $J = 1$ and $\bar{H}$ is already Hermitian. If a transformation of type 1 is used, either J may be computed or (132) used directly; the transformation is basically one-to-one and so occasions no further concern.

The Fluid Picture. In certain cases, the explicit form of the spurious wave functions of an extended Hamiltonian may be sufficiently transparent to suggest a direct method for their elimination. An extremely important instance of this kind is the Bogoliubov-Zubarev extended Hamiltonian (124) for a periodically-bounded Einstein-Bose system. With no interaction, this is

$$\bar{T} = (\hbar^2/2m)(\sum \mathbf{k} \cdot 1\, q_{k+1}\, \partial^2/\partial q_k\, \partial q_1 + \sum k^2 q_k\, \partial/\partial q_k) \tag{133}$$

Since the second term maintains the degree of a multinomial in the $\mathbf{q}_k$, while the first term decreases it by one or two, it is clear that starting with a term $\prod_k q_k^{n_k}$, one can iterate down a multinomial which is an eigenfunction of (133). But there is a sharp division between eigenfunctions of degree $\leq \mathcal{N}$, which transcribe uniquely to true eigenfunctions in x space, and those of degree $> \mathcal{N}$, which necessarily vanish. For example, if $\mathcal{N} = 2$, $\bar{\psi} = q_k^3 - 3q_k q_{2k} + 2q_{3k}$ vanishes as a function of $\mathbf{x}_1, \mathbf{x}_2$. For $\mathcal{N} < 4$, spurious levels appear explicitly [e.g., $2mE/\hbar^2 = (1^2 + 2^2 + 3^2) = 14$ is impossible for $\mathcal{N} = 2$], while for $\mathcal{N} \geq 4$, they are buried within the immense free-particle degeneracy, extractable only on fixing other constants of the motion. Numerically, the lowest spurious state occurs at an energy — the level of confusion — of $(\mathcal{N}+1)\hbar^2 k_0^2/2m$, so that (133) may indeed be used unmodified for states below this energy; however, with interaction, this energy per particle is small both temperature wise and compared to interaction energy shift, so that the undesirable states must be assumed to proliferate throughout the spectrum.

It is thus vital to ensure that the q dependence of a wave function is not that of a system of more than $\mathcal{N}$ particles; the condition $q_0 = \mathcal{N}$ is not enough. Now one severe restriction which has been unheeded is that for a particle density $\rho(\mathbf{x})$, not only does $\int \rho(\mathbf{x})\, d^3x = \mathcal{N}$ but also $\rho(\mathbf{x}) \geqq 0$ for all $\mathbf{x}$. This is still just a set of inequalities and is not complete, for it allows fractional particles, i.e., a fluid. Finally, if one adopts appropriate boundary conditions so that the mass points are discrete, i.e., $\int_R \rho(\mathbf{x}) \, d^3x$ is an integer for any region R, then our objective is achieved and indeed it may be shown that all relations between the $q_{\mathbf{k}}$ are thereby implied.

Let us now implement the procedure suggested above. First, one wishes to guarantee that $\rho(\mathbf{x}) \geqq 0$ for all $\mathbf{x}$, and this is most easily accomplished by switching to the

$$\rho(\mathbf{x}) = \sum_i \delta(\mathbf{x}-\mathbf{x}_i) \tag{134}$$

as new variables and defining the physical space by $\rho(\mathbf{x}) \geqq 0$ (a restricted eigenspace too since $\psi = 0$ when any $\rho(\mathbf{x}) = 0$). The "index" $\mathbf{x}$ is now continuous, but this occasions no essential difficulty; the momentum transformation (112) becomes

$$\mathbf{p}_i \rightarrow - \int \nabla \delta(\mathbf{x}-\mathbf{x}_i) \, \pi(\mathbf{x}) \, d^3x \tag{135}$$

where $\quad \pi(\mathbf{x}) = (\hbar/i) \, \delta/\delta\rho(\mathbf{x}) \quad : \quad [\pi(\mathbf{x}), \rho(\mathbf{y})] = (\hbar/i) \, \delta(\mathbf{x}-\mathbf{y})$

Hence using (118) to evaluate the kinetic energy, $2m\bar{T} = \sum p_i^2 = \iint \sum \nabla \delta(\mathbf{x}-\mathbf{x}_i) \cdot \nabla \delta(\mathbf{y}-\mathbf{x}_i) \pi(\mathbf{x}) \pi(\mathbf{y}) \, d^3x \, d^3y + (\hbar/i) \int \sum_i \nabla^2 \delta(\mathbf{x}-\mathbf{x}_i) \pi(\mathbf{x}) \, d^3x$, or integrating by parts,

$$\bar{T} = (1/2m) \int \rho(\mathbf{x}) \, \nabla\pi(\mathbf{x}) \cdot \nabla\pi(\mathbf{x}) \, d^3x - (\hbar/2mi) \int \nabla\rho(\mathbf{x}) \cdot \nabla\pi(\mathbf{x}) \, d^3x \tag{136}$$

Further, the potential energy $V = \frac{1}{2} \sum_{i \neq j} V(\mathbf{x}_i - \mathbf{x}_j)$ becomes, by direct use of (134),

$$\bar{V} = \tfrac{1}{2} \iint V(\mathbf{x}-\mathbf{y}) [\rho(\mathbf{x}) \rho(\mathbf{y}) - \rho(\mathbf{x}) \delta(\mathbf{x}-\mathbf{y})] \, d^3x \, d^3y \tag{137}$$

It is to be noted that neither (136) nor (137) involve the zeroth Fourier component $\pi_0 = \Omega^{-1} \int \pi(\mathbf{x}) \, d^3x$. If $q_0 = \mathcal{N}$ is regarded as an observable which happens to be a constant of the motion, then π_0 formally exists but does not conserve particle number, and because the eigenvalues of q_0 are integers, the relation $[\pi_0, q_0] = \hbar/i$ tells us that π_0 is necessarily multivalued ($-\pi_0$ and $\hbar q_0$ are an angle-action pair) with an additive non-uniqueness of nh. Correspondingly, $\pi(\mathbf{x}) = \pi_0 + \sum_{\mathbf{k} \neq 0} \pi_{\mathbf{k}} \exp(-i\mathbf{k} \cdot \mathbf{x})$ must have the same uniform ($\mathbf{x}$-independent) multivaluedness.

It is useful to consider the classical limit $\hbar \rightarrow 0$. With $\mathcal{N} = q_0$ a variable, we now have an essentially one-to-one transformation to a system of continuous particle number, a literal fluid. Since $\dot{\rho}(\mathbf{x}) = \delta H/\delta\pi(\mathbf{x})$, $\dot{\pi}(\mathbf{x}) = -\delta H/\delta\rho(\mathbf{x})$, the Hamiltonian of (136), (137) yields the equations of motion

$$\dot{\rho}(\mathbf{x}) + \nabla \cdot [\rho(\mathbf{x})\nabla\pi(\mathbf{x})]/m = 0$$

$$\dot{\pi}(\mathbf{x}) + \nabla\pi(\mathbf{x}) \cdot \nabla\pi(\mathbf{x})/m + \int V(\mathbf{x}-\mathbf{y})\rho(\mathbf{y})\, d^3y - \tfrac{1}{2}V(0) = 0 \tag{138}$$

the second of which serves to define π_0 via $\dot{\pi}_0 = \Omega^{-1}\int \dot{\pi}(\mathbf{x})\, d^3x$. Setting

$$\mathbf{v}(\mathbf{x}) = (1/m)\nabla\pi(\mathbf{x}) \tag{139}$$

and applying the gradient operation to the second of (138), the equations of motion become

$$\dot{\rho}(\mathbf{x}) + \nabla \cdot [\rho(\mathbf{x})\, \mathbf{v}(\mathbf{x})] = 0$$

$$\dot{\mathbf{v}}(\mathbf{x}) + \mathbf{v}(\mathbf{x}) \cdot \nabla\mathbf{v}(\mathbf{x}) + (1/m)\int \nabla V(\mathbf{x}-\mathbf{y})\rho(\mathbf{y})\, d^3y = 0 \tag{140}$$

appearing as hydrodynamic mass and momentum conservation. Thus $\pi(\mathbf{x})/m$ is a true velocity potential and correspondingly is undetermined to an arbitrary additive constant; the macroscopic local velocity $\bar{\mathbf{v}}(\mathbf{y}) = \int_\tau \rho(\mathbf{y}+\mathbf{x})\mathbf{v}(\mathbf{y}+\mathbf{x})\, d^3x/\int_\tau \rho(\mathbf{x})\, d^3x$ for a small volume τ, it is to be noted, no longer has a velocity potential. Finally, if (140) is converted to Lagrangian coordinates [34]: $\mathbf{x}(\mathbf{x}_0)$, where $\mathbf{x}_0$ is the initial position of a piece of matter which thereafter moves at local velocity $\mathbf{v}(\mathbf{x})$, we obtain

$$\rho(\mathbf{x})\, d^3x = \rho_0(\mathbf{x}_0)\, d^3x_0$$

$$\ddot{\mathbf{x}} + (1/m)\int \nabla V[\mathbf{x} - \mathbf{x}(\mathbf{x}_0')]\rho_0(\mathbf{x}_0')\, d^3x_0' = 0 \tag{141}$$

where ρ_0 is the initial density; thus if ρ_0 consists of a set of δ functions, the original particle equations of motion are recovered.

Transition to Second Quantization. In the quantum mechanical case, we also have a one-to-one transformation to a fluid, with fractional particles a fair game. This at least means that the Jacobian required to transform to a density representation and consequent Hermitian Hamiltonian will be unique. Thus, employing (131), we have

$$-\int \nabla\delta(\mathbf{x}-\mathbf{x}_i)\, \delta \ln J/\delta\rho(\mathbf{x})\, d^3x - \int [\delta/\delta\rho(\mathbf{x})]\nabla\delta(\mathbf{x}-\mathbf{x}_i)\, d^3x = 0 \quad (142)$$

Multiplying by $\delta(\mathbf{y}-\mathbf{x}_i)$ and summing over i, the first term of (142) becomes $\sum \int \delta(\mathbf{y}-\mathbf{x}_i)\delta(\mathbf{x}-\mathbf{x}_i)\nabla[\delta \ln J/\delta\rho(\mathbf{x})] \, d^3x = \rho(\mathbf{y})\nabla[\delta \ln J/\delta\rho(\mathbf{y})]$, while the second may be written as $\int [\delta/\delta\rho(\mathbf{x})] \sum \delta(\mathbf{y}-\mathbf{x}_i)\nabla\delta(\mathbf{x}-\mathbf{x}_i) \, d^3x$
$- \int \sum \nabla\delta(\mathbf{x}-\mathbf{x}_i)[\delta/\delta\rho(\mathbf{x})]\,\delta(\mathbf{y}-\mathbf{x}_i) \, d^3x = \int [\delta/\delta\rho(\mathbf{x})]\rho(\mathbf{y}) \, d^3x +$
$\sum \nabla_i\delta(\mathbf{y}-\mathbf{x}_i) = \int \delta(\mathbf{x}-\mathbf{y})\nabla\delta(\mathbf{x}-\mathbf{y}) \, d^3x - \nabla\rho(\mathbf{y})$. Hence (142) reads

$$\rho(\mathbf{y})\,\nabla[\delta \ln J/\delta\rho(\mathbf{y})] + \nabla\rho(\mathbf{y}) = 0 \qquad (143)$$

which clearly has the unique non-negative solution

$$J = \exp\left\{-\int [\rho(\mathbf{y}) \ln \rho(\mathbf{y}) - \rho(\mathbf{y})] \, d^3y\right\} \qquad (144)$$

Expression (144) is really quite familiar, for if space is divided into small volumes $d\tau_\alpha$ at $\mathbf{x}_\alpha$, and $\mathcal{N}_\alpha$ is the number of particles in $d\tau_\alpha$, the relative weight of the configuration $\{\mathcal{N}_\alpha\}$ is [35] $\prod_\alpha (d\tau_\alpha)^{\mathcal{N}_\alpha}/\mathcal{N}_\alpha!$
$\propto \prod_\alpha (d\tau_\alpha/\mathcal{N}_\alpha)^{\mathcal{N}_\alpha} e^{\mathcal{N}_\alpha} = \exp \sum_\alpha \{\rho(\mathbf{x}_\alpha) \, d\tau_\alpha[1 - \ln \rho(\mathbf{x}_\alpha)]\} = \exp$
$-\int [\rho(\mathbf{x}) \ln \rho(\mathbf{x}) - \rho(\mathbf{x})] \, d^3x$, coinciding with $J = J(x/\rho)$ of (144). This is very close to using (131'), a method which, incidentally, can be made to yield the same expression.

The density representation now results from $H = J^{\frac{1}{2}} \bar{H} J^{-\frac{1}{2}}$, which, since

$$J^{\frac{1}{2}}\pi(\mathbf{x})J^{-\frac{1}{2}} = \pi(\mathbf{x}) + (\hbar/2i) \ln \rho(\mathbf{x}) \qquad (145)$$

the principal value of $\ln \rho$ always being chosen, converts (136), (137) to

$$H = (1/2m) \int \{\rho(\mathbf{x}) \nabla\pi(\mathbf{x}) \cdot \nabla\pi(\mathbf{x}) + (\hbar/2i)\rho(\mathbf{x})[\nabla\pi(\mathbf{x}), \cdot \nabla\rho(\mathbf{x})/\rho(\mathbf{x})]$$
$$+ (\hbar^2/4)\nabla\rho(\mathbf{x}) \cdot \nabla\rho(\mathbf{x})/\rho(\mathbf{x})\} \, d^3x$$
$$+ \tfrac{1}{2}\iint V(\mathbf{x}-\mathbf{y})[\rho(\mathbf{x})\rho(\mathbf{y}) - \rho(\mathbf{x})\delta(\mathbf{x}-\mathbf{y})] \, d^3x \, d^3y \qquad (146)$$

The second term is an infinite c number. [It is interesting to note that although $\rho(\mathbf{x})\nabla\pi(\mathbf{x}) \cdot \nabla\pi(\mathbf{x})$ is Hermitian, with all factors commuting, the correct kinetic energy has additional $\hbar^2$ terms — this is an illustration of the futility of "quantization" per se]. Equation (146), or more accurately, an expansion about the classical solutions thereof, is the basis of Zilsel's approach (Chap. XXVI) to the many-body Bose system. Bogoliubov and Zubarev [29] adopt an intermediate procedure, transforming their wave function to render a major part of the Hamiltonian Hermitian, thus operating close to a ρ or q representation. The characteristic of (146) is of course the same as that of its classical analog: if $\rho(\mathbf{x}) \geq 0$, it represents a fluid in which total number is fixed, but the concept of an individual particle does not occur.

There remains the problem of assuring the discreteness of particles, i.e., that $\int_R \rho(\mathbf{y}) \, d^3y$ has only integral values for an arbitrary region R. But $[\pi(\mathbf{x}), \int_R \rho(\mathbf{y}) \, d^3y] = \hbar/i$ or 0 as $\mathbf{x}$ does or does not belong to R; it follows that we must extend the multivaluedness of π under a uniform change to a multivaluedness of $\pi(\mathbf{x})$ by nh for each value of x, and this suffices. An immediate consequence is that while an irrotational local velocity (139) may still be defined, its circulation need not vanish; indeed, $\oint \mathbf{v} \cdot d\mathbf{l}$ must be a multiple of h/m, and vortex strength is quantized. To compel this uncertainty in $\pi(\mathbf{x})$ requires a change of representation. Simplest is a π representation, with each $\pi(\mathbf{x})$ running periodically from 0 to h. Much more customary however is a transformation to new variables:

$$\psi(\mathbf{x}) = e^{i\pi(\mathbf{x})/\hbar} \rho^{\frac{1}{2}}(\mathbf{x}) \qquad \psi^*(\mathbf{x}) = \rho^{\frac{1}{2}}(\mathbf{x}) e^{-i\pi(\mathbf{x})/\hbar}$$

$$\text{with} \qquad [\psi(\mathbf{x}), \psi^*(\mathbf{y})] = \delta(\mathbf{x}-\mathbf{y}) \qquad (147)$$

as only non-vanishing commutator, solvable, using the commutation relations, as

$$\rho(\mathbf{x}) = \psi^*(\mathbf{x}) \, \psi(\mathbf{x})$$

$$\nabla \pi(\mathbf{x}) = (\hbar/2i)\{\psi^{-1}(\mathbf{x})\nabla\psi(\mathbf{x}) - \psi^{*-1}(\mathbf{x})\nabla\psi^*(\mathbf{x})\} \qquad (148)$$

The univalence of $\psi(\mathbf{x})$ is equivalent to the range and periodicity of $\pi(\mathbf{x})$. Substituting, (146) takes the form

$$H = (\hbar^2/2m) \int \nabla\psi^*(\mathbf{x}) \cdot \nabla\psi(\mathbf{x}) \, d^3x$$

$$+ \tfrac{1}{2} \int\int V(\mathbf{x}-\mathbf{y}) \, \psi^*(\mathbf{x}) \, \psi^*(\mathbf{y}) \, \psi(\mathbf{y}) \, \psi(\mathbf{x}) \, d^3x \, d^3y \qquad (149)$$

just the usual result of second quantization. Gross' treatment (Chap. XV) is guided by an expansion about classical solutions corresponding to eq. (149).

Comparison of Formulations. To examine (146) and (149), it is expedient to Fourier transform variables in each; such a transformation, being linear, maintains the representation. For the second quantized expression, we set $\psi(\mathbf{x}) = \Omega^{-\frac{1}{2}} \sum a_{\mathbf{k}} e^{i\mathbf{k} \cdot \mathbf{x}}$, as is customary, thus converting (149) to

$$H = \sum (\hbar^2 k^2/2m) a_{\mathbf{k}}^* a_{\mathbf{k}} + \tfrac{1}{2} \sum V_{\mathbf{k}} a_{\mathbf{m}-\mathbf{k}}^* a_{\mathbf{l}+\mathbf{k}}^* a_{\mathbf{l}} a_{\mathbf{m}} \tag{150}$$

while in (146) we revert to $\rho(\mathbf{x}) = \Omega^{-1} \sum q_{\mathbf{k}} e^{-i\mathbf{k} \cdot \mathbf{x}}$, which after a short computation yields

$$H = \sum (\mathbf{k} \cdot \mathbf{l}/2m) q_{\mathbf{k}-\mathbf{l}} \pi_{\mathbf{k}} \pi_{\mathbf{l}} - (\hbar^2/4m) \sum k^2 - \tfrac{1}{2} V(0) q_0$$
$$+ (\hbar^2/8m\Omega) \sum \mathbf{k} \cdot \mathbf{l} [1/\rho(\mathbf{x})]_{\mathbf{k}-\mathbf{l}} q_{\mathbf{k}}^* q_{\mathbf{l}} + \tfrac{1}{2} \sum V_{\mathbf{k}} q_{\mathbf{k}} q_{\mathbf{k}}^* \tag{151}$$

An obvious distinction between (150) and (151) (aside from the spurious state problem) is that in the former, the kinetic energy is diagonal in the pairs $a_{\mathbf{k}}, a_{\mathbf{k}}^*$, while in the latter the potential energy is diagonal in the pairs $q_{\mathbf{k}}, q_{\mathbf{k}}^*$. Now it is readily shown (Percus and Yevick, Chap. XVII) that if one drops the potential and off-diagonal terms in (151):

$$T' = \sum (k^2/2m) \{ q_0 \pi_{\mathbf{k}} \pi_{\mathbf{k}}^* - \tfrac{1}{2} \hbar^2 + \tfrac{1}{4} \hbar^2 [1/\rho(\mathbf{x})\Omega]_0 q_{\mathbf{k}} q_{\mathbf{k}}^* \} \tag{152}$$

with $[1/\rho(\mathbf{x})\Omega]_0 = q_0^{-1}$ for low excitation, $(q_0^2 - 4q_1 q_1^*)^{-\frac{1}{2}}$ for excitation at wave number **1** alone, then an excellent representation of free-particle energies and wave functions is obtained; for convenience, we rewrite (152), for low excitation, as

$$T' = \sum (k^2/2m)(q_0^{\frac{1}{2}} \pi_{\mathbf{k}}^* + \tfrac{1}{2} i\hbar q_0^{-\frac{1}{2}} q_{\mathbf{k}})(q_0^{\frac{1}{2}} \pi_{\mathbf{k}} - \tfrac{1}{2} i\hbar q_0^{-\frac{1}{2}} q_{\mathbf{k}}^*) \tag{153}$$

In a similar fashion, for excitation sufficiently low for the occupation of $\mathbf{k} = 0$ to be a finite fraction of all particles, we may neglect potential energy terms in (150) for which fewer than two $\mathbf{k} = 0$ states are involved (see Bogoliubov and Zubarev [29]; Brueckner and Sawada [36]), then (150) becomes

$$H' = \sum (\hbar^2 k^2/2m) a_{\mathbf{k}}^* a_{\mathbf{k}} + \tfrac{1}{2} \sum_{\mathbf{k} \neq 0} V_{\mathbf{k}} (a_0^* a_{-\mathbf{k}} + a_{\mathbf{k}}^* a_0)(a_0^* a_{\mathbf{k}} + a_{-\mathbf{k}}^* a_0)$$
$$+ \tfrac{1}{2} V_0 (a_0^* a_0)^2 - \tfrac{1}{2} V(0) a_0^* a_0 \tag{154}$$

We see then that the potential energy of (154), which approximates that of (150), is also obtained from the exact (151) if the identification

$$q_{\mathbf{k}} \to a_0^* a_{\mathbf{k}} + a_{-\mathbf{k}}^* a_0 \qquad q_0 \to a_0^* a_0 \tag{155}$$

can be made, while the kinetic energy of (153), approximating that of (150), is obtained from the exact (150) by the identification

$$a_0^* a_{\mathbf{k}} \to \tfrac{1}{2} q_{\mathbf{k}} + i q_0 / \hbar \pi_{-\mathbf{k}} \qquad a_0^* a_0 \to q_0 \qquad (156)$$

But (156) is derivable from (155) with the added relation, consistent with (155) at low excitation,

$$\pi_{\mathbf{k}} \to (i\hbar/2q_0)(a_{\mathbf{k}}^* a_0 - a_0^* a_{-\mathbf{k}}) \qquad (157)$$

Since (155) can be regarded simply as the result of applying the low excitation condition $a_{\mathbf{k}}^* a_{\mathbf{k}} \ll a_0^* a_0$ to $q_{\mathbf{k}} = \int \psi^*(\mathbf{x}) \psi(\mathbf{x}) e^{i\mathbf{k} \cdot \mathbf{x}} d^3 x = \sum a_{\mathbf{k}+\mathbf{l}}^* a_{\mathbf{l}}$, we conclude that for excitation low enough to validate (155), both (150) and (151) may be taken in pure diagonal form, while for higher excitation, (146), (151) or (149), (150) will be more useful according as the proper representation of potential or kinetic energy dominates the physical situation. In either event, these are longitudinal phonon-type excitations. Other classes presumably exist (see Chap. XXIII, Sec. 3) in which the above dichotomy is not appropriate.

Notes and References

1. H. Goldstein, *Classical Mechanics*, Addison-Wesley, Reading, Mass., 1950, Chap. 10.
2. M. Born, *Mechanics of the Atom*, George Bell & Sons, Ltd., London, 1927, Chaps. 8, 9.
3. E. Fermi, *Physik Z.* **24**, 261 (1923).
4. J. B. Keller, *Annals of Physics* **4**, 180 (1958).
5. R. B. Brout, *Phys. Rev.* **108**, 515 (1957).
6. See e.g. H. C. Corben and P. Stehle, *Classical Mechanics*, Wiley, New York, 1950, p. 316.
7. S. Tomonaga, *Progr. Theoret. Phys.* (*Kyoto*) **13**, 467 (1955); 482 (1955). See also D. ter Haar, *Introduction to the Physics of Many-Body Systems*, Interscience, New York, 1959, Chap. 6.1.
8. N. N. Bogoliubov, *J. of Phys.* (*U.S.S.R.*) **11**, 23 (1947).
9. G. J. Yevick and J. K. Percus, *Bull. Am. Phys. Soc.*, Ser. II, **4**, 15 (1959).
10. D. Pines and D. Bohm, *Phys. Rev.* **85**, 338 (1952).
11. Sawada, Brueckner, Fukuda, and Brout, *Phys. Rev.* **108**, 507 (1957).
12. M. Gell-Mann and K. A. Brueckner, *Phys. Rev.* **106**, 364 (1957); K. Sawada, *Phys. Rev.* **106**, 372 (1957);
P. Nozieres and D. Pines, *Phys. Rev.* **111**, 442 (1958).
13. G. Gamow and C. L. Critchfield, *Atomic Nucleus and Nuclear Energy-Sources*, Oxford, New York 1949, p. 165.
14. J. K. Percus and G. J. Yevick, *Phys. Rev.* **110**, 1 (1958).

15. E. C. Kemble, *Fundamentals of Quantum Mechanics*, McGraw-Hill, New York, 1937, p. 238.
16. J. K. Percus and G. J. Yevick, *Exact New Reformulation of Many-Body Problem*, unpublished O. N. R. report, 1955.
17. D. Bohm and D. Pines, *Phys. Rev.* **85**, 338 (1952).
18. See, e.g., L. I. Schiff, *Quantum Mechanics*, McGraw-Hill, New York, 1949, Chap. XIV.
19. T. Kinoshita and Y. Nambu, *Phys. Rev.* **94**, 598 (1954).
20. E. N. Adams, *Phys. Rev.* **98**, 947, 1130 (1955).
21. Bohm, Huang, and Pines, *Phys. Rev.* **107**, 71 (1957).
22. E. P. Wigner. *Phys. Rev.* **40**, 479 (1932).
23. W. Brenig, Z. *Physik* **144**, 488 (1956); *Nuclear Phys.* **4**, 363 (1957).
24. F. Villars, *Ann. Rev. Nuclear Sci.* **7**, 185 (1957).
25. Lipkin, de Shalit, and Talmi, *Nuovo cimento* **2**, 773 (1955).
26. R. Skinner, *Can. J. Phys.* **34**, 901 (1956).
27. See e.g., A. Bohr, *Rotational States of Atomic Nuclei*, Munksgaard, Copenhagen, 1954.
28. D. N. Zubarev, $ZETF$ **25**, 548 (1953).
29. N. N. Bogoliubov and D. N. Zubarev, $ZETF$ **28**, 129 (1955) [translation: $JETP$ **1**, 83 (1955)].
30. B. Zumino, private communication.
31. I. Gold and C. A. Levinson, private communication.
32. See, e.g., Z. Galasiewicz, *Acta Phys. Polon.* **15**, 49 (1956); 79 (1956).
33. E. P. Gross, private communication.
34. See, e.g., R. Courant and K. O. Friedrichs, *Supersonic Flow and Shock Waves*, Interscience, New York, 1948, p. 12.
35. A. A. Broyles, *Bull. Am. Phys. Soc.*, Ser. II, **3**, 201 (1958).
36. K. A. Brueckner and K. Sawada, *Phys. Rev.* **106**, 1117 (1957); 1128 (1957).

Long-Range Correlations in Classical and Quantum Systems*

N. N. Bogoliubov, D. N. Zubarev, V. V. Tolmatchev, and S. V. Tyablikov

In classical statistical mechanics, the range of force determines the character of the correlation between particles. Short-range forces correspond to correlations at distances of the order of the range of force; long-range forces, for example Coulomb forces, correspond to long-range correlations, at distances significantly greater than the mean interparticle separation.

In quantum statistical mechanics, the situation is different, and the range of force no longer determines the range of correlation. For non-ideal quantum gases, in addition to the well-known long-range exchange correlations, there exists a correlation, due to the interaction force, which has a long-range character even for short-range forces. Below, we wish to discuss questions connected with the role of long-range correlations in classical and quantum systems.

1. *Correlation function in classical statistical mechanics*

In classical statistical mechanics, the correlation between particles is described by the distribution functions:

$$F_s(\mathbf{q}_1, \ldots, \mathbf{q}_s) = V^s \int \ldots \int D_N(\mathbf{q}_1, \ldots, \mathbf{q}_N) \, d\mathbf{q}_{s+1} \ldots d\mathbf{q}_N \quad (1)$$

where D_N is the Gibbs distribution with respect to coordinates $\mathbf{q}_1, \ldots, \mathbf{q}_N$, V is the volume of the system, and N the number of

---

* Translated by D. Finkelstein.

particles. The functions F_s satisfy the chain of integro-differential equations [1]:

$$0 = \partial F_s / \partial q_1^\alpha + (1/\theta)(\partial U_s / \partial q_1^\alpha) F_s + (1/\theta v) \int [\partial \varphi(|\mathbf{q}_1 - \mathbf{q}_{s+1}|)/\partial q_1^\alpha F_{s+1} \, dq_{s+1} \quad (2)$$

$$(s = 1, 2, \ldots) \qquad (V \to \infty, \, \mathcal{N} \to \infty, \, V/\mathcal{N} = v = \text{constant}$$

where $\varphi(|\mathbf{q}_1 - \mathbf{q}_2|)$ is the interaction potential between particles, $U_s = \sum_{(1 \leq i < j \leq s)} \varphi(|\mathbf{q}_i - \mathbf{q}_j|)$ is the interaction energy of the complex of s particles, and $\theta \equiv kT$.

For the case of short-range forces, it is possible to apply an expansion in inverse powers of the specific volume to the solution of the system of eq. (2):

$$F_s = F_s^0 + v^{-1} F_s' + \ldots \tag{3}$$

This expansion makes it possible to break the chain (2) and determine [1] the coefficients of the expansion (3):

$$F_s = e^{-U_s/\theta} \{ 1 + v^{-1} \int [\prod_{(1 \leq i \leq s)} [1 + f(|\mathbf{q}_i - \mathbf{q}_{s+1}|)]] - 1$$

$$- \sum_{(1 \leq i \leq s)} f(|\mathbf{q}_i - \mathbf{q}_{s+1}|)] \, d\mathbf{q}_{s+1} + \ldots \} \tag{4}$$

$$f(|\mathbf{q}|) = e^{-\varphi(|\mathbf{q}|)/\theta} - 1$$

The correlation function F_2 of (4), upon substitution into the virial equation, gives the well-known Ursell-Mayer expansion of the equation of state.

From formula (4), we may convince ourselves that F_s differs from 1 only in domains in which the distance between particles is of the order of the range of interaction, i.e., to a short-range force correspond correlations at small distances, of the order of the range of the force.

For the case of long-range forces, e.g., for a system of charged particles interacting via Coulomb forces, an expansion of the type (3) is not suitable, for the integrals accompanying the inverse powers of v will diverge, a fact connected with the excessively slow vanishing of the interaction energy $\varphi(\mathbf{r})$ for large r.

However, in this case, if one takes into account the fact that the Debye radius r_D is significantly greater than the distance between particles $(v/r_D^3 \ll 1)$, it is possible to employ an expansion in powers of v [1]:

$$F_s = F_s^0 + vF_s' + \dots \tag{5}$$

which in first approximation gives the formula of Debye theory:

$$F_2(r) = 1 - (v/4\pi r_D^2)\, e^{-r/r_D}/r \tag{6}$$

(With the help of perturbation theory, we would get the formula $F_2(r) = 1 - (v/4\pi r_D^2)/r$ for the correlation at large distances). Consequently, the range of correlation for a system of particles interacting through Coulomb forces can be rather large, of the order of the Debye radius.

Formula (6) loses its utility for small distances, since as $r \to 0$, $F_2 \to -\infty$, which is not meaningful. This difficulty can be circumvented by a modified expansion of the form (5) (see [2]). Namely, instead of (5), we may use the expansion

$$F_s = e^{-\overline{U}_s/\theta}\{C_s^0 + vC_s' + \dots\} \tag{7}$$

where the factor $\exp(-\overline{U}_s/\theta)$ gives the behavior of the correlation function at small distances.

The function $\overline{U}_s$ in (7) is defined by $\overline{U}_s = \sum_{(1 \leq i < j \leq s)} \bar{\varphi}(|\mathbf{q}_i - \mathbf{q}_j|)$ where we require that, as $r \to 0$, $\bar{\varphi}$ have the same singularity as φ (of the form $1/r$ for a Coulomb force). The function $\bar{\varphi}$ is so determined that the first-order term C_s' vanishes. Thus, $\bar{\varphi}$ yields a cutoff of the Coulomb interaction at the Debye length

$$\bar{\varphi} = (e^2/r)\, e^{-r/r_D} \tag{8}$$

For the pair correlation function, we get correspondingly

$$F_2(\mathbf{r}) = e^{-\bar{\varphi}(r)/\theta}(1 + v^2 \dots) \tag{9}$$

The first term in the series expansion of the exponent in (9) gives formula (6). In this way, the difficulty of the divergence of the correlation function at small distances is removed.

Great interest is attached to the intermediary case in which it is impossible to use either an expansion in powers of the density (3) or the plasma-type expansion (5), (6). In this case, the chain of equations (2) can be cut if we use for the ternary distribution function the interpolation formula [1]:

$$F_3(\mathbf{q}, \mathbf{q}', \mathbf{q}'') = F_2(\mathbf{q}, \mathbf{q}')\, F_2(\mathbf{q}', \mathbf{q}'')\, F_2(\mathbf{q}'', \mathbf{q}) \tag{10}$$

Employing (10) we obtain for the binary distribution function the integral equation of [1], which was established earlier for the case of hard spheres by Kirkwood [3]. We observe that if we apply to the solution of this equation an expansion in powers of $1/v$, then we get the first two terms in (3), but if we expand the solution in powers of v, we get the first two terms in (5).

An analogous method of constructing the distribution function is also developed in the work of Born and Green [4].

2. *Correlation function in quantum statistics*

In quantum statistics, the correlation between particles is described by the density operator for a complex of s molecules

$$F_s(\mathbf{q}_1, \ldots, \mathbf{q}_s; \mathbf{q}_1', \ldots, \mathbf{q}_s') = V^s \operatorname{Tr}_{(s+1,\ldots,N)} \rho \qquad (11)$$

where ρ is von Neumann's statistical operator.

We can establish a simple equation for the function F_s by relating $\partial F_s/\partial t$ to F_{s+1}, suitable for the dynamic equations of quantum statistics. However, for the case of statistical equilibrium, the Gibbsian character of ρ is not taken into account in these equations. Equation (2), valid in classical statistics, cannot have, to our regret, a simple generalization in the case of quantum statistics. True, it is possible to set up a chain of equations connecting $\partial F_s/\partial\theta$ with F_s and F_{s+1}; however, these equations contain a multiplicity of terms proportional to the number of particles N, and so are not suitable for the treatment of asymptotic solutions corresponding to $V \to \infty$, $N \to \infty$, with $V/N = v$.

There exists another method of obtaining the correlation functions in cases in which it has been possible to compute the free energy $\mathscr{F}$ of the system. Then, one can make use of the relation

$$F_2(|\mathbf{q}_1 - \mathbf{q}_2|) = (2V/N^2)\, \delta\mathscr{F}/[\delta\varphi(|\mathbf{q}_1 - \mathbf{q}_2|)] \qquad (12)$$

which is valid both in classical and in quantum statistics.

We have computed the correlation for a weakly non-ideal Bose gas at low temperature by means of the previously developed theory of non-ideal Bose gases [7]. For this purpose, we point out that for ideal Bose gases at absolute zero, all of the molecules are in the cell of zero momentum, while for weakly non-ideal gases, this is still approximately valid. Thus, using the notation of second quantization, the number of particles in the cell with zero momentum, $\mathcal{N}_0 = a_0^+ a_0$, is significantly greater than 1; consequently, in the commutation relation $a_0 a_0^+ - a_0^+ a_0 = 1$, it is possible to neglect 1 in comparison with the left-hand side and so regard a_0, a_0^+ as ordinary numbers.

Assuming $a_{\mathbf{k}}$, $a_{\mathbf{k}}^+$ to be small compared to a_0, a_0^+, one may write the Hamiltonian of the system in the form

$$H = \tfrac{1}{2}(\mathcal{N}^2/V)\,v(0) + (1/2V)\sum_{(\mathbf{k}\neq 0)} v(\mathbf{k})\{a_0^2 a_{\mathbf{k}}^+ a_{-\mathbf{k}}^+$$
$$+ a_0^{+2} a_{\mathbf{k}} a_{-\mathbf{k}}\} + \sum_{(\mathbf{k}\neq 0)}\{\hbar^2 k^2/2m + \mathcal{N}_0 v(\mathbf{k})/V\}a_{\mathbf{k}}^+ a_{\mathbf{k}} \qquad (13)$$
$$v(\mathbf{k}) = \int \varphi(\mathbf{q})\,e^{-i\mathbf{k}\cdot\mathbf{q}}\,d\mathbf{q}$$

where we have restricted ourselves to terms not higher than second order in the operators $a_{\mathbf{k}}$, $a_{\mathbf{k}}^+$. Calculation of the discarded terms of third order gives an interaction between the elementary excitations of a Bose gas, and hence is essential for the construction of the dynamical equations for elementary excitations in a Bose gas.

Instead of the operators $a_{\mathbf{k}}$, $a_{\mathbf{k}}^+$ it is convenient to introduce new Bose operators

$$b_{\mathbf{k}}^+ = a_0 \mathcal{N}_0^{-\frac{1}{2}} a_{\mathbf{k}}^+ \qquad b_{\mathbf{k}} = a_0^+ \mathcal{N}_0^{-\frac{1}{2}} a_{\mathbf{k}} \qquad (14)$$

Transforming further from operators $b_{\mathbf{k}}$, $b_{\mathbf{k}}^+$ to new operators $\xi_{\mathbf{k}}$, $\xi_{\mathbf{k}}^+$ by the formula

$$\xi_{\mathbf{k}} = (b_{\mathbf{k}} - L_{\mathbf{k}} b_{\mathbf{k}}^+)/(1 - |L_{\mathbf{k}}|^2)^{\frac{1}{2}} \qquad \xi_{\mathbf{k}}^+ = (b_{\mathbf{k}}^+ - L_{\mathbf{k}}^* b_{-\mathbf{k}})/(1 - |L_{\mathbf{k}}|^2)^{\frac{1}{2}} \qquad (15)$$

where $L_{\mathbf{k}}$ is some known function of $\mathbf{k}$, it is easy to exhibit the Hamiltonian in diagonal form:

$$H = E_0 + \sum_{(\mathbf{k}\neq 0)} E(\mathbf{k}) n_{\mathbf{k}} \qquad n_{\mathbf{k}} = \xi_{\mathbf{k}}^+ \xi_{\mathbf{k}} \qquad (16)$$

Here

$$E(\mathbf{k}) = [(\mathcal{N}_0/V)(\hbar^2 k^2/m)\,v(\mathbf{k}) + (\hbar^2 k^2/2m)^2]^{\frac{1}{2}} \qquad (17)$$

is the energy of the elementary excitation, while

$$E_0 = (\mathcal{N}^2/2V)\,v(0) + \tfrac{1}{2}\sum_{(\mathbf{k}\neq 0)}\{E(\mathbf{k}) - \hbar^2 k^2/2m - (\mathcal{N}_0/V)\,v(\mathbf{k})\} \qquad (18)$$

is the energy of the lowest state of the system.

We point out, by the way, that the spectrum of elementary excitations of a non-ideal Bose gas (17) satisfies the well-known criterion of Landau [8], and makes it possible to partially explain the phenomenon of superfluidity [9].

The method presented has been somewhat generalized recently in the interesting work of Brueckner and Sawada [10], which starts from a Hamiltonian differing from (13) by replacing the matrix elements of the interaction energy by matrix elements of the scattering operator, in the spirit of the ideas of Brueckner.

By using the formulas (12), (18), (17), it is easy to get the following expression for the distribution function:

$$F_2(|\mathbf{q}|) = 1 + \mathcal{N}^{-1} \sum \{(\hbar^2 k^2/2m\,E(\mathbf{k}))(1 + 2\bar{n}_\mathbf{k}) - 1\}\, e^{-i\mathbf{k}\cdot\mathbf{q}} \qquad (19)$$

The very same connection between the correlation function and the energy of the elementary excitations was obtained by Feynman [11] for the case of zero temperature.

From eq. (19) for $T = 0$, we find the asymptotic expression, suitable for large $|q|$:

$$F_2(|\mathbf{q}|) \cong 1 + (\hbar V^{\frac{3}{2}}/\mathcal{N}^{\frac{3}{2}})/[2\pi^2(mv(0))^{\frac{1}{2}}](1/|\mathbf{q}|^4) \qquad (20)$$

From this, we see that even for short-range forces, for example the δ function type where $v(\mathbf{k}) = v(0)$, there can exist a correlation at large distances due to the interaction between particles.

The long-range character of the correlations of a quantum system can be further illustrated by examining the wave function of a weakly non-ideal Bose gas. Following the method of Bogoliubov and Zubarev [12], we will seek wave functions of a Bose gas of the form $\varphi(t,\ldots,\rho_\mathbf{k},\ldots)$ where

$$\rho_\mathbf{k} = \mathcal{N}^{-\frac{1}{2}} \sum_{(1 \le j \le N)} e^{-i\mathbf{k}\cdot\mathbf{r}_j} \qquad (\mathbf{k} \ne 0) \qquad (21)$$

are the supplementary collective variables introduced by Bohm and Pines [13] for Fermi gases. Inasmuch as the $\rho_\mathbf{k}$ are symmetric functions of the particle coordinates, this form of the wave function possesses the necessary symmetry properties. In order to get the usual representation of the wave function in terms of particle coordinates, it is only necessary to substitute $\rho_\mathbf{k}$ from (21) into the wave function φ.

The Schrödinger equation for the system of interacting Bose

particles can now be written in the form

$$i\hbar\, \partial\varphi/\partial t = H\Phi$$

$$H = E_0 + \tfrac{1}{2}\sum E(\mathbf{k})\{-\partial^2/\partial q_\mathbf{k}\,\partial q_{-\mathbf{k}} + q_\mathbf{k}q_{-\mathbf{k}} - 1\}$$

$$+\mathcal{N}^{-\frac{1}{2}}\sum_{(\mathbf{k}_1+\mathbf{k}_2\neq0)} (\hbar^2\mathbf{k}_1\cdot\mathbf{k}_2/2m)(\lambda_{\mathbf{k}_1+\mathbf{k}_2}/\lambda_{\mathbf{k}_1}\lambda_{\mathbf{k}_2}\sqrt{2})\, q_{\mathbf{k}_1+\mathbf{k}_2} \qquad (22)$$

$$\cdot\,(\partial/\partial q_{\mathbf{k}_1} + \lambda_{\mathbf{k}_1}^2 q_{-\mathbf{k}_1})(\partial/\partial q_{\mathbf{k}_2} + \lambda_{\mathbf{k}_2}^2 q_{-\mathbf{k}_2})$$

where

$$\Phi = \exp\{-\tfrac{1}{4}\sum_{(\mathbf{k}\neq0)}\rho_\mathbf{k}\rho_{-\mathbf{k}}\}\varphi \qquad (23)$$

$$q_\mathbf{k} = \rho_\mathbf{k}/\lambda_\mathbf{k}\sqrt{2}$$

$$\lambda_\mathbf{k}^4 = (\hbar^2 k^2/4m)(Nv(\mathbf{k})/V + \hbar^2 k^2/4m)^{-1}$$

$$E(\mathbf{k}) = [(N/V)(\hbar^2 k^2/m)\, v(\mathbf{k}) + (\hbar^2 k^2/2m)^2]^{\frac{1}{2}}$$

and E_0 coincides with the previously computed energy of the lowest state in first approximation. In order to obtain the representation of the Hamiltonian of the Bose gas in the form (22), we assume that the wave function φ depends upon the coordinates of the particles only through the $\rho_\mathbf{k}$, and also express the interaction energy in terms of the $\rho_\mathbf{k}$.

Introducing the Bose operators for annihilation and creation of phonons

$$b_\mathbf{k} = (q_\mathbf{k} + \partial/\partial q_{-\mathbf{k}})/\sqrt{2} \qquad b_\mathbf{k}^+ = (q_{-\mathbf{k}} - \partial/\partial q_\mathbf{k})/\sqrt{2} \qquad (24)$$

we write the Hamiltonian of the Bose gas in the form:

$$H = E_0 + \sum E(\mathbf{k}) b_\mathbf{k}^+ b_\mathbf{k}$$

$$+\mathcal{N}^{-\frac{1}{2}}\sum(\hbar^2\mathbf{k}_1\cdot\mathbf{k}_2/8m)(\lambda_{\mathbf{k}_1+\mathbf{k}_2}/\lambda_{\mathbf{k}_1}\lambda_{\mathbf{k}_2})(b_{\mathbf{k}_1+\mathbf{k}_2} + b_{-\mathbf{k}_1-\mathbf{k}_2}^+)$$

$$\times[(1+\lambda_{\mathbf{k}_1}^2) b_{-\mathbf{k}_1} + (\lambda_{\mathbf{k}_1}^2-1) b_{\mathbf{k}_1}^+][(1+\lambda_{\mathbf{k}_2}^2) b_{-\mathbf{k}_2} + (\lambda_{\mathbf{k}_2}^2-1) b_{\mathbf{k}_2}^+] \qquad (25)$$

If we restrict (25) to terms quadratic in $b_\mathbf{k}$, $b_\mathbf{k}^+$, then the energy of elementary excitations coincide with that of (16), obtained earlier by other methods. However, the method of introducing the variables $\rho_\mathbf{k}$ makes it possible to study in great detail the wave function of a weakly non-ideal Bose gas, and in particular its dependence on the particle coordinates.

The wave function of a weakly non-ideal Bose gas can be computed with the help of perturbation theory if it is observed that for ideal gases, $\lambda_{\mathbf{k}}^2 - 1 = 0$, so that $\lambda_{\mathbf{k}}^2 - 1$ can be regarded as small [12] for weakly non-ideal gases.

For the wave function of the lowest state, we get in first approximation

$$\varphi_0 = \exp \{\tfrac{1}{4} \sum (1 - \lambda_{\mathbf{k}}^{-2}) \rho_{\mathbf{k}} \rho_{-\mathbf{k}}\} \qquad (26$$

Formula (26) can also be written in the form:

$$\varphi_0 = \exp\{-(1/4\pi^2)(mV/\hbar^2 N) \sum_{i,j} (1/r_{ij}) \int_0^\infty [E(\mathbf{k}) - \hbar^2 k^2/2m](\sin \mathbf{k} \cdot \mathbf{r}_{ij}/k) dk$$
$$(27$$
$$r_{ij} = |\mathbf{q}_i - \mathbf{q}_j|$$

where (20) and integration over angular variables have been employed. For large r_{ij}, we get asymptotically:

$$\varphi \cong \exp \{-(V(mv(0))^{\tfrac{1}{2}}/4\pi^2 \hbar N) \sum_{i,j} 1/r_{ij}^2\} \qquad (28$$

It should be pointed out that the somewhat different methods of Bijl [14] lead to another asymptotic φ_0, namely with $1/r_{ij}$ instead of $1/r_{ij}^2$ in the exponent of the wave function. This, however, is connected with the fact that in Bijl's work, terms were discarded of the same order as those considered primary in [12].

The wave function of the state in which there is one phonon with wave vector $\mathbf{k}$ has the form:

$$\Phi_{\mathbf{k}} = b_{\mathbf{k}}^+ \Phi_0 = (1/N^{\tfrac{1}{2}} \lambda_{\mathbf{k}}) \sum_{(1 \leq j \leq N)} \exp \{i\mathbf{k} \cdot \mathbf{r}_j\} \varphi_0 \qquad (29$$

In form, it coincides with that proposed by Feynman [11], but the form of the wave function φ_0 was not considered in this work.

3. *Application of the method of correlations function to computing the energy of a system*

In recent times, Brueckner and collaborators [15] have discovered a new and very fruitful method for computing the ground state energy of a many-body system with strong interactions. Subsequently, Bethe [16] succeeded in clarifying some of the principles of this method.

It seems extremely interesting to connect the method of Brueckner with that of correlation functions. For this purpose, we shall start from the chain of equations for the correlation functions [5], [6]:

$$\partial F_s / \partial t = [H_s; F_s] + (1/v) \, \mathrm{Tr}_{(s+1)} \, [\sum_{(1 \leq i \leq s)} \varphi_{i, s+1}; F_{s+1}] \qquad (30)$$

where H_s is the Hamiltonian of a complex of s particles, and A, B is defined as $(AB - BA)/i\hbar$. We cannot here use a systematic expansion in powers of density, for this would automatically exclude the degenerate case and would lead to a Maxwellian, not to a Fermi distribution. Wishing to take into account the principal part of the short-range correlation in F_2, we point out that in the equation

$$\partial F_2 / \partial t = [H_2; F_2] + (1/v) \, \mathrm{Tr}_{(3)} \, [\varphi_{13} + \varphi_{23}; F_3] \qquad (31)$$

the first term plays the essential role for small r. Hence, we shall start from the approximate equation

$$\partial F_2 / \partial t = [H_2; F_2] \qquad (32)$$

and neglect terms $(1/v) \, \mathrm{Tr} \ldots$ corresponding to long-range correlations. The general solution of (32) is clearly given by

$$F_2(t) = e^{-iH_2 t/\hbar} F_2(0) e^{iH_2 t/\hbar} \qquad (33)$$

Considering a spatially homogeneous distribution and assuming that the initial distribution functions $F_1(0)$ and $F_2(0)$ satisfy the condition of weak correlation in the infinite past

$$\lim_{t \to -\infty} e^{-iH_2 t/\hbar} \{ F_2(0) - \gamma F_1^{(1)}(0) F_1^{(2)}(0) \} \, e^{iH_2 t/\hbar} = 0 \qquad (34)$$

one may show that for large t, $F_2(t)$ asymptotically approaches the expression

$$\gamma \Omega F_1^{(1)}(0) \, F_1^{(2)}(0) \, \Omega^+ \qquad (35)$$

In (34), γ designates the operation of symmetrization or antisymmetrization, the superscript on F_1 denotes the particle referred to, and Ω, appearing in (35), is the Møller operator

$$\Omega = \lim_{t \to \infty} e^{-iH_2 t/\hbar} e^{iH_1^{(1)} t/\hbar} e^{iH_1^{(2)} t/\hbar} \qquad (36)$$

transforming plane waves of the unperturbed operator $H_0 = H_1^{(1)} + H_1^{(2)}$ into scattered waves of the complete $H_2 = H_0 + \varphi$.

Now for the equilibrium correlation functions F_1 and F_2, we have

$$F_2 = \gamma \Omega F_1^{(1)} F_1^{(2)} \Omega^+ \qquad (37)$$

In view of spatial homogeneity, the unary correlation function F_1 commutes with H_1, and in view of (32), the equilibrium binary correlation function F_2 commutes with H_2. Hence, (37) is invariant with respect to changing Ω into $A\Omega B$, where A and B are unitary operators commuting with H_0 and H_2 respectively. Just this arbitrariness exists in the definition of the operator which transforms eigenfunctions of H_0 into eigenfunctions of H_2. Thus in (37), Ω can stand for any such operator.

We now introduce the formula required to compute the energy from the binary correlation function. Analogous to (12) we have

$$\delta\mathscr{F}(\varphi)/\delta\varphi_{12} = (1/2v^2)(\mathbf{x}_1\mathbf{x}_2|F_2|\mathbf{x}_1\mathbf{x}_2) \tag{38}$$

where $\mathscr{F}$ is the free energy of the system. From (38) one easily obtains the following expression for the contribution $\Delta\mathscr{F}$ to the energy of the free particles because of their interaction

$$\Delta\mathscr{F} = (1/2v^2)\int_0^1 \mathrm{Tr}\,[\varphi F_2(\tau)]\,d\tau \tag{39}$$

in which $F_2(\tau)$ designates the binary correlation function for the energy of interaction $\tau\varphi$. In (39) the operation Tr can be carried out consecutively, first taking T_{r_E} with respect to the subspace of H_0 with energy E, and then summing over all subspaces, i.e.

$$\Delta\mathscr{F} = (1/2v^2)\int_0^\infty\int_0^1 T_{r_E}[\varphi F_2(\tau)]\,dE\,d\tau \tag{40}$$

Substituting (37) into (40), we finally have

$$\Delta\mathscr{F} = (1/2v^2)\int_0^\infty T_{r_E}\left\{\int_0^1 \gamma\Omega_E^+(\tau)\,\varphi\Omega_E(\tau)\,d\tau\,F_1^{(1)}F_1^{(2)}\right\} dE \tag{41}$$

where Ω_E coincides with Ω on the subspace of H_0 with energy E; $\Omega_E(\tau)$ represents Ω_E for interaction potential $\tau\varphi$. Now $\Omega_E(\tau)$ can be chosen in the form

$$\Omega_E(\tau) = 1 + (P/E - H_0)\,R(\tau) \tag{42}$$

where

$$R(\tau) = \tau\varphi + \tau\varphi(P/E - H_0)\,R(\tau) \tag{43}$$

P denoting the principal part. As an immediate consequence of (43), it follows that

$$R^+(\tau) = R(\tau) \tag{44}$$

and also that $\partial R(\tau)/\partial \tau$ satisfies the equation

$$\partial R(\tau)/\partial \tau = \varphi + \varphi(P/E - H_0)R(\tau) + \tau\varphi(P/E - H_0)\,\partial R(\tau)/\partial \tau \quad (45)$$

On the other hand, it is easily proven, by use of (42) and (43), that $\Omega_E^+(\tau)\varphi\Omega_E(\tau)$ satisfies the same equation. We conclude that

$$\partial R(\tau)/\partial \tau = \Omega_E^+(\tau)\,\varphi\Omega_E(\tau), \quad (46)$$

so that (41) becomes

$$\Delta\mathscr{F} = (1/2v^2)\int_0^\infty T_{r_E}[\gamma R F_1^{(1)} F_1^{(2)}]\,dE \quad (47)$$

We observe that in computation, only the diagonal part of the operator R with respect to the eigenfunctions of the unperturbed H_0 is important.

The formula (47) can be applied to compute the correction energy to the ground state of a Fermi system for zero temperature. We get

$$\Delta E = \tfrac{1}{2}(N^2/8\pi^3)\sum_{s_1 s_2}\int_0^{K_F}\int_0^{K_F}\{\langle\mathbf{k}_1 s_1 \mathbf{k}_2 s_2|R|\mathbf{k}_1 s_1 \mathbf{k}_2 s_2\rangle$$

$$-\langle\mathbf{k}_2 s_2 \mathbf{k}_1 s_1|R|\mathbf{k}_1 s_1 \mathbf{k}_2 s_2\rangle\}\,d^3 k_1\,d^3 k_2 \quad (48)$$

where K_F is the Fermi limit of the wave vectors and s is the totality of ordinary and isotopic spin variables. Formula (48) coincides with the expression for the correction to the ground state energy, due to interactions of particles, which was given by Brueckner and collaborators [15].

We emphasize once more that our truncation of the equation for the binary correlation function F_2 leads to omission of terms corresponding to long-range correlations, which, as can be seen in the example of a Bose gas, exist even for short-range forces. It is clear that further improvement of the theory of Brueckner will require the study of long-range correlations in quantum systems.

Notes and References

1. N. N. Bogoliubov, *Problems in the Dynamical Theory of Statistical Physics*, M. L. 1946.
2. S. V. Tyablikov and V. V. Tolmatchev *Doklady Akad. Nauk U.S.S.R.* **114**, 1210 (1957).
3. J. G. Kirkwood and E. Monroe, *J. Chem. Phys.* **10**, 395 (1942).

274   N. N. BOGOLIUBOV *et al.*

4. M. Born and H. S. Green, *A General Kinetic Theory of Liquids*, Cambridge, New York, 1949; H. S. Green, *The Molecular Theory of Fluids* Interscience, 1952.
5. N. N. Bogoliubov, *Lectures on Quantum Statistics*, Kiev, 1949.
6. N. N. Bogoliubov and K. P. Gurov, $ZETF$ **17**, 614 (1947).
7. N. N. Bogoliubov. J. Phys. (U.S.S.R) **11**, 23 (1947); Isvest. *Akad. Nauk. U.S.S.R. (Ser. Fiz.)*, **11**, 77 (1947); *Moscow Univ. v.* **7**, 43, 1947.
8. L. Landau, $ZETF$ **11**, 592 (1941).
9. N. N. Bogoliubov, $ZETF$ **18**, 622 (1948).
10. K. A. Brueckner and K. Sawada, *Phys. Rev.* **106**, 1117 (1957).
11. R. P. Feynman, *Phys. Rev.* **94**, 262 (1954).
12. N. N. Bogoliubov and D. N. Zubarev, $ZETF$ **28**, 129 (1955); D. N. Zubarev, $ZETF$ **25**, 548 (1953).
13. D. Bohm and D. Pines, Phys. Rev. **82**, 625 (1951); Phys. Rev. **85**, 338 (1952); Phys. Rev. **92**, 609 (1953).
14. A. Bijl, *Physica* **7**, 869 (1940).
15. K. A. Brueckner, C. A. Levinson, H. M. Mahmond, *Phys. Rev.* **95**, 217 (1954); K. A. Brueckner and C. A. Levinson, *Phys. Rev.* **97**, 1344 (1955).
16. H. A. Bethe, *Phys. Rev.* **103**, 1353 (1956).

CHAPTER XV

Unified Theory of Interacting Bosons

EUGENE P. GROSS

1. *Introduction*

As we have heard, there has been quite a bit of progress recently in understanding the properties of liquid helium. However, there are certain matters to which not enough attention has been paid. In particular, most of the recent approaches have started from the gas point of view. If one looks in London's book on superfluids [1], one is impressed by the fact that the cohesive energy of the solid is almost equal to the cohesive energy of the liquid, and that the lattice packing parameters are close. For theories based on a gas picture, these features, in which the liquid is like the solid, are disquieting. It would be worth while to try to understand them.

One should also study in detail the liquid-solid phase transition at absolute zero, which takes place as the pressure is varied. The helium is then in a pure state. A unified theory of helium aims at giving insight into the cohesive energies and excitation spectra of liquid and solid by constructing wave functions for the systems from a common point of view. This is of course an ambitious task, and what will be presented is in no sense a finished theory. Nevertheless, I should like to investigate a line of thought which indicates that the problem of finding a unified theory of the solid and liquid states of a system of interacting Bosons is not quite as hard as one might believe at first sight.

We shall study Bosons interacting by two-body forces. This means we will not examine more detailed effects of the electronic structure of the atoms when put together in a many-body system. So strictly speaking we are not talking about a unified theory of the states of helium starting from first principles, but rather of a system of interacting Bosons.

275

2. *Classical limit*

We start with the following observations which are trivial, but which set the problem in a definite way. The states Φ_0 of the non-interacting Boson system form a complete set, and the set of states of the interacting Bosons can be obtained as some unitary operator U, operating on the complete set Φ_0. When you have found such a unitary operator, generating the complete set of states from the non-interacting set, all operators A_{op} transform as $UA_{op}U^{-1} = A'_{op}$, and we could call the primed operators the collective variables. If the exact U is given, we have an exact set of collective coordinates, but they would be hopelessly complicated. However, one is led to propose looking for approximate U's, which may be quite accurate, let us say, for the low-lying states of the system, but less accurate for another range of the spectrum. Now unitary transformations are basically of two types. We are familiar with some, which we can write explicitly in terms of the canonically conjugate coordinates and momenta. The simplest example is the displacement operator for a harmonic oscillator in an external electric field; this operator introduces coordinates relative to the equilibrium position. There is a second class of U's which we have to construct by giving the matrix elements in some basis system. Thus in the customary configuration-interaction procedure of molecular theory one builds U by using finite subspaces of orthogonal functions. We wish to adopt the first approach as far as we can. That is, we transform the entire set of non-interacting states with explicit U's, and at a later stage improve the theory for the desired portion of the spectrum by using the second type of transformation.

We now need a physical picture which indicates how to find U' that are appropriate. The argument is as follows: The Hamiltonian describing the system can be written in the language of second quantization

$$H = (\hbar^2/2M) \int \nabla\psi^+ \cdot \nabla\psi \, d^3x + \tfrac{1}{2}\int\int \psi^+(\mathbf{x})\psi^+(\mathbf{y}) V(\mathbf{x}-\mathbf{y})\psi(\mathbf{x})\psi(\mathbf{y}) \, d^3x \, d^3y$$

$$(1$$

This is rigorously equivalent to the ordinary many-dimensional configuration space representation. The two-body potential is $V(\mathbf{x}-\mathbf{x}')$ and will be unspecified as yet. The $\psi(\mathbf{x})$, $\psi^+(\mathbf{x})$ are operators obeying the commutation rules for a Bose field, typically $[\psi(\mathbf{x}), \psi^+(\mathbf{x}')]$ $= \delta(\mathbf{x}-\mathbf{x}')$. Associated with this is the full machinery of a field theory; namely there are a Lagrangian, a stress energy tensor, and differential conservation laws. The Heisenberg equations of motion for the time-dependent operators $\psi(\mathbf{x}, t)$, $\psi^+(\mathbf{x}, t)$ are

$$i\hbar\dot{\psi}(\mathbf{x}, t) \equiv [\psi, H] = -(\hbar^2/2M)\nabla^2\psi + \int V(\mathbf{x}-\mathbf{y})\,\psi^+(\mathbf{y})\,\psi(\mathbf{y})\,d^3y\,\psi(\mathbf{x}, t)$$

$$i\hbar\dot{\psi}^+(\mathbf{x}, t) \equiv [\psi^+, H] \qquad\qquad\qquad (2)$$

These are non-linear equations of motion.

Now let us go back to the fundamental idea behind the method of second quantization. For the Bose-Einstein case this is: find a classical wave field such that when quantized with the commutation rules it will describe the particle behavior of matter in accordance with the complementarity and correspondence principles. Let us take this point of view here and treat the Hamiltonian H as what governs the motion of a classical wave field. The Hermitian conjugate field operators

$$q(\mathbf{x}) = (\psi+\psi^+)(\hbar/2)^{\frac{1}{2}} \qquad p(\mathbf{x}) = (\psi-\psi^+)i(\hbar/2)^{\frac{1}{2}} \qquad (3)$$

which in the complete quantum theory obey commutation rules for conjugate quantities, are taken to satisfy classical Poisson bracket relationships. Planck's constant occurs in two somewhat different senses. First it enters in the term $(\hbar^2/2M)\int \nabla\psi^+ \cdot \nabla\psi\,d^3x$ which represents the wave character of the particles. This term and its effects remain in the semiclassical theory. $\hbar$ occurs in a second sense in measuring the quantum fluctuations of the field through the commutation rules, i.e., in the same characteristic sense in which electromagnetic theory introduces photons. The first occurrence of $\hbar$ is special to the intreacting matter system.

What we shall now do is go to this classical theory, mainly as motivation. We have to find satisfactory unitary transformations. The first step is to study the semiclassical theory, to understand something about the structure of the solutions of the equations of motion to a suitable approximation. The second step is to show that the information thus gained can be related to canonical transformations and thus to collective variables in the classical theory. We shall see that corresponding to the canonical analysis of the classical Hamiltonian, there is a simple quantum mechanical U, which goes with it. When we are through, we can drop the classical crutch, and simply use the U to evaluate the wave functions and energy spectrum of the completely quantum mechanical theory.

Let us look at the classical equations of motion, which are the same as the operator equations, but with no need to consider ordering of factors. There are certain special, exact solutions of the equations; they can only be set up by careful preparation of initial conditions. In particular, there are separable solutions in which $\psi = f(\mathbf{x}) \exp (-iEt/\hbar)$. Inserting this we see that $f(\mathbf{x})$ has to satisfy the differential equation

$$Ef(\mathbf{x}) = -(\hbar^2/2M)\nabla^2 f + f(\mathbf{x}) \int V(\mathbf{x}-\mathbf{y})|f(\mathbf{y})|^2 \, d^3 y \qquad (4)$$

There are however boundary conditions arising from the fact that the number operator $\mathcal{N}_{\mathrm{op}} = \int \psi^+ \psi \, d^3 x$ and the total momentum operator $P_{\mathrm{op}} = i\hbar \int (\psi \nabla \psi^+ - \nabla \psi \cdot \psi^+) \, d^3 x$ commute with the Hamiltonian, and that we are working with a definite number of particles. In the classical theory the condition is that $\int |\psi|^2 \, d^3 x = \mathcal{N} = \text{constant}$, independent of time; for the special solution it is $\int |f|^2 \, d^3 x = \mathcal{N}$. With $f(\mathbf{x})$ real we deal with states in which the total momentum is zero and the system as a whole is at rest.

Equation (4) with the boundary condition constitutes a non-linear eigenvalue problem. We notice that there is always one exact solution, namely the uniform solution $f(\mathbf{x}) = \sqrt{(\mathcal{N}/L^3)} = \text{constant}$. ($L^3$ is the volume over which we take spatial integrals.) The corresponding value of E is $E = (\mathcal{N}^2/L^3) \int V(\mathbf{x}) \, d^3 x$. However, there may be other exact solutions of this equation. Looking at it, we notice that it has the form of a Hartree equation for the classical field $f(\mathbf{x})$, with $V(\mathbf{x}-\mathbf{y})|f(\mathbf{y})|^2$ the self-consistent or collective interaction term. The boundary condition $\int |f|^2 \, d^3 x = \mathcal{N}$ is analogous to the normalization condition on the wave function. If the potential is suitably attractive in some portion of space, there may be periodic solutions. It's rather easy to establish this for simple potentials $V(\mathbf{x})$. For strongly repulsive interactions this is not the whole story. We discuss this case later. This distinction in the classical theory between solid- and gas-type modes of the non-linear fluid is then the basis for the distinction between solid and liquid in the full quantum theory.

3. *Uniform density*

Following the classical line of argument a bit further, we would say that we should next study the states of the non-linear field which correspond to small vibrations in the vicinity of each stable exact solution. In the classical theory, a field amplitude can be arbitrarily small — therefore, near any exact stable solution, there are others in which the field fluctuates with a small amplitude about it. Write $\psi = e^{-iEt/\hbar} [f(\mathbf{x}) + \varphi(\mathbf{x}, t)]$. All one has to do is insert this into the equation of motion, and linearize it; then one studies the spectrum of the small amplitude vibrations. The hermitian coordinate $q = (\varphi + \varphi^+)\sqrt{(\hbar/2)}$ then obeys the equation

$$-\hbar^2\ddot{q} = -(\hbar^2/2M)\{\nabla^2 - (\nabla^2 f)/f\}\{-(\hbar^2/2M)[\nabla^2 - (\nabla^2 f)/f] q(\mathbf{x}, t)$$
$$+2f(\mathbf{x}) \int V(\mathbf{x} - \mathbf{y}) f(\mathbf{y}) q(\mathbf{y}) \, d^3y\} \qquad (5)$$

The spectrum of course depends on the underlying exact solution $f(\mathbf{x}) e^{-iEt/\hbar}$. We now have to find the normal modes. In particular, let us take the solution that we know always exists; that is to say the one for which f is uniform. Then the Fourier transform $q_{\mathbf{k}}(t)$ of $q(\mathbf{x}, t)$ obeys the equation

$$-\hbar^2\ddot{q}_{\mathbf{k}} = q_{\mathbf{k}}(\hbar^2 k^2/2M)[(\hbar^2 k^2/2M) + 2f_0^2 V_k] \qquad (6)$$

The q_k are uncoupled from each other and we find Bogoliubov's [2] spectrum $\omega_k^2 = [(\hbar^2 k^2/2M)]^2 + 2V_k(\hbar^2 k^2/2M)(N/L^3)$. This has been written down and talked about many times — it has the phonons and individual particle excitations in it. Now, of course, a periodic solution $f(\mathbf{x})$ will have a different spectrum associated with it, this spectrum would be expected to describe the vibration excitations in the solid state. The approach to the solid state using second quantization is related to a remark of Schrödinger: "Indeed I deem the whole lattice to be something very akin to a standing de Broglie wave" [3].

Now, we must show how we can make this analysis into an actual quantum mechanical theory. We have to observe that we have only performed three elementary canonical transformations. The first, which we call U_1, is a simple time-dependent transformation; which removes the phase factor $e^{-iEt/\hbar}$. The second, U_2, may be written $U_2 = \exp S_2$, $S_2 = \int \{f(\mathbf{x})\,\psi^+(\mathbf{x}) - f^*(\mathbf{x})\,\psi(\mathbf{x})\}\,d^3x$. This is a linear shift; the transformed operator $U_2\psi U_2^{-1}$ differs from the original operator ψ by a c number $f(\mathbf{x})$. Thus the new operators obey the same Bose commutation rules as the original operators. The third transformation corresponds to the step of finding the normal modes for equation (5). If we write $U_3 = \exp S_3$, then S_3 is a suitable quadratic form functional of ψ, ψ^+. Now form the product unitary transformation $U = U_1 U_2 U_3$, and let it act on the states of the non-interacting system. Then our theory can be simply stated: Use the trial states $U\Phi_0$ to find the energy spectrum by forming the expectation values $\langle U\Phi_0, HU\Phi_0 \rangle$. It is clear that the method has a variational principle embedded in it as well. There is no reason why we need to restrict ourselves to taking $f(\mathbf{x})$ and the coefficients of the normal mode transform, i.e., S_3, from the linearized (small amplitude) classical analysis. In classical terms a better choice corresponds to the obvious point that if we had included additional, non-linear terms in the equations of motion, then, as with any anharmonic oscillator, there would be amplitude-dependent changes in the frequency of the modes. There will even be changes in the linear shifts $f(\mathbf{x})$, arising from essentially cubic terms. In the complete quantum theory some anharmonic effects have to be expected even for the ground and low-lying excited states because of minimum zero point amplitudes. Probably it does not pay to investigate the structure of the non-linear classical equations further, and one is inclined to go over to quantum mechanics directly, armed with the variational property (cf. below, however). An important property of the linear and quadratic S is that all calculations can be done explicitly. Let us now indicate how this procedure works for a uniform solution and for a possible periodic solution, and then come back to the original problem of the connection between the solid and the gas.

We look first at the uniform solution. We write the Hamiltonian in terms of the Fourier components $\psi_{\mathbf{k}}$ of $\psi(\mathbf{x})$. Then

$$H = (\hbar^2/2M) \sum_{\mathbf{k}} k^2 \psi_{\mathbf{k}}^+ \psi_{\mathbf{k}} + \sum_{k \neq 0} V_k \sum_{\mathbf{l},\mathbf{m}} \psi_{\mathbf{l}+\mathbf{k}}^+ \psi_{\mathbf{m}-\mathbf{k}}^+ \psi_{\mathbf{l}} \psi_{\mathbf{m}} + V_0 \mathcal{N}_{\mathrm{op}}(\mathcal{N}_{\mathrm{op}} - 1) \quad (7)$$

where

$$\psi_{\mathbf{k}} = \int \psi(\mathbf{x})\, e^{i\mathbf{k}\cdot\mathbf{x}}\, d^3x \qquad \text{(volume of periodic box} = 1)$$

$$\mathcal{N}_{\mathrm{op}} = \sum \psi_{\mathbf{k}}^{+}\psi_{\mathbf{k}}, \qquad [\psi_{\mathbf{k}}, \psi_{\mathbf{l}}^{+}] = \delta_{\mathbf{k},\mathbf{l}}$$

We have split off the term $V_0 \mathcal{N}_{\mathrm{op}}(\mathcal{N}_{\mathrm{op}}-1)$. The rigorous eigenfunctions of H correspond to a definite number of particles $\mathcal{N}$; we treat $V_0\mathcal{N}(\mathcal{N}-1)$ as a c number. This is equivalent to performing the time-dependent transformation U_1 for the uniform solution. Now $f(\mathbf{x}) = \sqrt{\mathcal{N}}$ so that $f_{\mathbf{k}} = 0$ except for f_0. We have $S_2 = -f_0(\psi_0 - \psi_0^{+})$ so that $U_2\psi_0 U_2^{-1} = \psi_0 + f_0$, $U_2\psi_{\mathbf{k}}U_2^{-1} = \psi_{\mathbf{k}}$, $k \neq 0$. The transformed Hamiltonian $H' = U_2 U_1 H U_1^{-1} U_2^{-1}$ is

$$H' = \sum_{i=0}^{4} H_i'$$

$H_0' = V_0\mathcal{N}(\mathcal{N}-1)$

$H_1' = 0$

$$H_2' = \sum_{k} (\hbar^2 k^2/2M)\psi_{\mathbf{k}}^{+}\psi_{\mathbf{k}} + \sum_{k\neq 0} (V_k/L^{\frac{3}{2}})\{f_0^{*2}\psi_{\mathbf{k}}\psi_{-\mathbf{k}} + \text{c.c.} + |f_0|^2 2\psi_{\mathbf{k}}^{+}\psi_{\mathbf{k}}\} \quad (8)$$

$$H_3' = \sum_{k\neq 0} (V_k/L^{\frac{3}{2}}) \sum \{f_0^{*}\psi_{\mathbf{m}}^{+}\psi_{-\mathbf{k}}\psi_{\mathbf{m}+\mathbf{k}} + \psi_{\mathbf{l}}^{+}f_0^{*}\psi_{\mathbf{l}-\mathbf{k}}\psi_{\mathbf{k}} + \text{c.c.}\}$$

$$H_4' = \sum_{k\neq 0} (V_k/L^{\frac{3}{2}}) \sum_{\mathbf{l},\,\mathbf{m}} \psi_{\mathbf{l}}^{+}\psi_{\mathbf{m}}^{+}\psi_{\mathbf{l}-\mathbf{k}}\psi_{\mathbf{m}+\mathbf{k}}$$

The transformation $U_3 = \exp S_3$, $S_3 = i\sum_{k_z>0} \{L_{\mathbf{k}}\psi_{\mathbf{k}}^{+}\psi_{-\mathbf{k}}^{+} + \text{c.c.}\}$ with $L_{\mathbf{k}} = L_{-\mathbf{k}}$ has the property that

$$\psi_{\mathbf{k}}' = U_3\psi_{\mathbf{k}}U_3^{-1} = (\psi_{\mathbf{k}} + L_{\mathbf{k}}\psi_{-\mathbf{k}}^{+})[1/\sqrt{(1-|L_{\mathbf{k}}|^2)}] \qquad (9)$$

One now forms $U_3 H' U_3^{-1}$, i.e., replaces $\psi_{\mathbf{k}}$ by $\psi_{\mathbf{k}}'$. With a proper choice of $L_{\mathbf{k}}$ the term $U_3 H_2' U_3^{-1}$ is thrown into the diagonal form $U_3 H_2' U_3^{-1} = \sum \varepsilon(k)\psi_{\mathbf{k}}^{+}\psi_{\mathbf{k}} + \text{(zero point constant)}$.

The terms $U_3(H_0' + H_2')U_3^{-1}$ thus give precisely Bogoliubov's theory. But we see that this theory is incomplete in several respects. First it is incomplete in that no attention has been paid to non-linear terms. There are contributions to expectation values from the quartic terms $U_3 H_4' U_3^{-1}$. These contributions modify the energy of the ground state, the spectrum of single excitations, and yield new types of multiple excitations. As expected, the corrections tend to vanish for very weak repulsive interactions, are more important for high values of k and for the highly excited states. For example, the complete ground state energy is

$$E_G = V_0 \mathcal{N}(\mathcal{N}-1) + \sum_{\mathbf{k} \neq 0} \beta_{\mathbf{k}}^2 \{[(\hbar^2 k^2/2M) + 2\mathcal{N}V_{\mathbf{k}}]L_{\mathbf{k}}^2 + 2\mathcal{N}V_{\mathbf{k}}L_{\mathbf{k}}\}$$

$$+ \sum_{\mathbf{k} \neq 0} V_{\mathbf{k}} \sum_{\mathbf{l}} \beta_{\mathbf{l}}^2 \beta_{\mathbf{l}-\mathbf{k}}^2 L_{\mathbf{k}}^2 L_{\mathbf{l}-\mathbf{k}}^2 + \sum_{\mathbf{k} \neq 0} V_{\mathbf{k}} |L_{\mathbf{k}/2}|^2 \beta_{\mathbf{k}/2}^4 \qquad (10)$$

Here $\beta_{\mathbf{k}}^2 = [1/(1-|L_{\mathbf{k}}|^2)]$ and we have taken the periodic box to have unit volume. Second, the approximate wave functions associated with the procedure are not eigenfunctions of the number operator $\sum \psi_{\mathbf{k}}^+ \psi_{\mathbf{k}}$, a property possessed by the exact wave functions. One may remedy this by using a projection operator on the above states and forming new orthonormal functions. The modifications are not serious for the low-lying states.

One is now free to choose the coefficients $L_{\mathbf{k}}$ to lower the total energy of the ground state, to take into account the quartic terms in a better way. With a slightly different choice (but still not the best possible $L_{\mathbf{k}}$) one recovers substantially the results of Bogoliubov and Zubarev [4], which they have shown to be equivalent to Feynman's theory [5]. There are other obvious ways of improving the wave functions. For example, one may form linear combinations of the above ground state and excited state wave functions and choose coefficients to give a more precise account of the cubic terms $UH_3'U^{-1}$. Another, more radical, idea will be discussed later. We have not yet undertaken a detailed analysis of the best that one can do with the above approach to the interacting Boson gas.

One can examine the configuration space wave functions corresponding to the transformations employed here. The basic operator $\exp i\{\sum' L_{\mathbf{k}} \psi_{\mathbf{k}}^+ \psi_{-\mathbf{k}}^+ + \text{c.c.}\}$ may be applied to, for example, the ground state. Neglecting the fact that the new state does not refer to a fixed number of particles we find the configuration wave function as a sum of powers of $\sum_{i,j} L_{\mathbf{k}} e^{i\mathbf{k} \cdot (\mathbf{x}_i - \mathbf{x}_j)}$. Application of a projection operator for $\mathcal{N}_{\text{op}}$ then gives a state with a definite number of particles which is a sum of powers of $\varphi(\mathbf{x}_i - \mathbf{x}_j)$. Thus the form of the wave function is such that with $L_{\mathbf{k}}$ chosen to drop to zero rapidly at high k we can obtain wave functions for the hard sphere gas in a binary collision approximation, as well as for the weakly interacting Boson gas.

4. Solid state

If one goes to the theory for the solid state, precisely the same steps are taken. If the choice of f is taken from the classical linearized theory, we must study the Hartree problem, eq. (4); then we analyze the spectrum of eq. (5). It is much easier and more intuitive to carry out the program in a slightly different way. Let us expand the original operators as $\psi(\mathbf{x}) = \sum_n a_n \varphi_n(\mathbf{x})$ where $\varphi_n(\mathbf{x})$ are c-number ortho-normal functions and a_n, a_n^+ are annihilation and creation operators associated with this basis. Now we can try to make contact with an intuitive "cage" model. One writes $\varphi_n(\mathbf{x})$ as a two-index affair $\varphi_{\mathbf{k}}^{(\alpha)}$. We take a particle in a cage of suitable size and potential height and find the associated localized orbitals. The index α refers to these states. Then we form Bloch tight-binding orbitals — the quasi-momentum vector $\mathbf{k}$ roams over the first zone. The $\varphi_{\mathbf{k}}^{(\alpha)}$ now form an appropriate set of one-particle functions. For $\mathbf{k} = 0$ they are strictly periodic; for $\mathbf{k} \neq 0$ there is a periodic portion and a modulating phase factor. We can build up the theory of the solid in a direct way by making the linear shift in the operators $a_{\mathbf{k}}^{(\alpha)}$, introducing a set of c-number functions. If we make the shifts only for $\mathbf{k} = 0$ we keep the periodicity of $\psi(\mathbf{x})$, of the correlation operator, of the density, etc. Then the leading terms in the energy are the terms in H_{op} with ψ replaced by the c-number shifts; this is related to London's old calculation of the cohesive energy. Now there are corrections which come in. First, when we make a normal mode transformation, there is a zero point depression of energy for the ground state. This term occurs in all theories involving normal modes. (We are referring to a new zero point energy term, not the usual one arising from the de Broglie wave character.) This type of contribution is already present in Bogoliubov's theory. There are also modifications coming from the expectation values of the non-quadratic terms. For the case helium, in which the potential contains a strongly repulsive portion, the normal mode transformation is essential in the calculation of the cohesive energy, since it keeps the atoms from coming close to each other (of the discussion of the form of the configuration space wave functions for the Bose gas).

We have not gone into the technical problems connected with the fact that the wave functions discussed are not eigenfunctions of the momentum and number operators. One way of remedying this defect is to apply projection operators. More important is the question of getting from the solid with its property of long-range correlation, to the liquid or gas. One suggestion is that one makes the linear shifts for $k \neq 0$ as well as for $k = 0$. The modulating factors in the Bloch wave functions will lead to a correlation function in which the periodicity is destroyed and is liquid-like. The use of projection operators gives the states the property that the expectation value of the density operator itself is uniform.

There is another idea, which possibly has some truth to it. Consider a particle in a potential which has several minima, maxima, and points of inflection: In the classical theory there are separate regions of configuration space, while the quantum theory if the regions are well separated the wave functions for the lowest states are oscillator wave functions. But if the regions are not well separated we have a tunnel effect. It is then appropriate to approximate the ground and low-lying states by linear combinations of terms referring to regions where, classically, the particle could remain for an appreciable time. In a similar way, here we can let the operators depend upon a parameter, r, which may range over both discrete or continuous values. We then form wave functions that are linear superpositions with a weight factor $G(r)$. One can then examine the connection between the solid and liquid. At absolute zero the phase transition from solid to liquid takes place for a pure quantum state as the density parameter is varied. Thus we have a situation similar to the transition from ionic to covalent bonding in a diatomic molecule when the internuclear separation is varied.

5. Concluding remarks

We shall now make some final remarks on the present approach. Suppose one adopts the program of obtaining wave functions for the interacting system from explicit unitary transformations acting on the states of the non-interacting system. The most direct procedure is to note that the basic elementary act conserving both particle number and momentum involves creating two particles and annihilating two particles. Thus S in $U = e^{iS}$ involves four operators ψ, ψ^+. Such a U

cannot be handled explicitly; it must be expanded, and cycles extracted from the expansion. In the limit of the number of particles approaching ∞ with the density constant, certain cycles survive. In the approach preferred here we have used S's containing at most two ψ, ψ^+. The transformation can then be handled explicitly but we violate one or more of the conservation laws. This is remedied by using projection operators. In the limit of the number of particles approaching ∞ these operators may not be necessary, corresponding to the relation between the grand and canonical ensembles in statistical mechanics. The use of projection operators leads to abandoning the straightforward approach of unitary transformation. By generalizing the modifications introduced by projection operators we are led to wave functions representing a superposition of resonant configurations and thus to a connection with customary methods of the theory of molecules.

ADDENDUM: *In response to query on validity of semiclassical approach*: It is true that the point of view which leads one to make the linear shift and then the quadratic diagonalization comes from a semiclassical point of view, and therefore one might expect it to break down in the limit of only a small number of particles excited in modes. However there is a well-known correspondance for Bosons, and particularly in the harmonic approximation, whereby the correspondance principle gives valid results down to the lowest state. In addition, if one compares the results with quantum mechanical perturbation theory, which is opposite from the semiclassical point of view, these results agree in the appropriate limit. This of course is based on our dealing with Bosons rather than Fermions.

6. Note Added in Proof

Among the numerous papers on the theory of interacting Bosons which have appeared since the symposium the following are closely related to the point of view and program presented. In the later work, some essential changes have been found necessary, particularly in the connection of the periodic state with a liquid rather than a solid. However no changes have been made in the original text.

E. P. Gross "Classical Theory of Boson Wave Fields" *Annals of Physics* **4**, 57 (1958); "Quantum Theory of Interacting Bosons" *Annals of Physics* **9**, 292 (1960); "Structure of a Quantized Vortex in Boson Systems" *Nuovo cimento* X, **20**, 454 (1961); "Periodic Ground States and the Many Body Problem" *Phys. Rev. Letters.* **4**, 599 (1960); "Motion of Foreign Bodies in Boson Systems" *Annals of Physics* (in press).

S. Pitaevski "Vortex Lines in a Non Ideal Bose Gas" *Soviet Phys. (JETP)* **13**, 451 (1961).

T. T. Wu "Non-Equilibrium Properties of a Bose System of Hard Spheres at Extremely Low Temperatures" *J. of Math. Phys.* **2**, 105 (1961).

J. G. Valatin and D. Butler "On the Collective Properties of a Boson System," *Nuovo cimento* **10**, 37 (1958).

M. Girardeau and R. Arnowitt "Theory of Many Boson Systems: Pair Theory" *Phys. Rev.* **113**, 755 (1959).

Notes and references

1. F. London, *Superfluids*, (Wiley, New York, 1952), Vol. II.
2. N. Bogoliubov, *J. Phys. (U.S.S.R.)* **11**, 23 (1947).
3. E. Schrödinger, *Statistical Thermodynamics*, Cambridge, New York, 1946, p. 67.
4. N. Bogoliubov and D. Zubarev, *JETP* **1**, 83 (1955).
5. R. P. Feynman, *Phys. Rev.* **94**, 262 (1954).

CHAPTER XVI

The Collective Description of Particle Interaction

DAVID PINES

1. *Introduction*

I should like to summarize the present status of the collective approach to those many-body problems in which one deals with systems of strongly interacting particles. I shall try to review briefly the general formulation and then discuss even more briefly the applications that have been made with this approach. I shall begin with the free electron gas, which is the problem for which Bohm and I developed the basic methods that I shall describe [1]; I shall then discuss electrons in solids, the dilute hard sphere Boson gas, liquid Helium, He³, and the nucleus. Finally I wish to consider two-plasma problems, as exemplified by electrons and ions in metals, and problems in which one has two distinct groups of electrons in a solid. What I shall be doing then is going over almost in reverse direction the territory covered by Professor Brueckner, and discussing quite a different approach which however seems to lead, in many problems, to very nearly the same answers.

2. *The general approach*

The basic philosophy behind the method is the recognition and exploitation of collective excited states. In all the systems which I have mentioned there are phonon-like elementary excitations brought about by the interaction between the particles. Where they exist, the many-body problem may be simplified by first going over to a description which is designed to take the phonon excitations into account explicitly. Having described the collective excitations, which involve the simultaneous excitation of many particles, one can then discuss in a much more straightforward fashion the remaining individual particle excitations in the system. (I should say the remaining excitations which may or may not have an individual particle character.)

For the purpose of recognition, it is instructive to discuss the equation of motion of the density fluctuations (2). In this fashion one obtains insight into the possibilities for collective motion and into the nature of the approximations that one has to make in carrying out a more detailed treatment. Consider the following general Hamiltonian:

$$H = \sum_i (p_i^2/2m) + \sum_k^{i>j} V_k \exp i\mathbf{k} \cdot (\mathbf{x}_i - \mathbf{x}_j) \qquad V_k = V_{-k} \qquad (1)$$

The first term represents the kinetic energy of the particles, the second, the particle interaction. The equation of motion of the density fluctuation, $\rho_k (= \sum_i e^{-i\mathbf{k} \cdot \mathbf{x}_i})$, may be written as [1]:

$$\ddot{\rho}_k + \omega_0^2 \rho_k = - \sum_i [(\mathbf{k} \cdot \mathbf{p}_i/m) + (\hbar k^2/2m)]^2 \, e^{-i\mathbf{k} \cdot \mathbf{x}_i} - \sum_{k' \neq k} (\mathbf{k} \cdot \mathbf{k}'/m) V_{k'} \rho_{k-k'} \rho_{k'}$$

$$(2)$$

where ω_0 is a frequency of collective oscillation, defined by

$$\omega_0^2 = nk^2 V_k/m \qquad (3)$$

and n is the density of particles.

In any general problem we might expect that the ρ_k will oscillate at the frequency ω_0 provided the two terms on the right-hand side of (2) are negligible. The first term there is essentially a kinetic term; it is present in the absence of any interaction between the particles. The second term comes from the potential energy of inter-action. We have separated out, and put on the left-hand side, the single term which corresponds to $\mathbf{k}' = \mathbf{k}$, for which $\rho_{k'-k} = n$, and for which this term reduces to $\omega_0^2 \rho_k$. The condition that the ρ_k oscil-late at a frequency ω_0 thus requires that kinetic effects be small, and that the non-linear coupling between the density fluctuations of different momenta be small.

We may use the equations of motion to estimate the importance of the kinetic term, provided we are correct in assuming that the non-linear effects arising from the coupling of the density fluctuations are small. Let us make that assumption, although one cannot justify it without a far more detailed treatment than the equations of motion provide. We estimate the strength of the kinetic term in (2) by approximating it as $-\langle \Omega_{\mathbf{k}}^2 \rangle_{\mathrm{Av}} \rho_{\mathbf{k}}$ where

$$\langle \Omega_{\mathbf{k}}^2 \rangle_{\mathrm{Av}} = \langle [(\mathbf{k} \cdot \mathbf{p}_i/m) + (\hbar k^2/2m)]^2 \rangle_{\mathrm{Av}} \tag{4}$$

is the averaged squared frequency of free particles which have absorbed a momentum $\mathbf{k}$. (In cases in which the particle momenta are properly regarded as not correlated with their positions, this is a quite good approximation.) $\Omega_{\mathbf{k}}$ is thus the characteristic frequency of the particle system in the absence of interaction, while ω_0 is the characteristic frequency due to that interaction, and is calculated neglecting kinetic effects. For a given problem it is generally useful to introduce collective coordinates only where $\omega_0^2 \gg \langle \Omega_{\mathbf{k}}^2 \rangle_{\mathrm{Av}}$, that is, where the collective modes of excitation are quite distinct from the individual particle modes.

TABLE 1

A Comparison of Free Particle (Ω) and Collective (ω_0) Frequencies for Many-Body Problems

System	$\langle \Omega_{\mathbf{k}}^2 \rangle_{\mathrm{Av}}$	ω_0^2
Free electron gas	$k^2 v_0^2$	$\omega_p^2 = 4\pi n e^2/m$
Electrons in solids	ω_{n0}^2	ω_p^2
Dilute hard sphere bosons	$\hbar^2 k^4/4m^2$	$4\pi nah^2 k^2/m^2$
Liquid helium	$\hbar^2 k^4/4m^2$	$s^2 k^2$
He^3	$k^2 v_0^2$	$nk^2 t_{\mathbf{k}}/m$
Nucleus	$k^2 v_0^2$	$nk^2 t_{\mathbf{k}}/m$

In Table I we compare the characteristic individual particle and collective frequencies for a number of many-body problems. For the free electron gas, $\langle \Omega_{\mathbf{k}}^2 \rangle_{\mathrm{Av}}$ is of the order of $k^2 v_0^2$, where v_0 is the velocity of an electron at the top of the Fermi distribution. At long wave lengths it is clear that $\langle \Omega_{\mathbf{k}}^2 \rangle_{\mathrm{Av}} \ll \omega_p^2$. For the case of actual electrons in solids, the characteristic free-particle frequencies are those calculated on the one-electron Bloch model of an electron moving in the periodic potential of the ion cores [2]. Such frequencies, ω_{n0}, correspond to inter-band or intra-band transitions. As we shall see, they may frequently be small compared to the plasma frequency of the valence electrons in the solid. For the free Boson gas near absolute zero, $\Omega_k = \hbar k^2/2m$, since nearly all the particles are in the ground state. In calculating the collective frequency arising from the hard sphere interaction, we should not use the Fourier transform of the potential, but rather t_k, the reaction matrix [3]. We have $\omega_0^2 = (nk^2 t_k/m) = 4\pi n a \hbar^2 k^2/m^2$, where a is the hard sphere radius. Again, $\langle \Omega_k^2 \rangle_{Av} \ll \omega_0^2$ at long wave lengths. The situation in actual liquid helium is quite similar, in that $\langle \Omega_k^2 \rangle_{Av} \ll s^2 k^2$, where s is the observed sound velocity.

In all of these systems, then, the interaction between the particles markedly modifies the excitation spectrum of the system, in such a way as to increase the characteristic frequency from Ω_k to ω_0. (We return later to He³ and the nucleus.) It seems desirable therefore to develop an approach in which one takes into account at the outset the interactions which determine the actual characteristic frequency of excitation. The approach which I shall describe is an extension of that which Bohm and I used for the free electron gas [4]. It is based on the idea of adding n' new variables to the system to describe the collective motion explicitly. The way we have done this is to extend the range of the original Hamiltonian; that is, to work not with the Hamiltonian (1), but to use an extended Hamiltonian in which we add a set of collective momenta π_k, for instance, and perhaps also an interaction between the collective momenta and the individual particles. A typical extended Hamiltonian is

$$H = \sum_i (p_i^2/2m) + \sum_k (V_k/2)(\rho_k^* \rho_k - n) + \sum_{k<k_c} [\pi_k^* \pi_k/2 + \sqrt{(V_k)} \pi_k^* \rho_k] \quad (5)$$

The new collective variables commute with the particle coordinates and momenta. We could guarantee that an extended Hamiltonian like (5) agree with the original Hamiltonian, (1) if we impose a set of n' subsidiary conditions on the extended system wave function, Ψ,

$$\pi_k \Psi = 0 \qquad (k < k_c) \qquad (6)$$

If our extended Hamiltonian is such that there is a lower bound for the system energy, it is actually not necessary to take the subsidiary conditions into account when solving for the ground state energy. The true ground state wave function may be shown to satisfy the subsidiary conditions automatically, so that the use of wave functions which do not satisfy the subsidiary conditions means only that the resultant energy eigenvalues will lie above the true ground state value appropriate to the original Hamiltonian, (1), [5].

I shall in what follows consider only families of positive definite Hamiltonians [of which (5) is an example] so that I may neglect the effect of the subsidiary conditions on the ground state energy of the system. Our basic approach is then equivalent to a variational method, in which we vary the Hamiltonian we consider, as well as the wave functions appropriate to a given Hamiltonian. The present application of the method is directed toward the introduction of phonons which we are going to describe in terms of collective coordinates and momenta. I believe the method may be extended to other problems in which perhaps phonons are not explicitly useful, but in which the introduction of a set of generalized collective coordinates may simplify the solution of the problem. In order to see how we work with an extended Hamiltonian like (5), let us consider a specific example, the free electron gas [3].

3. *Free electron gas*

We begin with the Hamiltonian (5), where $V_k = 4\pi e^2/k^2$. Here the collective coordinates have merely been introduced formally; they have not been related to any physical quantities in the system. We carry out this next step by making a canonical transformation which relates the π_k to the density fluctuations, ρ_k, and which couples the collective modes and the individual particle motion. The desired transformation is

$$\pi_k \rightarrow \pi_k - (\sqrt{V_k})\,\rho_k \tag{7a}$$

$$\mathbf{p}_i \rightarrow \mathbf{p}_i + i \sum_{k<k_c} (\sqrt{V_k})\,q_k\,\mathbf{k}e^{-i\mathbf{k}\cdot\mathbf{x}_i} \tag{7b}$$

where q_k is the collective coordinate which is canonically conjugate to π_k. The Hamiltonian (5) is transformed to

$$H = \sum_i (p_i^2/2m) + H_{sr} + \sum_{k<k_c} (\pi_k^*\pi_k/2 + (\omega_p^2/2)\,q_k^*q_k - 2\pi e^2 n/k^2) + H_{int} + U \tag{8}$$

where H_{sr} represents an interaction between the particles, of range k_c^{-1},

$$H_{\mathrm{sr}} = \sum_{\substack{i \neq j \\ k > k_c}} (2\pi e^2/k^2) \exp i\mathbf{k} \cdot (\mathbf{x}_i - \mathbf{x}_j)$$

and the third and fourth terms describe the plasma oscillations at the frequency ω_p. The remaining terms represent a linear interaction between the particles and the plasmons (the quantized plasma modes),

$$H_{\mathrm{int}} = i \sum_{\substack{k < k_c \\ i}} (\sqrt{V_{\mathbf{k}}}) (\mathbf{k} \cdot \mathbf{p}_i/m) + (\hbar k^2/2m)] q_{\mathbf{k}} e^{-i\mathbf{k} \cdot \mathbf{x}_i}$$

and a bilinear interaction,

$$U = \sum_{\substack{i(k, k' < k_c) \\ k' \neq k}} \sqrt{(V_{\mathbf{k}} V_{\mathbf{k}'})} \, q_{\mathbf{k}} q_{\mathbf{k}'}^* e^{i(\mathbf{k}' - \mathbf{k}) \cdot \mathbf{x}_i} \mathbf{k} \cdot \mathbf{k}'$$

The interaction, H_{int}, corresponds to a coupling between the particles and plasmons which is directly analogous to that arising from the kinetic term in our equation of motion, (2). In fact, the coupling constant which characterizes the strength of H_{int} is

$$g_1^2 = \langle \Omega_{\mathbf{k}}^2 \rangle_{\mathrm{Av}}/\omega_p^2 \cong \beta^2/2r_s \tag{9}$$

where β is $\mathbf{k}_c/\mathbf{k}_0$, $\mathbf{k}_0$ is the wave vector of an electron at the Fermi surface, and r_s is the interelectron spacing measured in units of the Bohr radius,

$$r_s = (3/4\pi n)^{\frac{1}{3}}/a_0$$

In the same way, U introduces a coupling which is analogous to the non-linear coupling between different $\rho_{\mathbf{k}}$ arising from the second term on the right-hand side of (2). Where $g_1^2 \ll 1$, it may easily be shown that the coupling arising from U has a strength

$$g_2^2 = (n'/48n) = \beta^3/96 \tag{10}$$

so that as long as $\beta \lesssim 1$ $(n' < n)$, the neglect of non-linear effects is an excellent approximation.

In general the method I have described will only be useful when we can get a better solution for the eigenfunctions and eigenvalues of the Hamiltonian (8) [or (5)] than we could for the original Hamiltonian

(1). This will be the case provided the coupling constants g_1^2 and g_2^2 may be regarded as small, which in turn requires that there be a clean-cut separation between the individual particle excitations and the collective excitations [6]. As we have seen, this will certainly be true for the long wave length plasmons in the electron gas. It turns out that a reasonable choice of k_c is $\beta \sim 0.35\, r_s^{\frac{1}{2}}$, which corresponds to a screening length, $\lambda_c \sim 1.3\, r_s^{\frac{1}{2}} a_0$, and a coupling constant, $g_1^2 \sim 1/16$ [7]. In this case, there is clearly no difficulty in solving accurately for the interaction between the plasmons and electrons, so that the long-range part of the problem $(k < k_c)$ may be regarded as satisfactorily solved.

The principle uncertainty in the calculation of the correlation energy of the electron gas therefore stems from H_{sr}. If one calculates its influence in perturbation theory (which seems not unreasonable since the interaction now has a range slightly less than the inter-electron spacing), one obtains a result for the correlation energy [8] in excellent agreement with the earlier calculation of Wigner [9]. I would estimate the error in this calculation as between 20 % and 30 %. One can probably improve the calculation somewhat by using a larger value of k_c. The choice I mentioned is one based on solving the low momentum part of the interaction accurately, and then getting the lowest value of the energy consistent with this so-lution. If we take a larger value of k_c, the energy associated with the long-range interactions is not much altered, and the treatment of H_{sr} by perturbation theory should be a better approximation. I might add that in the high density limit $(r_s \ll 1)$ one can show that the differences between our calculation and that of Brueckner and Gell-Mann [10] arise from our inaccurate treatment of H_{sr} so that the two approaches are essentially equivalent in that domain [11]. I believe that the usefulness of the approach which I have described lies in the fact that it is the only method at present which enables one to get reasonably accurate (10–30 %) results for a wide variety of metallic properties in the region of actual metallic densities $(2 < r_s < 5.5)$.

Thus far I have discussed only the ground state of our Hamilto-nian, (5), in which the plasmons are not excited. ($\hbar\omega_p$ is greater than the Fermi energy for all metals, and both energies are of course

large compared to kT.) There will be a· set of collective excited
states, corresponding to the plasmon spectrum. Such states play
a role only when an energy equal to or greater than $\hbar\omega_p$ is supplied
to the system. They are simply described, since, to the extent that
H_{Int} may be treated as a weak interaction, one can carry out a canonical transformation to a set of independent plasmon modes in which
the plasmons do not interact with the electrons and the plasmon
variables do not appear in the subsidiary conditions [4]. The subsidiary conditions act then only on the electrons, and a fairly detailed
discussion is required to make clear the effect which they have on the
excited-state electronic spectrum [5]. It appears likely that the low-
lying one-electron excitations are essentially unaffected.

4. *Electrons and plasmons in solids*

Let us now turn to the case of electrons in solids. Perhaps the first
question one would like to answer is whether the plasmons may be
regarded as a legitimate elementary excitation in actual solids. Thus
far we have considered only the free-electron gas and have neglected
the possible influence that band-band transitions might have on the
excitation spectrum of the electron system. Recently, Nozières and
I have carried out a treatment which takes into account the influence
of the inter-band transitions by using a model of electrons in a solid
in which the effect of the ion core may be represented by a simple
potential [12]. It is a fairly straightforward calculation to carry out.
The complications come in trying to account for the relative influence of the core electrons on the valence electrons for those solids
in which the characteristic frequencies of excitation of the individual
particles is of the order of the plasma frequency. Fortunately most
solids are fairly simple, in that the important free-particle excitation
frequency (which means the excitation frequency in the absence of
Coulomb interaction), is very low compared to the plasma frequency.
The reason for this is that the plasma frequency is so very high.
What comes in is the ratio of the squares of the frequencies. ω_p^2 may
easily be 225 ev, which means that even if you have an important
band-band transition with an energy of the order of 10 volts, the
correction coming from that to plasmon behavior will be relatively
small.

TABLE II

Comparison of Theoretical and Observed Values for Plasmon Excitation in Some "Simple" Solids [†]

Element	Be	B	C	Mg	Al	Si	Ge
z	2	3	4	2	3	4	4
$\hbar\omega_p$ (ev)	19	24	25	11	16	17	16
ΔE_{obs} (ev)	19	19	22	10	15	17	17

[†] From D. Pines (13).

Table II gives a comparison of the experimental and theoretical values of the plasmon excitation in some "simple" solids. In these solids one would expect to get very nearly free-electron plasmon behavior because the frequencies of the inter-band excitations are small compared to ω_p. We see that our expectation is well borne out by experiment. Similarly, one may understand, in a quite straightforward and consistent fashion, the experimental frequencies for plasmon excitation for solids throughout the whole range of the periodic table, including a wide variety of compounds [13].

Another of the results we find for electrons in solids is that the screening of electron interactions frequently occurs in just the same way as is found for the free-electron gas. This enables us to establish the validity of a quasi-independent particle model for electrons in solids. It is accordingly now possible to carry out a consistent band theory calculation which starts from first principles. Recently, Heine [14] has carried out just such a calculation for aluminium, with results which are in quite good agreement with experiment. Other applications which we have made concern the calculation of the optical properties and the dielectric constant; these will be discussed by Nozières later in the Conference [15].

5. *The dilute hard sphere boson gas and liquid helium*

One may apply exactly the formalism I have discussed for the free-electron gas to the calculation of the energy and excitation spectrum of a dilute gas of hard sphere Bosons. We need only regard the interaction between the particles as being characterized by a

$V_{\mathbf{k}}^{\text{eff}}$ which is

$$V_{\mathbf{k}}^{\text{eff}} = t_{\mathbf{k}} = 4\pi\hbar^2 a/m$$

where a is the hard sphere radius. Since we obtain results which are identical with those of many other investigators [16], I wish to make only a few brief remarks about the treatment.

We begin with the Hamiltonian, (5). After the first canonical transformation, analogous to (1), we obtain a set of phonons with frequency such that

$$\omega_0^2 = 4\pi\hbar^2 ak^2 n/m^2 = s_0^2 k^2$$

whose interaction with the individual Bosons is characterized by a coupling strength

$$g_B^2 = \langle \hbar^2 k^2/4m^2 s_0^2 \rangle_{\text{Av}}$$

We transform away this interaction, obtaining phonons with frequency such that

$$\omega^2 = \omega_0^2 + \hbar^2 k^4/4m^2$$

and a new effective interaction between the Bosons. When we minimize the long-range part of the interaction energy with respect to k_c, we obtain

$$\hbar k_c = (4/3)ms_0$$

which corresponds to a screening length in agreement with that of Lee, Huang, and Yang. This screening length is, as was the case for the electron gas, the wave length at which the phonon-Boson interaction becomes strong. If we now treat the remaining terms in the Hamiltonian in the random phase approximation (the linearization of the equations of motion for the $\rho_{\mathbf{k}}$), we obtain a result for the ground state energy in agreement with that given in [3].

How can we now go from this calculation to a consideration of liquid helium, which we know is far from being a dilute Bose gas? The answer, I believe, lies in the fact that for the long wave length part of the problem, our collective coordinate approach is by no means restricted in its applicability to a case of a dilute gas with weak interactions. In fact, as the interaction between the particles grows stronger, the treatment of the phonons as independent elementary excitations becomes more appropriate. As we have seen, it is based on

an expansion in powers of the squared ratio of the individual particle
frequencies to the phonon frequencies, and the latter increase with
the strength of the interaction.

In order to get a preliminary idea of how the collective coordinate
method would work for liquid helium, I have considered a semi-
phenomenological approach. The approach is designed to link our
methods with those employed by Feynman [17], who uses a structure
factor, $S(\mathbf{k})$, to describe the interaction between the particles. Let
us assume that the effective potential between the particles may be
represented by a $T_{\mathbf{k}}$, which is chosen to yield the current phonon
spectrum. We carry out a calculation directly analogous to that for
the dilute hard sphere Boson gas. We then find that it is sensible to
introduce the maximum number of phonon degrees of freedom, n,
and that the screening length is accordingly shortened to $r_0/2.4$,
where r_0 is the interparticle spacing. We have built the theory to
describe the phonons correctly; we must now consider the other
excitations of the system and the most important question of the self-
consistency of the approach.

To get the roton spectrum, we first decouple the phonon modes
by a series of canonical transformations analogous to those carried
out for the dilute Boson gas. We then obtain a Hamiltonian which
is given approximately by

$$H = \sum_i (p_i^2/2M^*) + \sum_{i>j} V(\mathbf{r}_i - \mathbf{r}_j) - \sum_{k<k_c} (T_{\mathbf{k}} \rho_{\mathbf{k}}^* \rho_{\mathbf{k}}/2) + \sum_{k<k_c} (P_{\mathbf{k}}^* P_{\mathbf{k}}/2)$$
$$+ \omega^2(Q_{\mathbf{k}}^* Q_{\mathbf{k}}/2) \quad (11)$$

The last two terms represent the independent phonon excitations,
while the first three describe individual particle motion. k_c is the
maximum phonon wave vector and is $\sim(6\pi^2 n)^{\frac{1}{3}}$. The helium atoms
in (11) carry with them a cloud of virtual phonons which results
from the particle-phonon coupling; this increases their mass to

$$M^* = [M/1 - (n'/3n)] \cong \tfrac{3}{2} M$$

We may calculate the roton spectrum from (11) in just the way that
Feynman does, by introducing a structure factor $S'(\mathbf{k})$ to charac-
terize the particle interaction. We find that the subsidiary conditions
prevent the appearance of any further long wave length excitations and

that there are short wave length excitations possessing an energy spectrum

$$E(\mathbf{k}) = \hbar^2 k^2 / 2M^* S'(\mathbf{k}) \qquad (k > k_c) \qquad (12)$$

If we now identify $S'(\mathbf{k})$ with the experimental structure factor, we find that (12) gives the experimentally observed roton excitation spectrum to within 10 per cent.

Expression (12) also agrees with the improved calculations of Feynman and Cohen [18], in which Feynman's original wave function was modified to take into account the interaction between the helium atoms. Feynman and Cohen discuss this interaction in terms of a back flow of other atoms about a given atom as it moves through the liquid. It is clear that the back flow may be understood in equivalent fashion as the phonon cloud surrounding each helium atom.

Our result, (12), is only suggestive, since we have not proven that $S'(\mathbf{k})$ is equivalent to the measured structure factor. It would be if the random phase approximation were applicable for the high densities actually encountered in the helium problem, since we have essentially assumed that the long wave length interactions are only weakly coupled to the short-range part of the interaction. In order to prove this assumption, which seems not completely unlikely, I believe that one should try to blend the two approaches which I have discussed. Thus I hope to develop a hybrid theory, which brings together the dilute Boson gas (where we know we are on safe ground), and the phenomenological approach, à la Feynman.

6. *He³ and the nucleus*

If we now consider, for the purpose of orientation, a dilute hard sphere gas of Fermions, we find that there are no collective phonon excitations of the kind we have been discussing. The condition that phonons exist is just the condition that the gas be dense, with a range of interaction comparable with the particle spacing. Such, of course, is the actual situation for He³. Whether there exist in He³ a set of low-lying collective phonon states, which possess a frequency determined by the interaction between the particles, we do not at present know. The sound velocity that one would estimate from knowledge of the He⁴ behavior is of the same magnitude as the velocity of the particles at the top of the Fermi distribution. Hence our simple criterion for a collective mode — that it have a frequency quite different from the individual particle frequencies — is not satisfied. We do not therefore expect to encounter a set of excitations directly analogous to those observed in He⁴. The difference in the behavior of the two systems arises from the statistics — in He⁴ the individual particle excitations are at an energy of $\hbar^2 k^2/2m$, while in He³ they possess the much higher value, $\hbar k v_0$, for long wave length excitations.

I have come to the same conclusion that Prof. Brueckner mentioned [19], that the attraction in He³ is, relatively speaking, much stronger than in the nucleus. As a result, the frequencies of collective excitation, which are determined by an interplay of the hard core repulsion and the attractive part of the interaction, should be relatively higher in the nucleus. There may therefore be a clean-cut separation between the nucleus' phonons and the individual particle nuclear excitations, so that the nuclear phonon may properly be regarded as an independent elementary excitation.

Some time ago, Ferentz, Gell-Mann, and I [20] proposed that the giant nuclear dipole resonance could be explained as an excitation of an isotopic spin nuclear phonon, that is, an oscillation of $\sum_i \tau_z^i \exp i\mathbf{k} \cdot \mathbf{x}_i$. The rough calculations we carried out led to good agreement with the experimental results. I believe that with our improved knowledge of nuclear forces it is now possible to work with the actual two-nucleon potential to verify whether our result follows from first principles.

7. Two-plasma problems

As examples of two-plasma problems, I would like to discuss the interaction between the electrons and ions in a metal, and the interaction between distinct groups of electrons in those solids in which they may be found. As a result of the interaction between the plasmas, the natural frequencies are very much altered. For instance if there were no electron-ion interaction in a metal, the collective excitations would be the electronic plasma oscillations, $(\omega \sim \omega_p)$, and ionic plasma oscillations $[\Omega_p = (4\pi N Z^2 e^2/M)^{\frac{1}{2}}]$, where N, Z, and M are the ionic density, charge, and mass. When we turn on the electron-ion interaction, we affect the high-frequency electronic mode only slightly; its frequency is increased to $\omega_e = (\omega_p^2 + \Omega_p^2)^{\frac{1}{2}}$. The low-frequency ionic mode is markedly altered, because the electrons follow the ionic motion in such a way as to screen out the ionic field quite effectively. We then find the usual sound waves in a metal which, for a simple model of screened electron-ion interaction, possess the dispersion relation

$$\Omega_s^2 = (k^2 v_0^2/3\omega_p^2)\Omega_p^2 = (k^2 v_0^2/3)(m/M)\mathcal{Z} \tag{13}$$

This result was first obtained for a system of free ions and electrons by Bohm and Staver [21]. Recently Bardeen and I [22] considered the influence of the periodic field in a metal on the system motion, and obtained essentially the same result. We were able to obtain a somewhat more accurate dispersion relation than (13), which was in good agreement with experiment for the sound waves in sodium.

We also reached the conclusion that the direct Coulombic electron-electron interaction is not of decisive importance for superconductivity. The direct electron-electron interaction, which is given by H_{sr}, can be treated more or less by perturbation theory. On the other hand, in just those metals which become superconductors, the electron-phonon interaction is sufficiently strong that electrons interacting via it, which lie within an energy $\hbar\omega$ of the Fermi surface, cannot be treated by perturbation theory. Hence it is the latter interaction which should be dominant.

A situation analogous to that of electrons and ions in a metal may arise in solids in which there are two quite distinct groups of electrons, such as electrons and holes of widely different masses in a semiconductor. In such solids, provided the light particle can move sufficiently quickly, and is present in sufficient density to screen out the field of the heavy particle, one expects to find two distinct kinds of plasmons. There will be a high-frequency optical plasmon, which corresponds to the out-of-phase motion of the different electrons, and a low-frequency acoustic plasmon associated with their in-phase motion. In advance of the discovery of this acoustic plasmon, I would like to propose a somewhat jocular term for it. We deal with a case of Distinct Electron Motion or a Double-band Excitation Mode. The wave could certainly have been anticipated classically. Therefore I propose, in honor of Maxwell, the name "demon".

Notes and references

1. D. Pines and D. Bohm, *Phys. Rev.* **85**, 338 (1952).
2. This may be seen by adding a potential energy term $V(\mathbf{r}_i)$ to (1) to describe the effect of the ion cores on the electronic motion. If one then works in the representation in which $\Sigma_i p_i^2 2m + V(\mathbf{r}_i)$ is diagonal, for which the excitation energies are given by $\omega_{n0}(k)$, the equations of motion yield the indicated result. See P. Nozières and D. Pines, *Phys. Rev.* **109**, 1062 (1958).
3. T. D. Lee, K. Huang, and C. N. Yang, *Phys. Rev.* **106**, 1135 (1957); K. A. Brueckner and K. Sawada, *Phys. Rev.* **106**, 1117 (1957).
4. D. Bohm and D. Pines, *Phys. Rev.* **92**, 608, (1953).
5. D. Bohm, K. Huang, and D. Pines, *Phys. Rev.* **107**, 71 (1957).
6. A more careful investigation shows that the $\langle \Omega_k^2 \rangle_{\mathrm{Av}}$ that appears in (9) should correspond to the averaged square excitation frequency approximate to the system of particles interacting via H_{sr}, that is, $\Sigma_i p_i^2 / 2m + H_{\mathrm{sr}}$.
7. D. Pines, in *Solid State Physics*, F. Seitz and D. Turnbull, eds., Academic, New York, 1955, Vol. I.
8. D. Pines, *Phys. Rev.* **92**, 625 (1953); [7].
9. E. P. Wigner, *Phys. Rev.* **46**, 1002 (1934).
10. M. Gell-Mann and K. A. Brueckner, *Phys. Rev.* **106**, 364 (1957).
11. At first sight it appears that we have an energy that depends on an expansion in powers of β; however, when the proper r_s dependence of β is included, one finds an expansion in powers of r_s analogous to that obtained in [10].
12. P. Nozières and D. Pines, *Phys. Rev.* **109**, 741 (1958); 762 (1958); 1062 (1958).
13. D. Pines, *Revs. Modern Phys.* **28**, 184 (1956); [12].
14. V. Heine, *Proc. Roy. Soc. (London)* **240**, 340; 361 (1957).
15. P. Nozières, Chap. XXI, this volume.
16. Lee et al., Brueckner and Sawada, [3]; N. N. Bogoliubov, *J. Phys., (U.S.S.R)* **11**, 23 (1947).
17. R. P. Feynman, *Phys. Rev.* **94**, 262 (1954).
18. R. P. Feynman and M. Cohen, *Phys. Rev.* **102**, 1189 (1956).
19. K. A. Brueckner, Chap. III, this volume.
20. M. Ferentz, Ph. D. Thesis, University of Pennsylvania, 1952; M. Ferentz, M. Gell-Mann, and D. Pines, *Phys. Rev.* **92**, 836 (1953).
21. D. Bohm and T. Staver, *Phys. Rev.* **84**, 336 (1952); T. Staver, Ph. D. Thesis, Princeton University, 1952 (unpublished).
22. J. Bardeen and D. Pines, *Phys. Rev.* **99**, 1140 (1955).

CHAPTER XVII

A Collective Coordinate Method
in the Many-Body Problem†

JEROME K. PERCUS and GEORGE J. YEVICK

1. Introduction

In investigating a system in classical mechanics, a recommended approach is to employ those variables in describing the problem which will present obvious qualitative characteristics in as simple a manner as possible. Now, in many-body systems, the existence of virtually unattenuated sound waves over a wide range of wave lengths is an omnipresent and striking phenomenon, not only in solids, in which lattice vibrations are unavoidable, but in fluids as well.

When the medium is uniform, such sound waves manifest themselves as harmonic vibrations of the matter density in space and time:

$$\rho(\mathbf{x}, t) = A \cos (\mathbf{k} \cdot \mathbf{x} - \omega_\mathbf{k} t) \tag{1}$$

An equivalent description is that the spatial Fourier components are separately excited in pairs by the sound wave; explicitly, the microscopic matter density is

$$\rho(\mathbf{x}) = \sum_{i=1}^{N} \delta(\mathbf{x} - \mathbf{x}_i) \tag{2}$$

so that the normalized Fourier components are

$$q_\mathbf{k} = \int \rho(\mathbf{x}) \, e^{i\mathbf{k} \cdot \mathbf{x}} \, d^3x$$

$$\text{or} \quad q_\mathbf{k} = \sum_{i=1}^{N} e^{i\mathbf{k} \cdot \mathbf{x}_i} \tag{3}$$

Then, except for microscopic fluctuations, eq. (1) becomes

$$q_\mathbf{k}(t) = \tfrac{1}{2} A L^3 e^{i\omega_\mathbf{k} t}$$
$$q_{-\mathbf{k}}(t) = \tfrac{1}{2} A L^3 e^{-i\omega_\mathbf{k} t} \tag{4}$$

† Supported by the Office of Naval Research.

all other q_k vanishing. Here L^3 is the volume of the container. The container will for convenience be regarded as a cube with periodic boundary conditions; thus, all wave vectors $\mathbf{k}$ will be vector multiples of

$$k_0 = 2\pi/L \tag{5}$$

If the system is completely represented by motions of type (4), it should then be specified by a prototype Hamiltonian

$$H = \sum_{\mathbf{k}} (1/\mu_{\mathbf{k}})(\pi_{\mathbf{k}}\pi_{-\mathbf{k}} + \mu_{\mathbf{k}}^2 \omega_{\mathbf{k}}^2 q_{\mathbf{k}} q_{-\mathbf{k}}) + \text{constant} \tag{6}$$

$\pi_{\mathbf{k}}$ being conjugate to $q_{\mathbf{k}}$. There are two complementary drawbacks: first, at very high k (close to the interparticle wave number) $q_{\mathbf{k}}$ is certainly not a pure independent harmonic oscillator; and second, since only $3N$ coordinates are available, all pertinent k could not be superposed (i.e., could not be independent) even if we knew their modes of oscillation. Possible alleviation [1] might involve employing more correctly individual variables for "high k". Or, if we insist on maintaining the simplicity of the set (3), we may take a sample [2] of $3N$ of the $q_{\mathbf{k}}$'s and make certain to restrict our attention to quantities which are determined by these $3N$ alone; the latter approach forms the philosophical basis of the present paper.

2. Non-interacting quantum systems

The coordinates $q_{\mathbf{k}}$, intertwining all particles, are clearly most appropriate for describing collective or system-wide behavior — that in which the system acts as a whole, associated with strong correlations between particles and high density. Since an individual, low correlation, or low density, situation appears to be a severe test of the fancied independence of the $q_{\mathbf{k}}$, let us introduce spin-independent quantum mechanics by considering the free particle case, in which the only correlation is that given by the Einstein-Bose or Fermi-Dirac statistics.

If $\pm \mathbf{k}$ excitation means exciting only the pair $q_{\mathbf{k}}$, $q_{-\mathbf{k}}$, then we would hope that the ratio of a $\mathbf{k}$-excited state to the ground state would be a function of $q_{\mathbf{k}}$ and $q_{-\mathbf{k}}$ alone. Now for an Einstein-Bose system we have ($\psi_{\mathbf{klm}...}$ denoting plane wave excitation at wave numbers

$\mathbf{k}, \mathbf{l}, \mathbf{m}, \ldots$), except for normalization,

$$\psi_{\mathbf{k}}/\psi_0 = \sum e^{i\mathbf{k}\cdot\mathbf{x}_i}/1 = q_{\mathbf{k}} \tag{7}$$

as desired, while

$$\psi_{\mathbf{k}-\mathbf{k}}/\psi_0 = |q_{\mathbf{k}}|^2 - \mathcal{N} \tag{8}$$

The first Laguerre polynomial in $|q_{\mathbf{k}}|^2$ has made its appearance. Moreover,

$$\psi_{\mathbf{k}\mathbf{l}}/\psi_0 = \sum_{i \neq j} e^{i(\mathbf{k}\cdot\mathbf{x}_i + \mathbf{l}\cdot\mathbf{x}_j)} \tag{9}$$
$$= q_{\mathbf{k}} q_{\mathbf{l}} - q_{\mathbf{k}+\mathbf{l}} \cong q_{\mathbf{k}} q_{\mathbf{l}}$$

$q_{\mathbf{k}}$, being a sum of $\mathcal{N}$ random unit vectors, is of order $\mathcal{N}^{\frac{1}{2}}$, so that $q_{\mathbf{k}+\mathbf{l}}$ is of order $\mathcal{N}^{-\frac{1}{2}} q_{\mathbf{k}} q_{\mathbf{l}}$.) Similar results obtain for further low excitations; this is most satisfactory.

On the other hand, for a Fermi-Dirac system, even the ground state is complicated in form. In the one-dimensional case, one can be fairly explicit and show that for state ψ in which wave numbers $k_1, \ldots, k_s$ below the ground state Fermi boundary are missing,

$$\psi/\psi_0 = \text{Det}\,(C_{k_a + bk_0}) \qquad a, b = 1, \ldots, s \tag{10}$$

where C_{jk_0} is the jth elementary symmetric function of the plane waves $e^{ik_0 x_i}$. Thus for n-fold excitation of k_0 (wave number $(n-1)k_0$ below the top is missing), eq. (10) becomes

$$\psi/\psi_0 = C_{nk_0} = (1/n!)q_{k_0}^n - [1/2(n-2)!]q_{k_0}^{n-2}q_{2k_0} + \cdots \tag{11}$$

which is essentially pure q_{k_0} excitation for sufficiently low n.

Putting aside the ψ/ψ_0 ratio, the antisymmetry of ψ itself in the Fermi-Dirac case would appear to introduce grave difficulties in the relatively naive collective coordinate treatment we envisage. However, it may be shown that in the one-dimensional problem, the Einstein-Bose type of calculation may be employed provided that we either insert the boundary condition that ψ vanish on the natural boundary of q space (difficult to accomplish in practice) or augment the potential energy by two-body infinite δ function potentials. In the general (three-dimensional) case, a preliminary division by a basic antisymmetric function converts the problem to an Einstein-Bose one. Or, of course, if evaluations at least are performed in x space, the difficulties vanish completely. These tricks which, as is well known, actually improve many approximational procedures, are nonetheless (with the exception of the configuration space approach) mere tricks from the present point of view, and so we henceforth restrict ouselves to Einstein-Bose statistics.

3. Representation of potential energy

To introduce the approximations appropriate to the method under investigation, consider the N-particle Einstein-Bose system of Hamiltonian

$$H = \sum (1/2m)\, p_i^2 + \tfrac{1}{2} \sum_{i \neq j} V(\mathbf{x}_i - \mathbf{x}_j) \qquad (12)$$

We shall suppose the system wave function to be an eigenstate of total momentum

$$\mathbf{P} = \sum \mathbf{p}_i \qquad (13)$$

which means that it is uniform in the sense of the expectation relations

$$\langle \delta(\mathbf{x} - \mathbf{x}_i) \rangle = 1/L^3$$
$$\langle \delta(\mathbf{x} - \mathbf{x}_i)\, \delta(\mathbf{x}' - \mathbf{x}_j) \rangle = \sigma(\mathbf{x} - \mathbf{x}')/L^6 \qquad (14)$$

The two-body coordinate distribution function σ, which enters prominently in the ensuing discussion, is a function of relative coordinates alone, and similarly for higher order distributions.

We now wish to transform to the (q, X) representation, where we use $3N-3$ $q_{\mathbf{k}}$'s and 3 $\mathbf{X}$'s:

$$q_{\mathbf{k}} = \sum e^{i\mathbf{k} \cdot \mathbf{x}_i} \qquad \mathbf{X} = (1/N) \sum \mathbf{x}_i \qquad (15)$$

First consider the potential energy: it is easy to show that

$$\tfrac{1}{2} \sum_{i \neq j} V(\mathbf{x}_i - \mathbf{x}_j) = \tfrac{1}{2} \sum_{\mathbf{k} \neq 0} V_{\mathbf{k}}(q_{\mathbf{k}} q_{-\mathbf{k}} - N) + [N(N-1)/2] V_0 \qquad (16)$$

where

$$V_{\mathbf{k}} \equiv 1/L^3 \int e^{i\mathbf{k} \cdot \mathbf{x}} V(\mathbf{x})\, d^3x \qquad (17)$$

is the Fourier transform of $V(\mathbf{x})$. Unfortunately, we have not all $\mathbf{k}$ but only a finite set denoted by $\{\mathbf{k}\}$ at our disposal; we should noneheless like to choose constant coefficients ν_k such that

$$\frac{1}{2}\sum_{i\neq j} V(\mathbf{x}_i-\mathbf{x}_j) \cong \frac{1}{2}\sum_{\{k\}}\nu_k(q_k q_{-k}-\mathcal{N})+[\mathcal{N}(\mathcal{N}-1)/2]\nu_0 \qquad (18)$$

1 some optimal fashion. The best expression for the ν_k depends on the etailed character of the state being considered. It is possible to determine [3] (although not uniquely) coordinate functions ν_k such that 18) is exactly satisfied; if the distribution of these ν_k can be shown to e sufficiently tight, then their averages may confidently be inserted 1 (18).

Without being required to follow the details of such a process, a easonable general criterion [2] for the ν_k is that

$$\langle[V(\mathbf{x}_i-\mathbf{x}_j)-V^*(\mathbf{x}_i-\mathbf{x}_j)]^2\rangle \qquad (19)$$

s to be minimized over the motion of the system, where

$$V^*(\mathbf{x}) = \sum_{\{k\}}\nu_k e^{ik\cdot\mathbf{x}}+\nu_0 \qquad (20)$$

Carrying out the minimization of (19), we readily obtain the conditions on the ν_k:

$$\sum_{\{1,0\}}\sigma_{k-1}\nu_1 = [V(\mathbf{x})\,\sigma(\mathbf{x})]_k \qquad (21)$$

r approximately, neglecting σ_1 for $1\neq 0$,

$$\nu_k = (V\sigma)_k \qquad (22)$$

The result (22) is eminently reasonable, for two particles at $\mathbf{x}, \mathbf{y}$

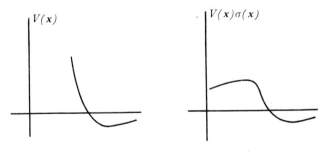

Figure 1

will never feel a potential unless the distribution function $\sigma(\mathbf{x}-\mathbf{y})$ allows them to achieve these positions; thus, crudely, the effective potential is $V(\mathbf{x})\,\sigma(\mathbf{x})$ which, incidentally, is itself much better represented by a finite Fourier series. We expect (21) or (22) to be valid for interactions weak enough so that the explicit criterion for $\nu_\mathbf{k}$ doesn't really matter; a more detailed examination will be deferred until later.

4. Representation of kinetic energy

Next we consider the quantum mechanical kinetic energy, which is to be transformed to the q representation so that q-space operations may be performed. It is more convenient to proceed with the canonical transformation in two steps; first we transform to the q picture, x representation, obtaining after a brief computation

$$\sum (p_i^2/2m) = (1/2m) \sum_{\{\mathbf{k},\mathbf{l}\}} \mathbf{k} \cdot \mathbf{l}\, q_{\mathbf{k}-\mathbf{l}}\, \pi_\mathbf{k}\, \pi_{-\mathbf{l}} + (1/2mN)P^2$$
$$+ (i\hbar/2m) \sum_{\{\mathbf{k}\}} q_\mathbf{k}\, \pi_\mathbf{k}(k^2 + (\mathbf{k}/N) \cdot (\mathbf{P}/\hbar)) \tag{23}$$

Since $q_0 = N$, whereas $q_{\mathbf{k}-\mathbf{l}} \sim N^{\frac{1}{2}}$ for $\mathbf{k} \neq \mathbf{l}$, it seems reasonable to restrict the summation in (23) to $\mathbf{l} = \mathbf{k}$; alternatively, we observe that $\langle q_{\mathbf{k}-\mathbf{l}} \rangle = 0$ for $\mathbf{k} \neq \mathbf{l}$, an immediate consequence of the fact that $\pi_\mathbf{k}$ and $\pi_\mathbf{l}$ belong to inequivalent representations of the translation group, under which the Hamiltonian is invariant.

Now to transform to the q representation, we use the fact that

$$\psi_q(q) = J(x/q)^{\frac{1}{2}}\, \psi_x(q) \tag{24}$$

where $J(x/q)$ is the transformation Jacobian. If the $q_\mathbf{k}$'s are to separate, this requires the Jacobian to separate as well

$$J(x/q) = \prod_{\{\mathbf{k}>0\}} J_\mathbf{k}(q_\mathbf{k}, q_{-\mathbf{k}}) \tag{25}$$

From (25), it follows that

$$J_\mathbf{k}(q_{\mathbf{k}'}, q_{-\mathbf{k}'}) = \int \delta[q_{\mathbf{k}'} - q_\mathbf{k}(x), q_{-\mathbf{k}'} - q_{-\mathbf{k}}(x)]\, J(x/q)\, dq^{3N}$$
$$= \int \delta[q_{\mathbf{k}'} - q_\mathbf{k}(x), q_{-\mathbf{k}'} - q_{-\mathbf{k}}(x)]\, dx^{3N} \tag{26}$$

which on evaluation becomes proportional to $e^{-q_{\mathbf{k}'} q_{-\mathbf{k}'}/N}$. Using (26) to transform (23), as approximated above, to the q representation, our new total Hamiltonian, kinetic plus potential energy, may be written as [4]

$$H = \sum_{\{k>0\}} H_k + (1/2mN) P^2 \tag{27}$$

where

$$H_k = [(Nk^2/m) \pi_k \pi_{-k} + (m\omega_k^2/Nk^2) q_k q_{-k}]$$
$$+ (i/2mN)(q_k \pi_k - q_{-k} \pi_{-k}) k \cdot P - \mathscr{E}_k \tag{28}$$

and

$$\hbar\omega_k = [(\hbar^2 k^2/2m)^2 + (N\hbar^2 k^2/m) \nu_k]^{\frac{1}{2}}$$
$$\mathscr{E}_k = N(\nu_k - \nu_0) + (\hbar^2 k^2/2m) \tag{29}$$

The first term in (28) represents a two-dimensional harmonic oscillator, as expected; one notes, from (29), that its energy quanta start off linearly in k for low k, corresponding to a speed of sound of

$$c = (\partial\omega_k/\partial k)_0 = [(N/m) \nu_k]^{\frac{1}{2}} \qquad k \to 0 \tag{30}$$

while at high k, $\hbar\omega_k$ reduces to the free particle value of $\hbar^2 k^2/2m$. The second term in H_k is diagonal in an angular momentum representation, and the third term is a constant.

To check the validity of (28), let us consider the free particle case: $V = 0$. Solving the Schrödinger equation for (28) in polar coordinates:

$$q_{\pm k} = Q_k e^{\pm i\varphi_k} \tag{31}$$

we readily obtain

$$\psi_{k,\,st} = (Q_k^2/N)^{(t-s)/2} e^{-Q_k^2/2N} L_s^{t-s} (Q_k^2/N) e^{i(s-t)\varphi_k} \tag{32}$$

L_s^{t-s} being the associated Laguerre polynomial, with energy and angular momentum

$$E_k = (s+t) \hbar^2 k^2/2m \qquad M_k = (s-t)\hbar k \tag{33}$$

On the other hand, the free-particle Einstein-Bose case is readily solved; if the q-space wave function were to decompose into separate (q_k, q_{-k}) wave functions, then one would have

$$|\psi_k(q_{k'}, q_{-k'})|^2 = \int \delta[q_{k'} - q_k(x), q_{-k'} - q_{-k}(x)] |\psi(x)|^2 dx^{3N} \tag{34}$$

For instance, let $s \ll \mathcal{N}$ particles of wave number $\mathbf{k}$ and $t \ll \mathcal{N}$ of wave number $-\mathbf{k}$ be excited; then a tedious computation [4] of (34) shows that, to order $1/\mathcal{N}$,

$$|\psi_{\mathbf{k}}|^2 = [(Q_{\mathbf{k}}^2/\mathcal{N})^{(t-s)/2} \, e^{-Q_{\mathbf{k}}^2/2N} \, L_s^{t-s}(Q_{\mathbf{k}}^2/\mathcal{N})]^2 \qquad (35)$$

precisely as in (32), whereas for $|\mathbf{l}| \neq |\mathbf{k}|$, the q_1 projection is strictly a ground state wave function. Further, we observe that the "k phonon" energy $E_{\mathbf{k}}$ is precisely the $\mathbf{k}$-excitation energy, and the angular momentum $M_{\mathbf{k}}$ is the linear momentum wrapped around the periodic cube.

The preceding generalizes to all low excitation; for high excitation, however $(\sim \mathcal{N})$, deviations occur which may be attributed to non-diagonality of the kinetic energy and non-separability of the Jacobian. For $\mathbf{k}$ excitation alone, they may be simulated by employing

$$m' = \mathcal{N}m/[\mathcal{N} - \tfrac{1}{2}(s+t)] \qquad s, t \sim \mathcal{N} \qquad (36)$$

in the kinetic energy, and replacing the Jacobian by

$$J_{\mathbf{k}'}(x/q) = [J_{\mathbf{k}}(x/q)]^{[N+(s+t)/2]/[N-(s+t)/2]} \qquad s, t \sim \mathcal{N} \qquad (37)$$

To a large extent, this is just a boundary effect: the $q_{\mathbf{k}}$'s are not free but must be restricted, e.g., to $|q_{\mathbf{k}}| < \mathcal{N}$, but actually by an interconnecting boundary. Physically, of course, an effect of this type is expected; no more than $\mathcal{N}$ particles can be excited in a given mode, so that apparent high excitation of coordinate $q_{\mathbf{k}}$ must correspond instead, energy wise at least, to excitation of higher $\mathbf{k}$. The transition in the present description must intrinsically be very complicated.

5. Classical statistics

We return to the problem of non-zero interaction. To isolate the interaction aspects, we consider the case of classical statistical mechanics; this means high excitation, but fortunately the kinetic energy can be integrated out and so does not bother us. Our major task is again to write

$$\begin{aligned} \tfrac{1}{2} \sum_{i \neq j} V(\mathbf{x}_i - \mathbf{x}_j) &\cong \tfrac{1}{2} \sum_{\{\mathbf{k} \neq 0\}} \nu_{\mathbf{k}}(q_{\mathbf{k}} q_{-\mathbf{k}} - \mathcal{N}) \\ &\equiv \tfrac{1}{2} \sum_{i \neq j} V^*(\mathbf{x}_i - \mathbf{x}_j) \end{aligned} \qquad (38)$$

in the best possible manner. Exact methods exist for accomplishing this. For example, we have mentioned the use of tightly distributed coordinate functions for the ν_k.

However, in the approach to be presented here, the ν_k really are uniquely determined constants, the approximation entering only in subsidiary computations. The pertinent fact is simply that we are at liberty to vastly restrict the knowledge which we wish to extract from the system; in particular, it suffices for most purposes to determine the two-body distribution function $\sigma(\mathbf{x})$ alone. Indeed, if $\{\mathbf{k}\}$ represents a good sampling of wave numbers, then since the Fourier coefficient σ_k is smooth in a statistical state, the values of σ_k for the set $\{\mathbf{k}\}$ alone are required. The ν_k are then determined uniquely by the condition that if they are used to simulate the potential, the σ_k so obtained are to be correct.

Given then that the potential energy has been replaced by its V^* image, how does one obtain the σ_k? From the definition (14) of σ, it is trivial to establish that [5]

$$\sigma_k = [1/\mathcal{N}(\mathcal{N}-1)](\langle q_k q_{-k}\rangle - \mathcal{N}) \tag{39}$$

But for a statistical state with potential V^*, the coordinate space probability density is

$$P(x) = \exp\left[-\tfrac{1}{2}\beta \sum \nu_k(q_k q_{-k} - \mathcal{N})\right] \qquad \beta = 1/kT \tag{40}$$

If the $\{\mathbf{k}\}$ are properly chosen (sufficiently widely spaced and relatively incommensurable), one may show that

$$L^{-3N}\int \prod f_k(q_k, q_{-k})\, dx^{3N} = \prod L^{-3N}\int f_k(q_k, q_{-k})\, dx^{3N} \tag{41}$$

is a good approximation, with easily computable error terms. The integration of a function of q_k and q_{-k} alone is not difficult, and so, inserting (40) and (41) into (39), we obtain

$$\sigma_k = -\beta\nu_k/(1+\mathcal{N}\beta\nu_k) \tag{42}$$

our first fundamental relation. A comment of interest: In the classical statistical case, one can calculate the effective (due to the transformation of volume from x to q space) harmonic oscillator frequency to be

$$\omega_k = (Nk^2/m)^{\frac{1}{2}}(\nu_k + 1/\mathcal{N}\beta)^{\frac{1}{2}}. \tag{43}$$

and from this the isothermal compressibility becomes

$$n \, \partial p/\partial n = n\mathcal{N}(\nu_{0+}+1/\mathcal{N}\beta) \qquad n \equiv \mathcal{N}/L^3 \tag{44}$$

Using (42), we thus obtain

$$n \, \partial p/\partial n = (n/\beta)(1/1+\mathcal{N}\sigma_{0+}) \tag{45}$$

reproducing the important Ornstein-Zernike relation [6].

Now how do we assure that the $\sigma_{\mathbf{k}}$ we have obtained are correct, i.e., identical with those resulting from the true potential $V(x)$? Clearly we must have identical expectations

$$\langle q_{\mathbf{k}}q_{-\mathbf{k}} \rangle_{V(x)} = \langle q_{\mathbf{k}}q_{-\mathbf{k}} \rangle_{V^*(x)} \tag{46}$$

for the probability densities $P(x)$ built on $V(x)$ and on $V^*(x)$; this will be the case if

$$\int \{\exp[-\beta \sum_{i>j} V^*(\mathbf{x}_i-\mathbf{x}_j)] - \exp[-\beta \sum_{i>j} V(\mathbf{x}_i-\mathbf{x}_j)]\} e^{i\mathbf{k} \cdot (\mathbf{x}_1-\mathbf{x}_2)} \, dx^{3N} = 0 \tag{47}$$

for all $\{\mathbf{k}, 0\}$, thereby determining the $\nu_{\mathbf{k}}$ in V^*. Removing the factor $\exp[-\beta \sum_{i>j} V(\mathbf{x}_i-\mathbf{x}_j)]$ from the integrand, we may write eq. (47) as

$$\left\langle \prod_{i>j} e^{\beta[V(\mathbf{x}_i-\mathbf{x}_j)-V^*(\mathbf{x}_i-\mathbf{x}_j)]} e^{i\mathbf{k} \cdot (\mathbf{x}_1-\mathbf{x}_2)} \right\rangle = \langle e^{i\mathbf{k} \cdot (\mathbf{x}_1-\mathbf{x}_2)} \rangle \tag{48}$$

Now if $V-V^*$ is small enough, or the $\{\mathbf{k}\}$ spectrum appropriate, the $\mathbf{x}_i, \mathbf{x}_j$ pairs may be averaged separately, as in

$$\left\langle \prod_{i>j} F_{ij}(\mathbf{x}_i-\mathbf{x}_j) \right\rangle = \prod_{i>j} \langle F_{ij}(\mathbf{x}_i-\mathbf{x}_j) \rangle \tag{49}$$

analogous to (41); eq. (48) then reduces to

$$[e^{\beta[V(\mathbf{x})-V^*(\mathbf{x})]} \sigma(\mathbf{x})]_{\mathbf{k}} = \sigma_{\mathbf{k}} \tag{50}$$

which for sufficiently rarified k spectrum may be solved for $\nu_{\mathbf{k}}$ to yield

$$\nu_{\mathbf{k}} = [(1/\beta)(e^{\beta V(\mathbf{x})}-1) \sigma(\mathbf{x})]_{\mathbf{k}} \tag{51}$$

our second fundamental relation. Observe that for small V, (51) reduces, as expected, to $\nu_{\mathbf{k}} = (V\sigma)_{\mathbf{k}}$.

6. Classical low density expansion

Our determining relations for σ, together with that of normalization of σ, are now [7]

$$\beta\nu_{\mathbf{k}} = [(e^{\beta V(\mathbf{x})} - 1)\,\sigma(\mathbf{x})]_{\mathbf{k}}$$
$$\sigma_{\mathbf{k}} = -\beta\nu_{\mathbf{k}}/(1 + \mathcal{N}\beta\nu_{\mathbf{k}}) \qquad \mathbf{k} \neq 0 \qquad (52)$$
$$\sigma_0 = 1$$

which may be combined to yield the single coordinate-space integral equation

$$e^{\beta V(\mathbf{x})}\sigma(\mathbf{x}) = 1 - n \int (e^{\beta V(\mathbf{y})} - 1)\,\sigma(\mathbf{y})[\sigma(\mathbf{x} - \mathbf{y}) - 1]\,d^3y \qquad (53)$$

which has a family resemblance to the Born-Green-Yvon and Kirkwood integral equations [8], but is quadratic rather than transcendental. For singular potentials, it is more convenient to use the ratio of σ to the two-particle σ:

$$\tau(\mathbf{x}) \equiv e^{\beta V(\mathbf{x})}\sigma(\mathbf{x}) \qquad (54)$$

in which case

$$\tau(\mathbf{x}) = 1 + n \int (e^{-\beta V(\mathbf{y})} - 1)\,\tau(\mathbf{y})[e^{-\beta V(\mathbf{x} - \mathbf{y})}\tau(\mathbf{x} - \mathbf{y}) - 1]\,d^3y \qquad (55)$$

Pertinent thermodynamic quantities can then be determined in principle from the compressibility relation (45) written in terms of τ;

$$\beta\,\partial p/\partial n = 1 - n \int (e^{-\beta V(\mathbf{x})} - 1)\,\tau(\mathbf{x})\,d^3x \qquad (56)$$

One notes in passing that

$$\tau(\mathbf{x}) = \sigma(\mathbf{x}) + \beta V^*(\mathbf{x}) \qquad (57)$$

thereby reducing to $\sigma(\mathbf{x})$ for large x and to $\beta V^*(\mathbf{x})$ for small x.

To check our integral equation (55), we must first solve it. In special cases, it would appear to be readily amenable to numerical solution, but for the general situation, solution is most readily accomplished by a low density (virial) expansion, for which purpose we write the equation for $\tau(\mathbf{x}_1 - \mathbf{x}_2)$ pictorially as

with the notation

$$\underset{\circ\!-\!\!-\!\circ}{1\quad 2} = \tau(\mathbf{x}_1 - \mathbf{x}_2) \qquad \underset{\circ}{3} = n \int d^3 x_3$$

$$\underset{\circ\!-\!-\!-\!\circ}{1\quad 3} = f_{13} = e^{-\beta V(\mathbf{x}_1 - \mathbf{x}_3)} - 1$$

Proceeding in this manner, one may compute a series for $\partial p / \partial n$ and so obtain the virial coefficients in

$$p\beta = \sum_{1}^{\infty} B_s n^s \tag{59}$$

It turns out that for $s > 1$,

$$B_s = -(1/s) \sum \text{plane irreducible [9] clusters of order } s \tag{60}$$

where only geometrically distinct diagrams are included. Thus the exact B_1, B_2, B_3 are reproduced correctly, while

$$B_4 - B_4^{\text{exact}} = \tfrac{1}{8} \int f_{12} f_{23} f_{34} f_{41} (1 + f_{24})(1 + f_{13}) \prod dx^3 \tag{61}$$

should quite generally be small. (The integrand is small except where the pairs 12, 23, 34, 41 are close but the pairs 24, 13 distant). In particular, for hard spheres, we find

$$B_4 / B_4^{\text{exact}} = 1.034 \tag{62}$$

(Our expression for B_4 was most ingeniously suggested, in the context of hard spheres, by Nijboer and Van Hove [10] some years ago.)

It appears then that even the fairly crude zeroth order theory presented here, essentially based upon independence of phonon oscillations and hence presumably superior for high density, may be valid over a wide range of density. In the few cases thus far tested, it compares very favorably with the results [8] of the Kirkwood superposition approximation for distribution functions.

7. Coupled Einstein-Bose systems

With free-particle Einstein-Bose systems and coupled classical statistical systems as background, we proceed to the case of coupled Einstein-Bose systems. Following the attack of Sec. 5, the major problem is once more to determine the ν_k such that σ_k, evaluated for potential V^*, coincides with that for V, or

$$\left\langle e^{i\mathbf{k} \cdot (\mathbf{x}_1 - \mathbf{x}_2)} \right\rangle_{H + \frac{1}{2}\sum U(\mathbf{x}_i - \mathbf{x}_j)} = \left\langle e^{i\mathbf{k} \cdot (\mathbf{x}_1 - \mathbf{x}_2)} \right\rangle_H \tag{63}$$

where

$$U(\mathbf{x}) \equiv V^*(\mathbf{x}) - V(\mathbf{x}) \tag{64}$$

The crude $\nu_\mathbf{k} = (V\sigma)_\mathbf{k}$ has been applied to the Landau spectrum of He II with good preliminary results [11] but is not a priori satisfactory. However, legerdemain similar to that employed in eqs. (48)–(50) allows us to approximate (63) by

$$\left\langle e^{i\mathbf{k} \cdot (\mathbf{x}_1 - \mathbf{x}_2)} \right\rangle_{H + U(\mathbf{x}_1 - \mathbf{x}_2)} = \sigma_\mathbf{k} \tag{65}$$

We thus require the state functions for $H + U(\mathbf{x}_1 - \mathbf{x}_2)$, and to first order we assume that these have the form

$$\psi(x) = f(\mathbf{x}_1 - \mathbf{x}_2)\,\psi_0(x) \tag{66}$$

where ψ_0 is the corresponding state for H, and f is a real function to be determined variationally. Carrying out the variation of $\langle H + U(\mathbf{x}_1 - \mathbf{x}_2)\rangle$ for the function of (66), we readily find that

$$-\hbar^2/m\, \nabla \cdot [\sigma(\mathbf{x})\, \nabla f(\mathbf{x})] + U(\mathbf{x}) f(\mathbf{x})\, \sigma(\mathbf{x}) = \Lambda f(\mathbf{x})\, \sigma(\mathbf{x}) \tag{67}$$

where Λ is the energy shift. Introducing

$$g(\mathbf{x}) = L^{-\frac{3}{2}} f(\mathbf{x})\, \sigma(\mathbf{x})^{\frac{1}{2}} \tag{68}$$

so that $[g(\mathbf{x}_1 - \mathbf{x}_2)]^2$ is the $\mathbf{x}_1$, $\mathbf{x}_2$ distribution function when the interaction between $\mathbf{x}_1$ and $\mathbf{x}_2$ alone is turned off, there results

$$-\hbar^2/m\, \sigma^{-\frac{1}{2}} \nabla \cdot \sigma\nabla\sigma^{-\frac{1}{2}} g + Ug = \Lambda g \tag{69}$$

as if the kinetic energy were determined by an altered σ-dependent metric. Writing

$$\varphi = L^{-\frac{3}{2}} \sigma^{\frac{1}{2}} \tag{70}$$

eq. (69) attains the more convenient form

$$-(\hbar^2/m)\nabla^2 g + [U + (\hbar^2/m)(\nabla^2 \varphi/\varphi)]\, g = \Lambda g \tag{71}$$

and the condition (65) may be rewritten

$$\int [g^2(\mathbf{x}) - \varphi^2(\mathbf{x})]\, e^{i\mathbf{k} \cdot \mathbf{x}}\, d^3x = 0 \tag{72}$$

Let the G_s be the "unperturbed" reduced wave functions

$$-(\hbar^2/m)\nabla^2 G_s + [(\hbar^2/m)(\nabla^2\varphi/\varphi) - V] G_s = \varLambda_s G_s \qquad (73)$$

Then, for sufficiently rarified **k** spectrum, one finds that V^*, by which (71) and (73) differ, may be regarded as a first-order perturbation; moreover, for insertion into (72), only the portion $2\nu_{\mathbf{k}} \cos \mathbf{k} \cdot \mathbf{x}$ of V^* need be included. Thus, applying first-order perturbation theory, the function g emanating from G_0 is given by

$$g = G_0 + 2\nu_{\mathbf{k}} \sum_{s \neq 0} [G_s \int G_s^* G_0 \cos \mathbf{k} \cdot \mathbf{x}\, d^3x / (\varLambda_0 - \varLambda_s)] \qquad (74)$$

Substituting into (72), there results the desired expression for $\nu_{\mathbf{k}}$:

$$\nu_{\mathbf{k}} = [(G_0^* G_0)_{\mathbf{k}} - \sigma_{\mathbf{k}}] / \{[L^6 \sum_{s \neq 0} |(G_s^* G_0)_{\mathbf{k}} + (G_s^* G_0)_{-\mathbf{k}}|^2] / (\varLambda_s - \varLambda_0)\} \qquad (75)$$

Under a wide variety of circumstances, the summation in eq. (75) can be performed, using the knowledge of G_0 alone, but we will not now consider these cases.

There remains the problem of determining the $\sigma_{\mathbf{k}}$ from the equivalent potential $V^*(\mathbf{x})$. Utilizing an approximation of the type (41), it suffices to find $\sigma_{\mathbf{k}}$ for an applied potential $2\nu_{\mathbf{k}} \cos \mathbf{k} \cdot \mathbf{x}$. Although even this problem is not solvable, the formulation eqs. (27)–(29) should be appropriate, especially if high excitation at any single **k** does not occur. Let us henceforth restrict ourselves, for convenience, to the ground state; then, solving (29) and applying (39), one easily obtains

$$\sigma_{\mathbf{k}} = (1/N)\{[1 + 2N\nu_{\mathbf{k}}/(\hbar^2 k^2/2m)]^{-\frac{1}{2}} - 1\} \qquad (76)$$

Indeed, it may be shown that for the potential $2\nu_{\mathbf{k}} \cos \mathbf{k} \cdot \mathbf{x}$, (76) is rigorously correct both in perturbation (small $\nu_{\mathbf{k}}$) and strong coupling (large $\nu_{\mathbf{k}}$) limits.

8. The ground state at low density

Recapitulating, the Einstein-Bose ground state correlation coefficients $\sigma_{\mathbf{k}}$ are determined in our approximation by the self-consistent set of equations

$$-(\hbar^2/m)\nabla^2 G_s + [(\hbar^2/m)(\nabla^2\varphi/\varphi) - V] G_s = \varLambda_s G_s \qquad (77a)$$

$$\nu_{\mathbf{k}} = [(G_0^* G_0)_{\mathbf{k}} - \sigma_{\mathbf{k}}]/\{[L^6 \sum_{s \neq 0} |(G_s^* G_0)_{\mathbf{k}} + (G_s^* G_0)_{-\mathbf{k}}|^2]/(\Lambda_s - \Lambda_0)\} \qquad (77b)$$

$$\sigma_{\mathbf{k}} = (1/\mathcal{N})\{[1 + 2\mathcal{N}\nu_{\mathbf{k}}/(\hbar^2 k^2/2m)]^{-\frac{1}{2}} - 1\} \qquad (77c)$$

$$\varphi = L^{-\frac{3}{2}} \sigma^{\frac{1}{2}} \qquad (77d)$$

An iterative process of solution might consist of guessing a σ, determining G_s from eq. (77a), then $\nu_{\mathbf{k}}$ from (77b), and finally recovering the new approximation to $\sigma_{\mathbf{k}}$ from (77c).

As an illustration of such an iteration, consider the case of low density. At vanishing density, our zeroth approximation $\sigma^{(0)}$ is simply the two-body relative coordinate probability density (not normalized), so that

$$(-\hbar^2/m \nabla^2 + V) \varphi^{(0)} = E^{(0)} \varphi^{(0)} \qquad (78)$$

Substituting into eq. (77a), G_s obeys the free particle equation, whence

$$G_{\mathbf{s}} = L^{-\frac{3}{2}} e^{i\mathbf{s} \cdot \mathbf{x}} \qquad \Lambda_{\mathbf{s}} - \Lambda_0 = \hbar^2 s^2/m \qquad (79)$$

which, for $\mathbf{k} \neq 0$, then yields at once

$$\nu_{\mathbf{k}} = -(\hbar^2 k^2/2m) \sigma_{\mathbf{k}}^{(0)} \qquad (80)$$

and, from (77c), the first-order approximation becomes simply

$$\sigma_{\mathbf{k}}^{(1)} = (1/\mathcal{N})[(1 - 2\mathcal{N}\sigma_{\mathbf{k}}^{(0)})^{-\frac{1}{2}} - 1] \qquad (81)$$

Further iterations are considerably more complicated.

For example, two hard spheres of diameter a have the ground state relative coordinate wave function

$$\varphi^{(0)} = (4\pi a)^{-\frac{1}{2}} r^{-1} \sin K(r-a) \qquad r \geqq a$$
$$\text{where} \qquad \tan K(R-a) = KR \qquad (82)$$

Here the periodic cube has been replaced by a periodic (projective) sphere of volume $L^3 = (4\pi/3)R^3$ and terms of order a/L have been omitted in the normalization. Thus, to first order in ka, one has

$$\sigma_{\mathbf{k}}^{(0)} = -(8\pi a/L^3)(1/k^2) \qquad (83)$$

and inserting in (81),

$$\sigma_{\mathbf{k}}^{(1)} = -(1/\mathcal{N}) + (1/\mathcal{N})[1 + (16\pi na/k^2)]^{-\frac{1}{2}} \qquad (84)$$

in agreement with the result of Lee, Huang, and Yang [12].

Knowledge of the σ_k should determine the principal physical parameters of the system, of which the ground state energy is one of the most important. However, the usual relation given by the quantum mechanical virial theorem [13] is not valid for the periodic boundary conditions we envisage. As an alternative approach, we compute the energy change under a change of volume of the periodic box (or equally well, with Dirichlet or Neumann conditions). If, for a cube of side $L+dL$, the wave equation is

$$[-(\hbar^2/2m) \sum \nabla_{\mathbf{y}_i}^2 + \tfrac{1}{2} \sum_{i \neq j} V(\mathbf{y}_i - \mathbf{y}_j)] \psi(\ldots \mathbf{y}_i \ldots)$$
$$= (E+dE) \psi(\ldots \mathbf{y}_i \ldots) \tag{85}$$

then the change of variable $\mathbf{y}_i = \mathbf{x}_i + (dL/L)\mathbf{x}_i$ converts (85) to a cube of side L, with an altered Hamiltonian given by

$$dH = 2(\hbar^2/2m)(dL/L) \sum \nabla_i^2 + \tfrac{1}{2}(dL/L) \sum_{i \neq j} (\mathbf{x}_i - \mathbf{x}_j) \cdot \nabla V(\mathbf{x}_i - \mathbf{x}_j) \tag{86}$$

Taking the expectation of (86),

$$dE = (dL/L)\{-2E + [N(N-1)/L^3] \int \sigma(\mathbf{x})[V(\mathbf{x}) + \tfrac{1}{2}\mathbf{x} \cdot \nabla V(\mathbf{x})] d^3x\} \tag{87}$$

which, switching from L to n (N taken as fixed) and integrating by parts, may be written as

$$\partial/\partial n(n^{-\frac{2}{3}} E/N) = -\tfrac{1}{3} n^{-\frac{2}{3}} \int V(\mathbf{x})[\sigma(\mathbf{x}) - \tfrac{1}{2}\nabla \cdot \mathbf{x}\sigma(\mathbf{x})] d^3x \tag{88}$$

We have our desired result.

The relation (88) is trivially applicable to the case of vanishing density since, in a periodic box (but *not* in a rigid box), $\sigma(\mathbf{x})$ is independent of n in this limit. Thus, eq. (88) integrates at once to yield

$$E/N = -n \int V(\mathbf{x})[\sigma(\mathbf{x}) - \tfrac{1}{2}\nabla \cdot \mathbf{x}\sigma(\mathbf{x})] d^3x \tag{89}$$

As a more interesting example, we again consider that of hard spheres at low density. Since $\sigma - \tfrac{1}{2}\nabla \cdot \mathbf{x}\sigma$ is regular at the origin, the hard sphere potential may be replaced, for low orders in a, by the pseudopotential [14]

$$V(\mathbf{x}) = (4\pi a\hbar^2/m) \delta(\mathbf{x}) \tag{90}$$

and so eq. (88) reduces to

$$\partial/\partial n(n^{-\frac{2}{3}}E/\mathcal{N}) = -(4\pi a/3)(\hbar^2/m)\,n^{-\frac{2}{3}}[\sigma(\mathbf{x})-\tfrac{1}{2}\nabla\cdot\mathbf{x}\sigma(\mathbf{x})]_{\mathbf{x}=0} \quad (91)$$

Inserting the first approximation (84) and recalling that $\sigma_0 = 1$, we have

$$\partial/\partial n(n^{-\frac{2}{3}}E/\mathcal{N}) = -(4\pi a/3)(\hbar^2/m)n^{-\frac{2}{3}}$$

$$\times\ (-\tfrac{1}{2}+(1/2\pi^2 n))\int_0^\infty k^2[1+(k/2)\,(d/dk)]\{-1+[1+(16\pi na/k^2)]^{-\frac{1}{2}}\}\,dk$$
$$(92)$$

All integrals are elementary; on evaluation, we obtain

$$\partial/\partial n(n^{-\frac{2}{3}}E/\mathcal{N}) = (4\pi a/3)(\hbar^2/2m)n^{-\frac{2}{3}}+(256\pi^{\frac{1}{2}}a^{\frac{5}{2}}/9)(\hbar^2/2m)n^{-\frac{1}{6}}$$
$$\text{or}\quad (E/\mathcal{N}) = 4\pi na(\hbar^2/2m)[1+(128/15\pi^{\frac{1}{2}})(na^3)^{\frac{1}{2}}] \quad (93)$$

again of course coinciding with the result of Lee, Huang, and Yang [12], [15].

Notes and references

1. D. Pines and D. Bohm, *Phys. Rev.* **85**, 338 (1952).
2. J. K. Percus and G. J. Yevick, *Phys. Rev.* **101**, 1192 (1956); *Nuovo cimento*, (Ser. 10) **5**, 65 (1957).
3. J. K. Percus and G. J. Yevick, *Phys. Rev.* **99**, 661 (A) (1955).
4. J. K. Percus and G. J. Yevick, *Collective Coordinate Analysis of Free Einstein-Bose Systems*, Office of Naval Research Report, 1956 (unpublished).
5. R. P. Feynman, *Phys. Rev.* **94**, 262 (1954).
6. L. S. Ornstein and F. Zernike, *Koninkl. Ned. Akad. Wetenschap. Proc.* **17**, 793 (1914).
7. J. K. Percus and G. J. Yevick, *Phys. Rev.* **110**, 1 (1958).
8. J. O. Hirschfelder, C. F. Curtiss, and R. B. Bird, *Molecular Theory of Gases and Liquids*, Wiley, New York, 1954, p. 330.
9. J. E. Mayer and M. G. Mayer, *Statistical Mechanics*, Wiley, New York, 1940, p. 285.
10. B. R. A. Nijboer and L. Van Hove, *Phys. Rev.* **85**, 777 (1952).
11. G. J. Yevick and J. K. Percus, *Phys. Rev.* **98**, 1164 (A) (1955).
12. T. D. Lee, K. Huang, and C. N. Yang, *Phys. Rev.* **106**, 1135 (1957).
13. J. O. Hirschfelder et al., op. cit., p. 68.
14. J. M. Blatt and V. F. Weisskopf, *Theoretical Nuclear Physics*, Wiley, New York, 1952, p. 76.
15. K. Huang, T. D. Lee, and C. N. Yang, Chap. X, this volume.

Part Four

CHAPTER XVIII

Normal States of Matter

JEROME K. PERCUS

1. Asymptotic Pair Distribution

A number of approaches to the many-body problem aim at approximate determination of the two-body distribution function, in terms of which most quantities of physical importance may be obtained. Some a priori knowledge of the form of this function would then be of great value. In Chap. XIX, Goldstein describes an early attempt of Zernike [1] to establish the asymptotic form for large particle separation. Zernike's analysis, elegant in conception, is weakened by uncertainties, both general and specific in nature, which deserve mention.

The conditional pair distribution or correlation function $n(\mathbf{r}'; \mathbf{r})$ is the expected particle density at $\mathbf{r}'$, given that there is a particle at $\mathbf{r}$; for an N-body system of temporally homogeneous one-body properties, the implied averaging process is one over time. So defined, $\int n(\mathbf{r}'; \mathbf{r}) \, d^3 r' = N-1$. Equally well, for translation invariance in space as well as time, and with n_a the limiting value of $n(\mathbf{r}'; \mathbf{r})$ for large $|\mathbf{r}'-\mathbf{r}|$ (note that $n_a \to N/\Omega$ for infinite volume Ω at fixed density), the deviation

$$g(\mathbf{r}'-\mathbf{r}) \equiv n(\mathbf{r}'; \mathbf{r})-n_a \tag{1}$$

is convenient to use; an alternative definition in terms of density fluctuations is given by Goldstein. The question arises whether $n(\mathbf{r}'-\mathbf{r})$ or $g(\mathbf{r}'-\mathbf{r})$ can in general be expressed in terms of some more fundamental quantity. Consider for example statistical equilibrium at temperature $T = 1/k\beta$ for a classical system of particles in a one-dimensional box of length $L \to \infty$, and with net repulsive interaction potential $V(x'-x)$ restricted to nearest neighbors. It can then be shown without difficulty that, for $x > 0$,

$$n(x) = h(x) + h(x) * h(x) + h(x) * h(x) * h(x) + \ldots \tag{2a}$$

$$\text{where} \quad a(x) * b(x) \equiv \int_0^x a(x-y) b(y) \, dy \tag{2b}$$

$$\text{and} \quad Lh(x) = \exp \{ -\beta[V(x) + (p - nkT)x - V_0] \} \tag{2c}$$

Here p is the system pressure, $n = \mathcal{N}/L$, and V_0 is adjusted such that $\mathcal{N} \int_0^L h(x) \, dx = \mathcal{N} - 1$. Equation (2a) may be interpreted as the probability of x_i being x away from x_j with no particles in between, plus the probability of one particle in between, the total separation being x, plus two particles, etc; the primitive or direct two-particle probability h simply employs a modified potential.

The conceptual decomposition of the correlation function g into iterated "direct" correlations has also occurred in approximate procedures of various authors for the general problem of classical statistical mechanics. Thus, in one formulation which has been employed (see Chap. XVII, Sec. 6),

$$g(\mathbf{r}) = f(\mathbf{r}) + \int g(\mathbf{r} - \mathbf{r}') f(\mathbf{r}') \, d^3 r' \tag{3a}$$

$$\text{where} \quad f(\mathbf{r}) = n(\mathbf{r})(1 - e^{\beta V(\mathbf{r})}) \tag{3b}$$

Equation (3a), on solving iteratively for g, is a three-dimensional generalization of eqs. (2a), (2b). An important characteristic of f, appearing as a modified correlation function for a pure two-body system (at density n), is that its range is of the order of that of the two-body interaction. Interpreting f as an intrinsic two-body probability whose iteration via arbitrary chains of interceding particles yields g, one now assumes with Zernike that the above property generally holds, and indeed, for a physical f to exist, its value, like that of g, should always exceed $-n$; otherwise, (3a) would merely define f and be of uncertain use.

Suppose then that f is physically significant. For an isotropic system, f and g are functions of $r = |\mathbf{r}|$ alone. We may readily expand $g(\mathbf{r} - \mathbf{r}')$ in (3a) as a Taylor series with remainder about $\mathbf{r}$, transforming (3a) to

$$[(1 - F) - \sum_1^S r_F^{(2j)} \Delta^j / (2j+1)!] g(\mathbf{r}) = f(\mathbf{r})$$
$$+ (1/2S!) \int_0^1 (1-t)^{2S} \int f(\mathbf{r}')(\mathbf{r}' \cdot \nabla_\mathbf{r})^{2S+1} g(\mathbf{r} + t\mathbf{r}') \, d^3 r' \, dt \tag{4}$$

where Δ is the Laplacian, the $r_F^{(2j)}$ are the even moments

$$r_F^{(2j)} = \int r^{2j} f(\mathbf{r}) \, d^3 r \tag{5}$$

and $F = r_F^{(0)}$. One cannot be confident of dispensing with the remainder term in (4), for only a few moments (5) may exist; for example, in the singular case of the ground state of a hard sphere Boson fluid, theoretical considerations [2] indicate that the extensive momentum correlation can produce very long range f and g in the presence of an interaction: even $F = r_F^{(0)}$ diverges. Estimates may be made [3] of the convergence of the series in (4) for large r, on the basis of asymptotic expressions for f and g, but such an approach runs the danger of being circular.

Assuming that the series in (4) exists and converges rapidly, Zernike's technique consists of retaining only the first two terms, so that (4) may be written in the form

$$(1-F)(1-\rho^2 \Delta) g(r) = f(r) \tag{6}$$

For r sufficiently large compared to the range of f, f may be regarded as a δ function, and so the asymptotic solution

$$g(r) = (3F/2\pi r_F^{(2)}) r^{-1} e^{-r/\rho} \tag{7}$$

is readily obtained. Unfortunately, an asymptotic form depends very sensitively upon its defining equation. Thus, if instead of approximating the differential operator in (5) by $(1-F)(1-\rho^2 \Delta)$, we use $(1-F) \exp(-\rho^2 \Delta)$, the asymptotic form $\exp(-r^2/4\rho^2)$ results, while even a change to $(1-F)(1-\frac{2}{3}\rho^2 \Delta)^{\frac{3}{2}}$ yields $(r)^{-\frac{1}{2}} \exp[-\frac{1}{2}\sqrt{3}(r/\rho)]$.

The uncertainty of the Zernike analysis stems from our inability to assess the physical attributes of the function f in a direct fashion, as well as from the chain of arguments required to carry out the differential equation approach. Both obstacles are circumvented by Goldstein (Chap. XIX), who employs the relation of $g(r)$ to the scattering intensity structure factor

$$g(r) = (1/2\pi^2 r) \int_0^\infty [F_L^2(k) - 1] k \sin kr \, dk \tag{8}$$

and observes that experimentally $F_L^2(k) - 1$ always appears parabolic for small k:

$$F_L^2(k) - 1 = a(1 - \rho^2 k^2 + \ldots) \qquad (9)$$

The new problem is that of extending (9) to larger k. Using the simplest extension $a/(1 + \rho^2 k^2)$, Goldstein reproduces the form (7), which, since $1 + \rho^2 k^2$ is the Fourier transform of the operator $1 - \rho^2 \Delta^2$, is not surprising. More generally, if $F_L^2 - 1$ can be represented as an algebraic function of k^2 which is integrable over the real axis, it is readily found that the asymptotic form (7) is obtained, with the exponent determined by the complex pole of smallest imaginary part.

Expression (9) represents information on the asymptotic form of g which may be obtained theoretically with a fair degree of certainty. If only low Fourier coefficients of $g[F_L^2(k) - 1 = \Omega g_k]$ are required, one may make use of the fact that the low wave vector density fluctuation coefficients $q_k = \sum \exp(i\mathbf{k} \cdot \mathbf{x}_i)$ are very nearly independent harmonic oscillators, coupled with the relation $\langle q_k q_k^* \rangle = \mathcal{N} + \mathcal{N} \int n(\mathbf{r}'; \mathbf{r}) \exp[i\mathbf{k} \cdot (\mathbf{r}' - \mathbf{r})] \, d^3 r'$, or

$$\mathcal{N} g_k = \Omega^{-1} \langle q_k q_k^* \rangle - n \qquad \text{for} \qquad \mathbf{k} \neq 0 \qquad (10)$$

Further, g_k is continuous at $\mathbf{k} = 0$. Now from the analysis of Bohm and Pines (see Chap. XVI, Sec. 2) or Tomonaga (see Chap. XIII, Sec. 2), the Hamiltonian for the kth oscillation is $H_k = (\mathcal{N} k^2/m) \pi_k \pi_k^* + (m/\mathcal{N} k^2) \omega_k^2 q_k q_k^*$, where

$$\omega_k^2 = (\mathcal{N} k^2/m)[\nu_k + (\hbar^2 k^2/4m\mathcal{N}) + \langle p^2 \rangle / 3m\mathcal{N}] \qquad (11)$$

ν_k being an effective interaction coefficient and m of the order of the particle mass. Since $\langle q_k q_k^* \rangle = (\mathcal{N} k^2/2m\omega_k^2)\langle H_k \rangle$, and $\langle H_k \rangle = \hbar\omega_k$ coth $(\frac{1}{2}\hbar\omega_k \beta)$ at temperature $T = 1/k\beta$, we then have

$$\Omega g_k = (\frac{1}{2}\hbar k^2/m\omega_k) \coth (\frac{1}{2}\hbar\omega_k \beta) - 1 \qquad (12)$$

We are interested in the region of low $\mathbf{k}$. Two possibilities exist. For the ground state $(\beta = \infty)$ of a system with short-range forces, ν_k approaches a constant ν_0 as $k \to 0$, and (11) may be written as $\omega_k = ck$, (12) as $\Omega g_k = (\frac{1}{2}\hbar k/mc) - 1$ as $k \to 0$. On Fourier transforming,

$$g(\mathbf{r}) = (\hbar/mc)(2\pi^2 r^4)^{-1} \qquad (13)$$

as $r \to \infty$ (depending only upon $g_{\mathbf{k}}$ at $k \sim 0$ as long as $g_{\mathbf{k}} \to 0$ smoothly as $k \to \infty$), which is a long-range correlation; "normal" states of matter do not fall into this category. On the other hand, for either Coulomb forces ($\nu_{\mathbf{k}} \propto 1/k^2$ as $k \to 0$), or finite temperature (and $\nu_{\mathbf{k}} = \nu_0 + \alpha k^2 + \ldots$), $g_{\mathbf{k}}$ is seen to have the form (9), so that the comments on eq. (9) apply. In particular, a restriction to something like an effective algebraic structure seems to be required; the non-algebraic examples: $F_L^2(k) - 1 = a \exp(-\rho^2 k^2)$ with $g(r) \to \frac{1}{2} a(\pi \rho^2)^{-\frac{3}{2}}$ $\exp(-\frac{1}{4} r^2 \rho^2)$, or: $F_L^2(k) - 1 = a(1 - \frac{1}{2}\rho^2 k^2)^2$ for $|k| < (\sqrt{2})/\rho$, or else 0, with $g(r) \to (2\sqrt{2})(a\rho/r^4) \cos [(\sqrt{2}r)/\rho]$, show that definitive statements on the asymptotic form cannot be made on the basis of (9) alone.

2. Ground state energy

Let us concentrate now upon the ground state energy of a many-body system. Of course, by ground state we need only mean the lowest state among simultaneous eigenstates of a commuting set of constants of motion, such as total linear momentum, but we will most often refer to the absolute ground state. Consideration is to be centered upon "normal" systems; superfluid properties will be dealt with in Part Five. Nonetheless, it is appropriate to extend the formal discussion to Einstein-Bose systems, and we shall do so. For definiteness and reality as well as for simplicity, the Hamiltonian will be taken as

$$H = \sum p_i^2/2m + \frac{1}{2} \sum_{i \neq j} V(\mathbf{x}_i, \mathbf{x}_j) \qquad (14)$$

A most convenient general expression for the energy is the Rayleigh-Ritz expression,

$$E = \langle \psi | H | \psi \rangle / \langle \psi | \psi \rangle \qquad (15)$$

an upper bound to the ground state energy (while a lower bound is obtainable by Weinstein's [4] method); expression (15), while second-order with respect to wave function deviations, does not necessarily produce a ψ that is good for calculating expectations of other observables. In any event, the problem will be to develop treatments which make use of (15) for the intrinsically complicated many-body system (14), indeed, which remain valid as the particle number $N \to \infty$, which is the "ideal" case of the many-body problem. Two types of approach can be specified loosely by nominal attempts at using respectively less and more information than that given by the wave function.

Suppose the system is bounded without artificial containment. Then for $H\psi = E\psi$, the kinetic energy may be converted to virial form:
$\langle\psi|\sum p_i^2/2m|\psi\rangle = \langle\psi|\frac{1}{2}(i/\hbar)[H,\sum \mathbf{x}_i\cdot\mathbf{p}_i]+\frac{1}{4}\sum(\mathbf{x}_i\cdot\nabla_i+\mathbf{x}_j\cdot\nabla_j)V(\mathbf{x}_i,\mathbf{x}_j)|\psi\rangle$
$= \frac{1}{4}\langle\psi|\sum(\mathbf{x}_i\cdot\nabla_i+\mathbf{x}_j\cdot\nabla_j)V(\mathbf{x}_i,\mathbf{x}_j)|\psi\rangle/\langle\psi|\psi\rangle$. Hence (15) becomes
$E = \langle\psi|\sum(\frac{1}{4}(\mathbf{x}_i\cdot\nabla_i+\mathbf{x}_j\cdot\nabla_j)V(\mathbf{x}_i,\mathbf{x}_j)|\psi\rangle/\langle\psi|\psi\rangle$, or choosing $V(\mathbf{x},\mathbf{y}) = V(\mathbf{x}-\mathbf{y})+U(\mathbf{x})/\mathcal{N}-1+U(\mathbf{y})/\mathcal{N}-1$ so that $V=\frac{1}{2}\sum_{i\neq j}V(\mathbf{x}_i-\mathbf{x}_j)+\sum U(\mathbf{x}_i)$,
then

$$E = \frac{1}{2}\mathcal{N}(\mathcal{N}-1)\int[V(\mathbf{x}-\mathbf{y})+\frac{1}{2}(\mathbf{x}-\mathbf{y})\cdot\nabla V(\mathbf{x}-\mathbf{y})]\,\sigma(\mathbf{x},\mathbf{y})\,d^3x\,d^3y$$
$$+\mathcal{N}\int[U(\mathbf{x})+\frac{1}{2}\mathbf{x}\cdot\nabla U(\mathbf{x})]\,\sigma(\mathbf{x},\mathbf{y})\,d^3x\,d^3y \qquad (16)$$

where $\sigma(\mathbf{x},\mathbf{y}) = n(\mathbf{y})n(\mathbf{x};\mathbf{y})/\mathcal{N}(\mathcal{N}-1)$ is a normalized pair distribution probability. It then appears that minimization with respect to $\sigma(\mathbf{x},\mathbf{y})$ is sufficient to determine the ground state E_0. There are two drawbacks. First, there are obvious restrictions to be imposed: normalization and positiveness of σ. These are certainly insufficient, for they would imply $E_0 \propto \mathcal{N}^2$ at very large $\mathcal{N}$. Second, there are indirect conditions: some properties of ψ and hence of σ have been used for the integration by parts leading to (16), and surely not every (two-body) σ can arise from some ($\mathcal{N}$-body) ψ. In fact, if $n^{(2)}(\mathbf{x},\mathbf{y})=n(\mathbf{y})n(\mathbf{x};\mathbf{y})$ vanishes over too large a region, it may be impossible to extend it not only to a $\psi^*\psi$ but even to a triplet distribution $n^{(3)}(\mathbf{x},\mathbf{y},\mathbf{z})$. Observing that $n^{(s)}(\mathbf{x}_1,\ldots,\mathbf{x}_s)$ must be symmetric in $\mathbf{x}_1,\ldots,\mathbf{x}_s$, the one-dimensional example, $n^{(2)}(x_1,x_2) = 0$ unless either $2 < x_1/x_2 < 4$ or $2 < x_2/x_1 < 4$, illustrates this point. Clearly, further consideration is necessary.

Striking out in the opposite direction, if, in the absence of spin dependence, one varies

$$I = \int F\psi^{-1}H\psi\,dx^{3N}/\int F\,dx^{3N} \qquad (17)$$

independently with respect to the full $3\mathcal{N}$-dimensional real functions ψ and F, there results $H(F/\psi) = \psi^{-2}FH\psi$, $\psi^{-1}H\psi = E$. Hence $H\psi = E\psi$, and $H(F/\psi) = E(F/\psi)$. The appropriate stationary condition is that, for non-negative F, the minimum with respect to ψ of the maximum of

I with respect to *F* (which is the maximum of $H\psi/\psi$) is an upper bound to the ground state energy (and $F = \psi^2$). The corresponding maximum condition applies for a lower bound. Since only ln ψ enters into (17), with a sufficiently simple ansatz for ψ, only various lower-dimensional integrals of *F* will be required. Thus, a pair product form for ψ (see Jastrow, Chap. XI), together with a Kirkwood superposition approximation [5] for the reduced three-body *F* in terms of two-body functions, has been suggested by Penrose [6] for treating the uniform many-Boson ground state. In practice, the mini-max condition is replaced by simple stationarity. Unless the guess for *F* is, roughly, as poor as that for ψ, *F* becomes sharply peaked, really choosing max $(H\psi/\psi)$, and the method is more suitable for accuracy of ψ than for E_0.

Density Matrix Approach. Let us make a somewhat more systematic analysis of the ground state energy problem, proceeding along lines similar to the above, but not restricting our considerations to coordinate space probability distributions. Quite generally, for the expectation of a many-body operator $A = (s!)^{-1} \sum' A[i_1, \ldots, i_s]$, where i_k indicates an operation involving particle i_k, and $\sum'$ is the sum over unequal indices, it is seen that [7]

$$\langle A \rangle = \mathrm{Tr}_{1\ldots s}[A(1, \ldots, s)\, \Gamma^{(s)}(\mathbf{x}_1 \ldots \mathbf{x}_s | \mathbf{x}_1' \ldots \mathbf{x}_s')] \qquad (18)$$

Here $\mathbf{x}_j$ stands for all coordinates, continuous and discrete, of particle j, $A(1, \ldots, s)$ operates only on $\mathbf{x}_1, \ldots, \mathbf{x}_s$, and $\mathrm{Tr}_{1\ldots s}$ indicates that we are to set all $\mathbf{x}_j' = \mathbf{x}_j$ $(j = 1, \ldots, s)$, then integrate (and sum as required) over the $\mathbf{x}_j$; the *s*th-order density matrix $\Gamma^{(s)}$ for an N-body system is then defined by

$$\Gamma^{(s)}(\mathbf{x}_1 \ldots \mathbf{x}_s | \mathbf{x}_1' \ldots \mathbf{x}_s') = \binom{N}{s} \mathrm{Tr}_{s+1\ldots N}[\psi(\mathbf{x}_1 \ldots \mathbf{x}_N)\, \psi^*(\mathbf{x}_1' \ldots \mathbf{x}_N')]$$

$$(19)$$

Only the relevant $\Gamma^{(s)}$, and not the detailed function ψ are required for expectations. In particular, for the Hamiltonian (14), one needs only $\Gamma^{(1)}$ and $\Gamma^{(2)}$, which are clearly related and normalized by

$$(2/N-1)\, \mathrm{Tr}_2\, \Gamma^{(2)}(\mathbf{x}_1 \mathbf{x}_2 | \mathbf{x}_1' \mathbf{x}_2') = \Gamma^{(1)}(\mathbf{x}_1 | \mathbf{x}_1')$$

$$(1/N)\, \mathrm{Tr}_1\, \Gamma^{(1)}(\mathbf{x}_1 | \mathbf{x}_1') = 1$$

$$(20)$$

In terms of $\Gamma^{(1)}$ and $\Gamma^{(2)}$ (T and U operating on $\mathbf{x}_1$ alone)

$$\langle H \rangle = \mathrm{Tr}_1\{[T(1)+U(1)]\,\Gamma^{(1)}(\mathbf{x}_1|\mathbf{x}_1')\}$$
$$+ \mathrm{Tr}_{12}[V(1,\,2)\,\Gamma^{(2)}(\mathbf{x}_1\mathbf{x}_2|\mathbf{x}_1'\mathbf{x}_2')] \qquad (21)$$

where $V(1,\,2) \equiv V(\mathbf{x}_1,\,\mathbf{x}_2)$, $T(1) = p_1^2/2m$, and an explicit external potential $U(\mathbf{x})$ has been included for convenience.

Now if one varies (21) subject to the conditions (20), the implicit relation satisfied by ψ which contributed to the difficulty in using (16) is no longer needed. There are of course obvious additional conditions which must be satisfied by a $\Gamma^{(2)}$ which arises from a many-body ψ: for (Fermi-Dirac) Einstein-Bose systems, $\Gamma^{(s)}(\mathbf{x}_1 \ldots \mathbf{x}_s | \mathbf{x}_1' \ldots \mathbf{x}_s')$ must be (anti-) symmetric in the sets $\mathbf{x}_1 \ldots \mathbf{x}_s$ and $\mathbf{x}_1' \ldots \mathbf{x}_s'$ separately, and non-negative as a matrix: $\int f^*(\mathbf{x}_1 \ldots \mathbf{x}_s)\,\Gamma^{(s)}(\mathbf{x}_1 \ldots \mathbf{x}_s | \mathbf{x}_1' \ldots \mathbf{x}_s') \times f(\mathbf{x}_1' \ldots \mathbf{x}_s')\,d\tau^s\,d\tau'^s \geqq 0$. The question is then whether these conditions suffice to render $\Gamma^{(s)}$ realizable. Since our interest is in the Hamiltonian (14), in which the operator $V(1,\,2)$ is diagonal in the coordinates, i.e., a function of $\mathbf{x}_1,\,\mathbf{x}_2$ alone, and is spin-independent, then only

$$n^{(2)}(\mathbf{x}_1\mathbf{x}_2) = 2\,\mathrm{Tr}_{\sigma_1\sigma_2}\,\Gamma^{(2)}(\mathbf{x}_1\sigma_1,\,\mathbf{x}_2\sigma_2 | \mathbf{x}_1\sigma_1',\,\mathbf{x}_2\sigma_2')$$
$$\Gamma(\mathbf{x}_1|\mathbf{x}_1') = \mathrm{Tr}_{\sigma_1}\,\Gamma^{(1)}(\mathbf{x}_1\sigma_1|\mathbf{x}_1\sigma_1') \qquad (22)$$

enter into $\langle H \rangle$, spin indices being spelled out explicitly. Further, for a translation-invariant state (with $U(\mathbf{x}) = 0$), (22) may be written, in Mayer's notation [8], as $n^{(2)}(\mathbf{x}_1\mathbf{x}_2) = [1-g(\mathbf{x}_1-\mathbf{x}_2)]n^2$, $\Gamma(\mathbf{x}_1|\mathbf{x}_1') = f(\mathbf{x}_1-\mathbf{x}_1')$. $\langle H \rangle$ is completely expressible in terms of the two functions f and g, and only the realizability of a pair $f,\,g$ is in question. Imposing a number of necessary conditions, Mayer [8] has computed the ground state energy of an electron gas in this fashion. However, Tredgold [9] and Mayer (Chap. XXII) have pointed out the inadequacy of these conditions, and Ayres [10] has added further restrictions, obtaining qualitatively reasonable results. A method of generating all required conditions has recently been reported [11] but it is not yet in practicable form.

Returning to the realizability of $\Gamma^{(2)}$ and $\Gamma^{(1)}$, one may also proceed as follows. It is readily seen that the Rayleigh-Ritz procedure may be replaced by the minimization of

$$\langle H \rangle = \text{Tr}_{1\ldots N}[H\Gamma^{(N)}(\mathbf{x}_1 \ldots \mathbf{x}_N | \mathbf{x}_1' \ldots \mathbf{x}_N')] \qquad (23)$$

subject to the sole conditions that $\Gamma^{(N)}$ be non-negative and normalized by $\text{Tr}_{1\ldots N}\Gamma^{(N)} = 1$; the stationary $\Gamma^{(N)}$ is precisely $\psi(\mathbf{x}_1 \ldots \mathbf{x}_N)\psi^*(\mathbf{x}_1' \ldots \mathbf{x}_N')$. If (19) is replaced by

$$\Gamma^{(s)}(\mathbf{x}_1 \ldots \mathbf{x}_s | \mathbf{x}_1' \ldots \mathbf{x}_s') = \binom{N}{s} \text{Tr}_{s+1\ldots N} \Gamma^{(N)}(\mathbf{x}_1 \ldots \mathbf{x}_N | \mathbf{x}_1' \ldots \mathbf{x}_N') \qquad (24)$$

then all results succeeding eq. (19) remain valid. Hence it is only necessary that $\Gamma^{(1)}$ and $\Gamma^{(2)}$ be obtainable from some non-negative normalized $\Gamma^{(N)}$. A possible approach in which $\Gamma^{(N)}$ is built up by a modified Kirkwood superposition principle [5] is briefly mentioned by Mayer (Chap. XXII, Sec. 3). Generally, if one chooses a $\Gamma^{(N)}$ depending upon an arbitrary function of four variables and integrates down to obtain $\Gamma^{(2)}(\mathbf{x}_1\mathbf{x}_2 | \mathbf{x}_1'\mathbf{x}_2')$ in terms of this function, then $\Gamma^{(2)}$ is certainly guaranteed to be realizable, but one must vary the function contained within, and not $\Gamma^{(2)}$ itself, which may be cumbersome. However, especially for Fermions, it may be less so than an analogous approach using wave functions (see Jastrow, Chap. XI, Sec. 4).

Independent Particle Model. As a prototype calculation for the Fermion case, let us use a variational ansatz based upon a function of two variables. In an independent particle picture, we have $\psi = \text{Det}\,[\varphi_k(\mathbf{x}_j)]$, so that $\Gamma^{(N)} = \text{Det}\,[\varphi_k(\mathbf{x}_j)]\,\text{Det}\,[\varphi_k^*(\mathbf{x}_j')] = \text{Det}\,[\sum_k \varphi_k(\mathbf{x}_i)\varphi_k^*(\mathbf{x}_j')]$. An obvious generalization is then the (unnormalized)

$$\Gamma_{\text{un}}^{(N)} = \text{Det}\,f(\mathbf{x}_i | \mathbf{x}_j') \qquad (25)$$

$\Gamma^{(N)}$ is seen to be non-negative if the continuous Hamiltonian matrix $f(\mathbf{x}|\mathbf{x}')$ is non-negative. The principal calculation is that of the normalization integral $\int \ldots \int \text{Det}\,f(\mathbf{x}_i|\mathbf{x}_j)\,d\tau^N$. It is only necessary to use the fact, familiar from Fredholm theory [12], that, with $\text{Det}^{(s)}$ denoting an $s \times s$ determinant,

$$\sum_0^\infty (z^s/s!) \int \ldots \int \text{Det}^{(s)} f(\mathbf{x}_i|\mathbf{x}_j)\,d\tau^s = \text{Det}\,[\delta(\mathbf{x}-\mathbf{x}')+zf(\mathbf{x}|\mathbf{x}')] \qquad (26)$$

coupled with the identity for any positive matrix M

$$\text{Det}\,M = \exp\,[\text{Tr}\,(\ln\,M)] \qquad (27)$$

Equating coefficients of z^s, we then obtain

$$\int \ldots \int \mathrm{Det}^{(N)} f(\mathbf{x}_i|\mathbf{x}_j) \, d\tau^N = (N!/2\pi i) \oint z^{-N} \exp\{\mathrm{Tr}\,[\ln(1+zf)]\} \, dz/z \tag{28}$$

Now (28) is readily evaluated by a saddle-point integration. The saddle point is at z_0, given by

$$\mathrm{Tr}\,(z_0 f/1+z_0 f) = N \tag{29}$$

and aside from the saddle-point value, z_0 occurs in the evaluation including correction terms only through the continuous matrix

$$F = z_0 f/(1+z_0 f) \tag{30}$$

whose eigenvalues are all between 0 and 1.

Finally, the reduced density matrices are found by noting that if one differentiates $\mathrm{Det}^{(N+1)}\, f(\mathbf{x}_i|\mathbf{x}_j)$ with respect to $f(\mathbf{x}_a|\mathbf{x}_b)$, $a \neq b$, moves column a to the left and row b to the top, and integrates over all but $\mathbf{x}_a, \mathbf{x}_b$, then $-(1/N)\Gamma_{\mathrm{un}}^{(1)}(x_b|x_a)$ results. On the other hand, for $a = b$, the process results in $\int \ldots \int \mathrm{Det}^{(N)} f(\mathbf{x}_i|\mathbf{x}_j) \, d\tau^N$. Thus, adding the various possibilities, and dividing by the normalizing factor,

$$\Gamma^{(1)}(\mathbf{x}_1|\mathbf{x}_1')$$
$$= \delta(\mathbf{x}_1-\mathbf{x}_1') - [(N+1) \int \mathrm{Det}^{(N)} f \, d\tau^N]^{-1} \delta \int \mathrm{Det}^{(N+1)} f \, d\tau^{N+1}/\delta f(\mathbf{x}_1'|\mathbf{x}_1) \tag{31}$$

But $\delta\,\mathrm{Tr}\,G(f)/\delta f(\mathbf{x}_1'|\mathbf{x}_1) = G'(f)(\mathbf{x}_1|\mathbf{x}_1')$, and so, inserting (28) and assuming that any additional factor in the integrand may be evaluated at z_0, we readily obtain

$$\Gamma^{(1)}(\mathbf{x}_1|\mathbf{x}_1') = F(\mathbf{x}_1|\mathbf{x}_1') \tag{32}$$

In a similar fashion, examining the effect of two successive variational derivatives with respect to f, we find

$$\Gamma^{(2)}(\mathbf{x}_1\mathbf{x}_2|\mathbf{x}_1'\mathbf{x}_2') = \tfrac{1}{2} \begin{vmatrix} F(\mathbf{x}_1|\mathbf{x}_1') & F(\mathbf{x}_2|\mathbf{x}_1') \\ F(\mathbf{x}_1|\mathbf{x}_2') & F(\mathbf{x}_2|\mathbf{x}_2') \end{vmatrix} \tag{33}$$

and the succeeding elementary superposition principle hierarchy is clear but unnecessary for our purposes. Since $\nabla^2 F(\mathbf{x}|\mathbf{x}')|_{\mathbf{x}'=\mathbf{x}}$ and

$- \nabla \cdot \nabla' F(\mathbf{x}|\mathbf{x}')|_{\mathbf{x}'=\mathbf{x}}$ have the same integrals, (21) now becomes

$$\langle H \rangle = (\hbar^2/2m) \int \nabla \cdot \nabla' F(\mathbf{x}|\mathbf{x}')|_{\mathbf{x}'=\mathbf{x}} \, d\tau + \int U(\mathbf{x}) \, F(\mathbf{x}|\mathbf{x}) \, d\tau$$

$$+ \tfrac{1}{2} \int\int V(\mathbf{x}, \mathbf{x}') [F(\mathbf{x}|\mathbf{x})F(\mathbf{x}'|\mathbf{x}') - F(\mathbf{x}|\mathbf{x}') \, F(\mathbf{x}'|\mathbf{x})] \, d\tau^2 \qquad (34)$$

Extension to non-condensed Einstein-Bose states is direct; use of a permanent in (25) together with the relation Det $(1+A)$ Perm $(1-A) = 1$ for continuous determinants results then in replacing (30) by $z_0 f/1 - z_0 f$ and (33) by the corresponding permanent. For condensed systems, a slight generalization of the permanent is required.

It appears at first sight that nothing has been lost in the approximations. By putting f in diagonal form and inserting it into (25), the minimizing f is clearly that in which precisely N eigenvalues ($\sim$ occupation numbers) are 1, the rest 0, i.e. the Hartree-Fock approximation; on the other hand, the Hartree-Fock approximation is seen to satisfy the variational equation corresponding to (34) as well. The trouble of course is that (34) may have a minimum value lower than the Hartree-Fock value and perhaps lower than the correct value; the fact that Tr $\Gamma^{(1)} = N$ but $\mathrm{Tr}_2 \, \Gamma^{(2)} = \tfrac{1}{2}(N - \Gamma^{(1)}) \Gamma^{(1)}$ indicates that something is amiss, unless $(\Gamma^{(1)})^2 = \Gamma^{(1)}$, as in the Hartree-Fock method. Since the $1/N$ correction terms to (32), (33) are readily found and appended perturbationwise at the end of the computation, the trouble is not serious. In fact, (26) is precisely a "grand" density matrix, analogous to a grand partition function, and the formulation does become rigorous as $N \to \infty$.

Various smoothed occupation number distributions may be tried for the sake of calculational simplicity; for example, one may paraphrase an ansatz due to Macke [13], leading to the Fermi-Thomas model, in the following fashion. The reduced one-body density for free spin $\tfrac{1}{2}$ Fermions in a box Ω is given, with explicit spin designation, by $F_0(\mathbf{y}\sigma | \mathbf{y}'\sigma') = (1/\Omega) \sum_{\mathbf{k}} [u(\sigma)u(\sigma') + v(\sigma)v(\sigma')] \exp i\mathbf{k} \cdot (\mathbf{y} - \mathbf{y}')$ $= (1/\Omega) \sum_{\mathbf{k}} \exp i\mathbf{k} \cdot (\mathbf{y} - \mathbf{y}') \, \delta_{\sigma\sigma'}$; hence for a large number of particles in a spherically symmetric ground state distribution, $F_0(\mathbf{y}\sigma | \mathbf{y}'\sigma')$ $= (2\pi)^{-3} \int \exp i\mathbf{k} \cdot (\mathbf{y} - \mathbf{y}') \, d^3 k \, \delta_{\sigma\sigma'}$, integrated over a sphere of radius k_f, where $N = \sum (1+1) = (\Omega/4\pi^3) \int d^3 k$. Thus,

$$F_0(\mathbf{y}\sigma | \mathbf{y}'\sigma') = (2\pi^2)^{-1} |\mathbf{y} - \mathbf{y}'|^{-3} (\sin k_f |\mathbf{y} - \mathbf{y}'| - k_f |\mathbf{y} - \mathbf{y}'| \cos k_f |\mathbf{y} - \mathbf{y}'|) \delta_{\sigma\sigma'}$$
$$\text{where} \qquad k_f = (3\pi^2 n)^{\tfrac{1}{3}} \qquad (35)$$

It is observed that $\mathrm{Tr}\, F_0 = \mathcal{N}$ and the eigenvalues of F_0 (obtained by Fourier transformation) are either 0 or 1, directly from the construction. Now eq. (35) corresponds to a uniform density $n(\mathbf{y}\sigma) = F_0(\mathbf{y}\sigma|\mathbf{y}\sigma) = n/2$ for each sign of spin. In a Fermi-Thomas atomic model, local uniformity exists, but the density varies; this may most simply be obtained by distorting the coordinate system: $\mathbf{y} = \mathbf{B}(\mathbf{x})$. Including the change in volume element, one then chooses

$$F(\mathbf{x}\sigma|\mathbf{x}'\sigma') = \{\mathrm{Det}\,[\partial B_\alpha(\mathbf{x})/\partial x_\beta]\,\mathrm{Det}\,[\partial B_\alpha(\mathbf{x}')/\partial x_\beta']\}^{\frac{1}{2}}$$
$$\times\, F_0[\mathbf{B}(\mathbf{x}),\,\sigma|\mathbf{B}(\mathbf{x}'),\,\sigma'] \tag{36}$$

whose properties — trace and eigenvalues — are precisely those of F_0. Further, the density is now

$$n(\mathbf{x}\sigma) = (n/2)\,\mathrm{Det}\,[\partial B_\alpha(\mathbf{x})/\partial x_\beta] \tag{37}$$

For insertion into (34), the leading terms of $F(\mathbf{x}\sigma|\mathbf{x}'\sigma')$ in an expansion about $\mathbf{x} = \mathbf{x}'$ are required; these are seen to be

$$F(\mathbf{x}\sigma|\mathbf{x}'\sigma') = \tfrac{1}{2}[n(\mathbf{x}\sigma)\,n(\mathbf{x}'\sigma')]^{\frac{1}{2}}[1 - \tfrac{1}{10}(3\pi^2 n)^{\frac{2}{3}}|\mathbf{B}(\mathbf{x}) - \mathbf{B}(\mathbf{x}')|^2 \dots]\delta_{\sigma\sigma'} \tag{38}$$

It follows that, setting $n(\mathbf{x}\sigma) = n(\mathbf{x})$,

$$\nabla\cdot\nabla' F(\mathbf{x}\sigma|\mathbf{x}'\sigma')\big|_{\mathbf{x}=\mathbf{x}',\,\sigma=\sigma'} = \tfrac{1}{2}\{\tfrac{1}{4}n(\mathbf{x})^{-1}|\nabla n(\mathbf{x})|^2$$
$$+ \tfrac{1}{5}(3\pi^2 n)^{\frac{2}{3}}n(\mathbf{x})\sum(\partial B_\alpha(\mathbf{x})/\partial x_\beta)^2\} \tag{39}$$

Consider a spherically symmetric state. Only a radial distortion is required; hence $\sum(\partial B_\alpha/\partial x_\beta)^2 = 3(\mathrm{Det}\,\partial B_\alpha/\partial x_\beta)^{\frac{2}{3}} = 3[n(\mathbf{x})/n]^{\frac{2}{3}}$, plus $(xB' - B)$ corrections, which we here omit. Introducing the total particle density $\rho(\mathbf{x}) = \mathrm{Tr}_\sigma n(\mathbf{x}\sigma) = 2n(\mathbf{x})$, (34) takes the form

$$\langle H \rangle = \hbar^2/2m \int \left[\tfrac{3}{10}(3\pi^2/2)^{\frac{2}{3}}\rho^{\frac{5}{3}} + \tfrac{1}{8}|\nabla\rho|^2/\rho\right] d^3x + \int U(\mathbf{x})\rho(\mathbf{x})\,d^3x$$
$$+ \tfrac{1}{2}\int \rho(\mathbf{x})\rho(\mathbf{y})\,V(\mathbf{x},\mathbf{y})\,d^3x\,d^3y - \tfrac{1}{2}\int \rho(\mathbf{x})\rho(\mathbf{y})\,V(\mathbf{x},\mathbf{y})\,G(\mathbf{x},\mathbf{y})\,d^3x\,d^3y \tag{40}$$

where $\quad G(\mathbf{x},\mathbf{y}) = \{3j_1[k_f|\mathbf{B}(\mathbf{x}) - \mathbf{B}(\mathbf{y})|]/k_f|\mathbf{B}(\mathbf{x}) - \mathbf{B}(\mathbf{y})|\}^2$

and $\quad k_f\mathbf{B}(\mathbf{x}) = (\int_0^x 9\pi^2 x^2 \rho(x)\,dx)^{\frac{1}{3}}\hat{x}$

Ordinary Thomas-Fermi as well as Weizsacker correction terms $(|\nabla\rho|^2/\rho)$ are included. Since $G(\mathbf{x},\mathbf{y})$ decreases from 1 to virtually zero at interparticle spacing, the exchange correction is a likely candidate for treatment by perturbation. For extensive discussion of the Thomas-Fermi model, see March [14].

Of course, an independent particle model is not realistic for singular potentials, and indeed the neglect of correlations makes it totally inapplicable in variational form for non-integrable singularities. The above prototype must then be extended to a $\Gamma^{(N)}$ ansatz, depending as well upon a function of four variables or a two-body matrix. This may be done by replacing the determinant (25) by a symmetrized Laplace expansion in 1×1 and 2×2 minors, with the second quantization formalism the most convenient for the purpose. The closed expression (33) however then becomes an infinite series, and although a graphical representation permits a number of closures to be made, definitive results have not as yet been obtained.

Dynamic Viewpoint. A technique such as the one outlined above is, by its nature, excessively formal and correspondingly tends to possess a motive power of its own, above and beyond the will of the physicist; this is unfortunate. A number of approaches have been formulated [15] in which some type of dynamics is built into the system. This is unnecessary for the problem at hand, but allows considerable play of physical and intuitive concepts in its solution. Inclusion of such additional information may be regarded in a sense as an extension of (17), although the principal forms thus far employed have not been variational. Let us consider this topic very briefly, and still quite formally.

Physical parameters whose alteration may shed light upon the structure of the system being considered include interaction potential, time, temperature, and many others. Kinematic variation of the interaction potential has been used in the main for reducing the information required to compute energy; i.e., in $E(V) = \int_0^V (\delta E/\delta V') \, \delta V'$, only the two-body distribution (and only a diagonal part thereof) may be needed to determine $\delta E/\delta V$. One may combine time dependence and interaction dependence into a dynamic change of interaction: Start with the appropriate density at $t = -\infty$ for an interactionless system, and slowly turn on the interaction. Recalling the dynamic equation for the unnormalized density matrix.

$$i\hbar \, \partial \Gamma^{(N)}/\partial t = [H_N, \, \Gamma^{(N)}] \qquad (41)$$

where H_s is the Hamiltonian for particles $1, \ldots, s$, and noting the identity $H_N = (1+\Delta)^{N-s} H_s = H_s + \binom{N-s}{1}(H_{s+1}-H_s) + \binom{N-s}{2}$ $(H_{s+2}-2H_{s+1}+H_s)+\ldots$, one readily obtains, on taking the trace of (41)

$$i\hbar \, \partial \Gamma^{(s)}/\partial t = [H_s, \Gamma^{(s)}]+(s+1) \, \mathrm{Tr}_{s+1}[H_{s+1}-H_s, \Gamma^{(s+1)}] \quad (42)$$

It is assumed here that at most two-body forces are present. The chain (42) may be solved iteratively, retaining only $\Gamma^{(0)} \ldots \Gamma^{(s)}$ at the sth stage, or may be closed by a truncation or by a super-position approximation for $\Gamma^{(3)}$ in terms of $\Gamma^{(2)}$. A temperature dependence may be similarly managed, or one may simply turn on the temperature. Thus, eq. (41) is replaced by the Bloch equation

$$\partial \Gamma^{(N)}/\partial \beta + H_N \, \Gamma^{(N)} = 0 \quad (43)$$

for the unnormalized Gibbs density $\exp(-\beta H)$, and eq. (42) accumulates an extra term:

$$\partial \Gamma^{(s)}/\partial \beta + H_s \, \Gamma^{(s)} + (s+1) \, \mathrm{Tr}_{s+1}(H_{s+1}-H_s)\Gamma^{(s+1)}$$
$$+\tfrac{1}{2}(s+1)\,(s+2)\,\mathrm{Tr}_{s+1,\,s+2}(H_{s+2}-2H_{s+1}+H_s)\Gamma^{(s+2)} = 0 \quad (44)$$

An obvious application is to carry the known infinite temperature $(\beta = 0)$ limit to $\beta = \infty$, and obtain the ground state energy from $E_0 = \lim -\partial \ln \Gamma^{(0)})/\partial \beta = \lim -\ln \Gamma^{(0)}/\beta$.

Even for a strictly time-independent (stationary) state, time correlations exist and are non-trivial. That is, one may ask for the probability distribution for particle $\mathbf{x}_1$ at t_1, $\mathbf{x}_2$ at t_2, etc., or more generally for the corresponding density matrix. It is simplest to use the second quantization notation. Defining the time translation $\psi(\mathbf{x}t) = \exp(-itH/\hbar) \, \psi(\mathbf{x}) \exp(itH/\hbar)$, expression (19) readily extends to

$$\Gamma^{(s)}(\mathbf{x}_1 \, t_1, \ldots, \mathbf{x}_s t_s | \mathbf{x}_1' t_1', \ldots, \mathbf{x}_s' t_s')$$
$$= (1/s!) \langle \psi^*(\mathbf{x}_1' t_1') \ldots \psi^*(\mathbf{x}_s' t_s') \psi(\mathbf{x}_s t_s) \ldots \psi(\mathbf{x}_1 t_1) \rangle \quad (45)$$

By virtue of the equation of motion (for one- and two-body forces),

$$i\hbar \, \partial \psi(\mathbf{x}_s t_s)/\partial t_s = T(s) \, \psi(\mathbf{x}_s t_s)$$
$$+ \int \psi^*(\mathbf{x}_{s+1} t_s) V(s, s+1) \, \psi(\mathbf{x}_{s+1} t_s) \, \psi(\mathbf{x}_s t_s) \, d\tau_{s+1} \quad (46)$$

the new chain of equations is at once found to be

$$i\hbar\, \partial \Gamma^{(s)}/\partial t_s = T(s)\,\Gamma^{(s)} + (s+1)\int V(s, s+1)$$

$$\times\ \Gamma^{(s+1)}\big(x_1 t_1, \ldots x_s t_s, x_{s+1} t_s \,|\, x_1' t_1', \ldots x_s' t_s', x_{s+1}' t_s\big)_{x_{s+1}' = x_{s+1}}\, d\tau_{s+1} \qquad (47)$$

to be solved by methods mentioned above, where standard field theoretical diagram compressions are appropriate. Expectations, such as energy, require only the special values $t_i = t_i' = 0$. As a boundary condition the fact that correlations are impotent when all time differences become infinite suffices. That is, the one-body distribution determines all others in the fashion of (32), (33). The formulation is valid for a statistical as well as for a pure state, and the separate introduction of many temperatures is unnecessary.

Notes and references

1. F. Zernike, *Koninkl. Ned. Akad. Wetenschap. Proc.* **19**, 1920 (1916).
2. Lee, Huang, and Yang, *Phys. Rev.* **106**, 1135 (1957).
3. L. Goldstein, *Annals of Physics* **1**, 33 (1957).
4. D. H. Weinstein, *Proc. Nat. Acad. Sci. US* **20**, 529 (1934).
5. J. G. Kirkwood and E. M. Boggs, *J. Chem. Phys.* **10**, 394 (1942).
6. O. Penrose, Kamerlingh Onnes Conference on Low Temperature Physics, Leiden, June, 1958.
7. See e.g., P. O. Löwdin, *Phys. Rev.* **97**, 1474 (1955).
8. J. E. Mayer, *Phys. Rev.* 100, 1579 (1955).
9. R. H. Tredgold, *Phys. Rev.* **105**, 1421 (1957).
10. R. U. Ayres, *Phys. Rev.* **111**, 1453 (1958).
11. J. K. Percus and G. J. Yevick, *Bull. Am. Phys. Soc.* **5**, 275 (1960).
12. See, e.g., W. V. Lovitt, *Integral Equations* McGraw-Hill, New York, 1924 Chap. III.
13. W. Macke, *Ann. Physik* **17**, 1 (1955).
14. N. H. March, *Advances in Phys.* **6**, 1 (1957).
15. See, e.g., Bogoliubov et al, Chap. XIV, this volume. P. C. Martin and J. Schwinger, *Bull. Am. Phys. Soc.* **3**, 202, (1958); *Phys. Rev.* **115**, 1342 (1959). A. Klein and R. Prange, *Phys. Rev.* **112**, 994 (1958).

CHAPTER XIX

On Pair Correlations in Liquids

Louis Goldstein

1. *Introduction*

The various attempts of interest at establishing the statistical mechanics of liquids at equilibrium, starting from first principles [1], necessitate the use of approximations in deriving some of the properties of these systems that are determined by the distribution of pairs of atoms or molecules. The difficulties inherent in the formalism of the rigorous theory leave completely open those indirect lines of investigation through which partial properties of liquids can be reached with some degree of rigor. Results obtained thereby should be general enough and should follow essentially from the rigorous theory once the latter is transformed to become more tractable or methods are devised allowing for a more rigorous derivation of the physical content of the general theory.

Such an indirect line of attack on the theory of liquids originated in the investigations of Einstein [2] on the scattering of long wave visible radiation by liquids. The scattering arises from density fluctuations, whose macroscopic statistical thermodynamic evaluation is based ultimately on the fuller use of the Boltzmann principle connecting the statistical configurational probability with the entropy of the system under consideration. It should be noted here that density fluctuations were first discussed by Gibbs [3] within the canonical ensemble formalism.

The Einstein [2] theory of radiation scattering accounted correctly, in a qualitative way, for the observed very large increase of the intensity of the scattered radiation at the approach of the critical temperature in liquids. However, it failed quantitatively since it predicted a physically inacceptable infinitely large scattering cross section per

339

atom at the critical point. Inasmuch as a highly interesting attempt at a quantitative theory of critical opalescenĉe by v. Smoluchowski [4], prior to Einstein's work [2], was not entirely satisfactory, Ornstein and Zernike [5] undertook a reconstruction of the theory through a deeper analysis of the density fluctuation processes. This resulted in the recognition of correlations between the accidental deviations of the density from the mean value in two volume elements within the liquid.

The analysis led thus to the introduction of two types of correlations. One of these is a direct one which measures the effect of a density excess or defect from the mean in some element of volume dv_i on the similar quantity in another volume element dv_j, assuming that in all the other volume elements the density is maintained at its equilibrium mean value. The direct interaction between these fluctuations is thus expected to be determined by the actual interatomic or intermolecular interactions between the atoms or molecules located within the two volume elements, and its range is expected to be of the order of the range of interatomic forces. In addition, the density deviations from the mean in dv_i could also affect the density deviations in dv_j indirectly, step by step, through their direct effect on the elements dv_k which in turn would tend to modify the density deviations indirectly in dv_j. The indirect and direct correlations are described through the local density deviations $g(|\mathbf{r}_i-\mathbf{r}_j|, T)$ and $f(|\mathbf{r}_i-\mathbf{r}_j|, T)$, respectively, from the mean atomic density $n_0(T)$ at temperature T; $\mathbf{r}_i$ and $\mathbf{r}_j$ are the radius vectors of the centers of the volume elements dv_i and dv_j. Hence, if dv_i is supposed to be centered at the origin of a coordinate system, then (omitting the subscript j of dv_j) with one atom in dv_i,

$$n(r, T) = n_0(T)+g(|\mathbf{r}|, T) \tag{1}$$

is the density of pairs of atoms formed by the one located at the origin and those in the volume element $dv(r)$ near the point $\mathbf{r}$: $n(r, T)\, dv(r)$ is the mean number of such pairs in $dv(r)$ at the temperature T. The quantity $n(r, T)$ is the pair density distribution function, or briefly pair distribution function, which appears in the general theory of liquids as one of the series of distribution functions relative to three, four, ..., n, atoms, which prove to be necessary for a complete physical description of liquids [1].

We shall here be concerned with some general properties of the pair correlation concentrations or simply pair correlation functions, $f(r, T)$ and $g(r, T)$, which, though connected, are fundamental elements of any theory of liquids based on first principles.

2. *The asymptotic large separation behavior of pair correlation functions*

One of the main results of the analysis of density fluctuation processes was the derivation of the connection between the direct and indirect pair correlation functions $f(r, T)$ and $g(r, T)$ so that if one of them is known the other can be obtained rigorously in principle. This connection is expressed by the integral equation

$$g(r, T) = f(r, T) + \int_V g(|\mathbf{r}-\mathbf{r}'|, T) f(r', T) \, dv(r') \qquad (2)$$

with the integral extended over the whole volume V of the system, or over the whole space. Surface effects will be neglected throughout. Equation (2) states that if there is an atom at the origin of the coordinate system, then the indirect correlation function $g(r, T)$ between this atom and one at the distance $r = |\mathbf{r}|$ is determined by their direct correlation $f(r, T)$, augmented by the indirect correlations $g(|\mathbf{r}-\mathbf{r}'|, T)$ of all atoms $\mathbf{r}'$, weighted by the strength of the direct correlations of the latter atoms $f(|\mathbf{r}'|, T)$ with the one at the origin [6]. As mentioned in Sec. 1, the range of the function $f(r, T)$ may be reasonably expected to be of the order of magnitude of the range of the intermolecular forces.

The various distribution functions of any particle group, including the pair distribution function $n(r, T)$, have been discussed in a rather general way by Mayer and Montroll [7] who have shown that these functions are, apart from a volume factor, the configurational integrals appearing in the partition function of statistical systems, the integrals being extended over the coordinates of $(N-m)$ of the N particles for the distribution function associated with m particles. The pair distribution function is thus the configurational integral extended over the coordinates of $(N-2)$ of the N atoms forming the system. In imperfect gases they could thus evaluate these various distribution functions using the formalism of the theory of Mayer [8, 9].

In liquids the generalized Boltzmann equation of the pair distri-

bution function necessitates the knowledge of the three-atom distribution function, which appears in this equation through a term
involving an integration over this function [1]. However, even assuming the simplest approximate form for this three-atom distribution
function [1] in terms of the pair distribution functions associated with
the three pairs of the three atoms, the approximate equation so
obtained for $n(r, T)$ or $g(r, T)$ is a non-linear integral equation. Since
a straightforward analytic attempt at solving this approximate
equation of pair distribution functions in liquids encounters difficulties, it appears useful to derive as many partial analytical properties of the pair correlation functions as possible, provided that these
properties be general enough so that they would appear automatically
in the eventual rigorous statistical mechanical description of liquids.

It was in this sense that Zernike [10] was able to exploit eq. (2)
in deriving from it the asymptotic large separation behavior of $g(r, T)$.
Inspection of eq. (2) shows that, expanding $g(|\mathbf{r}-\mathbf{r}'|, T)$ near r,
one is led to a linear differential equation of infinite even order. The
even character of this equation is due to the fact that the differential
operators appearing in the expansion have as coefficients the moments
of the function $f(r, T)$, which are all even because of the even character
of $f(r, T)$. The same is true with $g(r, T)$. The various even moments
are defined by

$$r_F^{2n}(T) = \int_V r^{2n} f(r, T) \, dv(r) \tag{3}$$

$$r_G^{2n}(T) = \int_V r^{2n} g(r, T) \, dv(r) \tag{4}$$

the integrals being extended over the volume V of the whole system,
or over the whole space. Equation (2) is found to be equivalent to the
following differential equation in a Cartesian coordinate system:

$$[\sum_1^\infty (r_F^{2n}(T)/(2n+1)!) \Delta^{2n} - (1 - F(T))] g(x, y, z, T) = -f(x, y, z, T) \tag{5}$$

where Δ^{2n} is $(\partial^2/\partial x^2 + \partial^2/\partial y^2 + \partial^2/\partial z^2)^n$, and

$$F(T) = \int_V f(r, T) \, dv(r) \tag{6}$$

is the moment of zero order of $f(r, T)$. At the present time, it will suffice to assume the convergence of the expansion appearing on the left-hand side of eq. (5).

Since the functions are regular throughout space, either one being determined by the other through eq. (2), the differential equation of infinite order which determines $f(x, y, z, T)$ in terms of $g(x, y, z, T)$ is easily shown to be

$$[\sum_{n=1}^{\infty} [r_G^{2n}(T)/(2n+1)!]\Delta^{2n} + (1+G(T))]f(x, y, z, T) = g(x, y, z, T) \quad (7)$$

Keeping the first term in the expansion on the left hand side of eq. (5), one obtains the linear second order equation used by Zernike [10] in his derivation of the approximate asymptotic form of the correlation function $g(r, T)$. While implied, [10], this derivation can be shown to be better justified the higher the temperature of the liquid. A closer inspection of eq. (5) with plausible assumptions on the ratios of the first successive moments $r_F^2(T)$, $r_F^4(T)$, ..., as well as on the results of the operations with the Laplacians Δ^2, Δ^4, ..., on $g(x, y, z, T)$, shows that at low temperatures the expansion tends to diverge, in the sense that an increasing number of terms of the series will be needed for a satisfactory determination of $g(r, T)$ in terms of $f(r, T)$ and its moments. The characteristic temperature T_0, above which the sole use of the Laplacian Δ^2 in eq. (5) is justified, is that temperature at which $F(T)$ vanishes [11].

The same discussion extended to eq. (7), expressing $f(r, T)$ in terms of $g(r, T)$ and the moments of the latter, shows that here again the use of the first term in the expansion is justified provided the temperature of the liquid is low in comparison with T_0. The complementary character of the two correlation functions in these two temperature intervals clearly appears here.

The possibility of keeping only a few terms in the expansion of eqs. (5) and (7) is determined by the short range of the functions defining the nonhomogeneity of these equations. This range may be taken approximately as the square root of the absolute value of the second moments $r_F^2(T)$ or $r_G^2(T)$, or the square root of the mean square extensions $r_F^2(T)/F(T)$ and $r_G^2(T)/G(T)$. The connection between the moments of the same order $r_F^{2n}(T)$ and $r_G^{2n}(T)$ is, from eq. (2), of the type [11]

$$r_G^{2n}(T) = \gamma(r_F^{2n}, r^{2n-2}, \ldots, r_F^2, F) \tag{8}$$

$$r_F^{2n}(T) = \varphi(r_G^{2n}, r_G^{2n-2}, \ldots, r_G^2, G) \tag{9}$$

showing that the $2n$th moment of either function is a relatively simple combination of all the moments of order $2n$, $2n-2$, etc., of the other function.

A direct discussion of the second-order differential equations contained in eqs. (5) and (7) yields, using standard techniques of solution, the following asymptotic forms of the g and f functions, respectively:

$$\lim g(r, T) = [3F(T)/2\pi r_F^2(T) r][\exp -r/\rho_G(T)] \tag{10}$$

$$\text{for} \quad r \gg [r_F^2(T)]^{\frac{1}{2}} \quad \text{and} \quad T_0 < T \leq T_c$$

with

$$[\rho_G(T)]^2 = \tfrac{1}{6} r_F^2(T)/[1-F(T)] \tag{11}$$

$$\lim f(r, T) = (3G(T)/2\pi |r_G^2(T)| r)(\exp -r/\rho_F(T)) \tag{12}$$

$$\text{for} \quad r \gg [|r_G^2(T)|]^{\frac{1}{2}} \quad \text{and} \quad T_M \leq T \ll T_0$$

where

$$[\rho_F(T)]^2 = \tfrac{1}{6} |r_G^2(T)|/[1+G(T)] \tag{13}$$

T_M and T_c stand for the temperature of the melting and critical points, respectively. The r dependence of both of these functions is the same, with the appropriate temperature-dependent quantities, in the respective temperature ranges.

It appears of interest to comment here briefly on the temperature dependence as well as the interconnections of the first two moments $F(T)$, $G(T)$, $r_F^2(T)$ and $r_G^2(T)$ of the two correlation functions. One obtains easily from eq. (2),

$$G(T) = F(T)/[1-F(T)] \tag{14}$$

and with the expression of $G(T)$ in terms of the mean square fluctuation $\langle \Delta N^2 \rangle_{\mathrm{Av}}$ of the total number of atoms N of the system, per atom [5],

$$\langle \Delta N^2 \rangle_{\mathrm{Av}}/N = 1+G(T) = n_0(T)kT\chi_T \tag{15}$$

k being Boltzmann's constant, and χ_T the isothermal compressibility of the liquid,

$$F(T) = G(T)/1 + G(T) = 1 - [n_0(T)kT\chi_T]^{-1} \tag{16}$$

It will be seen that the temperature T_0 introduced above is that temperature at which the macroscopic correlations, as measured by the density fluctuations, vanish and the liquid behaves as an ideal gas of the same density as the liquid at T_0.

The functions $G(T)$ and $F(T)$ are both increasing functions of the temperature throughout the range (T_M, T_c). These functions are both negative at $T < T_0$, and positive at $T > T_0$; they vanish at T_0 where their representative curves have a common tangent. These two curves have a simple external contact at T_0, with $G(T)$ being always concave upward and $F(T)$ always concave downward, or $d^2G/dt^2 > 0$ and $d^2F/dt^2 < 0$ throughout the temperature range (T_M, T_c). The various limiting values of $G(T)$ and $F(T)$ at the limits of this temperature range result easily [11] from eqs. (15) and (16).

The connection between the second moments is found to be [11]

$$r_G^2(T)/r_F^2(T) = (n_0(T)kT\chi_T)^2 \tag{17}$$

and with the definitions given above for the mean square extensions

$$\langle r_G^2(T) \rangle_{\mathrm{Av}} / \langle r_F^2(T) \rangle_{\mathrm{Av}} = n_0(T)kT\chi_T \tag{18}$$

This shows that $g(r, T)$ is the longer range function at high temperatures $T > T_0$, where $n_0(T)kT\chi_T > 1$, while at $T < T_0$, the $f(r, T)$ function becomes of longer range — or $g(r, T)$ shrinks in range with decreasing temperatures.

3. A new derivation of the asymptotic (large separation) forms of the correlation functions

The preceding method of obtaining the asymptotic forms of correlation functions involves the fundamental eq. (2) which connects the two types of correlations. At the present time, the indirect but practical method of deriving the approximate correlation functions from the observed scattering properties of liquids is customarily used. The problem we consider is the derivation of the asymptotic forms of the correlation functions from their definitions in terms of the liquid scattering structure factors.

The indirect correlation function is obtained [12] from

$$g(r, T) = (1/2\pi^2 r) \int_0^\infty [F_L^2(k, T) - 1](k \sin kr) \, dk \qquad (18)$$

where $F_L^2(k, T)$ is the scattering intensity structure factor per atom of the liquid at equilibrium, at temperature T, associated with a scattering process in which the momentum change on scattering is $|\mathbf{k}|$, in units of $h/2\pi$. Similarly, the direct correlation function is given by [11]

$$f(r, T) = (1/2\pi^2 r) \int_0^\infty [1 - F_L^{-2}(k, T)] \, k(\sin kr) \, dk \qquad (19)$$

Our problem is to find the asymptotic behavior (for large r) and form of these functions. While a solution of this problem within the formalism of the general theory of Fourier integral transformations does not seem to be available, one may attempt to obtain an answer along the following lines of reasoning.

Clearly, the behavior of these functions at very large r should be determined by the properties of either the collective structure factor $[F_L^2(k, T) - 1]$ as $k \to 0$, or by those of $[1 - F_L^{-2}(k, T)]$ near the origin in k space. Now, a rather general feature of the liquid structure factors at small values of k is their parabolic character [11], that is, effectively, up to terms quadratic in k,

$$\lim_{k \to 0} F_L^2(k, T) - 1 = G(T)[1 - k^2 r_G^2(T)/6G + \ldots] \qquad (20)$$

Since we are concerned only with the asymptotic (large r) behavior of $g(r, T)$, it would appear justified to substitute for the rigorous structure factor $F_L^2(k, T)$ another function $\varphi_L^2(k, T)$ which reduces to the former at small and vanishing k values. The two plane curves $F_L^2(k, T)$ and $\varphi_L^2(k, T)$, T being a parameter, will thus have a first-order contact at vanishing k. Defining this new function resulting from eq. (20) by

$$\varphi_L^2(k, T) - 1 = G(T)/[1 + k^2 r_G^2(T)/6G(T)] \qquad (21)$$

one sees that $\varphi_L^2(k, T)$ is the first-order osculator of $F_L^2(k, T)$ at vanishing k. It will be noted [13] that the coefficient of k^2 is positive at $T > T_0$. At T_0, the problem loses its meaning because of the peculiar absence of macroscropic or integral pair correlations at this characteristic temperature, as illustrated by the scattering of long wave length radiation at T_0.

From the rigorous result [11] which states that the structure factor at small or vanishing k values has the precise value

$$\lim_{k \to 0} F_L^2(k, T) = 1 + G(T) = n_0(T) k T \chi_T \qquad (22)$$

and the behavior of the first few positive even moments of the function $g(r, T)$ [14], one shows that the second moment $r_G^2(T)$ has at least one root T_2 such that $T_2 < T_0$. Hence, at $T < T_2$, $r_G^2(T) < 0$, and with $G(T) < 0$ at $T < T_0$, one sees that $[\varphi_L^2(k, T) - 1]$ is negative at $k \to 0$ — it increases continuously with k and tends to vanish at large k values. At temperatures $T_2 < T < T_0$, the osculator (21) becomes, $G(T)$ being negative,

$$\varphi_L^2(k, T) - 1 = -|G(T)|/[1 - k^2 r_G^2(T)/6|G(T)|] \qquad T_2 < T < T_0 \quad (23)$$

and this function, becoming infinite at k equal to $(6|G(T)|/r_G^2(T))^{\frac{1}{2}}$, differs fundamentally from the osculators in the temperature regions $T_M < T < T_2$ and $T_0 < T < T_c$, which are finite throughout the whole k range.

Replacing (20) by (21) in (18) one obtains [15],

$$\begin{aligned} \gamma(r, T) &= [G(T)/4\pi^2 r] \int_0^\infty k \, (\sin kr)/[1 + (k^2 r_G^2/6G)] \, dk \\ {}_{T_c > T > T_0} \\ &= \{3G(T)/[2\pi r_G^2(T) r/G(T)]\} \exp[-r/(r_G^2/6G^{\frac{1}{2}})] \end{aligned} \qquad (24)$$

which shows that the algebraic, first-order osculator $\varphi_L^2(k, T)$ of the rigorous structure factor $F_L^2(k, T)$ correctly reproduces the asymptotic behavior of $g(r, T)$ at large r, as obtained directly from the linear second-order differential equation approximating the rigorous integral equation (2). Actually, (24) can be transformed at once to yield the same asymptotic form as obtained by the direct method in the temperature interval (T_0, T_c). Indeed, eq. (11) may be written, with eqs. (14)–(17), as

$$[\rho_G(T)]^2 = \tfrac{1}{6} r_G^2(T)/[1 + G(T)] = r_G^2(T) G(T)/6G(T)[1 + G(T)] \quad (25)$$

and the factor on the right-hand side of (24) may be rewritten as

$$G^2(T)/r_G^2(T) = F(T)\{1 + [G(T)]^{-1}\}^{-1}/r_F^2(T) \qquad (26)$$

Hence,

$$\lim g(r,\,T) = \gamma(r,\,T) = [3F(T)/2\pi r_F^2(T)r](1+G^{-1})^{-1}$$
$$\times \{\exp\,[-r/\rho_G(1+G^{-1})^{\frac{1}{2}}\}\quad(27)$$

for r large and $T_0 < T < T_c$

and, since for $T > T_0$, G is large, it is seen that the above osculator method yields practically the same asymptotic form of $g(r,\,T)$ as derived directly in the temperature range where the direct differential equation method is valid. At the critical temperature, $\gamma(r,\,T)$ reduces completely to the asymptotic form resulting from the differential equation approach,

$$\lim g(r,\,T) = \gamma(r,\,T_c) = 3/2\pi r_F^2(T_c)r\quad(28)$$

for r large and $T \to T_c$

since at T_c, G^{-1} vanishes together with ρ_G^{-1}, while $F(T_c)$ is unity.

At low temperatures, where the direct method ceases to be valid because of the diverging character of the expansion in eq. (5), at least up to terms of the fourth order [15] the osculator method appears to be still valid. Equation (24) may now be written as

$$\lim g(r,\,T) = -\{3[G(T)]^2/2\pi|r_G^2(T)|r\}\{\exp\,[-r/\rho_G'(T)]\}\quad(29)$$

for r large and $T_M < T < T_2$

where $\rho_G'(T) = [r_G^2(T)/6G(T)]^{\frac{1}{2}} = [<r_G^2(T)>_{\mathrm{Av}}/6]^{\frac{1}{2}}$

An important qualitative change in the asymptotic behavior of $g(r,\,T)$ is that at high temperatures, $g(r,\,T)$ tends to vanish from positive values, while at low temperatures this vanishing proceeds from negative values. This qualitative difference is to be associated with the behavior of the structure factor at small values of k. At high temperatures, $T_0 < T < T_c$, the structure factor decreases from its value at vanishing k values, where it has a maximum larger than unity, while at low temperatures, $T_M < T < T_2$, the structure factor has a minimum less than unity at vanishing k and increases at small k values.

At the intermediate temperatures, $T_2 \leqq T \leqq T_0$, both the differential equation approach and our osculator method fail. The failure in the latter method is due to the impossibility of obtaining the required first-order algebraic osculator of the structure factor at the origin that is regular throughout the k interval as shown by eq. (23).

We now have to extend our discussion to cover the case of the indirect correlation function $f(r, T)$, using eq. (19), its definition in terms of the structure factor. One finds with the expansion (20) that

$$\lim_{k \text{ small}} [1 - F_L^{-2}(k, T)] = G/(1+G)[1 + k^2 r_G^2(T)/6G(1+G)]^{-1} \quad (30)$$

is valid up to terms in k^2. Substituting into (19), one obtains

$$\varphi(r, T) = \lim_{r \text{ large}} f(r, T)$$

$$= (G/1+G)(1/2\pi^2 r) \int_0^\infty k(\sin kr)/[1 + k^2 r_G^2/6G(1+G)] \, dk \quad (31)$$

$$= (3G/[\pi r r_G^2(T)/G])(\exp \{-r/[r_G^2/6G(1+G)]^{\frac{1}{2}}\})$$

At low temperatures, $T_M < T < T_2$, $G(T) = (-1+\varepsilon)$, $\varepsilon \ll 1$, so that, with $r_G^2(T) < 0$, it is seen that $\varphi(r, T)$ is essentially the same as the asymptotic form (12) obtained above. In normal liquids and even near the melting point temperature T_M, $f(r, T)$ conserves the asymptotic form of the type $-[\exp(-\alpha r)]/r$, where α is finite, and the approach toward its vanishing limit is from below.

In the temperature interval $T_2 < T < T_0$, expression (30) becomes an inacceptable osculator of the function $[1 - F_L^{-2}(k, T)]$ because of the zero of its denominator at $k = [6G(1+G)/r_G^2(T)]^{\frac{1}{2}}$. The osculator method fails† as well to yield the asymptotic form of $f(r, T)$ in this temperature range. However, at the higher temperatures, $T_0 < T \leqq T_c$, the form (31) appears to retain its full significance, as was the case with the asymptotic form of $g(r, T)$ when extended into the low temperature region, eq. (29).

It seems then that we are justified in saying that our osculator method of deriving the asymptotic (large separation) form of the pair correlation functions in monatomic liquids yields essentially the same results as the method based on approximating the integral eq. (2) by the linear second-order differential equations included in eqs.

† Formal extension of the method yields for both g and f, at $T_2 < T < T_0$, a $\cos \alpha(T) r/r$ behavior whose significance is less direct than that of the asymptotic forms outside this temperature interval.

(5) and (7), in the temperature ranges where this latter method is valid. In addition, the osculator method appears to yield the asymptotic forms of both $f(r, T)$ and $g(r, T)$ in those temperature intervals where the differential equation approach tends to become invalid. Our method requires the formation of first-order osculators of the scattering structure factor complement $[F_L^2(k, T)-1]$, that is the collective structure factor, near the origin of k space as well as the same type of osculator of the function $[1-F_L^{-2}(k, T)]$ near vanishing k values. These osculators have to be algebraic, and regular throughout the k interval, and vanish at infinity in k space.

4. *The asymptotic (large momentum) change behavior of the scattering structure factors of liquids*

The results obtained by the osculator method can be further exploited essentially by inverting them in the following sense. Since one knows [11] the rigorous behavior of the indirect correlation function at close separations r, one would expect, on the basis of the results obtained in Sec. 3, that this should fully determine the asymptotic behavior, at large momentum changes k, of the scattering structure factors of monatomic liquids. The same results should remain essentially valid in molecular liquids, as far as the intermolecular part of their structure factors is concerned.

One has indeed [11], [12]

$$F_L^2(k, T) = 1 + (4\pi/k) \int_0^\infty g(r, T)(\sin kr)r\, dr \qquad (32)$$

and, according to our method of deriving the asymptotic form of the function on the left-hand side, we need to obtain the required first-order osculator of $g(r, T)$ near the origin of the coordinate system and at vanishing r.

Now, up to terms quadratic in r, one has essentially at all temperatures, $T_M \leqq T \leqq T_c$,

$$\lim_{r \to 0} g(r, T) = -n_0(T)[1-\tfrac{1}{6}r^2\langle k^2(T)\rangle_{\mathrm{Av}}+\ldots] \qquad (33)$$

where

$$\langle k^2(T)\rangle_{\mathrm{Av}} = \int_0^\infty k^2[F_L^2(k, T)-1]k^2\, dk \Big/ \int_0^\infty [F_L^2(k, T)-1]k^2\, dk \qquad (34)$$

One can equally well prove that, over the whole temperature interval (T_M, T_c) with the possible exception of one or a few points T, the possible roots of the second moment of $(F_L^2 - 1)$ appear in the numerator on the right-hand side of (34), one has $\langle k^2(T) \rangle_{Av} > 0$. Hence, the required first-order osculator of $g(r, T)$ at vanishing r is

$$\Gamma(r, T) = -n_0(T)/[1 + \tfrac{1}{6} r^2 \langle k^2(T) \rangle_{Av}] \qquad (35)$$

The asymptotic (large k) form of $F_L^2(k, T)$ or of $[F_L^2(k, T) - 1]$ is thus obtained by substituting $\Gamma(r, T)$ for $g(r, T)$ in the Fourier sine integral on the right-hand side of eq. (32). One finds [15],

$$\lim_{k \text{ large}} [F_L^2(k, T) - 1]$$

$$= -(4\pi n_0(T)/k) \int_0^\infty r(\sin kr)/[1 + \tfrac{1}{6} r^2 \langle k^2(T) \rangle_{Av}] \, dr$$

$$= -[12\pi^2 n_0(T)/k \langle k^2(T) \rangle_{Av}](\exp{-k/[\langle k^2(T) \rangle_{Av}/6]^{\frac{1}{2}}}) \qquad (36)$$

showing that the structure factors of liquids behave as $\exp[-\beta(T)k]/k$ at large k, and that they tend toward their limits of unity from below. The latter qualitative behavior results from the fact that at small separations the pair correlation function always increases from its minimum value of $[-n_0(T)]$ at vanishing r. This result is similar to the one mentioned above in connection with the qualitative asymptotic behavior of the functions $g(r, T)$ and $f(r, T)$ in the various temperature ranges.

The results obtained using the osculator method of deriving the asymptotic behavior of pair correlation functions, or of the scattering structure factors in liquids, appear to be limited owing to the approximation which reduces an integral equation to a linear second-order differential equation. However, as far as the correlation functions are concerned, the osculator method is capable of overcoming the limitations arising from convergence difficulties in the differential equation approach.

Beside the general physical results obtained here concerning some partial properties of liquids, it would seem that the above studies have led to a problem of some possible mathematical interest; namely, there appears to exist some class of functions for which the asymptotic form of their Fourier sine integral transform can be obtained directly, to a certain approximation. The investigations of the analytical problem connected with the osculator method might thus be of interest for the theory of integral Fourier transforms.

Notes and references

1. J. G. Kirkwood and E. M. Boggs, J. Chem. Phys. **10**, 394 (1942); M. Born and H. S. Green, *Proc. Roy. Soc. (London)* **A188**, 10 (1946), and *A General Kinetic Theory of Liquids*, M. Born and H. S. Green, eds., Cambridge, New York, 1949.
2. A. Einstein, *Ann. Physik* **33**, 1275 (1910); see also W. H. Keesom, *Ann. Physik* **35**, 591 (1911).
3. J. W. Gibbs, *Elementary Principles in Statistical Mechanics*, (Yale University Press, New Haven, Conn., 1902).
4. M. v. Smoluchowski, *Ann. Physik* **25**, 205 (1908).
5. L. S. Ornstein and F. Zernike, *Koninkl. Ned. Akad. Wetenschap. Proc.* **17**, 793 (1914) see also Y. Rocard, *J. phys. radium* **4**, 165 (1933).
6. For a discontinuous transcription of eq. (2), see M. J. Klein and L. Tisza, *Phys. Rev.* **76**, 1861 (1949).
7. J. E. Mayer and E. Montroll, *J. Chem. Phys.* **9**, 2 (1941).
8. J. E. Mayer, *J. Chem. Phys.* **5**, 67 (1937).
9. The functions $g(r,T)$ and $f(r,T)$ in imperfect gases have been discussed recently by G. S. Rushbrook and H. I. Scoins, *Proc. Roy. Soc. (London)* **A216**, 203 (1953).
10. F. Zernike, *Koninkl. Ned. Akad. Wetenschap. Proc.* **19**, 1920 (1916).
11. L. Goldstein, *Phys. Rev.* **84**, 466 (1951).
12. F. Zernike and J. A. Prins, *Z. Physik* **41**, 184 (1927).
13. L. Goldstein, *Phys. Rev.* **85**, 35 (1952).
14. L. Goldstein and J. Reekie, *Phys. Rev.* **98**, 857 (1955).
15. L. Goldstein, *Annals of Physics* **1**, 33 (1957).

CHAPTER XX

Effect of Defects on
the Vibration of Crystal Lattices[†]

E. W. Montroll, A. A. Maradudin, G. H. Weiss

1. *Introduction*

A considerable fraction of today's research activity in solid state physics is devoted to the investigation of the influence of defects on the behavior of solids. Typical defects are vacancies, impurities, disorder, dislocations, and stacking faults. One is no longer surprised to discover that small numbers of defects contribute to striking macroscopic effects. To list only a few: surface catalysis is due to irregularities and impurities on solid surfaces; the electric properties of semiconductors are a consequence of localized electronic impurity levels which lie in the energy gap between bound electron and conduction electron bands; the attraction of vacancies to grain boundaries and dislocation lines probably causes the growth of cavities which lead to creep and fatigue failures of metals; localized normal modes of vibration around defects may lead to non-spherically symmetric fields in which normally forbidden electronic transitions may occur (some transitions associated with luminescence may be of this type).

The purpose of this paper is to discuss the general mathematical theory of the effect of defects on lattice vibrations and to deduce various qualitative physical results. Since a crystal lattice with its accompanying defects can be represented rather well by a set of coupled springs and masses, the appropriate many-body problem is "solvable" in the sense of Whittaker's *Analytical Dynamics*. A perfect lattice is analogous to a vacuum; and defects, to particles inserted into the vacuum. Our problem is the discrete analogue of the one solvable

† Supported by Air Force Office of Scientific Research.

problem in quantum field theory, the meson pair theory. Our mathematical methods are similar to those introduced by Wentzel [1] for the development of pair theory.

This paper is a continuation of the work of R. B. Potts and one of the authors [2]. Since their papers were published we have found that a parallel (and older) program has been developed along similar lines by I. M. Lifshitz [3] and his collaborators (older references to the Russian literature are given in [3]). Analogous work on the effect of impurities on electronic states has been done by Koster and Slater[4].

Space limitations have forced us to restrict most of our presentation to one-dimensional examples. The corresponding three-dimensional examples, as well as the application of our methods to the theory of lattice vibrations of disordered lattices, will be published elsewhere.

2. On the evaluation of additive functions of normal mode frequencies

Let the normal mode frequencies of our crystal be $\omega_1, \omega_2, \omega_3, \ldots$. Various additive functions of the frequencies

$$S = \sum_j f(\omega_j) \tag{1}$$

are of considerable interest. For example the zero point energy of the crystal is given by (1) with $f(z) = (1/2)\hbar z$, while $f(\alpha)$, the characteristic function of the squares of the frequencies, corresponds to $f(z) = \mathcal{N}^{-1} \exp(i\alpha z^2)$. The distribution function of the squares of the frequencies $G(\omega^2)$ is the Fourier transform of $f(\alpha)$. Furthermore, most thermodynamic functions are additive functions of the frequencies.

Let us suppose the ω_j's to be the zeros of the secular determinant corresponding to a matrix M, i.e., det $M(\omega_j) = 0$. Then we may write for S,

$$S = (1/2\pi i) \int_C f(z) \, d[\ln \det M(z)] \tag{2}$$

where the closed contour C extends in a counterclockwise direction around the relevant zeros of det $M(z)$ and where it is assumed that $f(z)$ has no poles inside or on the boundary of C. Certain corrections are necessary when the latter condition is not satisfied.

Now suppose the matrix M to be the sum of two matrices

$$M = M_0 + \delta M = M_0[I + M_0^{-1} \delta M] \tag{3}$$

Here M_0 is to be associated with a perfect lattice and δM is to contain variations from the perfect lattice. We represent the elements of M_0, M_0^{-1}, and δM by $\{a_{ij}\}$, $\{a_{ij}^{(-1)}\}$, and $\{\varepsilon_{ij}\}$ respectively and define a matrix Δ by $\Delta = I + M_0^{-1}\delta M$. Then $\det M = (\det M_0)(\det \Delta)$. Substitution of this factored form of $\det M$ into (2) leads us to an expression for the change in S, ΔS, due to the insertion of defects:

$$\Delta S = (1/2\pi i) \int_C f(z)\, d[\ln \det \Delta(z)] \tag{4}$$

Since the elements of the matrix $M_0^{-1}\delta M$ are

$$(M_0^{-1}\delta M)_{ij} = \sum_k a_{ik}^{(-1)} \varepsilon_{kj} \tag{5}$$

those of Δ are

$$\Delta_{ij} = \delta_{ij} + \sum_k a_{ik}^{(-1)} \varepsilon_{kj} \tag{6}$$

The determinant of Δ is easily computed when only a small number of non-vanishing ε_{kj}'s exist. For example, suppose only one element of M_0 is perturbed; viz. $\varepsilon_{\alpha\alpha} \neq 0$, while all other ε's vanish. Then $\varepsilon_{kj} = \varepsilon_{\alpha\alpha}\, \delta_{k\alpha}\, \delta_{\alpha j}$ and

$$\Delta_{ij} = \delta_{ij} + a_{i\alpha}^{(-1)} \delta_{\alpha j} \varepsilon_{\alpha\alpha} \tag{7}$$

Hence we have

$$\det \Delta = \det \Delta_{ij} = 1 + a_{\alpha\alpha}^{(-1)} \varepsilon_{\alpha\alpha} \tag{8}$$

As a slightly more complicated example we consider the change in M_0 due to the substitution of an impurity for a normal atom in a linear chain of N identical atoms of mass M connected by springs, whose force constant is γ. The matrix M_0 has elements

$$(M_0)_{ij} = (2\gamma M^{-1} - \omega^2)\delta_{ij} - \gamma M^{-1}(\delta_{i,j-1} + \delta_{i,j+1}) \tag{9}$$

The correction matrix associated with an impurity of mass M' at the αth position has elements

$$\varepsilon_{ij} = \delta_{i,\alpha-1}\varepsilon_{\alpha-1,\alpha-1}\delta_{\alpha-1,j} + \delta_{i,\alpha}\varepsilon_{\alpha,\alpha}\delta_{\alpha,j} + \delta_{i,\alpha+1}\varepsilon_{\alpha+1,\alpha+1}\delta_{\alpha+1,j} \tag{10a}$$
$$+\delta_{i,\alpha}\varepsilon_{\alpha,\alpha-1}\delta_{\alpha-1,j} + \delta_{i,\alpha}\varepsilon_{\alpha,\alpha+1}\delta_{\alpha+1,j} + \delta_{i,\alpha-1}\varepsilon_{\alpha-1,\alpha}\delta_{\alpha,j} + \delta_{i,\alpha+1}\varepsilon_{\alpha+1,\alpha}\delta_{\alpha,j}$$

where

$$\varepsilon_{\alpha-1,\alpha-1} = \varepsilon_{\alpha+1,\alpha+1} = (\gamma'-\gamma)/M = \varepsilon_1 = -\varepsilon_{\alpha-1,\alpha} = -\varepsilon_{\alpha+1,\alpha}$$
$$\varepsilon_{\alpha,\alpha-1} = \varepsilon_{\alpha,\alpha+1} = (\gamma/M) - (\gamma'/M') = \varepsilon_2 = -\tfrac{1}{2}\varepsilon_{\alpha,\alpha} \tag{10b}$$

Here γ' is the force constant of a spring which connects an atom of mass M with one of mass M'.

The determinant of $\varDelta$ is then

$$\det \varDelta =$$

$$\begin{vmatrix} 1+g(-1)\varepsilon_2+g(0)\varepsilon_1 & -[g(0)+g(-2)]\varepsilon_1-2g(-1)\varepsilon_2 & g(-1)\varepsilon_2+g(-2)\varepsilon_1 \\ g(0)\varepsilon_2+g(1)\varepsilon_1 & 1-[g(1)+g(-1)]\varepsilon_1-2g(0)\varepsilon_2 & g(0)\varepsilon_2+g(-1)\varepsilon_1 \\ g(1)\varepsilon_2+g(2)\varepsilon_1 & -[g(2)+g(0)]\varepsilon_1-2g(1)\varepsilon_2 & 1+g(-1)\varepsilon_2+g(0)\varepsilon_1 \end{vmatrix}$$

where $g(k) = a_{j+k,j}^{(-1)}$, is independent of j if periodic boundary conditions are imposed.

The elements of the inverse of M_0 are

$$g(j-k) = (M_0^{-1})_{jk} = \frac{1}{N} \sum_{l=1}^{N} \frac{\exp 2\pi i(j-k)(l/N)}{[(2\gamma M^{-1}-\omega^2)-2\gamma M^{-1}\cos 2\pi l/N]}$$

$$= \frac{1}{2\pi} \int_0^{2\pi} \frac{\exp [i(j-k)\varphi]}{(2\gamma M^{-1}-\omega^2)-2\gamma M^{-1}\cos \varphi} d\varphi \qquad \text{as} \qquad N \to \infty$$

$$= \begin{cases} \dfrac{1}{\omega_L^2} \dfrac{[\sqrt{(f^2+1)}-\sqrt{f^2}]^{2|j-k|}}{\sqrt{[(f^2+1)f^2]}} & \text{if} \quad (\omega/\omega_L)^2 < 0 \quad (12a) \\[3mm] -\dfrac{(-1)^{|j-k|}}{\omega_L^2} \dfrac{[\sqrt{(f^2-1)}-(\sqrt{f^2})]^{2|j-k|}}{\sqrt{[(f^2-1)f^2]}} & \text{if} \quad (\omega/\omega_L)^2 > 1 \quad (12b) \end{cases}$$

where $f = \omega/\omega_L$ and $\omega_L^2 = 4\gamma/M$. Note that $g(j) = g(-j)$.

Det $\varDelta$ can be factored into

$$\det \varDelta$$
$$= \{1+[g(0)-g(2)]\varepsilon_1\}\{1+[g(2)-2g(1)+g(0)]\varepsilon_1-2\varepsilon_2[g(0)-g(1)]\}$$

However, since

$$g(2)-2g(1)+g(0) = -(M\omega^2/\gamma)g(1)$$
$$g(0)-g(1) = (M/2\gamma)[1+\omega^2 g(0)]$$

$$\det \varDelta = \{1+[(\gamma'-\gamma)/M][g(0)-g(2)]\}\{(\gamma'M/\gamma M')$$
$$-[(\gamma'-\gamma)/\gamma]\omega^2 g(1) \qquad (13)$$
$$-[1-(\gamma'M/\gamma M')]\omega^2 g(0)\}$$

The expressions for det $\varDelta$ appropriate for other selections of ε_{kj} can easily be deduced in a similar manner.

If we can assume that the elements of δM are small in some sense and that the elements of $M_0^{-1}(\omega)$ are easily found, then an expansion of $\ln [\det \Delta(\omega)]$ in powers of the elements of $\delta M(\omega)$ would seem to be appropriate. Let the matrix $M_0^{-1}(\omega)\delta M(\omega)$ be denoted by $D(\omega)$ and let the characteristic values of $D(\omega)$ be $\{\lambda_j\}$. Then,

$$\det \Delta = \prod_j (1+\lambda_j) \tag{14}$$

Hence, if $|\lambda_j| < 1$ for all j,

$$\ln \det \Delta(\omega) = \sum_j \ln (1+\lambda_j)$$

$$= \sum_j (\lambda_j - \tfrac{1}{2}\lambda_j^2 + \tfrac{1}{3}\lambda_j^3 - \ldots) \tag{15}$$

$$= \operatorname{Tr} D - \tfrac{1}{2}\operatorname{Tr}D^2 + \tfrac{1}{3}\operatorname{Tr}D^3 - \ldots$$

where $\operatorname{Tr} D = \operatorname{trace} D$. Finally the change in an additive function, ΔS, becomes

$$\Delta S = (1/2\pi i) \int_C f(z) \, d\{\operatorname{Tr} D(z) - \tfrac{1}{2}\operatorname{Tr} D^2(z) + \tfrac{1}{3}\operatorname{Tr} D^3(z) - \ldots\} \tag{16}$$

The retention of only the first two terms in the bracket generally gives results equivalent to second-order perturbation theory.

3. Localized modes

It has long been understood that if one attempts to drive a crystal at a frequency outside the band of normal mode frequencies the driven wave is attenuated in a short distance, the penetration distance diminishing as the displacement of the frequency from band edges increases. Hence, if the existence of a lattice defect introduces a new isolated frequency into the frequency spectrum, the associated normal mode of vibration must be localized around the defect, because the defect is a source of waves whose frequency is such as to ensure attenuation. Such localized modes are analogous to bound states of electrons around impurity centers in semiconductors.

A detailed analysis of the effect of constraints and variations of parameters on dynamical systems undergoing small vibrations was made by Rayleigh [5] and Routh many years ago. Several of their results are useful for a qualitative understanding of the development of localized defect modes in crystal lattices. We have schematically sketched the vibrational frequencies of a diatomic linear chain of N atoms in Fig. 1. The upper band of frequencies is the optical band; and the lower, the acoustical. The separation of adjacent levels in a given band is of order $1/N$ [except near band edges where it is $O(1/N^2)$]. The density of levels becomes continuous as $N \to \infty$ and the band

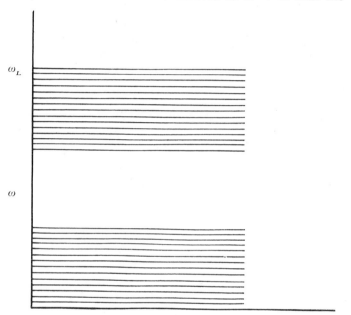

Figure 1. The vibrational frequencies of a diatomic linear chain.

gap has a finite value in this limit. It was shown by Rayleigh that if a single mass is reduced by δM, all frequencies are increased, but *by no more than the distance* to the next higher unperturbed frequency. Hence, as $N \to \infty$ in our lattice, all frequencies suffer a change of at most $O(1/N)$ except those associated with the upper edge of each band. These are raised by amounts proportional to $(\delta M)^2$, when δM is small, but independent of N as $N \to \infty$. These frequencies, which are displaced out of the band, are those of localized modes. An increase of a single mass by δM reduces all frequencies by amounts no greater than the distance to adjacent lower unperturbed frequencies. Since the lowest frequency is only of order $1/N^2$ away from zero, the only localized mode which can develop is the one associated with the displacement of the lower optical band edge frequency. The increase (decrease) of a single force constant has the same effect as a reduction (enhancement) of a single mass.

The following generalization of Rayleigh's theorems, which is useful in studying the effect of changes in boundary conditions, as well as the introduction of defects on normal mode frequencies, has been derived by Ledermann [6]: If, in a Hermitian matrix, the elements of r rows and their corresponding columns are modified in any way, provided only that the matrix remains Hermitian, then the number of characteristic values of the matrix which lie in a given real interval cannot increase or decrease by more than $2r$.

The frequencies of localized modes are roots of det $\Delta = 0$ [see eq. (6)]. The expressions to be used for the $a_{ij}^{(-1)}$ which appear in det Δ are those appropriate to frequencies not in the normal mode bands of the perfect lattice [eq. (12b) in a $1-D$ system] [2], [7], [8].

As an example, consider the localized modes associated with an impurity in a linear chain of atoms. The frequencies of these modes are obtained by setting det Δ of eq. (13) equal to zero. One factor of det Δ yields roots of

$$1 + (\gamma/M)[(\gamma'/\gamma) - 1][g(0) - g(2)] = 0 \qquad (17)$$

where $g(0)$ and $g(2)$ are given by (12b). Then if $\gamma'/\gamma > 2$, a localized mode with frequency

$$\omega = \omega_L P/(P-1)^{\frac{1}{2}} \qquad P = \gamma'/\gamma > 2 \qquad (18)$$

exists. An examination of the second factor of (13) yields a localized mode if $2 > P > 0$ and $P > Q(2-P)$ with $Q = M'/M$. Similar conditions must be satisfied for the existence of localized modes with frequencies in the gap between the acoustical and optical bands of a diatomic chain and with frequencies higher than those of the optical band. The exchange in position of a pair of nearest-neighbor atoms in an ordered diatomic lattice creates a local disorder with an associated localized mode.

The elements $a_{ij}^{(-1)}$ required for the investigation of localized modes in three-dimensional lattices are considerably more complicated than (12). They have recently been tabulated [14].

If two identical widely separated point defects exist in a lattice, each is the source of a localized mode of the same frequency. As the distance between the two is diminished the frequency degeneracy is split, at first symmetrically, about the original frequencies. At separations greater than several lattice spacings the splitting depends only on the distance between the two defects (at smaller separations the direction of the line of centers relative to the crystal axes becomes important). Hence all defect levels are broadened in a system with a small but finite concentration of randomly distributed defects. The line width at low concentrations can be estimated by weighting a given frequency separation by the number of nearest-neighbor defect pairs whose distance leads to that splitting. Interactions between more distant neighbors can be neglected at low concentrations.

Let $\Omega = f(r)$ be the level spacing appropriate to a pair of defects separated by a distance r. Furthermore, let $W(r)\, dr$ be the probability that the nearest neighbor to a given defect be between r and $r+dr$. Then the fraction of levels split into a pair with separation less than Ω is

$$\mathcal{N}(\Omega) = - \int_0^{\Omega} W(r)(dr/d\Omega)\, d\Omega \tag{19}$$

The distribution of nearest-neighbor distance between random points was derived by Paul Hertz (see also Chandrasekhar [9]). If ρ is the average number of points per unit volume (unit length in one dimension and unit area in two), the distribution function is

$$W(r) = \begin{cases} 2\rho e^{-2\rho r} & \text{one dimension} \\ 2\pi r\rho \exp\left(-\pi\rho r^2\right) & \text{two dimensions} \\ 4\pi r^2\rho \exp\left(-\tfrac{4}{3}\pi\rho r^3\right) & \text{three dimensions} \end{cases} \tag{20}$$

It is known [2] that the splitting due to a pair of defects separated by a distance r (greater than several lattice spacings) is

$$\Omega = \begin{cases} Ae^{-\alpha r} & \text{in one dimension} \\ (A/r)\, e^{-\alpha r} & \text{in three dimensions} \end{cases} \tag{21}$$

The constants A and α depend on the nature of the defects. Hence the fraction of defect pair frequencies split by amounts $< \Omega$ are

in one dimension:
$$\mathcal{N}(\Omega) = \begin{cases} (\Omega/A)^{2\rho/\alpha} & \Omega < A \\ 1 & \Omega > A \end{cases} \tag{22}$$

in three dimensions: $\mathcal{N}(\Omega) = \exp\left\{-\tfrac{4}{3}\pi\rho\left[r(\Omega)\right]^3\right\}$

where $r(\Omega)$ is obtained by solving (21) for r. We have plotted $\mathcal{N}(\Omega)$ in Fig. 2 for the particular choice $A = \alpha = 1$, $\rho = 0.2$.

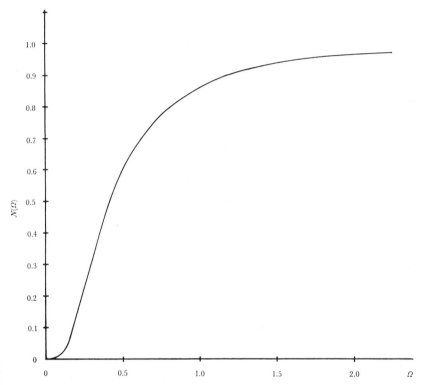

Figure 2. The fraction of defect pair frequencies split by an amount less than Ω. $A = \alpha = 1$; $\rho = 0.2$.

The line width of a defect level due to concentration splitting is

$$\bar{\Omega} = -\int_0^\infty \Omega \, d\mathcal{N}(\Omega)/d\Omega \, d\Omega = \int_0^\infty \Omega(r) W(r) \, dr$$

$$= \begin{cases} 2\rho A/(\alpha+2\rho) & \text{in one dimension} \tag{23} \\ 4\pi A\rho \int_0^\infty r \exp\left\{-\alpha r - \tfrac{4}{3}\pi\rho r^3\right\} dr & \text{in three dimensions} \end{cases}$$

As $\rho \to 0$ in the three-dimensional case,

$$\bar{\Omega} \sim 4\pi A(\rho/\alpha^2) \qquad (24)$$

As a specific example, it has been shown that the localized mode due to an isotopic impurity in a linear chain is split by

$$\Omega = \omega_L[Q(2-Q)]^{\frac{1}{2}}[(1-Q)^2/(2-Q)][Q/(2-Q)]^{r/a} \quad 0 < Q < 1 \quad (25)$$

when two isotopes of mass M' are separated by r/a lattice spacings. Here M is the normal mass with $Q = M'/M$, a the lattice spacing, and ω_L the largest frequency in the band associated with a perfect lattice. Then

$$A = (1-Q)^2 Q^{-\frac{1}{2}}(2-Q)^{-\frac{3}{2}}$$
$$\alpha = (1/a) \ln \{(2-Q)/Q\} \qquad (26)$$

Hence the width of the band of isotopic impurity frequencies is

$$\bar{\Omega} = [2\rho(1-Q)^2 Q^{-\frac{1}{2}}(2-Q)^{-\frac{3}{2}} a\omega_L]/\{2\rho a + \ln[(2-Q)/Q]\} \qquad (27)$$

The product ρa is the number of light isotopes per lattice spacing. It should probably be less than 0.2 in order for this calculation to be valid.

Extended defects such as dislocation lines and stacking faults also might give rise to bands of localized modes. A discussion of the effects of these defects would be too long to be included here.

A method similar to this has been used by Schmidt [10] to obtain an approximation to the frequency spectrum of a disordered many-component linear chain.

4. *Vibrational Self Energy and Interaction Energy of Defects*

The vibrational free energy of a crystal is changed by introducing defects into it. We shall call this change the vibrational self energy of the defect. At low temperatures it is merely the change in zero point energy due to the existence of the defect.

As an example we compute the self energy of an impurity in a linear chain at high and low temperatures. Reference to equations (4) and (13) imply that

$$\Delta E_0 = (1/2\pi i) \int_C \tfrac{1}{2}\hbar z \, d\{\ln \det \Delta(z)\}$$

We shall perform our integration by choosing a D-shaped contour which goes from $-i\infty$ to $i\infty$ along the imaginary axis and along a large semicircle in the right half plane. In the limit as the circle radius approaches infinity the contribution of that part of the contour to ΔE_0 vanishes. As can be noted from (12a) and (13), $\Delta(z)$ is an even function of f^2. Hence the integrand of (28) also has this property and we finally find

$$\Delta E_0 = (-\hbar\omega_L/2\pi)\left[\int_0^\infty f d\ln\{1+(P-1)[(f^2+1)^{\frac{1}{2}}-f]^2\} + \int_0^\infty f d\ln \right. \tag{29}$$
$$\left. \times([P/Q]+(P-1)\{f[(f^2+1)^{\frac{1}{2}}-f]^2/(f^2+1)^{\frac{1}{2}}\}+[1-(P/Q)]f/(f^2+1)^{\frac{1}{2}})\right]$$

where $P = \gamma'/\gamma$, $Q = M'/M$. These integrals are elementary but have different forms depending on the values of P and Q. For example under the conditions

$$P > (4/Q)[2-(P/Q)-P] > 0 \qquad Q > 0 \tag{30}$$

we have

$$\Delta E_0 = (\hbar\omega_L/2\pi)\{P/2\sqrt{(P-1)}\cos^{-1}[(2-P)/P] - 1\}$$
$$+(\hbar\omega_L/2\pi)\{1-(\pi/2)+(A-B\alpha)/(\beta-\alpha)(\alpha-1)+(A-B\beta)/(\alpha-\beta)(\beta-1)$$
$$+[\alpha(A-B\alpha)]/[(\beta-\alpha)(1-\alpha)](1-\alpha^2)^{-\frac{1}{2}}\ln[1+(1-\alpha^2)^{\frac{1}{2}}]/\alpha$$
$$+[\beta(A-B\beta)]/[(\alpha-\beta)(1-\beta)](1-\beta^2)^{-\frac{1}{2}}\ln[1+(1-\beta^2)^{\frac{1}{2}}/\beta]\} \tag{31}$$

where

$$A = \frac{(PQ-2P)}{(2Q-P-PQ)} \qquad \alpha = \frac{P+\{P^2-(4P/Q)[2-(P/Q)-P]\}^{\frac{1}{2}}}{2[2-(P/Q)-P]}$$
$$B = \frac{(4Q-2P-3PQ)}{(2Q-P-PQ)} \qquad \beta = \frac{P-\{P^2-(4P/Q)[2-(P/Q)-P]\}^{\frac{1}{2}}}{2[2-(P/Q)-P]} \tag{32}$$

At high temperatures the vibrational contribution to the thermo-dynamic properties of crystals can be expressed as a series of inverse powers of kT. For example, the Helmholtz free energy is [for $(\hbar\omega_L/kT) < 2\pi$ and a system with N degrees of freedom]

$$A = kT \sum_j \ln \hbar\omega_j/kT - NkT \sum_{n=1}^\infty (-1)^n B_n(\hbar/kT)^{2n}/(2n)(2n)!\mu_{2n} \tag{33}$$

while the heat capacity is

$$C_V = Nk - Nk \sum_{n=1}^{\infty} (-1)^n [(1-2n)B_n/(2n)!] (\hbar/kT)^{2n} \mu_{2n} \qquad (34)$$

where the B_n's are Bernoulli numbers with

$$B_1 = \tfrac{1}{6} \qquad B_2 = \tfrac{1}{30} \qquad B_3 = \tfrac{1}{42} \qquad \text{etc.} \qquad (35)$$

μ_{2n} is the $2n$th moment of the frequency distribution of normal modes of vibration. It is well known that these moments are related to traces of powers of the matrix M, which is associated with the characteristic determinant whose roots are squares of normal mode frequencies. If M is an $N \times N$ matrix

$$\mu_{2n} = (1/N) \, \mathrm{Tr} \, M^n \qquad (36)$$

also

$$\sum_j \ln \omega_j = \tfrac{1}{2} \ln (\prod_j \omega_j^2) = \tfrac{1}{2} \ln \det M(0) \qquad (37)$$

We now find the high temperature contribution of an impurity to the Helmholtz vibrational free energy of a linear chain. The determinant of the matrix M is given by (13) with $\omega = 0$. Since, as $\omega \to 0$

$$g(0) - g(1) = (1/2\pi) \int_0^{2\pi} [(1 - \cos \varphi)/2\gamma M^{-1}(1 - \cos \varphi)] d\varphi = M/2\gamma \qquad (38a)$$

while

$$g(0) - g(2) = (1/2\pi) \int_0^{2\pi} [(1 - \cos 2\varphi)/2\gamma M^{-1}(1 - \cos \varphi)] d\varphi = M/\gamma \qquad (38b)$$

Hence (13) becomes

$$\det \Delta = (\gamma'/\gamma)^2 (M/M') \qquad (39)$$

The trace of $M(0)$ in a system with a single impurity is easily shown to be

$$\mathrm{Tr} \, M(0) = 2\gamma N M^{-1} - (2\gamma/M)(1 - \gamma'\gamma^{-1}) - (2\gamma/M)(1 - \gamma'\gamma^{-1}MM'^{-1}) \qquad (40)$$

as compared with $2\gamma N M^{-1}$ for a perfect chain.

The high temperature change in the Helmholtz free energy of a chain due to the insertion of a single impurity is then

$$\Delta A = +\tfrac{1}{2} kT \ln (\gamma'/\gamma)^2 (M/M') - (\hbar\omega_L/24)[(\hbar\omega_L/kT)]$$
$$\{1 - \tfrac{1}{2}(\gamma'/\gamma)[1 + (M/M')]\} + \ldots \qquad (41)$$

The change in heat capacity at high temperatures per impurity atom is

$$\Delta C_V = -(k/12)(\hbar/kT)^2 \Delta \operatorname{Tr} M(0)$$
$$= (k/24)(\hbar\omega_L/kT)^2\{2-(\gamma'/\gamma)[1+(M/M')]\} \quad (42)$$

Stripp and Kirkwood [12] were the first to discuss the classical high temperature limit of self energies and interaction energies of defects.

The interaction between two defects can be discussed in a similar manner. Let us first consider the classical high temperature interaction between two isotopic defects in a linear chain. We let atoms of mass M' replace normal ones at lattice points α and β. The contribution to the interaction free energy that is proportional to kT is also proportional to $\det M(0)$, which is this case turns out to be

$$\det M(0) = \{1+\varepsilon[g(1)-2g(0)+g(-1)]$$
$$+\varepsilon[g(\beta-\alpha+1)-2g(\beta-\alpha)+g(\beta-\alpha-1)]\}$$
$$\times \{1+\varepsilon[g(1)-2g(0)+g(-1)]$$
$$-\varepsilon[g(\beta-\alpha+1)-2g(\beta-\alpha)+g(\beta-\alpha-1)]\} \quad (43)$$

However, if $\omega = 0$

$$g(\beta-\alpha+1)-2g(\beta-\alpha)+g(\beta-\alpha-1) = \begin{cases} -M/\gamma & \text{if} \quad \beta = \alpha \\ 0 & \text{if} \quad \beta \neq \alpha \end{cases} \quad (44)$$

Hence

$$\ln \det M(0) = 2 \ln (M/M') \quad (45)$$

This is exactly twice the value of $\log \det M(0)$ which is associated with an isolated isotopic defect. Hence, a pair of interacting isotopic defects contributes the same amount to the term in the defect free energy that is proportional to kT as two independent isotopic defects. We then observe from (33) that the free energy of interaction at high temperature is not proportional to kT but to some negative power of kT.

We shall show below that the free energy of interaction of a pair separated by $|\alpha-\beta|$ lattice points is qualitatively

$$\Delta A = O[(\hbar\omega_L/kT)^{-|\alpha-\beta|}(1-M/M')^2] \quad (46)$$

First we notice from eq. (33) that (because the kT term in ΔA vanishes)

$$\Delta A = -NkT \sum_{n=1}^{\infty} [(-1)^n B_n (\hbar/kT)^{2n} \Delta \mu_{2n}/(2n)(2n)!] \qquad (47)$$

where

$$\Delta \mu_{2n} = (1/N) \Delta \operatorname{Tr} M^n \qquad (48)$$

means the difference between $N^{-1} \operatorname{Tr} M^n$ for a matrix associated with two defects and twice that associated with one defect. We note that the elements of $M_0 = (a_{ij})$ which must be changed when defects are introduced at lattice points α and β are in the neighborhood of the diagonal elements $a_{\alpha\alpha}$ and $a_{\beta\beta}$. As $M = M_0 + \delta M$ is raised to successive powers the effect of the defect elements spreads further through the matrix. However, $\Delta \mu_{2n}$ remains zero until the power M^n is such that the defect elements from α and β interfere with each other. This occurs first when $n = O(|\alpha - \beta|)$. The first interference term in the lowest order non-vanishing $\Delta \mu_{2n}$ is of $O[1 - M/M']^2$. Higher powers of M lead to terms of higher order in $[1 - M/M']$. We can then expect (46) to be qualitatively correct and interaction free energies to diminish exponentially with distance of separation if $(\hbar\omega_L/kT) < 2\pi$, i.e., at temperatures above $\Theta_D/2\pi$, where Θ_D is the Debye Θ.

It has been shown however that at very low temperatures a longer range interaction exists. For example [2], the interaction energy which results from a change in zero point energy due to a pair of like isotopic defects corresponds to an attraction with

$$\Delta E/\tfrac{1}{2}\hbar\omega_L = -\{[1 - M'/M]^2(n+1)! \, a^{2n+1}/16n^{\frac{1}{2}}(4\pi)^n R^{2n+1}\} \qquad (49)$$

n being the number of dimensions, a the lattice spacing, and R the distance between lattice points. A stronger attraction of $O(R^{-4})$ exists between a light isotopic defect and a free boundary in a three-dimensional lattice. These results indicate that if a mixture of two isotopes were kept at a very low temperature, a separation (and ordering of the crystal) would take place, leaving a frosting of light isotope on the boundary. The equilibrium state of separation into two phases was suggested by Prigogine, Bingen, and Jeener [13] from the fact that the zero point energy of two phases is less than of a disordered mixture of the two components.

The zero point energy of interaction (attraction) of a pair of vacancies [2], is of $O(R^{-3})$ (in a three-dimensional lattice), while the fact that a vacancy is attracted to a free boundary as R^{-2} indicates that, as equilibrium is reached at low temperatures, vacancies would be spewed out of a lattice. Of course the relaxation time of these low temperature processes would be extremely long.

5. *Effect of Large Numbers of Defects on Additive Functions of Frequencies*

When defects are present in a lattice in large numbers their influence on thermodynamic quantities can usually be expressed as a power series in the defect concentration. The coefficient of the kth power of the concentration in such an expansion depends on the influence of *only* k defects on the function of interest.

Let us suppose that we have three defects located at $\mathbf{r}_1$, $\mathbf{r}_2$, and $\mathbf{r}_3$ and that we are concerned with a function $S(\mathbf{r}_1, \mathbf{r}_2, \mathbf{r}_3)$. Then if $S(\mathbf{r}_i, \mathbf{r}_j)$, $S(\mathbf{r}_i)$, and $S(0)$ are the values of the function in the presence of two, one, and no defects, we have the identity

$$
\begin{aligned}
S(\mathbf{r}_1, \mathbf{r}_2, \mathbf{r}_3) = \; & S(0) + \sum_{i=1}^{3} [S(\mathbf{r}_i) - S(0)] \\
& + \tfrac{1}{2} \sum_{i,j=1}^{3} [S(\mathbf{r}_i, \mathbf{r}_j) - S(\mathbf{r}_i) - S(\mathbf{r}_j) + S(0)] \\
& + [S(\mathbf{r}_1, \mathbf{r}_2, \mathbf{r}_3) - S(\mathbf{r}_1, \mathbf{r}_2) - S(\mathbf{r}_1, \mathbf{r}_3) \\
& - S(\mathbf{r}_2, \mathbf{r}_3) + S(\mathbf{r}_1) + S(\mathbf{r}_2) + S(\mathbf{r}_3) - S(0)]
\end{aligned}
\tag{50}
$$

where the prime on the second summation indicates that $\mathbf{r}_i \neq \mathbf{r}_j$.

This identity can immediately be generalized to the case of n defects. Then,

$$
\begin{aligned}
S(\mathbf{r}_1, \mathbf{r}_2, \ldots, \mathbf{r}_n) = \; & S(0) + \sum_{i=1}^{n} [S(\mathbf{r}_i) - S(0)] \\
& + \tfrac{1}{2} \sum_{i,j=1}^{n}{}' [S(\mathbf{r}_i, \mathbf{r}_j) - S(\mathbf{r}_i) - S(\mathbf{r}_j) + S(0)] \\
& + \tfrac{1}{6} \sum_{i,j,k=1}^{n}{}' [S(\mathbf{r}_i, \mathbf{r}_j, \mathbf{r}_k) - S(\mathbf{r}_i, \mathbf{r}_j) - S(\mathbf{r}_i \mathbf{r}_k) - S(\mathbf{r}_j \mathbf{r}_k) \\
& + S(\mathbf{r}_i) + S(\mathbf{r}_j) + S(\mathbf{r}_k) - S(0)] + \cdots
\end{aligned}
\tag{51}
$$

This expansion is exact.

The average of this function over all positions of defects has a simple form when all defects are identical. Let us denote by $S(k)$ the value of S when there are just k identical defects in the lattice. Then eq. (51) averaged over all possible positions of defects becomes

$$\langle S(n) \rangle = S(0) + n \langle S(1) - S(0) \rangle + [n(n-1)/2!] \langle S(2) - 2S(1) + S(0) \rangle$$
$$+ n(n-1)(n-2)/3! \langle S(3) - 3S(2) + 3S(1) - S(0) \rangle + \ldots \quad (52)$$

where the kth average is taken over the distribution function of the positions of only k defects.

For convenience we express $S(k) - S(0)$ by $\Delta S(k)$, and with this notation we obtain the following expressions:

$$S(1) - S(0) = \Delta S(1)$$
$$S(2) - 2S(1) + S(0) = \Delta S(2) - 2\Delta S(1) \quad (53)$$
$$S(3) - 3S(2) + 3S(1) - S(0) = \Delta S(3) - 3\Delta S(2) + 3\Delta S(1) \quad \text{etc.}$$

It must be kept in mind that $\Delta S(k)$ depends explicitly on the coordinates of k particles.

If we denote by $W(\mathbf{r}_1, \mathbf{r}_2, \ldots, \mathbf{r}_k)$ the probability that there is a defect at each of the k lattice points with position vectors $\mathbf{r}_1, \mathbf{r}_2, \ldots, \mathbf{r}_k$ respectively, then we obtain for the necessary averages

$$\langle \Delta S(1) \rangle = \sum_{\mathbf{r}_1} W(\mathbf{r}_1) \Delta S(1)$$
$$\langle \Delta S(2) - 2\Delta S(1) \rangle = \sum_{\mathbf{r}_1 \mathbf{r}_2}' W(\mathbf{r}_1, \mathbf{r}_2)[\Delta S(2) - 2\Delta S(1)] \quad (54)$$
$$\langle \Delta S(3) - 3\Delta S(2) + 3\Delta S(1) \rangle$$
$$= \sum_{\mathbf{r}_1 \mathbf{r}_2 \mathbf{r}_3}' W(\mathbf{r}_1, \mathbf{r}_2, \mathbf{r}_3)[\Delta S(3) - 3\Delta S(2) + 3\Delta S(1)]$$

If there is no correlation between the positions of the defects then

$$W(\mathbf{r}_1, \mathbf{r}_2, \ldots, \mathbf{r}_j) = 1 \left/ \binom{N}{j} \right. \quad (55)$$

where N is the total number of particles in the lattice.

This is valid in all dimensions. When using the cyclic boundary condition one must be extremely careful in averaging since it is possible to define more than one distance between two point defects. Therefore a proper convention must be established for any formula containing a distance variable. For example, with two defects on a circle, the convention adopted is that the distance is always the shorter of the two possible distances.

Now the concentration of defects is

$$c = n/N \tag{56}$$

If as $N \to \infty$

$$
\begin{aligned}
S(0) &= S_0 \\
\langle \Delta S(1) \rangle &= S_1/N \\
\langle \Delta S(2) - 2\Delta S(1) \rangle &= S_2/N^2 \\
\langle \Delta S(3) - 3\Delta S(2) + 3\Delta S(1) \rangle &= S_3/N^3 \quad \text{etc.}
\end{aligned}
\tag{57}
$$

and if $n \to \infty$ while $N \to \infty$ in such a manner that $n/N = c$, the value of $\langle S(n) \rangle$ becomes

$$S(c) = S_0 + S_1 c + \tfrac{1}{2} S_2 c^2 + \ldots \tag{58}$$

Convenient expressions can be obtained for the S_j's when S is an additive function of the normal mode frequencies of the crystal

$$S = \sum_j f(\omega_j) = (1/2\pi i) \int_C f(z) \, d \ln \det M(z) \tag{59}$$

Let us denote by $|M_n(z)|$ the determinant whose zeroes give the frequencies, $\omega_1, \omega_2, \ldots$, of a lattice which contains n defects. Then by an obvious extension of the notation developed in Sec. 2, we express $M_n(z)$ as

$$
\begin{aligned}
M_n(z) &= M_0(z) + \delta M(z) \\
&= M_0(z)[I + M_0^{-1}(z)\delta M(z)] = M_0(z)\Delta_n(z)
\end{aligned}
\tag{60}
$$

Now with the aid of eqs. (59) and (60) we can express $\Delta S(k)$ as

$$\Delta S(k) = (1/2\pi i) \int_C f(z) \, d \ln |\Delta_k(z)| \tag{61}$$

so that

$$\Delta S(1) = (1/2\pi i) \int_C f(z) \, d \ln |\Delta_1(z)| \tag{62a}$$

$$\Delta S(2) - 2\Delta S(1) = (1/2\pi i) \int_C f(z) \, d \ln (|\Delta_2(z)|/|\Delta_1(z)|^2) \quad \text{etc.} \tag{62b}$$

Equations (54), (57), (58), and (62) constitute a formal solution to our problem.

As a simple example we calculate the first three terms in the expansion (58) of the zero point energy per particle for a two-component linear chain of N particles. We assume that cN particles ($c < 1$) have mass m and $(1-c)$ N particles have mass M, where with no loss of generality we put $m < M$. c thus represents the concentration of light particles in the chain. For simplicity we assume that the chain's force constants are not altered by the introduction of the lighter particles and that there is no correlation between the positions of the two kinds of masses. We set $m = M(1-\varepsilon)$ with $0 < \varepsilon < 1$. $f(z)$ in eq. (59) becomes $\hbar z/2N$.

The zero point energy per particle of the monatomic chain composed of masses M alone is

$$E_0(0) = \hbar \omega_L/\pi \tag{63}$$

where $\omega_L = 2(\gamma/M)^{\frac{1}{2}}$ and γ is the force constant of the springs joining the masses.

The expression for $\Delta E_0(1)$ is given by eq. (62a) as

$$\Delta E_0(1) = (1/2\pi Ni) \int_C \tfrac{1}{2}\hbar z \, d \ln |\Delta_1(z)| \tag{64}$$

An expression for $|\Delta_1(z)|$ was obtained in Sec. 2 for the more general case in which the addition of the defect mass alters the force constants joining it to its nearest neighbors. Our case corresponds to setting $\gamma' = \gamma$ and $M' = M(1-\varepsilon)$ in eq. (13). Our contour of integration C is the D-shaped contour of Sec. 4, and again the only non-vanishing contribution to the integral comes from the integration down the imaginary axis. Thus $\Delta E_0(1)$ becomes

$$\Delta E_0(1) = -(\hbar \omega_L/2\pi N) \int_0^\infty f \, d \ln \left[1 - \varepsilon \omega^2 g(0; i\omega)\right]$$

$$= -(\hbar \omega_L/2\pi N) \int_0^\infty f \, d \ln \left[1 - \varepsilon f/\sqrt{(f^2+1)}\right] \tag{65}$$

$$= (\hbar \omega_L/2\pi N) \left[-(\pi/2) + (1-\varepsilon^2)^{-\frac{1}{2}} \cos^{-1}(-\varepsilon)\right]$$

This result is independent of the position of the particle; thus we see from (54) and (55) that

$$\langle \Delta E_0(1) \rangle = S_1/N = (\hbar \omega_L/N\pi)\left[-(\pi/4) + \tfrac{1}{2}(1-\varepsilon^2)^{-\frac{1}{2}} \cos^{-1}(-\varepsilon)\right] \tag{66}$$

To calculate $\Delta E_0(2) - 2\Delta E_0(1)$ we assume that the two defects are introduced into the chain at lattice sites α and β. We will subsequently average this expression over all configurations of the two defects. $\Delta E_0(2) - 2\Delta E_0(1)$ is the interaction energy between two identical isotope defects, one at α the second at β. This problem has been studied by Montroll and Potts [2]. In our notation their result becomes

$$\Delta E_0(2) - 2\Delta E_0(1)$$
$$= -(\hbar\omega_L/2\pi N) \int_0^\infty f\, d\ln\{1 - \varepsilon^2\omega^4[g(\alpha-\beta; i\omega)]^2/[1 - \varepsilon\omega^2 g(0; i\omega)]^2\} \quad (67)$$

$$= -(\hbar\omega_L/2\pi N) \int_0^\infty f\, d\ln\left(1 - \varepsilon^2\frac{\{[\sqrt{(f^2+1)} - f]^{4|\alpha-\beta|}/(f^2+1)\}}{[1 - \varepsilon f/\sqrt{(f^2+1)}]^2}\right) \quad (68)$$

An integration by parts and the substitution $f = \sinh z$ transforms this into

$$\Delta E_0(2) - 2\Delta E_0(1)$$
$$= (\hbar\omega_L/2\pi N) \int_0^\infty \ln\left[1 - \varepsilon^2\frac{(\tanh^2 z\; e^{-4|\alpha-\beta|z})}{(1 - \varepsilon\tanh z)^2}\right] \cosh z\, dz \quad (69)$$

Montroll and Potts have evaluated only the leading term (in ε^2) in the weak defect limit $\varepsilon \to 0$. Since we are less interested in the value of $\Delta E_0(2) - 2\Delta E_0(1)$ than in its average over α and β, we can do somewhat better. If we expand the integrand of eq. (69) in powers of ε we obtain

$$\Delta E_0(2) - 2\Delta E_0(1) = -(\hbar\omega_L\varepsilon^2/2\pi N) \int_0^\infty \tanh^2 z\, \cosh z\, e^{-4|\alpha-\beta|z}\, dz$$

$$- (2\hbar\omega_L\varepsilon^3/2\pi N) \int_0^\infty \tanh^3 z\, \cosh z\, e^{-4|\alpha-\beta|z}\, dz$$

$$- (\hbar\omega_L\varepsilon^4/2\pi N) \int_0^\infty \tanh^4 z\, \cosh z\, [e^{-4|\alpha-\beta|z}$$

$$+ \tfrac{1}{2}\, e^{-8|\alpha-\beta|z}]\, dz + \ldots \quad (70)$$

These integrals can all be evaluated in closed form in terms of polygamma functions. However, it turns out to be much simpler to interchange the order of integrating and averaging, because the resulting integrals take a particularly simple form. Since we have assumed no correlation between the positions of the two defects eqs. (54) and (55) give us

$$\langle \Delta E_0(2) - 2\Delta E_0(1) \rangle = [2/N(N-1)] \sum_{\alpha, \beta}' [\Delta E_0(2) - 2\Delta E_0(1)] \quad (71)$$

In the limit $N \to \infty$ this result gives, in connection with eq. (70),

$$\langle \Delta E_0(2) - 2\Delta E_0(1) \rangle = -(\hbar\omega_L \varepsilon^2/4\pi N^2) \int_0^\infty e^{-2z} \sinh z/\cosh^2 z \, dz$$

$$- (\hbar\omega_L \varepsilon^3/2\pi N^2) \int_0^\infty e^{-2z} \sinh^2 z/\cosh^3 z \, dz$$

$$- (\hbar\omega_L \varepsilon^4/4\pi N^2) \int_0^\infty (\sinh^3 z/\cosh^4 z)$$

$$[3 \, e^{-2z} + (e^{-4z}/4 \cosh 2z)] \, dz - O(\varepsilon^5) \quad (72)$$

These integrals are all elementary and our final result is

$$\langle \Delta E_0(2) - 2\Delta E_0(1) \rangle = (S_2/N^2)$$
$$= -(\hbar\omega_L/\pi N^2)\{\varepsilon^2[(\pi-3)/4] + \varepsilon^3[(16-5\pi)/8]$$
$$+ \varepsilon^4[(21\pi/16) - (25/6) + (\sqrt{2}/16) \tanh^{-1} 1/\sqrt{2}] + O(\varepsilon^5)\} \quad (73)$$

Higher order terms in this expansion could be obtained in the same way.

Combining eqs. (63), (66), and (73) we finally obtain, the following expansion for the zero point energy per particle in powers of concentration

$$E_0(c)/N = (\hbar\omega_L/\pi) \{1 + c[-(\pi/4) + \tfrac{1}{2}(1-\varepsilon^2)^{-\frac{1}{2}} \cos^{-1}(-\varepsilon)]$$
$$- c^2[\varepsilon^2((\pi-3)/8) + \varepsilon^3((16-5\pi)/16)$$
$$+ \varepsilon^4(63\pi - 200 + 3\sqrt{2} \tanh^{-1}(1/\sqrt{2}))/96 + \ldots] + O(c^3)\} \quad (74)$$

An interesting check on the validity of this result is made by setting $c = 1$ and expanding the coefficients of c^k in powers of ε up to ε^2. The result is

$$E_0(c = 1)/N = (\hbar\omega_L/\pi)\{1 + \tfrac{1}{2}\varepsilon + \tfrac{3}{8}\varepsilon^2 + \ldots\} \quad (75)$$

Alternatively we know the exact expression for $E_0(c = 1)/N$, for this is simply the zero point energy per particle for a monatomic chain composed of particles of mass $M(1-\varepsilon)$. The result in this case is

$$E_0(c = 1)/N = (\hbar\omega_L/\pi)(1-\varepsilon)^{-\frac{1}{2}} = (\hbar\omega_L/\pi)\{1 + \tfrac{1}{2}\varepsilon + \tfrac{3}{8}\varepsilon^2 + \ldots\} \quad (76)$$

While we would have expected eq. (74) to be a good approximation for $c \ll 1$ and ε small, the agreement between the expansion of that equation for $c = 1$ and eq. (76) implies that it is a good approximation over the entire composition range.

Expansions similar to eq. (58) have been proposed by Lifshitz and Stepanova [11] for the determination of additive functions of the normal mode frequencies, but they have not applied their method to any specific calculation.

Notes and References

1. G. Wentzel, *Helv. Phys. Acta* **15**, 111 (1942).
2. E. W. Montroll and R. B. Potts, *Phys. Rev.* **100**, 525 (1955); **102**, 72 (1956); P. Mazur, E. Montroll and R. Potts, *J. Wash. Acad. Sci.* **46**, 2 (1956).
3. I. M. Lifshitz, Nuovo cimento **3**, *Suppl.*, 591 (1956).
4. G. F. Koster and J. C. Slater, *Phys. Rev.* **95**, 1167 (1954); G. F. Koster, *Phys. Rev.* **95**, 1436 (1954). See also M. Lax, *Phys. Rev.* **95** 1391 (1954).
5. Lord Rayleigh, *Theory of Sound*, Dover, New York reprint, (1945), p. 119.
6. W. Ledermann, *Proc. Roy. Soc. (London)* **A182**, 362 (1944).
7. R. J. Elliott, *Phil. Mag.* **1**, 298 (1956).
8. R. L. Bjork, *Phys. Rev.* **105**, 456 (1957).
9. S. Chandrasekhar, *Revs. Modern Phys.* **15**, 1 (1943).
10. H. Schmidt, *Phys. Rev.* **105**, 425 (1957).
11. I. M. Lifshitz and G. I. Stepanova, *JETP* **3**, 626 (1956).
12. K. F. Stripp and J. G. Kirkwood, *J. Chem. Phys.* **22**, 1579 (1954).
13. I. Prigogine, R. Bingen, and J. Jeener, *Physica* **10**, 383; 516 (1954).
14. A. Maradudin, E. Montroll, G. Weiss, R. Herman, and H. Milnes, *Acad. Roy. Belg., Classe Sci.*, Mem. 1709 (1960).

CHAPTER XXI

A Collective Approach to the Dielectric Constant

PHILIPPE NOZIÈRES

Abstract

A collective approach to the dielectric constant is developed for high polarizability electrons, using the Bohms-Pines technique. It is shown that the local field corrections are in many cases negligible, and in any event much smaller than the ones predicted by the Lorentz-Lorenz formula.

CHAPTER XXII

Round Table on Normal States of Matter

Participants:

C. Herring, *Moderator*

B. J. Alder	E. Montroll
K. A. Brueckner	R. K. Nesbet
E. P. Gross	P. Nozières
J. G. Kirkwood	D. Pines
M. Lax	P. J. Price
J. E. Mayer	J. M. Richardson

G. Wannier

C. Herring: This is, to read the program, a round table on normal states of matter; I guess it becomes a round table in spite of its one-dimensional character if one uses periodic boundary conditions. The normal states of matter, I think, would include everything except superconductivity and superfluids, and that is quite a lot. We are going to try to comment on a few topics that pertain to three of the normal states of matter: the behavior of electrons in atoms and molecules, of molecules in fluids, and of electrons in crystals.

1. The atomic and molecular many-body problem†

E. P. Gross: Of all those discussing many-body methods thus far, we have had no representative of the people who calculate electronic structure in molecules by Hartree-Fock and configuration mixing methods. I understand that they feel that they have been doing much the same thing as those using the more novel methods we have heard about, and I would like Dr. Nesbet to make some remarks from this point of view.

† The remarks of Drs. Gross, Nesbet, and Brueckner were, of necessity, originally presented at the Round Table on Superfluids; they have been shifted to this more appropriate location.

R. K. Nesbet: I should like to call your attention to the fact that there have been some significant developments in the theory of many-particle systems arising from calculations of atomic and molecular wave functions. These developments have come primarily since the war, and not very much work has been published as yet. The Hartree-Fock approximation was used during the 1930s for atomic calculations and turned out to be such a good approximation, on the basis of providing a qualitative explanation of atomic spectra, that there was no great need to consider the electron correlation. The most important correlation effects could be taken into account by relatively simple methods.

However if more accurate wave functions are needed, for instance to calculate the electronic contribution of quadrupole coupling with the nucleus, the Hartree-Fock method is not adequate and simplified correlation calculations are not very reliable. Also, in molecular work more accuracy is needed for one is more often interested in properties of the wave function or in differences between closely spaced energy levels than in gross electronic energy. This has led to reconsideration of the many-particle problem from first principles and to several prescriptions for practicable, converging methods of solution of the general problem [1]. A reasonable procedure is to carry out a Hartree-Fock calculation and then do a variational calculation including all determinantal functions which have matrix elements with the Hartree-Fock wave function for the Hamiltonian of the system. According to a result first stated by Brillouin [2] this limits the calculation to determinantal functions which involve two-particle correlations. The Hartree-Fock determinant is already stationary for changes of single orbitals (single-particle wave functions), and the Coulomb operator has no matrix elements between determinants differing by more than two orbitals.

Higher correlation effects can be taken into account by a bootstrapping procedure of selecting configurations by second-order perturbation theory, diagonalizing a finite matrix based on the most important of these, and using a matrix eigenvector as zeroth-order approximation in a further round of second-order perturbation theory calculations. This is a convergent process which involves only finite calculations at each successive stage. In practice, this process is refined by the use of group theoretical techniques and variants on straight perturbation theory.

The Brueckner theory also emphasizes two-particle correlations. When the Hartree-Fock orbitals are plane waves it is essentially identical with the approach that I have been considering at this level of approximation and in the limit of uniform particle densities. However, there are discrepancies which might be important if one tried to do a calculation on a system where plane wave orbitals were no longer of practical value (e.g., an atom or molecule). Since the Brueckner theory is based on a perturbation approach, there is no way, short of a calculation to arbitrarily high order, of estimating the error in truncating any of the matrix product expansions in the theory, as one might be forced to do when working with orbitals which do not fall into convenient sets of complete functions. In a paper that will be published [3] I have tried to express the variational approach in language as similar as possible to the Brueckner theory in order to provide a theoretical frame in which to analyze such problems.

In conclusion it might be of value to remark that, in molecular wave function calculations in particular (and the same must be true to a large extent in the solid state), the formalism of a correlation calculation is a relatively trivial problem compared with that of organizing the calculation of the large number of difficult integrals required in all known workable approaches. Any reliable method which reduces the extent of such calculations for finite nuclei below the requirements of a Hartree-Fock boot-strapping procedure would be of great value in molecular physics.

K. A. Brueckner: I quite agree with the point that the configuration mixing methods used in the shell model are actually analogous to those used in electronic systems. The methods we use are of course very much simplified when one deals with infinite systems, because then the Hartree-Fock solutions are actually known, and one has a very simple starting point instead of having first to determine all Hartree-Fock solutions. Now in dealing with non-uniform systems using the Hartree-Fock approximation and trying to correct for the correlation energy, it seems to me that there is an approximation one can make which is in the spirit of the Slater treatment of exchange energy [4]. That is, the correlation effects that give rise to the correlation energy are of even shorter range than the correlation effects which arise from the exchange interactions, and therefore it is, I think, fully legitimate to compute these correlation effects as if the system really were locally uniform in density.

Thus one can compute the interaction operators, which in the nuclear case we call reaction operators, as if the system were uniform in density; these can then be transformed to coordinate space as non-local interaction operators. These non-local interactions, if now treated using the Hartree approximation for a finite system, will give the correlation energy to an extremely high degree of accuracy. Certainly an approximation of this sort is very much more accurate in treating the correlation energy than the Slater method is in treating the exchange energy.

2. Molecules in a fluid

C. Herring: On the subject of molecules in fluids, I think that Dr. Kirkwood has some remarks to make on Monte Carlo calculations.

[EDITOR'S NOTE: The information which was outlined here by Dr. Kirkwood is presented in abstract in Chap. XXX. Briefly, Dr. Kirkwood stressed the agreement of Monte Carlo calculations of the classical radial distribution function for hard spheres and Lennard-Jones potentials with the corresponding results obtained from the Born-Green-Yvon [5], [6] and Kirkwood [7] integral equations, which are terminated by use of the superposition approximation [8]. He also discussed the empirical evidence, on the basis of the Monte Carlo calculations, for a first-order phase transition in a classical fluid of hard spheres.]

C. Herring: Dr. Alder, do you have any comments on these calculations or the assumptions that underlie it?

B. J. Alder: I just want to say that the calculations we are doing [9], where we follow the equations of motion, are only in quantitative disagreement with the Monte Carlo calculations [10], and some of these differences will certainly be resolved as a result of further calculations. It appears that the number of particles has at least some effect in our calculations, and it appears almost certain that there is a transition, although the quantitative aspects have not as yet been completely determined.

C. Herring: Would either of you care to comment on the variable which is different in the higher and lower temperature phases. What is the qualitative nature of the transition?

J. G. Kirkwood: It would appear to be first-order. Presumably one is making a transition from a fluid phase to a crystalline phase, and the difference would be in the long-range order in the pair correlation function in the latter case, as opposed to the short-range order in the former case.

C. Herring: There seems to me to be a qualitative argument against having an ordered crystalline phase with only repulsive forces, because you can reason this way: Suppose you have an ordered phase, and suppose you have a slight excess volume. Then by removing atoms from the ordered structure, and removing them in a disordered fashion, you do no work. On the other hand, while doing no work, you increase the entropy; therefore, one would feel that with only repulsive forces, there is an intrinsic instability of the ordered phase.

J. G. Kirkwood: Will you allow me to repeat your argument by taking soft spheres — a soft repulsion. If you take an r^{-12} repulsion with no attraction, or perhaps an exponential repulsion, I think you can convince yourself that, if you are willing to squeeze the particles into a small enough volume, then you can find a potential energy minimum in the configuration space of the entire system. Then you can make a harmonic expansion of the potential energy as a function of the displacements of the atoms, and you get a perfectly good crystal with repulsive forces alone. I admit that it is difficult to pass to the limit of the hard sphere, but I will not accept your statement that you cannot have a crystalline phase with repulsive forces alone.

C. Herring: I am willing to modify my objection as you indicate. Incidentally, the periodic conditions on a cube that are used would introduce anisotropy in phase space. Wouldn't that mean that the pair distribution function at the surface of a hard sphere would be angle-dependent — and one needs this function to get the hard sphere equation of state.

J. G. Kirkwood: I think that what has been done is a calculation of a cumulative radial distribution function. That means that an integration is performed to obtain all pairs within a sphere of radius *r* of a given atom, and then this is differentiated. Angle dependence has not been investigated; it would be interesting but I don't know whether it would be practical to do so.

3. *Ground State Correlations*

C. Herring: If there are no further comments from members of the panel, perhaps we ought to go on to the next topic. There are quite a number of things to be discussed on the subject of electron correlations in solids — if we get to them. There is first of all the question of the ground state energy of many-electron systems. Then — what we hope to devote the principle time to — the elementary excitations of the various kinds of electron systems in solids. Starting with the ground state correlation problem, I think Dr. Mayer has some comments.

J. E. Mayer: I'd just like to make one comment on a method of approach which is very similar to one that Jastrow used and spoke of in a previous talk [11] — at least in spirit — but differs from it in one way. That is, one talks about the reduced density matrix for pairs, which of course in a coordinate representation has four coordinates, and which is just the integral of the complete density matrix over the diagonal parts of $d\mathbf{r}_3 \ldots d\mathbf{r}_n$. Then of course it is clear that if you are using potentials which depend on single particles and pairs only, and one usually does that (for instance with electrons it is obviously correct), then the energy is determined by this reduced two-body matrix alone. Of course, then, one thing one immediately thinks of is; why not put in a variational calculation, simply minimize the energy and find the function which minimizes the energy. Now the trouble with that, as with any minimization problem, is to put on the right boundary conditions, that is, to know what are allowed functions. Certain conditions pertaining to symmetry are necessary, and simple to ascertain.

I wrote a paper on electron correlation [12], and I believe that there is a paper in *The Physical Review* by Tredgold [13], pointing out that with the conditions that I had set, which are certainly necessary and just have to do with symmetry, one can get a ridiculous answer. That is, those conditions alone are not sufficient. I should have known this when I wrote the paper, for it is a familiar story in the classical case, where you only need ρ_2, the pair density in the classical system. This $\rho_2(\mathbf{r}_1, \mathbf{r}_2) = \rho_2(\mathbf{r})$, where $\mathbf{r} = |\mathbf{r}_1 - \mathbf{r}_2|$, is just the diagonal element of the reduced pair density matrix. For instance, if I draw $\rho_2(\mathbf{r})$ versus r, and draw the kind of curve that Dr. Kirkwood just had on the board, one which rises from zero at $r > 0$, perhaps one-third atomic spacing and then levels off, it looks perfectly good; but suppose I put in numbers, and suppose I say that $\rho_2(r \to \infty) = 1$. That is, I have chosen units such that the density is unity. Then let's say that where ρ_2 starts to rise at small r, $r = 10$ atomic spacings. Well, it is obvious nonsense, because I am saying that every particle is surrounded by a sphere of volume $4\pi/3 \times 10^3$ in which there is no other particle, and that I have several thousand in the first coordination zone. It's clear that I have violated something, and of course it is clear here that there are conditions other than symmetry and the requirement that ρ_1, when brought into diagonal form (if it is the antisymmetric case), never have more than one particle in each state. However there is a simple way out — it's even numerically practical in some cases, and I think perhaps it is worth commenting on as a method.

In principle, just by the Kirkwood closure [8], you can go up to the triple density from the pair density by assuming the triple density to be a product of pair density functions. Similarly, one may build up all the higher density probabilities so that they are consistent with the assumed pair probability. There is a completely analogous way, for any reduced pair density matrix, to build up reduced density matrices for n particles, where n has any finite value, providing these are defined in an infinite volume. But you can't do this if you assume that the density is large — n/V is large. However if the density is uniform in the volume, then you can take the problem of infinite volume, go up to a finite n, and then ask what this unreduced density matrix would be in a small volume out of the infinite volume. There is then, from this, a perfectly good way of computing the density matrices for the isolated particles in the volume, and the method is perfectly analogous to the one in the classical case. Now if these functions have the right symmetry, and are positive when brought into diagonal form, then one has constructed an acceptable ensemble which would lead to the reduced pair density matrix. One might say that this is an impossible job, for I have to compute an infinite number of them and must examine them at all diagonal elements to see if they are acceptable. It isn't so bad. The symmetry conditions are easy to satisfy. The condition on the diagonal elements that they must be positive and real can be assured by building the entropy out of them, and if the entropy is positive, it means that you have got a satisfactory set.

It is rather amusing that this works rather easily in the case in which you know the answer, namely a perfect gas of Fermions. In that case the condition for the lowest energy state turns out to be almost the same, in a numerical sense, as the condition for a Bose-Einstein transition; that is, in going from the reduced set to the complete sets, there is an alternation of signs which you get from the antisymmetry; the resulting series looks like the Bose-Einstein series. The lowest energy case is the one in which the series is just at the point of divergence. I believe that this method is at least worth looking at more seriously than it has been.

P. J. Price: I want to mention an idea that I think is relevant when you are working with Bosons. It was suggested by Penrose a few years ago [14] that although the classical one-particle density matrix goes to zero as $|\mathbf{r}_1 - \mathbf{r}'_1|$ tends to infinity, what is characteristic of the Bose-Einstein fluid in the ground state is that ρ_1 remains finite, corresponding to a δ function in the momentum distribution. Similarly you can infer something about ρ_2 for large separation, and perhaps these, or their generalization, are conditions you may want to impose.

4. Elementary Excitations in Semiconductors

C. Herring: Perhaps we should turn now to elementary excitations. The one-electron theory of solids, as you know, has had great success for many years in the theory of metals and semiconductors. It has gradually become evident that what one is dealing with here is not a set of free electrons oblivious to the existence of others, but rather elementary excitations of a many-electron system which have in many respects properties very similar to those of individual particles. The simplest case in which this can be seen is the case of the insulator, or the insulator with an extra electron or extra hole — in other words, a semiconductor — in which the existence of a finite gap enables one very easily to prove some rigorous theorems about the band structure. May we have some comments on this point to start with.

M. Lax: I think, first of all, we should point out that Walter Kohn is the one who is responsible for treating this problem [15]. What he was trying to establish was that the usual procedure for dealing with an extra electron in a solid, in an otherwise empty band, can be adequately treated from the point of view of an effective mass and dielectric constant, but without making a one-body approximation. I don't think that there is much point in my going through his analysis, except to state that this primary assumptions are that there is an energy gap, and that one can get the usual effective mass type of equation for slowly varying potentials. This is the same assumption that is made in one-body theories, so that he has a many-body theory which has no more assumptions in it than the one-body theory.

The essential success of this procedure is based on the fact that for the many-body problem you have translation invariance; you know therefore that you can set up a wave function which, if I use n to denote a band number and $\mathbf{k}$ a propagation constant, has the form of $\exp(i\mathbf{k} \cdot \mathbf{r}_1)$ times a function with the full periodicity of the lattice. This is of course an N-body function. Then if you have, say, an impurity present or a Coulomb potential, you assume a solution of the form $\sum A_{nk}\psi_{nk}$, and this is precisely the same form of solution as was previously assumed in the one-body problem. All the same formal manipulations can then be carried through, and you end up with a set of equations looking something like this:

$$[(1/2m^*)k^2 - E^*]A_{\mathbf{k}} - (q/K^*)(4\pi/V) \sum_{\mathbf{k}' \neq \mathbf{k}} (1/|\mathbf{k}-\mathbf{k}'|^2) A_{\mathbf{k}'} = 0 \qquad (1)$$

I have already dropped the index n because Kohn assumed a band gap, and the interband coupling is small for a slowly varying potential. Here K^* plays the part of the dielectric constant and the term in $|\mathbf{k}-\mathbf{k}'|^{-2}$ is just the Fourier transform of q/r. So this is the usual equation for effective mass in the presence of a dielectric constant, but the point is that he didn't introduce the dielectric constant — it appears automatically in his theory.

In particular, what Kohn found was that although the ψ's are normalized, i.e. $(\psi_k, \psi_k) = 1$, if you take a pair of such functions with slightly different k and k', then instead of being close to unity, the overlap

$$(\psi_{\mathbf{k}}, \psi_{\mathbf{k}'}) \simeq [(\mathcal{N}+1)K^*]^{-1} \qquad (2)$$

goes as the reciprocal of $(\mathcal{N}+1)$ times a constant, and this constant he then defined as the dielectric constant. Now of course this is a very formal definition, and what he does is to verify that this definition is a suitable one by inserting a couple of test charges inside the crystal and calculating the interaction energy. He finds that he does get an interaction energy of the form $q_1 q_2/(K^* |\mathbf{r}_1 - \mathbf{r}_2|)$ so that K^* is indeed the dielectric constant of the material. The point is that the approach is rather formal. One never says anything about the precise nature of the wave functions; one merely derives a result with a certain unknown constant which one prefers to call the dielectric constant, which is then verified by doing another example in which the dielectric constant is well defined.

C. Herring: May I add one or two footnotes to this before we go on, just by way of clarification. The assumption of a band gap that is referred to in this calculation simply means the following: If we just have an $\mathcal{N}$-electron system without the extra electron, then we assume that there is a certain ground state, probably translationally invariant, and that the lowest excited energy state, corresponding physically to an exciton, electron-hole pair, or the like, lies a finite distance above it. Now if we picture the energy plotted as a function of the wave vector, defined as the eigenvalue of the translation operation for the entire many-body system, it's not hard to show that if there is a finite energy gap in the above sense for the lowest excited energy state, then the excited states must be discrete for any given **k**, up to a certain minimum level — that is, where the excited particles have enough energy to create more pairs. From this point on, there is a continuum for all **k**, and the only thing that is used in Kohn's work is the topological nature of the energy spectrum of the many-body system, but nothing beyond that.

I should add another footnote, that although I think the work of Kohn is by far the most general and practical that has been published, a number of people in a number of countries have worked on similar things, especially the Russians [16], who have gone at the problem of elementary excitations in semiconductors from the point of view of an almost atomic approach. That is, the elementary excitations are then states in which you have two electrons instead of one electron on an atom, with some atoms having no electrons, and so forth.

[P. J. Price discussed the f-sum rules obtained when Kohn's ψ_{nk} are employed analogously to one-body periodic Bloch functions, and remarked on the influence of the dielectric constant on the band gap.]

J. M. Richardson: I would like to make a few remarks reflecting my personal prejudices on the most expeditious ways of treating problems of this class. My remarks will be concerned explicitly with the calculation of the equilibrium properties of a system of many particles. However, it should be made clear that the determination of the energy spectrum is part of the above problem, since the density of states on the energy axis may be expressed as an appropriate Fourier transform of the partition function.

Let me confine my remarks to a system containing many Fermions of one type. The Pauli exclusion principle is most conveniently incorporated in the formulation by using the second quantization scheme. It is most natural and convenient then to employ the grand canonical ensemble instead of the canonical ensemble. Our central problem is now the calculation of $Q = \mathrm{Tr}\,\exp\,(\gamma N - \beta H)$ where N

and H are the number of particles and the Hamiltonian, respectively, expressed in terms of creation and desctruction operators. Here, the trace is the dagonal sum in the vector space in which these operators are defined. The coefficients of N and H are defined by $\gamma = \mu/kT$ and $\beta = 1/kT$, where μ is the chemical potential or Fermi level, T is the absolute temperature, and k is the Boltzmann constant. The calculation of Q may be approached by means of the following variational principle:

$$\text{Tr } \rho \; (\ln \rho - \gamma N + \beta H) = \text{minimum} = -\ln Q \qquad (3)$$

in which the variations are on the density matrix ρ, subject to the restriction Tr $\rho = 1$. This principle, related to the maximization of entropy with the average energy and number fixed, is in its present form called the pressure maximization principle.

If the variational problem is solved exactly, the minimum value of the variational function is independent of the choice of wave functions used as the basis of the second quantization scheme. However, if ρ is restricted in some way that excludes the exact solution, the minimum is dependent upon the basis. In this case, it is worthwhile varying the basis to obtain the "best" solution within the restrictions on ρ.

Let us now consider a collection of interacting electrons moving in a periodic potential (due to the nuclei or ion cores, as one wishes). Let the basis of the second quantization scheme be a set of Bloch type functions $\psi_k(\mathbf{r}) = \varphi_k(\mathbf{r}) \exp (i\mathbf{k} \cdot \mathbf{r})$, where $\varphi_k(r)$ has the periodicity of the lattice but is otherwise undetermined as yet. For economy of bookkeeping, we allow the vector $\mathbf{k}$ to range over all of $\mathbf{k}$ space so that different bands are labelled without the introduction of additional quantum numbers. The density matrix ρ has elements which are labeled by the occupation numbers η_k defined with the above basis in mind. As a first step, let us consider maximizing the pressure with respect to variations on the basis (more explicitly, on the form of the functions $\varphi_k(\mathbf{r})$, preserving periodicity, orthogonality, and normalization, of course) but keeping the density matrix fixed. The formal solution of this problem constitutes a generalization of the Hartree-Fock equations for the case of electrons in a crystal.

As a second step, let us consider the maximization with respect to variations on ρ. There are many levels and types of approximations we could consider here. A simple but meaningful approximation is to write ρ as a product of factors, each diagonal and dependent on one η_k. The equations resulting from the maximization correspond to each Bloch function being occupied to a degree dependent upon the average occupation of all other Bloch functions with correlation effects explicitly neglected. The correlation problem can be treated within the present framework by considering a more complicated expression for ρ, i.e., one including factors referring to pairs of points in **k** space, etc.

5. *Elementary Excitations in Metals*

C. Herring: Having seen how the elementary excitation concept gives a rigorous justification to many of the considerations of use in the theory of semiconductors, perhaps we should turn our attention to the corresponding problem in the case of metals. Here again, I think that a number of people have had, for some years, the idea that it may be possible to give a rigorous meaning to the concept of individual particles, or quasi particles, in metals that have a certain energy versus wave number functional dependence in the neighborhood of the Fermi surface. Some of the general developments we heard about previously (see Parts One and Three) may provide the key that takes this from an intuitive speculation into an essentially rigorously established fact. Would you care to say something about this, Dr. Pines.

D. Pines: The basic question one faces is how the interaction between the electrons may alter the elementary excitation spectrum. We can discuss this first of all for the free electron gas, for we certainly face the problem in this case. Here, as Gell-Mann has recently emphasized [17], it is clear that if we are talking about sufficiently low temperatures, and we have only a few electrons excited above the Fermi sea, then the notion of a one-particle-like elementary excitation, for which one could rigorously write the energy as a function of momentum, should make sense. As long as the number of electrons is small in comparison with the number of electrons in the sea, the interaction of the excited electrons with the electrons in the sea is the dominant interaction; one may neglect the interaction between the excited electrons. That is statement one. Statement two is that the interaction of the excited electrons with the electrons in the sea can be gotten from a suitable theory, à la Brueckner, perhaps. If one defines the energy levels for a free gas of Fermi particles and then turns on the interaction between the excited electrons and the electrons in the sea, one should be able to derive a set of E versus k curves, which, while not corresponding to free electrons, can be given the same meaning — that of elementary excitations of the Fermi sea.

The principal difficulty that one runs into with this approach is that the Coulomb interaction between the electrons might lead to a possible excitation, not of a few electrons above the Fermi sea, but of a great many, and so destroy the notion that one may neglect the interaction between the excited electrons. This in turn could mean that one has to go to a much more accurate treatment, and in so doing, one would most likely really destroy the notion of an elementary one-electron-like excitation. Here I think the answer is also clear on physical grounds. There are collective excitations brought about by the Coulomb interaction in which many electrons are excited from the Fermi sea. However, these collective excitations have a very high energy — a frequency at least of the order of the plasma frequency. Therefore, as long as one talks about reasonable temperatures, or about any physical situation in which there is not enough energy around to exite a plasmon, then one can forget about the complications introduced by the long range of the Coulomb interaction, which could in principle lead to the excitation of many electrons and destroy the notion of a one-electron excitation.

It is physically clear that this is the situation, but a mathematical proof of the fact that things go through in this way is not in such a tidy state. One encounters the following difficulty. When we introduce the plasmons [18] and so take out the long-range part of the Coulomb interaction, what we have left over is well-behaved in that there is a short-range interaction between the electrons. One can compute its effect, by perturbation theory, on the E versus k curves (and they behave very much as free electron curves do), and one can compute a number of other one-electron properties. But in all of these computations, one is ignoring the fact that not only does the long range of the Coulomb interaction give rise to the plasmons, which have a very high excitation frequency, but it also introduces correlations between the electrons such that the over-all wave function must satisfy a set of subsidiary conditions of the approximate form

$$\rho_{\mathbf{k}}\psi = 0 \qquad (k < k_c) \qquad (4)$$

where k_c is the maximum plasmon momentum.

One can give physical arguments which indicate that the effect of the subsidiary conditions on the over-all energy of the system will be small. The argument is that they involve long-range correlations in the electron positions, which do not cost much in the way of kinetic energy, and that they do not couple into the short-range interaction energy. Therefore, you would not expect them to influence the energy of the system very much. One can also argue that the subsidiary conditions will not influence the specific heat markedly. They essentially come into play (limiting the number of degrees of freedom) only if you have enough energy in the system to excite a plasmon. It is only at this point that one is faced with a possible "duplicity" of the degrees of freedom, i.e., that a question arises as to whether you are talking about an individual-electron excitation, or a plasmon. But to establish furthermore that the subsidiary conditions do not alter the shape of the Fermi surface is by no means a simple matter, and I for one have not seen how to do this. I think it is likely that they do not, from the simple physical arguments that we gave — that the real alteration of the Fermi surface comes only when one puts enough energy into the system to excite a plasmon. In other words, I believe that the essentially virtual alteration corresponding to the zero point correlations of the electrons (that give rise to the plasmon) is not really a large one, but it is hard to prove that in fact this is the situation.

P. Nozières: I'd like to make a very short point about the subsidiary conditions, relating to my calculation of the dielectric constant [19]. The total energy is the mean energy for the electrons, plus the short-range interaction, plus the screened long-range interaction, which must be considered together with a set of subsidiary conditions, eq. (4). Now if one tries to select a small number of electrons — very small compared to the total number — and to average their effective interaction in the average field of the others, one finds the following facts: First, the minority electrons disappear from the subsidiary relations, so as long as one considers these, one does not have to worry. Secondly, the effective screened interaction of the remaining electrons may be written in the following way:

$$H^{\text{scr}}_{\text{Coul}} = \sum_{k > k_c} (2\pi e^2/k^2)\, r_{\mathbf{k}} r_{\mathbf{k}}^{\text{scr}} \tag{5}$$

where $r_{\mathbf{k}}$ is the density fluctuation of the minority electrons of wave vector $\mathbf{k}$, and r_k^{scr} a screened density fluctuation:

$$(r_{\mathbf{k}}^{\text{scr}})_{mn} = (r_{\mathbf{k}})_{mn}/\mathscr{E}(\omega_{mn}) \tag{6}$$

where $\mathscr{E}(\omega_{mn})$ is the dielectric constant at frequency ω_{mn}. I think that this is just a generalization of Kohn's result [15] to the case of interband electron transitions. It shows that in this case, one does not have to worry about subsidiary conditions.

[There was at this point some discussion of the validity, for real solids, of Koopmans' theorem [20] which establishes the identity of the Hartree-Fock calculation with an E versus k curve, and therefore with the energy gap picture.]

6. *Mobility and Transport Theory*

C. Herring: Perhaps we should go on to the last topic that is to come up for discussion. Having set up the concept of elementary excitations, what can we do with them? Well, one of the most important things one can calculate with them is theory of transport phenomena, but until recently, there has been some difficulty in even formulating the transport problem for cases in which the scattering-type interactions are very strong. I believe that Dr. Lax has something to say about this.

M. Lax: The study of mobility, of say, electrons in a solid, usually starts with a slightly arbitrary separation of the Hamiltonian into an unperturbed part describing the free motion of the electron (and the scattering system if the latter possesses a dynamics) plus a perturbation: the interaction with the scattering system. The perturbation is used to calculate transition probabilities for collisions, and the latter are inserted into the customary transport equation. The presence of an electric field is accounted for by a drift term. The perturbation is supposed at the start to be small, but the field may be either large or small.

For the purposes of calculating the ohmic conductivity however, one is concerned only with the part of the current that is linear in the field. One may then regard the field as arbitrarily small. It has for many years seemed logical to me that one should then regard the electric field contribution to the Hamiltonian, $V(t) = -e\mathbf{E}(t) \cdot \mathbf{r}$, as a genuinely small perturbation producing transitions between the combined states of the system composed of electron plus scattering system. If $\mathbf{E}(t) = \mathbf{E}(0) \exp(i\omega t)$, then transitions of the combined system can be produced with an energy gain of $\hbar\omega$ or an energy loss of $\hbar\omega$. Callen and Welton [21] suggested that the power dissipated by the field in the system be computed by multiplying $\hbar\omega$ by the net rate of energy-gaining transitions. In this way, Callen and Welton compute the real part of the conductivity.

In principle, the Callen-Welton procedure is preferable to the usual one, since no splitting of the Hamiltonian into an unperturbed part plus a perturbation is required. However the resulting formula for the conductivity requires a knowledge of matrix elements of $\mathbf{r}$ between eigenstates of the combined system. Such matrix elements must be handled with care because $\mathbf{r}$ is not a bounded operator. Furthermore, our knowledge of the combined eigenstates is rather limited. Callen and Welton did not derive their formula with the intention of making a practical calculation of conductivity; rather they used it, in conjunction with a calculation of the integrated noise spectrum, to derive an integral Nyquist theorem [22].

There is a need, however, for a formula of the Callen-Welton type that makes no assumptions other than that the electric field is small — for the usual conductivity theory depends on a particular way of splitting the Hamiltonian, and on the existence of a transport theory. And the existence of a transport theory is questionable for strong-coupling problems in which the time between collisions becomes comparable with the duration of a collision — so that the electron hasn't sufficient time to lose the phase information of the last collision. (Such phase information is ignored in transport theory, which considers probabilities, but not probability amplitudes.)

A number of people [23] – [28] independently, and at nearly the same time, recognized these difficulties, and proposed another scheme for calculating the conductivity: (a) Calculate the modification of the wave functions or density matrix produced by the electric field, regarding the latter as a small perturbation. (b) Calculate the current with respect to the new wave functions or density matrix. The ratio of the current to the field will give the conductivity, including both real and imaginary parts.

The real part of the conductivity calculated in this way must, of course, agree with the Callen-Welton result. An easy way to check this is to verify the Nyquist relation [29]. The chief advantage of the present result [eq. (11)], is a purely formal one: it is written as a trace, thus permitting the use of any representation and facilitating approximate computations, instead of being written in the energy representation of Callen and Welton. While the Callen-Welton result does not bear the faintest resemblance to conventional conductivity expressions, our result can be written in a form such that when a relaxation time exists, the coventional results are immediately obtained.

When the coupling between the electron and lattice is sufficiently weak, Van Hove [30], and Kohn and Luttinger [31] have shown that a transport equation exists. We shall now come to the work of Van Hove, and show (for the first time, I believe) that *our generalized conductivity reduces to the conventional one in the limit of weak coupling, regardless of the existence of a relaxation time.* For simplicity, we adopt a one-electron viewpoint (for further discussion, and generalization to a many-electron viewpoint, see [29]) and start with the density-matrix equation:

$$i\hbar \, \partial\rho/\partial t + [\rho, H - e\mathbf{E}(t) \cdot \mathbf{r}] + i\hbar\alpha(\rho - \rho_0) = 0 \qquad (7)$$

where $\mathbf{E}(t) = \exp(i\omega t)\mathbf{E}(0)$ represents a single-frequency electric field. (A knowledge of the response of a system to an arbitrary time-dependent $\mathbf{E}(t)$ can be synthesized from either the single-frequency response or the pulse response.) We represent by H the Hamiltonian of the electron plus the scattering system plus the interaction between the two. The last term represents the fact that the crystal is not isolated but may interact weakly with the surroundings in such a way that in the absence of a field the system approaches the equilibrium density matrix

$$\rho_0 = \mathcal{Z}^{-1} \exp{(-\beta H)} \qquad \text{or} \qquad \rho_0 = \rho^F = [1 + \exp{\beta(H - E_F)}]^{-1} \quad (8)$$

where $\beta = 1/kT$ and $\mathcal{Z} = \mathrm{Tr}\,[\exp{(-\beta H)}]$. The second form applies when Fermi statistics are necessary and E_F, the Fermi energy, is chosen so that $\mathrm{Tr}\,\rho^F = \mathcal{N} =$ the total number of electrons.

Since $\mathbf{E}$ is regarded as arbitrarily small, a result accurate to first order in $\mathbf{E}$ may be obtained by approximating $[\rho, r]$ by $[\rho_0, r]$ in eq. (7). If the system starts at $t = -\infty$ at equilibrium, $\rho(-\infty) = \rho_0$, then the term in ρ of first order in $\mathbf{E}$ is given precisely by

$$\rho_1(t)\,e^{-i\omega t} = -ie\mathbf{E}(0) \cdot \int_0^\infty e^{-i\omega t} e^{-\alpha t} e^{-iHt/\hbar}[\rho_0,\, \mathbf{r}]e^{iHt/\hbar}\, dt \quad (9)$$

The interaction with the universe, as represented by $\exp{(-\alpha t)}$, damps out contributions of oscillatory transients that would otherwise appear in ρ. We see from (9) that at any finite time t, $\rho_1(t)\,\exp{(-i\omega t)}$ is independent of time, i.e., a steady state has been reached.

The current density in the presence of a uniform electric field can be calculated from

$$\mathbf{j} = ne\,\mathrm{Tr}\,(\mathbf{v}\rho_1) \quad (10)$$

where n represents the number of non-interacting electrons in a cubic centimeter and $\mathbf{v} = [\mathbf{r}, H]/i\hbar$ is the velocity. The resulting conductivity dyadic is given by

$$\boldsymbol{\sigma}(\omega) = (ne^2/i\hbar) \int_0^\infty dt \exp{(-i\omega t)}\,\mathrm{Tr}\,\{\mathbf{v}(t)[\rho_0,\, \mathbf{r}]\} \quad (11)$$

$$\text{where} \qquad \mathbf{v}(t) = \exp{(iHt/\hbar)}\mathbf{v}\exp{(-iHt/\hbar)} \quad (12)$$

is the Heisenberg operator for the velocity and the convergence factor $\exp{(-\alpha t)}$ is suppressed.

We now wish to examine eq. (11) in the limit of weak coupling to compare it with the results of conventional transport theory. If $H = H_0 + \lambda H_1$, where H_1 represents the scattering interaction, one certainly neglects the influence of the interaction H_1 on the occupancy statistics of the electron (and of the scattering system) in conventional theory, i.e., we approximate $\rho_0(H)$ by $\rho_0(H_0)$. Since $H_0 = H_{\text{electron}} + H_{\text{scattering system}}$, averages may be performed separately over the motion of the electron and the scatterer. For simplicity of notation we do not show the latter average explicitly. Assuming $H_{\text{electron}} = E(\mathbf{p})$ is a function of the electrons' momentum only, we may replace $\rho_0(H_0)$ by $f_0(\mathbf{p})$, an operator diagonal in the momentum representation, corresponding to the usual Boltzmann or Fermi distribution. (This assumption specifically neglects magnetic fields. The analysis up to this point is valid in the presence of magnetic fields provided the Hamiltonian H contains the magnetic field terms.) But

$$[\mathbf{r}, f_0(\mathbf{p})] = i\hbar \, \partial f_0(\mathbf{p})/\partial \mathbf{p} \tag{13}$$

so that

$$\boldsymbol{\sigma}(\omega) = -ne^2 \int_0^\infty \exp\left(-i\omega t\right) dt \, \text{Tr} \, [\mathbf{v}(t) \, \partial f_0/\partial \mathbf{p}] \tag{14}$$

We may of course write

$$\partial f_0/\partial \mathbf{p} = \mathbf{v} \, \partial f_0/\partial E \qquad \mathbf{v} = \partial E(\mathbf{p})/\partial \mathbf{p} \tag{15}$$

Let us now consider the case in which a relaxation time exists. This implies that we may make the replacement

$$\mathbf{v}(t)\mathbf{v}(0) = \mathbf{v}(0)\mathbf{v}(0) \exp\left[-t/\tau(\mathbf{v})\right] \tag{16}$$

Equation (14) then yields

$$\boldsymbol{\sigma}(\omega) = -ne^2 \, \text{Tr} \left\{ [\mathbf{v}(0) \, \mathbf{v}(0) \, \tau(\mathbf{v})/1 + i\omega\tau(\mathbf{v})] \, \partial f_0/\partial E \right\} \tag{17}$$

where the trace is now simply an integral over $\mathbf{v}$ or $\mathbf{p}$ since all operators are now diagonal in the momentum representation. Equation (17) can be recognized as one that is obtained from conventional transport theory when a relaxation time exists [32].

Similar proofs have been given by the authors of references [23]–[28]. Although our results have the correct form, we have not proven that the τ appearing in eq. (16) is identical to the one computed conventionally. We shall establish this point in a general way by reconsidering eq. (14) and showing that it reduces to the conventional transport result whether or not a relaxation time exists. Equation

(14) can be written in the momentum representation

$$\sigma = -ne^2 \int_0^\infty e^{i\omega t}\, dt \int \mathbf{v}\, d\mathbf{p} \int W(\mathbf{p}, \mathbf{p}'; t)\, \partial f_0(\mathbf{p}')/\partial \mathbf{p}'\, d\mathbf{p}' \qquad (18)$$

$$\text{where} \qquad W(\mathbf{p}, \mathbf{p}'; t) = |\langle \mathbf{p} \mid \exp\left(-iHt/\hbar\right) \mid \mathbf{p}'\rangle|^2 \qquad (19)$$

represents the probability that an electron with momentum $\mathbf{p}'$ at time $t = 0$ will have a momentum $\mathbf{p}$ at time t, and the normalization factors incurred in converting sums to integrals can be absorbed by renormalizing $f_0(\mathbf{p})$ so that $\int f_0(\mathbf{p})\, d\mathbf{p} = 1$.

To verify that (18) is indeed equivalent to the conventional result we start from the conventional transport equation

$$\partial f/\partial t + e\mathbf{E}(t) \cdot \partial f/\partial \mathbf{p} + Kf = 0 \qquad (20)$$

(where K is a linear operator and Kf is an abbreviated way of writing the collision terms) and solve, as in the quantum mechanical case, by treating the electric field term as a known inhomogeneous term. Then $f = f_0 + f_1 + \ldots$ where f_1, the term linear in the field obeys

$$\partial f_1/\partial t + Kf_1 = \varphi(\mathbf{p}, t) = -e\mathbf{E}(t) \cdot \partial f_0/\partial \mathbf{p} \qquad (21)$$

An immediate solution of eq. (21) can be obtained by introducing a Green's function $W(\mathbf{p}, \mathbf{p}', t-t')$ obeying

$$\partial W/\partial t + KW = \delta(\mathbf{p}-\mathbf{p}')\,\delta(t-t') \qquad (22)$$

$$W = 0 \qquad \text{for} \qquad t < t' \qquad (23)$$

then

$$f_1(\mathbf{p}, t) = \int d\mathbf{p}' \int_{-\infty}^{t} dt'\, W(\mathbf{p}, \mathbf{p}'; t-t')\, \varphi(\mathbf{p}', t') \qquad (24)$$

where the upper limit t arises because of (23). If we now consider the periodic case, $\mathbf{E}(t) = \exp\left(i\omega t\right)\mathbf{E}(0)$, eq. (24) can be rewritten as

$$f_1(\mathbf{p}, t) = -e\mathbf{E}(t) \cdot \int \partial f_0(\mathbf{p}')/\partial \mathbf{p}'\, d\mathbf{p}' \int_0^\infty W(\mathbf{p}, \mathbf{p}'; t)\, \exp\left(-i\omega t\right) dt \quad (25)$$

This result may be compared directly with $\langle \mathbf{p} \mid \rho_1(t) \mid \mathbf{p}\rangle$ using (9) and (13), or one may simply calculate the current density from

$$\mathbf{j} = ne \int \mathbf{v} f_1(\mathbf{v})\, d\mathbf{p} \qquad (26)$$

and compare the resulting conductivity with (18). In either case, the results are seen to be identical providing $W(\mathbf{p}, \mathbf{p}'; t)$ as defined by (22) and (23) is equal to $W(\mathbf{p}, \mathbf{p}'; t)$ as defined by (19).

An examination of (22) and (23) shows that W suffers a jump of $\delta(\mathbf{p}-\mathbf{p}')$ from $t = t'-0$ to $t = t'+0$ so that

$$W(\mathbf{p},\ \mathbf{p}'; 0) = \delta(\mathbf{p}-\mathbf{p}') \tag{27}$$

$$\text{and} \qquad \partial W(\mathbf{p}, t)/\partial t + KW(\mathbf{p}, t) = 0 \qquad t \neq 0 \tag{28}$$

where $\mathbf{p}'$ in (28) is a parameter and may be suppressed. According to (28), $W(\mathbf{p}, \mathbf{p}'; t)$ represents the probability of finding an electron at $\mathbf{p}$ at time t if by (27) it starts at $\mathbf{p}'$ at time 0. Thus W has the same *meaning* as the quantum mechanical expression (19).

The work of Van Hove [30] shows that in the limit of weak coupling W defined by (19), obeys the transport equation (20) with the collision terms calculated in the usual way. Indeed, a simple proof of Van Hove's result, based on Weisskopf-Wigner perturbation theory, will be presented in a future publication. This proof does not require the coupling strength to go toward zero but makes the less restrictive assumption that the "duration of a collision" is short compared to the mean „time between collisions."[†] In other words, the generalized conductivity expression (11) bears a close relation to the corresponding conventional expression whenever a transport equation may reasonably be expected to exist. This conclusion applies equally well to the case of Fermi as well as Boltzmann statistics [29] and does not depend on the structure of the relation between energy and momentum $E = E(\mathbf{p})$. A proof that the one-body approach adopted in this paper is suitable for electrons that possess Pauli but not dynamical correlations has been given [29].

C. Herring: Well, we have run very much over time. I am afraid that any further discussion will have to take place over the teacups, since we are due back in here for the next session a few minutes ago.

[†] Van Hove's recent elegant paper (33) develops a non-Markoffian transport equation, when higher orders of perturbation theory are considered. He states that the usual Markoffian form of transport theory can only be used consistently with transition probabilities calculated to the lowest order of perturbation theory. However, we shall show that it is consistent to use the (exact) transition probabilities calculated to all orders of perturbation theory, provided only that the time between collisions is large compared to a suitably defined duration of a collision.

Notes and References

1. S. F. Boys, *Proc. Roy. Soc. (London)* **A200**, 542 (1950). P. O. Lowdin, *Phys. Rev.* **97**, 1474 (1955); 1490 (1955); 1509 (1955). R. K. Nesbet, *Proc. Roy. Soc. (London)* **A230**, 312 (1955).
2. L. Brillouin, *Les champs self-consistent de Hartree et de Fock*, Hermann et Cie, Paris, 1934. No. 159 in the series: *Actualites Scientifiques et Industrielles*.
3. R. K. Nesbet, *Phys. Rev.* **109**, 1632 (1958).
4. J. C. Slater, *Revs. Modern Phys.* **6**, 209 (1934).
5. M. Born and H. S. Green, *Proc. Roy. Soc. (London)* **A188**, 10 (1946).
6. J. Yvon, *Actualites Scientifiques et Industrielle* Hermann et Cie, Paris, 1935, p 203.
7. J. G. Kirkwood, *J. Chem. Phys.* **3**, 300 (1935).
8. J. G. Kirkwood and E. M. Boggs, *J. Chem. Phys.* **10**, 394 (1942).
9. B. J. Alder and T. Wainwright, Chep. XXIX, this volume.
10. Wood, Parker, and Jacobson, Chap. XXX, this volume.
11. R. Jastrow, Chap. XI, this volume.
12. J. E. Mayer, *Phys. Rev.* **100**, 1579 (1955).
13. R. H. Tredgold, *Phys. Rev.* **105**, 1421 (1957).
14. O. Penrose, *Phil. Mag.* **42**, 1373 (1951).
15. W. Kohn, *Phys. Rev.* **105**, 509 (1957).
16. Cf T. I. Liberberg and K. B. Tolpygo, *ZETF* **26**, 35 (1954).
17. M. Gell-Mann, *Phys. Rev.* **106**, 369 (1957).
18. D. Pines, Chap. XVI, this volume.
19. P. Nozieres, Chap. XXI, this volume.
20. Cf F. Seitz, *Modern Theory of Solids*, McGraw-Hill, New York, 1940, p. 313.
21. H. B. Callen and T. R. Welton, *Phys. Rev.* **83**, 34 (1951). See also Callen, Barasch, and Jackson, *Phys. Rev.* **88**, 1382 (1952).
22. H. Ekstein and N. Rostoker, *Phys. Rev.* **100**, 1023 (1955). These authors considered the noise spectrum at a given frequency, and used the Callen-Welton conductivity to verify the Nyquist theorem at each frequency.
23. R. Kubo, *Can. J. Phys.* **34**, 1274 (1956).
24. M. Lax, *Phys. Rev.* **100**, 1808 (1955).
25. I. M. Lifshitz, *JETP* **32**, 1509 (1957).
26. H. Mori, *J. Phys. Soc. Japan* **11**, 1029 (1956).
27. H. Nakano, *Prog. Theor. et Phys. (Kyoto)* **15**, 77 (1956).
28. R. P. Feynman, private communication.
29. For details of the present author's calculations on these points, see M. Lax, *Phys. Rev.* **109**, 1921 (1958).
30. L. Van Hove, *Physica* **21**, 513 (1955).
31. W. Kohn and J. Luttinger, *Phys. Rev.* **108**, 590 (1957); **109**, 1892 (1958).
32. C. Herring, *Bell System Tech. J.* **34**, 237 (1955), eq. (45).
33. L. Van Hove, *Physica* **23**, 441 (1957).

Part Five

CHAPTER XXIII

Superfluids

Jerome K. Percus

1. *Introduction*

Superfluidity is a quantum mechanical many-body phenomenon associated with an abnormally low density of energy levels in the vicinity of the ground state. It is not merely a macroscopic manifestation of quantum mechanics, as is evidenced, e.g., by the behavior of normal solids; in fact, one can thus far apply the term only to He^4 and to the valence-electron fluid in a number of solids (and perhaps to some collective states of nuclei). Since superfluidity disappears at a sufficiently high temperature, the nature of the transition region is of interest, and certainly involves further specific properties of the fluid in question. Similarly, there are various other effects which are concomitant with, but not implied by, the existence of the low density of states. We shall consider the nature of the energy spectra and transition probabilities, the resulting superfluid properties, and current thoughts on the explanation of spectra and properties from basic principles.

For the purpose of orientation, let us recount the characteristic properties of superfluids. Helium (of atomic weight 4 : He^4) liquefies at a temperature of 5.2°K; if this liquid, termed helium I, is further cooled under its own vapor pressure, another transition takes place at 2.1°K, producing helium II, which remains liquid down to 0°K. Thermodynamically, He II has a low-temperature specific heat varying as T^3, while at the He II – He I transition, the specific heat shows a logarithmic (lambda point) singularity as well as a finite discontinuity. Mechanically, He II flows through narrow channels with no apparent resistance, as long as a certain critical velocity is not exceeded; it will follow a slowly rotating cylinder only after an extended period. Thermo-mechanically, the heat conductivity of He II is an order of magnitude greater than that of other fluids; a temperature gradient can also be transmitted as a wave with characteristic velocity (second sound). There is a pressure gradient associated with a temperature gradient, leading to the fountain effect; conversely, in the mechano-caloric effect, the He II pushed through a fine capillary is cooled. Finally, the Rollin film which covers the walls of a vessel containing He II depends crucially on Van der Waals adhesion and will not be further considered. For detailed properties of helium II, see London [1], Daunt and Smith [2], and Wilks [3].

A number of metals and metallic alloys show a phase transition of the second kind — a finite discontinuity in the specific heat variation with temperature — at a temperature of a few degrees; at lower temperatures, the specific heat varies as $\exp(-a/T)$. In the superconducting region, below the transition, D.C. electric current not exceeding a certain critical current will flow without apparent resistance and D.C. magnetic fields below a (geometry-independent) critical field will not penetrate the metal beyond a very small depth; at higher frequencies, the normal characteristics of the metal come increasingly into play. A gyromagnetic ratio of unity indicates that the carriers of the superconductivity are electrons without spin coupling; a very small thermal conductivity in the superconducting state, that the electrons responsible do not transfer heat; and a very small thermoelectric coefficient, that they do not possess entropy. On the other hand, the variation of the transition temperature with isotopic mass (proportional to the Debye temperature) for a lattice of fixed composition shows that the lattice interactions are important, and this is emphasized by the marked change in thermodynamic and electromagnetic parameters on straining the lattice or altering the crystal form (Such treatment is prone to produce characteristics intermediate between normal and superconducting, which also occur in various alloys). The lattice structure is nonetheless little different between normal and superconducting states, as verified by X-ray diffraction pattern and heat capacity measurements. For further details, see Shoenberg [4], Von Laue [5], London [6], Kittel [7], and Bardeen [8].

2. Low-Temperature Specific Heat

A free-particle system obeying Einstein-Bose statistics has a low-temperature specific heat which ([1], Chap. C) varies as $T^{\frac{3}{2}}$; the electronic specific heat of the Sommerfeld-Bloch independent-particle model ([7], Chap. 12) for a normal solid is linear in T at low temperatures. On the other hand, the specific heat for He II decreases more rapidly with temperature ([1], Chap. C) as T^3, while that for a superconductor drops very sharply [9], as exp $(-a/T)$. Thus, the low-energy density of levels for the superfluids must be significantly lower than that for the corresponding "normal" cases.

In order to examine the level structure of superfluids in greater detail, we tentatively assume that the ground state may be regarded as a medium through which excitations can propagate independently, with excitation energy spectrum $\varepsilon(\mathbf{k})$ thus far unspecified. This is an independent-particle model insofar as energy is concerned — $E = \Sigma_{\mathbf{k}} \, \mathcal{N}_{\mathbf{k}} \, \varepsilon(\mathbf{k})$ for $\mathcal{N}_{\mathbf{k}}$-fold occupation of state $\mathbf{k}$ — but not for wave functions; we will return to consider the validity of this picture. In the absence of external forces, the effective one-body levels of a uniform many-body system may be indexed by momentum (and any required spin variables); if $\mathbf{k}$ denotes the corresponding wave vector, then for the total momentum, $\mathbf{P} = \Sigma_{\mathbf{k}} \, \mathcal{N}_{\mathbf{k}} \, \hbar\mathbf{k}$. This designation is useful as well for Bloch states in a periodic lattice, and also for a fluid in an ideal box, the pair $\{\mathbf{k}, -\mathbf{k}\}$ then being represented by only one member and a subscript denoting oddness or evenness appended. We now inquire as to the effective one-body excitation spectrum needed to reproduce the observed specific heat at low temperature.

Helium II. For an elementary excitation spectrum, $\varepsilon(\mathbf{k})$, the occupation-number distribution of an independent $\mathcal{N}$-particle Einstein-Bose system at temperature T is given by [10]

$$\mathcal{N}_k = 1/[A \, e^{\beta \varepsilon(\mathbf{k})} - 1] \qquad \beta = 1/kT \tag{1}$$

where A is determined by the normalization condition

$$\sum_k 1/[A \, e^{\beta \varepsilon(\mathbf{k})} - 1] = \mathcal{N} \tag{2}$$

Taking $\varepsilon(\mathbf{k})$ as the excitation energy from the ground state, we have

$\varepsilon(0) = 0$; at low temperature the preponderant occupation is at $\mathbf{k} = 0$, and A is then very close to unity. Separating out the $\mathbf{k} = 0$ contribution, and converting the remaining $\mathbf{k}$ summation to integration, (2) becomes

$$1/(A - 1) + (\Omega/2\pi^2) \int_0^\infty k^2/[e^{\beta\varepsilon(\mathbf{k})} - 1] \, dk = \mathcal{N} \tag{3}$$

where Ω is the system volume and $\varepsilon(\mathbf{k})$ is assumed to be isotropic. Similarly, the mean energy per particle is clearly

$$\bar{E} = (1/2\pi^2)(\Omega/\mathcal{N}) \int_0^\infty k^2 \, \varepsilon(\mathbf{k})/[e^{\beta\varepsilon(\mathbf{k})} - 1] \, dk \tag{4}$$

as if the excitations were separately occupied since, at low temperature, any total occupation for $k > 0$ is available — the $\mathbf{k} = 0$, $\varepsilon = 0$ state takes up the slack. The free energy $\bar{F} = \beta^{-1} \int_\beta^\infty \bar{E} \, d\beta$ and specific heat per particle $\bar{C}_v = -k\beta^2 \, \partial\bar{E}/\partial\beta$ are then

$$\bar{F} = (\Omega/2\pi^2\mathcal{N}\beta) \int_0^\infty \ln [1 - e^{-\beta\varepsilon(\mathbf{k})}] k^2 \, dk$$

$$\bar{C}_v = (k\beta^2\Omega/2\pi^2\mathcal{N}) \int_0^\infty [e^{\beta\varepsilon(\mathbf{k})} - 1]^{-2}\varepsilon(\mathbf{k}) \, e^{\beta\varepsilon(\mathbf{k})} \, k^2 \, dk \tag{5}$$

Neglecting 1 as small compared to $e^{\beta\varepsilon(\mathbf{k})}$, while not exact even in the $T \to 0$ limit, is often an excellent approximation in this limit.

Now we have noted that the specific heat of the Einstein-Bose fluid He⁴ varies as T^3 for low T. Inserting $\varepsilon(\mathbf{k}) \propto k^a$ for small k in (5), we find at once that $\bar{C}_v \propto \beta^{-3/a} \propto T^{3/a}$, and conclude that the specific heat of He⁴ is consistent with a particle excitation spectrum $\varepsilon(\mathbf{k}) \propto k$ for small k. We shall write

$$\varepsilon(\mathbf{k}) = \hbar \, c \, k \tag{6}$$

and, evaluating (5) as $\bar{C}_v = (2\pi^2k/15)(\Omega/\mathcal{N})(kT/\hbar c)^3$, then find experimentally that $c = 2.4 \times 10^4$ cm/sec. $c = d\varepsilon(k)/\hbar dk$ should also be the group velocity for a packet of low wave vector excitations.

Bose Condensation. At sufficiently high temperature, eqs. (2), (3) can no longer be satisfied by infinitesimal $A - 1$, and the principal occupation of the $\mathbf{k} = 0$ state disappears. Thermodynamic parameters are not all continuous at this point, and it is reasonable to identify the He II – He I transition at 2.18°K --- not an ordinary change of state — as such an Einstein-Bose condensation. According to (3), $\mathcal{N}_0 = (A - 1)^{-1}$ falls to zero (to relative order $1/\mathcal{N}$) at the critical temperature T_c determined by

$$\int_0^\infty k^2 \, dk / [e^{\beta_c \varepsilon(\mathbf{k})} - 1] = 2\pi^2 \mathcal{N}/\Omega \tag{7}$$

If (6) is to be maintained for high $\mathbf{k}$ as well, then, employing (7), we obtain $kT_c = \hbar c[\pi^2/\zeta(3)]^{\frac{1}{3}}(\mathcal{N}/\Omega)^{\frac{1}{3}}$ or $T_c = 10.3°K$. Thus, the $\varepsilon(\mathbf{k})$ curve must fall substantially below eq. (6) for $\hbar c k \sim 10°K$; in fact, a "normal" spectrum in this region, $\varepsilon(\mathbf{k}) = \hbar^2 k^2/2m^*$ with $m^* \sim 1.5 \, m_{\mathrm{He}}$, does produce the correct value of T_c. The corresponding rapid rise of energy-level density with k must also be manifested by a more rapid rise in specific heat, and this is experimentally observed.

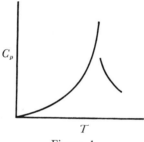

Figure 1

If one examines details of the He II – He I transition, the pure elementary-excitation picture must nonetheless appear naive. At the very least, excitation energies in a ground state medium will depend on how much of the medium remains available, that is, on the unexcited density $\mathcal{N}_0/\Omega : \varepsilon(\mathbf{k}; \mathcal{N}_0/\Omega)$. In the opposite limit, there will be effects of coherent saturation of amplitudes, $\varepsilon(\mathbf{k}; \mathcal{N}_k)$, and, in particular, modes which cannot be excited many times. Finally, there is the intermediate region in which $\varepsilon(\mathbf{k})$ depends separately upon so many other $\mathcal{N}_{k'}$ that the concept of independent excitations fails completely. Of course, there may also be several classes $\varepsilon_\gamma(\mathbf{k})$ of excitations of wave vector $\mathbf{k}$, although they are not distinguishable in the energy-level density

$$\mathcal{N}(\varepsilon) = \sum_\gamma (\Omega/2\pi^2) k^2 \, |dk/d\varepsilon_\gamma| \tag{8}$$

which, even for $\varepsilon(\mathbf{k}; \mathcal{N}_0/\Omega)$, is all that is relevant to thermodynamic evaluations, and to many dynamic quantities as well. The equivalent single spectrum may in various regions of $\mathbf{k}$ bear little resemblance to the component $\varepsilon(\mathbf{k})$ curves.

The specific heat C_v just below T_c is a sensitive indicator of the required spectrum. Experimentally (see Buckingham, Chap. XXVII), there is a $\ln (T_c - T)$ singularity in specific heat at vapor pressure, and hence essentially in C_p. For an ideal condensed Einstein-Bose system, pressure is a function of T alone, so that C_p cannot be defined; but C_v can. The C_p singularity (always crucially dependent upon the equation of state) appears to be mirrored by one of the same form $\ln (T_c - T)$ in α, the coefficient of thermal expansion [11], so that, the adiabatic compressibility κ_s being related to the nonsingular sound velocity,

$$C_v = C_p/[1 + (\alpha^2 T \Omega/\kappa_s C_p)] \qquad (9)$$

is nonsingular as T approaches T_c. However, $\partial C_v/\partial T$ is then singular, and the discontinuity in C_v at T_c equal to that of C_p. Now, assuming an elementary spectrum, $-\partial(\beta^2 \bar{C}_v)/\partial\beta \propto \int \varepsilon^2 e^{\beta\varepsilon} (e^{\beta\varepsilon}+1)(e^{\beta\varepsilon}-1)^{-3} k^2 dk$ cannot be singular at β_c for a system which also exists at $\beta < \beta_c$; further, one can then show in general that a discontinuity $\bar{C}_v{}^{\mathrm{II}} - \bar{C}_v{}^{\mathrm{I}} \sim k[\beta_c \bar{E}(\beta_c)]^2$ exists at the transition, and this is wrong by a factor of 5.

A fixed elementary-excitation spectrum is thus not acceptable. Since the "underlying density" $\mathcal{N}_0/\Omega$ is changing rapidly at the transition, the modification $\varepsilon(\mathbf{k}; \mathcal{N}_0/\Omega)$, coupled with the "ground state energy" $E_0(\mathcal{N}_0/\Omega)$, is suggested [12]. The parameter A is no longer required to count the unoccupied states and so eqs. (2, 3) are replaced by

$$(\Omega/2\pi^2) \int_0^\infty [A(\beta, \mathcal{N}_0) \, e^{\beta\varepsilon(\mathbf{k}, N_0)} - 1]^{-1} k^2 \, dk = \mathcal{N} - \mathcal{N}_0 \qquad (2')$$

to determine $A(\beta, \mathcal{N}_0)$. The free energy per particle becomes

$$\bar{F} = \bar{E}_0(\mathcal{N}_0) + (\Omega/2\pi^2 \mathcal{N}\beta) \int_0^\infty \ln [1 - e^{-\beta\varepsilon(\mathbf{k}, N_0)}/A(\beta, \mathcal{N}_0)] k^2 \, dk \qquad (5')$$

and the equilibrium value of $\mathcal{N}_0$ at temperature $T = 1/k\beta$ is then obtained from $\partial \bar{F}/\partial \mathcal{N}_0 = 0$, or

$$-(\mathcal{N}-\mathcal{N}_0/\beta)\,\partial\ln A/\partial\mathcal{N}_0$$
$$= \partial E_0/\partial\mathcal{N}_0 + (\Omega/2\pi^2)\int_0^\infty (Ae^{\beta\varepsilon}-1)^{-1}(\partial\varepsilon/\partial\mathcal{N}_0)\,k^2\,dk \qquad (10)$$

Although a detailed analysis of (2′), (5′), (10) is not easy, one qualitative remark is surely pertinent, and this is that by controlling the variation of $\mathcal{N}_0$ with β, one can impart an almost arbitrary temperature dependence (via $\mathcal{N}_0(\beta)$) to the spectrum. Thus, any desired singularity in the vicinity of T_c should be available. Further, if the temperature dependence of the effective spectrum $\varepsilon(\mathbf{k}) + \beta^{-1}A$ (note the gap) and base energy E_0 is regarded as known, [e.g., from eqs. (2′), (5′), (10)] all statistical thermodynamic computations proceed as in (1) – (5).

Of course, no theoretically derived spectrum does yield the observed specific heat singularity. Moreover, for $T > T_c$, $\mathcal{N}_0/\Omega$ is fixed at zero, so that the behavior is again that of independent excitations, and hence unsatisfactory. The independence of excitations must be further destroyed, low modes be required or non-linear excitation introduced, or both. But this reminds one of the problem of normal fluids, and it is a fine place to stop.

Superconductors. The electron fluid in a superconductor constitutes a Fermi-Dirac system. Although the lattice interaction is spatially anchored, we may still index the single-particle type of excitations by momentum $\mathbf{k}$, in the manner of Bloch states [13]. Now if the energy increases monotonically with $\mathbf{k}$, and if the effect of lattice anisotropy is neglected [ordinarily a dangerous assumption, as in the case of alkaline earth conductivity (see [7], p. 261), but presumably not crucial in comparing normal and superconductors], then, with two-fold spin degeneracy, the system's ground state ($T = 0°$) has all levels occupied for $k \leq k_f$, and none beyond, where

$$(\Omega/\pi^2)\int_0^{k_f} k^2\,dk = \mathcal{N} \qquad (11)$$

It is then convenient to designate excitations by electrons — states with $k > k_f$, $\varepsilon(\mathbf{k})$ being defined with respect to the ground state Fermi energy $\varepsilon_f = \varepsilon(k_f)$, and holes — missing states with $k \leq k_f$, $\varepsilon(\mathbf{k})$ being defined as the positive energy distance to ε_f.

The occupation-number distribution at temperature T for the states so defined is

$$\mathcal{N}_{\mathbf{k}} = 2/\{1 + \exp \beta[\varepsilon(\mathbf{k}) \mp \varepsilon_f(T)]\} \tag{12}$$

the upper sign for electrons, the lower for holes, where the temperature-dependent Fermi energy $\varepsilon_f(T)$ is determined by the normalization condition that the total number of electrons and holes be the same:

$$\int_0^{k_f} k^2/\{1 + \exp \beta[\varepsilon(\mathbf{k}) + \varepsilon_f]\}\, dk = \int_{k_f}^{\infty} k^2/\{1 + \exp \beta[\varepsilon(\mathbf{k}) - \varepsilon_f]\}\, dk \tag{13}$$

Further, the mean energy per particle (above ground state) is clearly

$$\bar{E}(T) = (\Omega/N\pi^2) \int_0^{k_f} \varepsilon(\mathbf{k}) k^2/\{1 + \exp \beta[\varepsilon(\mathbf{k}) + \varepsilon_f]\}\, dk$$
$$+ (\Omega/N\pi^2) \int_{k_f}^{\infty} \varepsilon(\mathbf{k}) k^2/\{1 + \exp \beta[\varepsilon(\mathbf{k}) - \varepsilon]\}\, dk \tag{14}$$

where now $\varepsilon_f \equiv \varepsilon_f(T)$. As the temperature is raised from absolute zero, the states for $k > k_f$ become excited, but it is readily seen that if the density of states at k_f is neither zero nor infinite (the same holding for the slope of the ε versus k curve), then only the density of states at k_f enters into, e.g., the initial specific heat [14]. For an anomalously low specific heat, one therefore expects $d\varepsilon/dk = \infty$ at k_f; the greatest effect is obtained by having a discontinuous jump in energy, say from $-\frac{1}{2}\varDelta$ to $\frac{1}{2}\varDelta$ at k_f, which is equivalent to a gap in the density of elementary excitations as a function of energy.

For a discontinuity of $\varDelta$ at k_f, if we assume that $-\frac{1}{2}\varDelta < \varepsilon_f(T) < \frac{1}{2}\varDelta$, then at low temperatures (high β), the exponentials in (11) are dominant, so that we can solve at once for $\varepsilon_f(T)$:

$$e^{\beta \varepsilon_f(T)} = \left[\int_0^{k_f} k^2\, e^{-\beta \varepsilon(k)}\, dk \Big/ \int_{k_f}^{\infty} k^2\, e^{-\beta \varepsilon(k)}\, dk \right]^{\frac{1}{2}} \tag{15}$$

thereby validating the assumption. Inserting (15) into (14), with the same assumptions, and using only the boundary values $-\frac{1}{2}\varDelta$ and $\frac{1}{2}\varDelta$ for ε, we obtain

$$e^{\frac{1}{2}\beta\varDelta}\bar{E}(T) = (\Omega/N\pi^2)\varDelta \left[\int_0^{k_f} k^2\, e^{-\beta(\varepsilon(\mathbf{k}) - \frac{1}{2}\varDelta)}\, dk \int_{k_f}^{\infty} k^2\, e^{-\beta(\varepsilon(\mathbf{k}) - \frac{1}{2}\varDelta)}\, dk \right]^{\frac{1}{2}} \tag{14'}$$

Thus $\bar{E}$, and hence $\bar{C}_v$, have the desired exponential dependence, $\exp\left(-\frac{1}{2}\beta\varDelta\right)$, in addition to some undetermined form factors.

Superconducting Transition. At the critical temperature, marking the shift from the normally conducting to the superconducting phase, there is, experimentally, a second-order transition — continuous entropy but discontinuous specific heat. It is once more easy to see that, although the effect of the energy gap will certainly not be strong at $kT \sim \varDelta$, a specific-heat singularity is incompatible with a

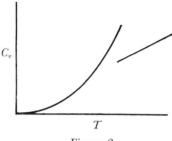

Figure 2

fixed elementary excitation spectrum. Now the transition appears rather like a typical order-disorder transition [15] (the fact that He II – He I resembles the special case of a two-dimensional Ising model [16] more is neither amazing nor, at this stage, understandable) and this suggests a cause for non-independence of excitations. The highly ordered structure necessary to maintain a gap above the ground state sea will suffer interference from any excitations present, so that the gap (and with it the remaining spectrum) should be a decreasing function of the level of excitation. In a statistical state, the excitation level $[\varSigma \mathcal{N}_\mathbf{k} \text{ (hole)} + \varSigma \mathcal{N}_\mathbf{k} \text{ (electron)}]$ will be a sharply defined function of temperature [analyzed as in $(2')$, $(3')$, (10)], and hence the gap will be as well; when $\varDelta(T)$ falls to zero, the normal phase sets in.

The concept of a temperature-dependent gap may seem strange at first, but is a consequence of the dependence of the gap upon total excitation, which is then averaged over in a statistical state. It is valid for non-thermodynamic processes as well, such as photon absorption, because of the sharpness of the excitation level in a statistical state. Once more, there are no computational difficulties as long as the spectrum at each temperature is known.

3. *Dissipationless Flow in He II*

While it is true that there is a very low density of states (rapid rise of energy with wave number) near the ground state of a superfluid, one can without rising too far in energy uncover many classes of states, each class having a low state density above its own ground state; the superfluidity properties arise to a large extent from the difficulty of making transitions from one class to another. Let us catalog the states that exist more carefully, confining our attention to low temperature and hence to temperature-independent spectra.

Excitation Structure. As has been indicated from specific heat data, the low-wave-number excitations in He^4 have a constant group velocity $\partial\varepsilon(\mathbf{k})/\partial\hbar k = c$, and are clearly consistent with an ordinary density fluctuation or phonon interpretation. At intermediate wave

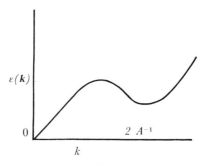

Figure 3

numbers, the specific heat indicates [17] a minimum in the $\varepsilon - k$ curve, and this has been validated experimentally [18] by direct excitation by cold neutrons. The corresponding quanta, denoted "rotons" by Landau, may probably be interpreted, on the basis of work by Feynman and Cohen [19], as symmetrized moving atoms, each surrounded by a dipole velocity counterflow in the surrounding medium. For still higher wave numbers, the fluid presumably having no time to adjust to a high-velocity atom shooting through, the latter is surrounded by a cloud of comoving atoms; hence an effective-mass excitation structure $\varepsilon = \hbar^2 k^2/2m^*$ might be expected. An exact stationary state of this kind (if it exists at all) would be a very complex object, with counterflow and boundary reflections delicately adjusted to keep it stationary and would be impossible to prepare. In practice, approximate stationary excitations above phonons will rapidly decay under the residual interactions into kinematically available lower modes.

There also exist states of bulk motion, of high energy compared with phonons but low ratio of energy to momentum (which may not be diagonal), and which are incapable of being excited more than once. They are quite analogous to electronic levels of molecules, as opposed to vibrational excitations, and also come with qualitatively different selection rules. An interactionless system serves as the prototype, and these states are then simply formed

$$\psi = \prod_i \chi(\mathbf{x}_i) \tag{16}$$

as product states, where χ satisfies the one-body Schrödinger equation. Equation (16) describes a completely correlated motion, in which all particles follow exactly in step. It is a primitive hydrodynamic state, and, defining local velocity and mass density as usual by

$$\mathbf{u}(\mathbf{x}) = \mathrm{Re} \left\langle \sum \delta(\mathbf{x} - \mathbf{x}_j)\mathbf{p}_j/m \right\rangle / \left\langle \sum \delta(\mathbf{x} - \mathbf{x}_j) \right\rangle$$
$$\rho(\mathbf{x}) = m \left\langle \sum \delta(\mathbf{x} - \mathbf{x}_j) \right\rangle \tag{17}$$

we see that if χ is normalized,

$$\mathbf{u}(\mathbf{x}) = (\hbar/m) \, \mathrm{Im} \, (\nabla\chi(\mathbf{x})/\chi(\mathbf{x})) \tag{18a}$$

$$\rho(\mathbf{x}) = \mathcal{N} m \, |\chi(\mathbf{x})|^2 \tag{18b}$$

Assuming the one-body equation $i\hbar\dot{\chi} = -(\hbar^2/2m)\nabla^2\chi + V\chi$, the mass and momentum conservation laws

$$\dot{\rho} + \nabla \cdot (\rho\mathbf{u}) = 0$$
$$\dot{\mathbf{u}} + \mathbf{u} \cdot \nabla\mathbf{u} + (1/m)\nabla[V - \rho^{-\frac{1}{2}}(\hbar^2/2m)\nabla^2\rho^{\frac{1}{2}}] = 0 \tag{19}$$

readily follow; $-\rho^{-\frac{1}{2}}(\hbar^2/2m)\nabla^2\rho^{\frac{1}{2}}$ is an effective quantum mechanical potential (tending to explode any localization of density).

The flow pattern for (16) is characterized by its infinite singularities, and these, according to (18), correspond to the nodes of χ. The basic nonsingular flow is given by $\chi = e^{i\mathbf{k}\cdot\mathbf{x}}$, whence $\mathbf{u} = \hbar\mathbf{k}/m$, a "moving state" of uniform velocity. If Re (χ) and Im (χ) vanish simultaneously at only a point, a point singularity in the flow appears; in the absence of symmetry, this is an exceptional case, as is that of a stagnation point, $\mathbf{u} = 0$. But Re (χ) and Im (χ) will usually vanish together on a line. The standard line singularity is a vortex, typefied by a local dependence $\chi = x + iy$, leading to $\mathbf{u} = (\hbar/m)(-y, x, 0)/(x^2 + y^2)$ $= (\hbar/m)\hat{\varphi}/r$; for example, a free-particle wave function $\sin k_0 x + i \sin k_0 y$ in a periodic box produces a quartet of vortices. Since $\rho \propto x^2 + y^2$, the fluid kinetic energy remains finite. Infinitely rapid oscillations can also yield a line singularity without vorticity, e.g., $\chi = \exp [i(x^2 + y^2)^{-1}]$ implies $\mathbf{u} \propto (x, y, 0)/(x^2 + y^2)^2$, but these will not be of interest. Finally, surface singularities do not occur, but nulls do, either at real boundary surfaces or internal stagnation surfaces.

If one linearizes the motion (19) about $\mathbf{u} = 0$, $\rho = $ constant, (with $V = 0$), the wave equation $\ddot{\rho} + (\hbar\nabla^2/2m)^2\rho = 0$, and similarly for $\mathbf{u}$, is easily obtained. The elementary solutions yield $\chi = 1 + Ae^{i\mathbf{k}\cdot\mathbf{x}} e^{-i\omega_{\mathbf{k}} t}$, where $\hbar\omega_{\mathbf{k}} = \hbar^2 k^2/2m$, and the leading term of $\psi = \prod \chi(\mathbf{x}_j)$ is $\exp (Aq_{\mathbf{k}} e^{-i\omega_{\mathbf{k}} t})$, where $q_{\mathbf{k}} = \sum e^{i\mathbf{k}\cdot\mathbf{x}_j}$, suggesting an interpretation of ψ as a packet of what pass here for phonons. But "phonon" excitations can occur separately as well here. Indeed, based on any hydrodynamic state, we can construct a band of states with superimposed phonon excitations; for, considering the independent particles, it is only necessary to multiply the hydrodynamic and phonon wave functions. At first sight, the bands appear to join, since, e.g., the uniform translation $\psi = \prod e^{i\mathbf{k}\cdot\mathbf{x}_j}$ is just the result of exciting a $\mathbf{k}$ phonon N times. However, such N-fold excitation of a real fluid is highly artificial; the qualitative nature of the state, and the whole concept of independence of phonons, is distinctly altered before any amplitude approaches even a fraction of full saturation. Thus, the various moving states are certainly in qualitatively distinct bands.

Hydrodynamic Modes. We proceed to examine the hydrodynamic modes of the real fluid He II. For the purpose of orientation, consider first a uniformly moving state. Let ψ be an eigenstate of energy E and total momentum $\mathbf{P}$ in a direction in which the helium, including any boundary constraints, is translationally invariant. We may impart a momentum $\hbar\mathbf{s}$ (in a similar direction) to each particle by a change of reference frame:

$$\psi' = \exp(i\mathbf{s} \cdot \textstyle\sum \mathbf{x}_j)\psi \tag{20}$$

Since $\exp(-i\mathbf{s} \cdot \sum \mathbf{x}_j)\,\mathbf{p}_i \exp(i\mathbf{s} \cdot \sum \mathbf{x}_j) = \mathbf{p}_i + \hbar\mathbf{s}$ (a simple Galilean transformation), and $H = \sum p_i^2/2m + V(\ldots \mathbf{x}_j \ldots)$, the energy and momentum of ψ and ψ' are related by

$$E' = E - P^2/2m\mathcal{N} + (\mathbf{P} + \mathcal{N}\hbar\mathbf{s})^2/2m\mathcal{N}$$
$$\mathbf{P}' = \mathbf{P} + \mathcal{N}\hbar\mathbf{s} \tag{21}$$

The probability densities of ψ and ψ' are identical.

Determining the moving frame of a moving state is easy if we recall that a free Einstein-Bose system below condensation is characterized by a finite fraction of particles occupying the single momentum state $\mathbf{k} = 0$; thus the moving wave vector of a moving state is that of its most populous excitation. Similarly, a condensation in momentum space may be used [20] to define interacting condensed Einstein-Bose systems in any frame. It is to be noted that the proper descriptive analogue is a free system, not, for example a strongly coupled system. In the latter one can readily and uniquely separate the center of mass mode from the oscillating modes, only to find [21] that the oscillating modes all have zero momentum (the difference is crucial — a Boson solid at low temperature is not a superfluid — e.g., it resists the passage of a slow projectile).

The generalization of the moving state (20) to a more complex flow is clear from (16). Restricting one's attention to unexcited phonons, and setting $\chi = e^{i\lambda}$, it is

$$\psi'_0 = \exp[i \textstyle\sum \lambda(\mathbf{x}_j)]\psi_0 \tag{22}$$

where ψ_0 is the absolute ground state. This may validly be regarded as a position-dependent moving state if there is no variation within a typical correlation distance. Correspondingly, if $\mathrm{Im}\,(\lambda) = 0$ asymptotically, the normalization factor for (22) is approximately $\exp(\tfrac{1}{2}\Delta)$, where Δ is the number of particles missing at density nodes. Relation (18a), expressed as $\mathbf{u} = \hbar/m\,\mathrm{Re}\,(\nabla\lambda)$, is still valid, but there is no simple form for ρ. Now, ψ'_0 of (22), to the extent that it is a true state, is *not* characterized by a unique condensation momentum.

To see whether (22) satisfies the dynamic Schrödinger equation $i\hbar\dot\psi_0' = [\sum p_i^2/2m + V(\ldots \mathbf{x}_j \ldots)]\psi_0'$, we have on inserting (22) and realizing that ψ_0 is itself a solution,

$$-\hbar \sum \dot\lambda(\mathbf{x}_i)\psi_0 = (\hbar^2/2m) \sum \nabla \lambda(\mathbf{x}_i) \cdot \nabla\lambda(\mathbf{x}_i)$$
$$+ (\hbar/2m) \sum [\nabla\lambda(\mathbf{x}_i) \cdot \mathbf{p}_i\psi_0 + \mathbf{p}_i \cdot (\nabla\lambda(\mathbf{x}_i)\psi_0] \tag{23}$$

Two assumptions are now required. First is that (see Chap. XIII) the (phonon) excitations of a Boson system, at least for low wave vector, correspond to harmonic oscillations of the density Fourier components $q_\mathbf{k} \equiv \sum \exp i\mathbf{k} \cdot \mathbf{x}_i$. For frequency $\omega_k = \varepsilon(\mathbf{k})/\hbar$, the ground state is then specified [22] by $(\dot q_{-\mathbf{k}} - i\omega_\mathbf{k} q_{-\mathbf{k}})\psi_0 = 0$, or since $\dot q_\mathbf{k} = (i/\hbar)[H, q_\mathbf{k}]$ where $H = \sum p_i^2/2m + V$, by

$$(\hbar/2m) \sum(\mathbf{k} \cdot \mathbf{p}_i \, e^{i\mathbf{k} \cdot \mathbf{x}_i} + e^{i\mathbf{k} \cdot \mathbf{x}_i} \mathbf{k} \cdot \mathbf{p}_i)\psi_0 = \varepsilon(\mathbf{k}) \sum e^{i\mathbf{k} \cdot \mathbf{x}_i} \psi_0 \tag{24}$$

Secondly, the ground state, having no viscosity, cannot support shear modes, so that the transverse wave momenta $\pi_\mathbf{k}^T \equiv \sum \exp(i\mathbf{k} \cdot \mathbf{x}_i)\mathbf{k} \times \mathbf{p}_i$ must vanish. Thus $\pi_k^T \psi_0 = 0$, and (24) generalizes to

$$(\hbar/2m) \sum (\mathbf{p}_i \, e^{i\mathbf{k} \cdot \mathbf{x}_i} + e^{i\mathbf{k} \cdot \mathbf{x}_i} \mathbf{p}_i)\psi_0 = -i(\varepsilon(\mathbf{k})/k^2) \sum (\nabla_i \, e^{i\mathbf{k} \cdot \mathbf{x}_i})\psi_0 \tag{24'}$$

Equations (24'), it may be noted, are self-consistent only for sufficiently low $\mathbf{k}$ or in the special case $\varepsilon(\mathbf{k}) \propto k^2$. Now if $\mathbf{f}$ contains low enough wave vectors, it follows from (24') that

$$\sum (\mathbf{p}_i \cdot \mathbf{f}(\mathbf{x}_i) + \mathbf{f}(\mathbf{x}_i) \cdot \mathbf{p}_i)\psi_0 = (\hbar/i) \sum \int G(\mathbf{x}_i - \mathbf{y})\nabla \cdot \mathbf{f}(\mathbf{y}) \, dy^3 \, \psi_0$$
$$\text{where} \quad G(\mathbf{x}) = \sum_{k \neq 0} (2m\varepsilon(\mathbf{k})/\hbar^2 k^2 \Omega) \, e^{i\mathbf{k} \cdot \mathbf{x}} \tag{25}$$

the $\mathbf{k} = 0$ contribution vanishing because $\sum \mathbf{p}_i\psi_0 = 0$. Employing (25) in (23), the factor ψ_0 separates out, and the same equation

$$\dot\lambda + (\hbar/2m)(\nabla\lambda)^2 - (\hbar/2m)iG(\nabla^2\lambda) = 0 \tag{26}$$

results for each i; G denotes the integral operator $\int G(\mathbf{x} - \mathbf{y})(\quad) d^3y$. Thus a hydrodynamic mode exists for any λ satisfying (26). To interpret (26), set $\lambda = (m/\hbar)\varphi - \frac{1}{2}i \ln \bar\rho$ for real φ, $\bar\rho$, and define $\mathbf{u} = \nabla\varphi$; we thus obtain

$$\dot{\bar\rho} + \mathbf{u} \cdot \nabla\bar\rho + \bar\rho G(\nabla \cdot \mathbf{u}) = 0 \tag{27a}$$

$$\dot{\varphi} + \tfrac{1}{2}u^2 = (\hbar^2/8m^2)(\nabla \ln \bar\rho)^2 + (\hbar^2/4m^2)G(\nabla^2 \ln \bar\rho) \qquad (27\text{b})$$

or $\quad \dot{\mathbf{u}} + \mathbf{u}\cdot\nabla\mathbf{u} - (\hbar^2/4m^2)\nabla[\tfrac{1}{2}(\nabla \ln \bar\rho)^2 + G(\nabla^2 \ln \bar\rho)] = 0 \qquad (27\text{c})$

which is clearly the generalization of the flow pattern of (19) (for no interaction, $G = 1$ except when operating on constants). $\bar\rho$ is only related to the density, and it may be shown that for small deviations from uniformity, the identification of (27a) as a mass conservation equation requires $\varepsilon(\mathbf{k}) = (\hbar^2/2m)(k^2/1 + \mathcal{N}\sigma_{\mathbf{k}})$, where σ is the two-body distribution function; the significance of this remark will appear in Sec. 7. Although hydrodynamic distributions cannot in general be superposed, this does become possible when they are orthogonal, $\nabla\lambda_1 \cdot \nabla\lambda_2 = 0$, as seen from (26).

The classification of hydrodynamic modes proceeds just as in the interactionless case, with the correspondence $\chi = \exp i\lambda = [\exp i(m/\hbar)\varphi]\bar\rho^{\frac{1}{2}}$. A single-valued velocity potential φ necessarily produces a curl-free velocity field, an instance of which is the oscillating packet $\lambda = Ae^{i\mathbf{k}\cdot\mathbf{x}}e^{-i\omega_{\mathbf{k}}t}$ with $\hbar\omega_{\mathbf{k}} = \varepsilon(\mathbf{k})$. A line of multivaluedness, which must be a multiple of h/m, gives rise to a vortex of strength quantized in units of h/m; the density field for the system with interaction of course recovers its uniform value quite rapidly. There are bounding surfaces as well. For a stationary state of energy E, clearly $\dot{\varphi} = -(E - E_0/\mathcal{N}m)$. Hence, integrating (27b) over volume,

$$E - E_0 = \mathcal{N}\int[\tfrac{1}{2}mu^2 - (\hbar^2/8m)(\nabla \ln \bar\rho)^2]\,d^3x/\Omega \qquad (28)$$

is divided into kinetic and redistributed density contributions; on the other hand, by the methods of eqs. (57, 58) one readily finds $E - E_0 = \tfrac{1}{2}\int\rho\,[u^2 + (\hbar^2/4m^2)(\nabla \ln\bar\rho)^2]\,d^3x$. The energies, corresponding to a simultaneous correlated motion of all particles, are typically multiples of $\mathcal{N}(h^2/\Omega^{\frac{2}{3}})/2m$, and their approximate "excitation," by linear multiplication of each velocity, produces a quadratic mode-number dependence, while their juxtaposition in space, if possible, is linear in mode number. Feynman speculates [24] that lower energy entities such as ring vortices may exist and correspond to roton states.

At any rate there is clearly an immense number of hydrodynamic states available, while (Fig. 4) each class will have a low associated density of states; the counting process is quite simple in the prototype case of interactionless particles. Thermodynamically, their high energy precludes their importance at low temperature, but they may play a major role in the form of the He II – He I transition and in He I.

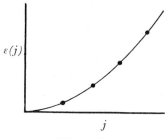

$\varepsilon(j)$

j

Figure 4

Externally Produced Transitions. Suppose one sets up a moving state with low velocity inside a narrow (say $< 10^{-3}$ cm) tube or channel; even neglecting end effects, as we shall, the motion of an ordinary fluid will soon be damped out by wall interactions. The situation is dramatically different for He II below a certain critical velocity. Dimensionally, there are two obvious velocities available, h/md and h/mb, where b is a channel dimension and d an atomic spacing; both will enter our discussion. For simplicity, we shall assume $T = 0^0$, and hence consider the possible degradation of a moving ground state. In analogy with the onset of turbulence in normal fluids, eq. (26), with its omission of viscosity and boundary layer effects, is probably incapable of eliciting the dynamics of this situation. We therefore ask the simpler question: When is it *possible* for energy degradation to result from a wall interaction?

Consider first a transition to a final state in which the moving velocity **v** is maintained, an energy decrease resulting from reversed momentum excitations. From (21), if a state of energy ΔE, momentum $\Delta \mathbf{P}$ (in a direction of translation invariance) with respect to the ground state is moved at velocity **v**, its energy with respect to the corresponding moving ground state is

$$\Delta E' = \Delta E + \mathbf{v} \cdot \Delta \mathbf{P} \qquad (29)$$

Hence an energy decrease $\Delta E' < 0$ can occur only if

$$v > \Delta E/\Delta P \qquad (30)$$

For independent excitations, $\Delta E/\Delta P = \Sigma N_k \varepsilon(\mathbf{k})/|\Sigma N_k \hbar \mathbf{k}|$ equals or exceeds the lowest value of $\varepsilon(\mathbf{k})/\hbar k$, so that energy can be transferred only if $\varepsilon(\mathbf{k})/\hbar k < v$ for some $\mathbf{k}$. But for phonons, $\varepsilon(\mathbf{k})/\hbar k = c(\sim \hbar/md) = 240$ m/sec; and even in the roton region, $\varepsilon(\mathbf{k})/\hbar k > 70$ m/sec. There is then no mechanism in the spectrum of Fig. (3) for disturbing "superflow" below the very large velocity of 70 m/sec.

Surely one can alter the motion of He II — a piston or the force of gravity are quite effective. But these involve a change of hydrodynamic mode, and we can disregard phonon excitation. Although the stationary states of (22) are not in general eigenstates of total momentum, $\mathbf{P} = \Sigma \mathbf{p}_i$, their projections

$$(1/\Omega)\int e^{-i\mathbf{y}\cdot\mathbf{P}} \exp\left[i\Sigma \lambda(\mathbf{x}_j + \mathbf{y})\right] d^3y \, \psi_0 \qquad (31)$$

onto momentum $\mathbf{P}$ in any direction of translation invariance are again energy eigenstates, unless we are trying to extract more detail than is built into the approximation. These states may be regarded as distant branches of Fig. (3). Now we know that the energy of such a mode is $\Delta E \sim \int \frac{1}{2}\rho u^2 \, d^3x$; to estimate the maximum momentum, one may integrate the magnitude of $\mathbf{v}$-component momentum elements (as if they were all lined up). Hence (30) becomes

$$v_{\min} \sim \tfrac{1}{2}\int \rho u^2 \, d^3x / \int \rho \, |u_{\mathbf{v}}| \, d^3x \qquad (32)$$

As a typical case, consider a vortex line of minimum strength h/m formed inside a parallel-plate channel of separation b. Assuming $u_x + iu_y = (ih/mb)$ csc $[\pi(x + iy)/b]$ and stopping density compensation at distance d (of the order of atomic size) from the line, one obtains $\Delta E = (\rho/2\pi)(\hbar/m)^2 \ln (b/d)$, $\Delta P = (\rho/2)(\hbar/m)b$ per unit channel width, and so v is of order h/mb ($\sim$ cm/sec), which is qualitatively verified experimentally without very good quantitative correlation.

If the final state is also permitted a change in moving state velocity, (30) is replaced by $v > (1 + \bar{P}/\Delta P)^{-1}[v_0 + (\bar{P}mN)(1 + \frac{1}{2}\bar{P}/\Delta P)]$, where $\bar{P}$ is the momentum of the "excited" moving state, and $v_0 = \Delta E/\Delta P$. Thus, if $\bar{P}$ is a multiple of ΔP (for a channel of height b and length L, $\bar{P}$ is indeed quantized in units of $N(\hbar 2\pi/L) = \rho(h/m)b$

per unit width), $v_{\min}$ may be substantially reduced, ultimately to the very small value $\sim \frac{1}{2}(\Delta E/mN)^{\frac{1}{2}}$. (The hydrodynamic energy is then reduced to its "internal" value $E - P^2/2mN$ — see, e.g., Penrose [25].) A direct reduction of the initial moving velocity without imposition of further hydrodynamics is even more effective, requiring no minimum velocity. These kinematically allowed transitions will not occur owing to the immense difficulty of producing a correlated many-body alteration via a one-body wall potential (as a typical agent).

The transition matrix element between moving states $(\exp i\mathbf{k}_1 \cdot \sum \mathbf{x}_i)\psi_0$ and $(\exp i(\mathbf{k}_1 - \mathbf{k}) \cdot \sum \mathbf{x}_i)\psi_0$ via wall potential $\sum U(\mathbf{x}_i)$ is clearly $\mathscr{M} = NU_{Nk}\langle\psi_0|\exp (i\mathbf{k} \cdot \sum \mathbf{x}_j) \exp (-iN\mathbf{k} \cdot \mathbf{x}_1)|\psi_0\rangle = NU_{Nk}\langle\psi_0| \exp (-iN\mathbf{k} \cdot \overline{\mathbf{x}}_1)| \psi_0\rangle$ where $\overline{\mathbf{x}}_1$ is the position of $\mathbf{x}_1$ relative to the center of mass. For the high momentum desired, the rest of the particles may be considered uncoupled and their positions then averaged over. As an upper bound to $\mathscr{M}$, we take the reduced $\psi_0^2(\overline{\mathbf{x}}_1)$ as the space between an a-radius (~ 2 Å) sphere in a d-radius (~ 4 Å) hole, and thus obtain $\mathscr{M} \sim 3NU_{Nk} (\sin Nkd - \sin Nka)/[(Nkd^3) - (Nka)^3]$. But even for $k = k_0 = 2\pi/L$, since $N \sim L\mathscr{A}/d^3$, we have $Nkd \sim 2\pi\mathscr{A}/d^2$, the number of particles in a cross-sectional channel area $\mathscr{A}$, and this is a macroscopic quantity $\sim 10^6$. For a potential contribution $\overline{U}$ at each atom of the wall, typically, $N\overline{U}_{Nk} \sim N(N_{\text{wall}})^{\frac{1}{2}} \overline{U}_{Nk} \sim N(N_{\text{wall}})^{\frac{1}{2}} (Nkd)^{-2} \overline{U} \sim (L^2/\mathscr{A})^{\frac{3}{4}} \overline{U}/4\pi^2 \sim 10^3 \overline{U}$. Thus (subject to examination of the final state density) the first-order transition probability is vanishingly small, a situation which is not improved in higher order.

On the other hand, consider a transition in which only the $\mathbf{K} \sim Nk_0 \hat{v}$ component of a vortex mode is excited. Because of the velocity and density singularities there will be a considerable contribution from states in which the hydrodynamic momentum $N\hbar k_0$ is shared among a small number, s, of particles. If the potential factor exp $(-iN\mathbf{k} \cdot \mathbf{x})$ is similarly shared, then for an s-order transition, Nka in the above analysis reverts to a value of unity or less, leading to a non-vanishing transition rate. This situation does not persist if a sufficient part of a moving state (or any pattern with large-scale motion) is so appended that the total momentum cannot be found among a comparatively small number of particles. From the configuration-space point of view, the activating potential is required to contact a large enough fraction of the alteration of the flow pattern. Thus as some mean velocity of (30) or (32) for localized flow patterns is approached, the state density of kinematically available states rises even more rapidly. The resulting turbulent flow encompasses interactions of vortices, phonons, and container, with viscous effects playing an important role in the degeneration of vortices into thermal excitations. A limited amount of locally uniform flow can be transmitted at each interaction, and the end result is inevitably a uniform flow, below the critical velocity, in thermal equilibrium with the container.

4. Persistent Currents in Superconductors

Equivalent Interaction. The forces acting on a superconducting electron fluid are rather more complicated than those relevant to superfluid helium. Our discussion will be facilitated by some preliminary approximations.

The Hamiltonian for a crystal composed of interacting (monatomic) spherical ions $(\mathbf{y}_\alpha, P_\alpha)$ and valence electrons $(\mathbf{x}_i, \mathbf{p}_i)$ may be written as

$$H = \sum p_i^2/2m + \tfrac{1}{2} \sum_{i \neq j} e^2/|\mathbf{x}_i - \mathbf{x}_j| + \sum U(\mathbf{x}_i - \mathbf{y}_\alpha)$$
$$+ \sum P_\alpha^2/2M + \tfrac{1}{2} \sum_{\alpha \neq \beta} W(\mathbf{y}_\alpha - \mathbf{y}_\beta) \qquad (33)$$

where interelectron (Coulomb) and central interionic potentials have been included. For a perfect crystalline state, one may expand each term about the regular lattice positions: $\mathbf{y}_\alpha = \mathbf{y}_\alpha^{(0)} + \mathbf{Y}_\alpha$, to first effective order in the $\mathbf{Y}_\alpha$, and then switch to interactionless normal lattice modes or phonons: $\mathbf{Y}_\alpha = (\mathcal{N}M)^{-\frac{1}{2}} i \sum \mathbf{u}_{s\lambda} q_{s\lambda} \exp(-i\mathbf{s} \cdot \mathbf{y}_\alpha^{(0)})$, the $\mathbf{u}_{s\lambda}$ being polarization vectors. Now if lattice anisotropy is neglected by performing a spherical average over lattice positions, transverse components, $(\mathbf{s} \cdot \mathbf{u}_{s\lambda} = 0)$ of the $q_{s\lambda}$ do not appear in the potential energy. Thus, dropping constant and transverse kinetic energy terms, H becomes

$$H = \sum [p_i^2/2m + V(\mathbf{x}_i)] + \tfrac{1}{2} \sum_{i \neq j} e^2/|\mathbf{x}_i - \mathbf{x}_j|$$
$$+ \tfrac{1}{2} \sum (\pi_s \pi_s^* + w_s^2 q_s q_s^*) + \sum q_s K_{-s}(\mathbf{x}_i) \qquad (34a)$$

where $\quad w_{\mathbf{s}}^2 \equiv M^{-1} \sum_\gamma (1 - \exp i\mathbf{s} \cdot \mathbf{y}_\gamma^{(0)})(\mathbf{s} \cdot \nabla)^2 W(\mathbf{y}_\gamma^{(0)})$

$$V(\mathbf{x}) \equiv \sum_\alpha U(\mathbf{x} - \mathbf{y}_\alpha^{(0)})$$

$$K_{-\mathbf{s}}(\mathbf{x}) \equiv -i(NM)^{-\frac{1}{2}} \sum_\alpha e^{-i\mathbf{s} \cdot \mathbf{y}_\alpha^{(0)}}(\mathbf{s} \cdot \nabla)U(\mathbf{x} - \mathbf{y}_\alpha^{(0)}) \qquad (34b)$$

and $\pi_{\mathbf{s}}$ is conjugate to the longitudinal $q_{\mathbf{s}}$.

If U is regarded as being long-range, the α summation in $K_{\mathbf{s}}$ of (34b) may be replaced by an integration, yielding $K_{-\mathbf{s}}(\mathbf{x}) = s(N/\Omega)(NM^{-\frac{1}{2}})(\int U(\mathbf{y}) e^{-i\mathbf{s} \cdot \mathbf{y}} d^3y) e^{-i\mathbf{s} \cdot \mathbf{x}}$. That is, the umklapp terms of $U(\mathbf{x})$, those involving wave vectors differing from $\mathbf{s}$ by a Bragg vector, are eliminated. If U were really long-range, V of (34b) would become a constant. Actually, V is responsible for the "unperturbed" electron wave functions of $p^2/2m + V(\mathbf{x})$ being Bloch functions $e^{i\mathbf{k} \cdot \mathbf{x}}\varphi_{\mathbf{k}}(\mathbf{x})$ and not pure plane waves, resulting in a strongly modified one-body spectrum $\mathscr{E}(\mathbf{k})$. But $\varphi_{\mathbf{k}}$ has the lattice periodicity and hence is a constant in a coarse-grained fashion. For expectation values and matrix elements of slowly varying quantities, we may therefore replace $\varphi_{\mathbf{k}}$ by 1 and, correspondingly, $p^2/2m + V(\mathbf{x})$ by $\mathscr{E}(\mathbf{p}/\hbar)$. The further interactions may perhaps modify the form of $\mathscr{E}(\mathbf{p}/\hbar)$, viewed self-consistently, and we shall accept such modifications. Equation (34a) now appears as

$$H = \sum \mathscr{E}(\mathbf{p}_i/\hbar) + \tfrac{1}{2} \sum_{i \neq j} e^2/r_{ij}$$
$$+ \tfrac{1}{2} \sum(\pi_{\mathbf{s}}\pi_{\mathbf{s}}^* + w_{\mathbf{s}}^2 q_{\mathbf{s}} q_{\mathbf{s}}^*) + \sum K_{-\mathbf{s}} q_{\mathbf{s}} e^{-i\mathbf{s} \cdot \mathbf{x}_i} \qquad (35)$$
$$K_{\mathbf{s}} = -\mathbf{s}(N/\Omega)(NM)^{-\frac{1}{2}}(\Omega U_{\mathbf{s}})$$

The first two terms of (35) describe the normal solid, if somewhat approximately. The last or phonon interaction term, which would be absent for rigid lattice points, $M = \infty$, must carry the burden of explaining superconductivity.

Finally, there are interactions responsible for resistance to current flow, those in which energy is transferred from electron fluid to lattice by virtue of lattice imperfections (residual resistance), or real scattering of electrons by thermally excited phonons (ideal resistance). The persistance of a current in an superconductor must stem from the impotence of perturbations of this character (which include errors due to our enforcement of translation invariance).

Excitation Structure. The elementary excitation spectrum $\mathscr{E}(\mathbf{k})$ of the independent-particle model is somewhat modified by the influence of Coulomb forces in a normal metal and by high-energy collective modes that are introduced (see Chap. XIII). At low temperatures, the uncoupled phonons of (35) may be taken to be in their ground state, and we have seen that the principal effect of the electron-phonon coupling is to introduce a gap at the Fermi surface, producing a further modified $\varepsilon(\mathbf{k})$. It may be shown on the basis of the approximate theory of Sec. 8 that the creation operators for the canonically redefined (electron plus associated phonon cloud) particles $\mathbf{k}\sigma$, holes $\mathbf{1}\sigma$, and pairs $(\mathbf{k}\sigma, -\mathbf{k} -\sigma)$, $(\mathbf{1}\sigma, -\mathbf{1} -\sigma)$, have the (second-quantized) form

$$a_{\mathbf{k}\sigma}^*, \qquad a_{\mathbf{1}\sigma}, \qquad b_{\mathbf{k}\sigma}^* - b_{\mathbf{k}\sigma}(\mathscr{C}^*)^2, \qquad b_{\mathbf{1}\sigma} - b_{\mathbf{1}\sigma}^* \mathscr{C}^2 \qquad (36)$$

where
$$b_{\mathbf{k}\sigma} \equiv a_{\mathbf{k}\sigma} a_{-\mathbf{k}-\sigma} \qquad \mathscr{C} \equiv \sum \cot \tfrac{1}{2}\theta_{\mathbf{m}\sigma} b_{\mathbf{m}\sigma}$$
$$b_{\mathbf{k}\sigma}^* \equiv a_{-\mathbf{k}-\sigma}^* a_{\mathbf{k}\sigma}^* \qquad \mathscr{C}^* = \sum \tan \tfrac{1}{2}\theta_{\mathbf{m}\sigma} b_{\mathbf{m}\sigma}^*$$

with the ground state (J. M. Blatt, private communication) correspondingly given by $(\mathscr{C}^*)^{\frac{1}{2}N} |0\rangle$.

Since the system (35) is translation invariant, the total momentum $\mathbf{P} = \sum \mathbf{p}_i + \sum \hbar \mathbf{s} q_{\mathbf{s}} \pi_{\mathbf{s}}$ is a constant of the motion. Equally well, the mean current density

$$\mathbf{J} = (-e/\Omega) \sum \dot{\mathbf{x}}_i \qquad (37)$$

is very closely constant, for in $\sum \dot{\mathbf{x}}_i = \sum \nabla \mathscr{E}(\mathbf{p}_i) = \sum \mathbf{p}_i (d\mathscr{E}(\mathbf{p}_i)/p_i \, dp_i)$, the one-body momentum distribution of the states we shall deal with is constant except near the Fermi surface. Thus, $(1/p) \, d\mathscr{E}/dp$ may be evaluated at the Fermi surface; also, the phonon momentum will vanish in states of interest. Now to produce a uniform current, we may construct a moving state, which we similarly approximate. Using precisely the transformation of (20), we have
$H' = \exp(-im\mathbf{v} \cdot \sum \mathbf{x}_i/\hbar) H \exp(im\mathbf{v} \cdot \sum \mathbf{x}_i/\hbar) = H - (i/\hbar)m[\mathbf{v} \cdot \sum \mathbf{x}_i, H]$
$+ \tfrac{1}{2}(i/\hbar)^2 m^2 [\mathbf{v} \cdot \sum \mathbf{x}_i, [\mathbf{v} \cdot \sum \mathbf{x}_i, H]] + \ldots, \mathbf{J}' = \mathbf{J} - (i/\hbar)m[\mathbf{v} \cdot \sum \mathbf{x}_i,]$
$+ \ldots$, or

$$H' = H - (\Omega/e)m\mathbf{v} \cdot \mathbf{J} + \tfrac{1}{2}(\Omega n/m^*)m^2 v^2$$
$$\mathbf{J}' = \mathbf{J} - (ne/m^*)m\mathbf{v} \qquad (38)$$

where the reciprocal effective mass $1/m^* = \tfrac{1}{3}\nabla_p^2 \mathscr{E}(p)$, evaluated at the Fermi surface, is a scalar owing to our assumption of isotropy.

A vital requirement is that of the nonsingularity of $1/m^*$. For an insulator, at $T = 0°$, with one-electron levels occupied up to an energy gap, a uniform motion applied to the electrons results in an energy discontinuity: $m^* = 0$. For a superconductor, the gap occurs on the insertion of phonon interaction and moves — so to speak — with the reference frame.

For a real system with sharp boundaries, the existence of a gross magnetic field precludes that of a totally uniform current. Rather than attempt an analysis of the depth of eqs. (22) – (28), let us simply assume on the basis of this analysis that a "hydrodynamic" mode may be achieved by conceptually dividing the volume into cells large compared to electron spacing, and moving the ground state electron fluid in each cell by a velocity field $\mathbf{v}(\mathbf{x})$. Appending the magnetic field energy of the current distribution — assuming negligible magnetic susceptibility — we obtain from (38) for an excitationless hydrodynamic or current-carrying mode

$$E = E_0 + \tfrac{1}{2}\int (m^2/m^*)n\, v^2\, d^3x + (1/8\pi)\int B^2\, d^3x \tag{39}$$
$$\mathbf{J}(\mathbf{x}) = -ne(m/m^*)\, \mathbf{v}(\mathbf{x})$$

Let us now determine the ground state velocity distribution for fixed total current. By fixed current we refer to the values $I_\nu = \int \mathbf{J} \cdot d\mathbf{S}_\nu$ for a prescribed set of independent surfaces which cut the conductor, e.g., a single minor cross section for a ring-shaped conductor. Employing Ampere's law in the form $\nabla \times \mathbf{B} = (4\pi/c)\mathbf{J}$ in (39), the energy above the ground state is given by

$$8\pi\Delta E = (m^* c^2/4\pi e^2) \int \nabla \times \mathbf{B} \cdot \nabla \times \mathbf{B}n^{-1}\, d^3x + \int B^2\, d^3x \tag{40}$$

and, minimizing at fixed I_ν, one has in the interior

$$(m^* c^2/4\pi e^2)\nabla \times n^{-1}\nabla \times \mathbf{B} + \mathbf{B} = 0$$
$$\mathbf{J} = (c/4\pi)\nabla \times \mathbf{B} \qquad \nabla \cdot \mathbf{B} = 0 \tag{41}$$

for a current-carrying ground state (the consistent condition $\nabla \cdot \mathbf{B} = 0$ need not be applied during the variation). Introducing the vector potential through $\mathbf{B} = \nabla \times \mathbf{A}$, one can say that Ohm's law $\mathbf{J} = \sigma\mathbf{E}$

is replaced in a superconductor at $T = 0°$ by London's relation

$$\mathbf{J} = -(c/4\pi\lambda^2)\mathbf{A} \qquad \lambda^2 = m^*c^2/4\pi ne^2 \qquad (42)$$

According to (41), λ is of the nature of a skin depth, for $B \propto \exp(-x/\lambda)$ at a plane boundary. Since, typically, $\lambda \sim 10^{-6}$ cm, miscroscopic magnetic field variations are not necessarily ignorable. Indeed, it is found appropriate [43] to introduce a screening length $\xi \sim 10^{-4}$ for the field, modifying (42) to $\mathbf{J}(\mathbf{r}_1) = -(c\xi/16\pi^2\lambda^2) \cdot \int \mathbf{A}(r_2) e^{-r_{12}/\xi} r_{12}^{-2} d^3 r_2$ and correspondingly changing the field energy.

Decay of Current. Suppose one sets up at $T = 0°$ a current-carrying ground state (a process which physically involves cooling down through the transition temperature); the energy (40) is certainly higher than that of the absolute ground state [26], so that a persistent current will be metastable. While a direct diminution of the current amplitude is possible, we surmise in the fashion of the analysis for He II that the transition rate for such a correlated change via essentially one-body perturbations is vanishingly small. Thus it is only necessary to investigate transitions to elementary excitations or localized velocity patterns that ride along with the moving state.

Since a rapid change of magnetic field pumps energy into an induced electric field, let us confine our attention to the kinematics of transitions which decrease the kinetic energy of the current distribution. From (38), it is clear that the energy shift from a moving ground state with current pattern $\mathbf{J}_c$ to an excited state $(\Delta E, \mathbf{J})$ moving in the same manner is

$$\Delta E' = \Delta E + \int (m^*/ne^2)\mathbf{J} \cdot \mathbf{J}_c \, d^3x \qquad (43)$$

Consider a particle-hole excitation. For the shell current of a current-carrying ground state, a counteracting excitation should move as a surface wave packet, but it suffices to examine a stationary component, which is then uniform over the conductor's cross section. But we have seen that the total momentum is $\mathbf{P} = (-\bar{m}\Omega/e)\mathbf{J}$, where $1/\bar{m} = (1/p)\partial\mathscr{E}/\partial p$ is of the order of $1/m^*$. Hence the condition that $\Delta E' < 0$ in (43) reduces at once to

$$I_c > (\bar{m}/m^*)(ne\mathscr{A})\Delta E/\Delta P \qquad (44)$$

for total ground state current I_c and cross-sectional area $\mathscr{A}$.

A particle-hole excitation at diametrically opposite points of the Fermi surface can transfer the macroscopically finite momentum $2p_f$, where p_f is the maximum Fermi momentum. Thus, unlike the case of He II, a macroscopic gap must appear in ΔE to prevent (44) from being satisfied at arbitrarily small I_c. A gap is present, and so a high critical current, of the order of 10^7 $\mathscr{A}$ amps, does exist for (44).

As for excitation of a local hydrodynamic mode, we do not really know the form of such distributions. For an estimate, we may however copy the typical He II results. These would yield $\Delta E \sim \mathscr{C} n \hbar^2 / 2m^*$, $\Delta P \sim 4\mathscr{A} n \hbar$, where $\mathscr{C}$ is the circumference of the cross section. Hence $I_c / \mathscr{C} \sim n e \hbar m / 8(m^*)^2$, entailing a corresponding surface magnetic field $B_c = (4\pi/c) I_c / \mathscr{C}$

$$B_c \sim n\pi(m/m^*)(e\hbar/2m^*c) \tag{45}$$

which is of the order of 10^3 gauss. In the naive picture presented here, no account has been taken of the field energy inside the conductor. If this energy is included, using the shielding or correlation length ξ mentioned above, it is easily seen that B_c rises when the dimension of the conductor is less than ξ. This is an experimentally validated observation.

Finally, if an external stationary current source is applied to a superconductor which carries no current initially, eq. (41) remains valid for the ground state, and only the external boundary conditions are modified — source singularities are required. Because a poorly penetrating surface magnetic field again results at the conductor, current flow is then induced, with the same local characteristics as a self-maintained current. In particular, the surface current density $I_c / \mathscr{C}$ may be exceeded; in any region in which this occurs, current decay is no longer prohibited and the material acts as a normal conductor. The field configuration thus determines the normal-superconductor distribution, and the associated boundary conditions determine the field; a complicated intertwined domain structure may ensue [27], and be further confused by any natural domains in the conductor.

5. Two-Fluid Model

We next consider thermodynamic, hydrodynamic, and electromagnetic properties of superfluids above absolute zero. The energy spectrum for combined particle-type and hydrodynamic excitations must then be determined. For He II, this may be done by a simple modification of the argument of Sec. 3: first apply a gross motion and then excite the desired phonons. Phonon excitations in the absolute ground state ψ_0 may be produced as $\psi = \prod (A_k^*)^{N_k} \psi_0$, using the unnormalized phonon creators $A_k^* = \dot{q}_k + i\omega_k q_k$. If for the combined state, we correspondingly choose $\psi = \exp[-\sum \lambda(\mathbf{x}_i)] Q(\cdots A_k^* \cdots) \psi_0$, it can be shown that the energy increment due to excitation is $\Delta E_{ex} = \sum \mathcal{N}_k(\hbar\omega_k + \mathbf{u}_0 \cdot \hbar\mathbf{k})$, where $\mathbf{u}_0$ is the zeroth Fourier component of the local velocity $\mathbf{u} = (\hbar/m) \operatorname{Re} \nabla\lambda$. Only the mean velocity $\mathbf{u}_0$ seems to be Doppler shifting the phonons, but if we instead write

$$\Delta E_{ex} = \int \sum (\mathcal{N}_k/\Omega)[\varepsilon(\mathbf{k}) + \hbar\mathbf{k} \cdot \mathbf{u}(\mathbf{x})] \, d^3x \qquad (46)$$

then, because $\varepsilon(\mathbf{k}) + \hbar\mathbf{k} \cdot \mathbf{u}(\mathbf{x})$ is precisely the phonon energy quantum for a frame moving with velocity $\mathbf{u}(\mathbf{x})$, one may say that insofar as total energy (and quite trivially, total momentum) is concerned, it is literally correct to compute on the basis of small uniformly moving cells, whose contributions are then summed. This is a somewhat tortuous way to arrive at a conclusion which would scarcely have been contested, and we shall without further ado consider the conclusion to be valid for the superconducting electron fluid as well.

Two-Fluid Decomposition. Consider then a small volume consisting of excitations in a uniformly moving state with velocity $\mathbf{v}_s$; at absolute zero there are no excitations, and $\mathbf{v}_s$ totally specifies the motion. At $T > 0°\mathrm{K}$, dynamical interchange of excitations occurs, e.g., through container friction and fluid viscosity, but $\mathbf{v}_s$, if sufficiently small, may be regarded as thermodynamically isolated. Further, the total momentum $\mathbf{P}$ may also be fixed by external means — a pressure differential or the like. The availability of two vector parameters to describe the stae of the fluid suggests the possible interpretation that there are two distinct coexisting fluids; such a decomposition, strictly formal or mathematical, may be introduced in the following manner.

Eschewing the particle-hole formulation for a Fermion system, and continuing to assume isotropy, we observe from both (21) and (38) that for a single excitation, the energy and momentum in a moving state $\mathbf{v}_s$ are related to the corresponding "static" quantities by a transformation of the form (for simplicity, we shall no longer explicitly indicate effective masses)

$$\varepsilon(\mathbf{k}, \mathbf{v}_s) = \varepsilon_0(\mathbf{k}) + \mathbf{v}_s \cdot \mathbf{p}_0(\mathbf{k}) + \tfrac{1}{2}mv_s^2$$
$$\mathbf{p}(\mathbf{k}, \mathbf{v}_s) = \mathbf{p}_0(\mathbf{k}) + m\mathbf{v}_s \tag{47}$$

(47) also implies (21) and (38) for states of arbitrary excitation. Now, in general, the one-body entropy of a mixed state of independent excitations of mean occupation number $\mathcal{N}_k$ is given by

$$S = (k/\gamma) \sum [(1 + \gamma\mathcal{N}_k) \ln (1 + \gamma\mathcal{N}_k) - \gamma\mathcal{N}_k \ln \mathcal{N}_k] \tag{48}$$

where $\gamma = 1$ for Einstein-Bose statistics, -1 for Fermi-Dirac statistics. Fixing the total particle number $\mathcal{N} = \sum \mathcal{N}_\mathbf{k}$, energy $E = \sum \varepsilon(\mathbf{k}, \mathbf{v}_s)\mathcal{N}_\mathbf{k}$, and momentum $\mathbf{P} = \sum \mathbf{p}(\mathbf{k}, \mathbf{v}_s)\mathcal{N}_\mathbf{k}$, the entropy will have a sharp maximum at some set of values $\mathcal{N}_\mathbf{k}$ which may therefore be taken as the occupation numbers for the statistical state. Using Lagrange parameters β', μ'', and $\mathbf{v}_n$ (a generalized velocity), the stationary entropy is given by $dS + k\beta'[\mu''d\mathcal{N} - dE + \mathbf{v}_n \cdot d\mathbf{P}] = 0$, or $\ln (1 + \gamma\mathcal{N}_\mathbf{k}) - \ln \mathcal{N}_\mathbf{k} + \beta'[\mu'' - \varepsilon(\mathbf{k}, \mathbf{v}_s) + \mathbf{v}_n \cdot \mathbf{p}(\mathbf{k}, \mathbf{v}_s)] = 0$, whence the required distribution is

$$\mathcal{N}_k = [\exp \beta'(\varepsilon_0(\mathbf{k}) - \mu') + (\mathbf{v}_s - \mathbf{v}_n) \cdot \mathbf{p}_0(\mathbf{k}) - \gamma]^{-1} \tag{49}$$

where we have inserted (47) and set $\mu' = \mu'' - \tfrac{1}{2}mv_s^2 + m\mathbf{v}_s \cdot \mathbf{v}_n$.

We wish to divide the energy and momentum into internal and kinetic parts. Assuming that the mechanical motion is adiabatic, the internal state (and associated true thermodynamic temperature β and chemical potential μ) is that state satisfying $\mathbf{v}_s = \mathbf{v}_n = 0$ which goes over to the physical state by adiabatically turning on moving and imposed velocities. The kinetic or hydrodynamic energy and momentum are then the differences between initial internal and final total values; let us obtain these to second order in $\mathbf{v}_s$, $\mathbf{v}_n$ for E, and to first order for $\mathbf{P}$ (whose "internal" value is of course zero). Using (49), an easy computation shows that the hydrodynamic increments are

$$\Delta \mathcal{N} = -\Sigma[(e^{\alpha}-\gamma)^{-2}e^{\alpha}\,\Delta\alpha + \ldots]$$
$$\Delta S = -k\Sigma[(e^{\alpha}-\gamma)^{-1}e^{\alpha}\,\alpha\Delta\alpha + \ldots]$$
$$\Delta \mathbf{P} = \Sigma[(e^{\alpha}-\gamma)^{-1}\,\Delta\mathbf{p}-(e^{\alpha}-\gamma)^{-2}e^{\alpha}\,\mathbf{p}_0\Delta\alpha + \ldots]$$
$$\Delta E-\Delta\mathcal{N}-(1/k\beta)\Delta S =$$
$$\Sigma[(e^{\alpha}-\gamma)^{-1}\,\Delta\varepsilon+(e^{\alpha}-\gamma)^{-2}e^{\alpha}\,\Delta\alpha(\Delta\varepsilon-\tfrac{1}{2}\beta^{-1}\Delta\alpha) + \ldots] \quad (50)$$

where $\alpha = \beta[\varepsilon_0(\mathbf{k})-\mu]$

$$\Delta\varepsilon = \mathbf{v}_s \cdot \mathbf{p}_0(\mathbf{k})+\tfrac{1}{2}mv_s^2$$
$$\Delta\mathbf{p} = m\mathbf{v}_s$$
$$\Delta\alpha = -\Delta(\beta\mu)+(\varepsilon_0(\mathbf{k})+(\mathbf{v}_s-\mathbf{v}_n)\cdot\mathbf{p}_0(\mathbf{k}))\Delta\beta$$
$$+\beta(\mathbf{v}_s-\mathbf{v}_n)\cdot\mathbf{p}_0(\mathbf{k})$$

Since $\Delta S = 0$, $\Delta \mathcal{N} = 0$, one sees that $\Delta\beta$, $\Delta\mu$ are of second order and hence do not enter into $\Delta\mathbf{P}$ or ΔE. The sums for $\Delta\mathbf{P}$ and ΔE simplify materially by virtue of parity and isotropy considerations, leading at once to hydrodynamic energy and momentum per unit volume

$$U_H \equiv \Delta E/\Omega = \tfrac{1}{2}\rho_n v_n^2 + \tfrac{1}{2}\rho_s v_s^2$$
$$J_H \equiv \Delta P/\Omega = \rho_n \mathbf{v}_n + \rho_s \mathbf{v}_s \quad (51a)$$

where $\rho_n = (\beta/\beta\Omega)\,\Sigma p_0(\mathbf{k})^2 \exp\beta(\varepsilon_0(\mathbf{k})-\mu)/\{\exp\beta[\varepsilon_0(\mathbf{k})-\mu]-\gamma\}^2$

$$\rho_s = nm-\rho_n \quad (51b)$$

According to (51a), it is eminently reasonable to interpret ρ_s and ρ_n as mass densities of "superfluid" and "normal" fluid components which co-occupy the volume. ρ_s is related to, but not identical with, the occupation of the $\mathbf{k} = 0$ moving state in helium, or of the moving Fermi sphere for superconductors; it is clearly associated with velocity $\mathbf{v}_s$. Further, if in the case of helium we increase $\mathcal{N}$ at constant temperature and volume. assuming no change of excitation spectrum, then only $\mathcal{N}_0$ changes; thus only ρ_s is increased, while there is no increase in internal energy and entropy. Consequently, one can say that the residual normal fluid is carrying all of the internal energy and entropy. A similar result obtains for superconductors at temperatures low enough that only the vicinity of the Fermi surface is involved. It is to be observed that there is very little normal fluid at low temperatures in helium, for inserting the phonon spectrum

$\varepsilon_0(\mathbf{k}) = \hbar c k$ into (51b), one obtains

$$\rho_n = [4\zeta(4)/\pi^2](kT)^4/\hbar^3 c^5 \tag{52}$$

The normal component for a superconductor drops even faster with temperature.

6. *Qualitative Aspects of Two-Fluid Model*

Hydrodynamics of He II at T > 0. Thermodynamic and hydrodynamic consequences readily follow [1], [12], [29], [30], from the two-fluid picture, irrespective of the excitation spectrum which originally gave rise to it. These are generally carried out on the basis of empirical thermodynamic arguments, with the confidence that they could be validated on a microscopic basis, such as eqs. (27), (46), if desired. As indicated by (46), one further uses the principle that if the helium properties change slowly in space and time, each element of the volume may be analyzed as if it were uniform; if local thermal equilibrium is to be maintained, there must also be no change within a typical mean free path of a phonon. For completeness, let us briefly review the empirical arguments commonly employed.

If density dependence has been established (even by appending a density-dependent net attraction [93] to an elementary excitation picture), pressure, entropy, and partial densities ρ_n and ρ_s are known state functions of density and temperature. By virtue of (51a) and the fact that only "normal" fluid carries entropy, equilibrium hydrodynamics results from conservation of mass, momentum, and entropy. But five equations are not enough to determine the eight quantities $\mathbf{v}_n$, $\mathbf{v}_s$, ρ, T. To obtain another vector relation, the Gibbs potential per unit mass, $g(\rho, T)$, may be introduced; g will be the same [32] for super and normal fluids if local thermal equilibrium exists at all points. If any superfluid is added to a fixed volume, $dS = dV = 0$, so that the internal energy relation $dU = TdS - pdV + gdM$ identifies g as the potential energy per unit mass seen by the superfluid. Hence superfluid momentum conservation yields

$$(\partial/\partial t + \mathbf{v}_s \cdot \nabla)\,\mathbf{v}_s + \nabla g = 0 \tag{53}$$

which is the required second vector relation.

Owing to the two-fluid character of He II, one may propagate not only longitudinal waves of density fluctuation, but also of fluctuations of relative density, and hence of temperature. Indeed, linearizing the hydrodynamic relations, the corresponding *first sound* and *second sound* both appear as normal modes, with velocities given closely by $c_1 = (\partial p/\partial \rho)^{\frac{1}{2}}$ and $c_2 = [(\rho_s/\rho_n)TS^2/C_v]^{\frac{1}{2}}$, which agree with observation except at low T. As $T \to 0°\text{K}$, one finds [17] from the above that $c_2 = c_1/3^{\frac{1}{2}}$, which is reasonable, because an isotropic sea of phonons associated with a thermal distribution has an rms. velocity in any direction of $c_1/3^{\frac{1}{2}}$. However, phonon mean free path effects become important and $c_2 = c_1/3^{\frac{1}{2}}$ is exceeded at low temperatures [35], wave propagation being severely in the process.

Viscous Effects. For many phenomena associated with He II, a knowledge of viscosity is necessary. We know that at $T = 0°\text{K}$, a moving ground state, and so presumably the superfluid component in general, exhibits neither friction nor viscosity for sufficiently low velocity. For $T > 0°\text{K}$ one sees according to eq. (49) that the minimum of $\mathcal{N}_k$ at $\mathbf{k} = 0$ for $\mathbf{v}_s = \mathbf{v}_n = 0$ remains at $\mathbf{k} = 0$ when $\mathbf{v}_s$, $\mathbf{v}_n \neq 0$ only if $\varepsilon_0(\mathbf{k}) + \mathbf{p}_0(\mathbf{k}) \cdot (\mathbf{v}_s - \mathbf{v}_n) > 0$ for all $\mathbf{k} \neq 0$; applying this condition to hydrodynamic excitations modifies the criterion, following (32), to $|\mathbf{v}_s - \mathbf{v}_n|_{\text{crit}} \sim h/mb$. On the other hand, the normal fluid, depending upon excitations above the ground state that will have some sort of scattering cross section [33], should show the viscous behavior of a normal gas.

These attributes are verified qualitatively and quantitatively by a number of experiments — (a) Mechano-Caloric Effect [36]: if He II is pushed gently through a fine orifice (superleak), the inviscid superfluid passes through, exiting at a temperature close to zero; (b) Andronikashvili Experiment [38]: only the viscous normal fluid follows the motion of a rotationally oscillating plate viscometer; (c) Fountain Effect [38]: two vessels connected by a superleak must have [see (53)] the same value of g when $\mathbf{v}_s = 0$; if the temperature in one is raised, fluid rushes into it to raise the pressure to its required value; (d) Thermal Superconductivity [39]: the superfluid pressure generated by a temperature difference sets up a large counterflow (internal convection) of the low-viscosity normal fluid; (e) Wide

Channel Hydrodynamics: since the critical velocity is exceeded, a viscous drag between normal and superfluid is required; the empirical theories (see, e.g., Gorter and Mellink [40]) are not yet satisfactory.

Electrodynamics of Superconductors. London ([6], Chap. B) fixes the gauge of the vector potential $\mathbf{A}$ by imposing the conditions $\nabla \cdot \mathbf{A} = 0$, $A_4 = 0$; $\partial \mathbf{A}/\partial n = 0$ at the surface of a superconductor; and total flux $\varphi = \int \mathbf{A} \cdot d\mathbf{S}$ for each independent section of a non-simply connected conductor. $\mathbf{A}$ then necessarily drops to zero with the magnetic field. By assuming that the wave function for the system does not change when $\mathbf{A}$ is applied to the ground state, he directly obtains relation (42). For time-varying currents, eq. (42) implies that $\mathbf{E} = (4\pi/c^2)\partial\lambda^2\mathbf{J}/\partial t$; this was originally found by Becker, Sauter, and Heller [44] who observed that if current flows without resistance, an electron in an electric field moves according to $m^*d\mathbf{v}/dt = -e\mathbf{E}$, which, since $\mathbf{J} = -ne\mathbf{v}$ implies the above expression in the low-velocity limit.

Above absolute zero, the effective density of the entropyless coherent single state — the superfluid — is only n_s; the remaining normal fluid presumably conducts normally, and so we have

$$\mathbf{J}_s = -(c/4\pi\lambda^2)\,\mathbf{A} \qquad \mathbf{J}_n = \sigma\mathbf{E} \qquad \lambda^2 = m^*c^2/4\pi n_s e^2 \qquad (42')$$

As previously indicated, this should be modified [43] in a non-local fashion.

Thermodynamics of Superconductors. At moderately low temperatures, low compared to the energy gap Δ and low insofar as changes in $\varepsilon(\mathbf{k})$ are concerned, the normal density of eq. (51b) reduces to $n_n = (\beta m)(\hbar k_f^2/\pi)^2 \int_0^\infty \exp\left[-\beta\varepsilon(\mathbf{k})\right] dk$; the integral will occur in most statistical calculations, so that the ubiquity of n_n might be predicted. In particular, the superconductor free energy above the ground state, per unit volume, is found to be

$$F_s = -3m(\beta\hbar k_f)^{-2}n_n \qquad (54)$$

Because $F = -(\pi^2/4)m(\beta\hbar k_f)^{-2}n$ for a normal metal, the interpretation of n_n as a density of normally conducting electrons is strengthened.

At any temperature below T_c, we may speak of a "corresponding"

ıormal metal as one with the gap turned off; a realization presumably
ıccurs when a higher than critical magnetic field decouples the highly
ırganized but individually very weak electron-phonon interactions
·esponsible for the gap. If the free energy is measured above the
ground state of this corresponding normal metal, and if the tail of
the gap disappears at an energy of the order of Δ, one must add

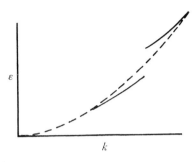

Figure 5

to the normal fluid contribution (54) a bulk term $-\frac{1}{4}\alpha\mathcal{N}(0)\Delta^2$,
with α of order unity, and $\mathcal{N}(0) = k_f^2 \, dk/\pi^2 \, d\varepsilon$ the state density per
unit volume at the Fermi surface. Knowing $n_n(\Delta, T)$, minimization
of F at a given temperature then yields Δ and all thermodynamic
properties, a sophisticated two-fluid model [30], [41].

If the "normal" metal above the critical field if really an extra-
polation of the true normal metal to below the transition temperature,
then the reversible change at B_c implies relations between normal and
superconducting thermodynamic properties. Since the internal field
in a superconductor cancels an applied magnetic field, it represents
a stored energy of $B^2/8\pi$ per unit volume. But the Gibbs free energies,
given by F if there is no mechanical change, should be the same at
the critical field for both phases. There results the relation

$$F_s + B_c^2/8\pi = F_n \qquad (54')$$

between field-free normal and superconducting free energies. As a
consequence, using $C = -\partial^2 F/\partial T^2$ for the specific heat at constant
volume, we see [45] that at critical temperatures (where $B_c = 0$),
$C_s - C_n = T(\partial B_c/\partial T)^2$. This is well verified experimentally, offering
another check on the underlying picture.

7. Level Structure of He⁴ Fluid

Basic Interaction. We now consider the superfluidity problem from a more fundamental point of view: given the particle interaction, to determine the energy levels and consequent properties of the fluid. In the case of He⁴, it is simple in principle to obtain the effective potential between two He atoms in their ground states. At the low temperature that we are presently interested in, there can be no excitation of internal degrees of freedom, and no significant velocity dependence in the interatomic potential. Thus, only the ground state energy of two fixed He⁴ atoms need be treated. The practical problem is not however an easy one; perhaps the most reliable computation to date is the Rosen-Margenau-Page potential (see Hirschfelder, Curtiss, and Bird [46])

$$V(r) = (925\ e^{-4.40r} - 560\ e^{-5.33r} - 1.39r^{-6} - 3.0r^{-8}) \times 10^{-12}\ \text{erg} \quad (55)$$

r in Å, including valence (1st order perturbation), exchange (second-order exchange) and dispersion (second-order Coulomb) forces.

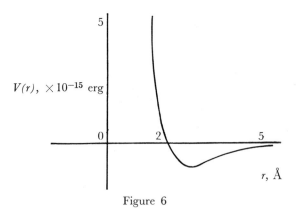

Figure 6

This differs somewhat from the best empirical potentials obtained from specific heat data, enough so that the possible existence of a very weakly bound vibrational state is still an open question, although not an important one for our purposes. Finally, there is of course the problem of three-body and higher forces at the separations of interest; in this respect, it may be noted that a comparison of gaseous argon and solid argon equations of state shows [47] that the same pair potential will represent both. We shall restrict our attention to pair interactions.

General Properties. Knowledge that the excitation spectrum $\varepsilon(\mathbf{k})$ for helium must rise at most as rapidly as k near the origin in $\mathbf{k}$ space in order to produce superfluidity also yields some information on ground state wave-function properties. Again supposing that the first excited states consist essentially of plane waves traveling in the ground state medium ψ_0, an upper bound to the excited energies (the lowest of total momentum $\hbar k$) may be obtained [19] in the standard Rayleigh-Ritz fashion;

$$E_0 + \varepsilon(\mathbf{k}) \leqq \langle q_\mathbf{k}\psi_0|H|q_\mathbf{k}\psi_0\rangle / \langle q_\mathbf{k}\psi_0|q_\mathbf{k}\psi_0\rangle$$
$$H = \sum p_i^2/2m + \tfrac{1}{2}\sum_{i\neq j} V(\mathbf{x}_i - \mathbf{x}_j) \tag{56}$$
$$q_\mathbf{k} = \sum_j \exp i\mathbf{k}\cdot\mathbf{x}_j$$

Since $Hq_\mathbf{k}\psi_0 = [H, q_\mathbf{k}]\psi_0 + q_\mathbf{k}H\psi_0 = [H, q_\mathbf{k}]\psi_0 + q_\mathbf{k}E_0\psi_0$, then

$$\varepsilon(\mathbf{k}) \leqq \langle\psi_0|q_{-\mathbf{k}}[H, q_\mathbf{k}]|\psi_0\rangle / \langle\psi_0|q_{-\mathbf{k}}q_\mathbf{k}|\psi_0\rangle \tag{57}$$

But, ψ_0 being real, expectations are unchanged under the combined operations of Hermitian adjoint (*) and complex conjugate (^{c}) — actually time inversion — $\langle\psi_0|A|\psi_0\rangle = \langle\psi_0|A^*|\psi_0\rangle^c = \langle\psi_0|A^*|\psi_0\rangle$; since H is real, the numerator of (57) may then equally well be taken as $\langle\psi_0|[q_\mathbf{k}, H]q_{-\mathbf{k}}|\psi_0\rangle$, or, combining with (57),

$$\varepsilon(\mathbf{k}) \leqq \tfrac{1}{2}\langle\psi_0|[q_{-\mathbf{k}}, [H, q_\mathbf{k}]|\psi_0\rangle / \langle\psi_0|q_{-\mathbf{k}}q_\mathbf{k}|\psi_0\rangle \tag{58}$$

Carrying out the indicated operations, one has

$$\varepsilon(\mathbf{k}) \leqq (\hbar^2 k^2/2m)/[1+(\mathcal{N}-1)\sigma_k] \tag{59}$$

where $\sigma_\mathbf{k} = \langle\psi_0|\exp i\mathbf{k}\cdot(\mathbf{x}_i - \mathbf{x}_j)|\psi_0\rangle$ is the Fourier coefficient of the two-body correlation function $\sigma(\mathbf{r})$ in the ground state.

According to (59), $1 + (\mathcal{N} - 1)\sigma_\mathbf{k}$ must rise from 0 at least as rapidly as k with increasing k in order to achieve the desired excitation spectrum. If the behavior were exactly as k, which would be the case if (59) were a good estimate, the asymptotic form of $\sigma(\mathbf{r})$ for large $\mathbf{r}$ would then be r^{-4}, a long-range correlation. Certainly, however, the necessity that $1 + (\mathcal{N} - 1)\sigma_\mathbf{k}$ approach 0 as $k \to 0$ [indeed, as $\hbar k/mc$, where c is the velocity of sound in helium if (59) is accurate] is a considerable restriction on any process which may be envisaged for obtaining eigenfunctions and values for H of (56). In particular, suppose one were to attempt a perturbation calculation from the free-particle system; for unit volume, the relevant states are $\psi_0^{(0)} = 1$, $\psi_{\mathbf{k}, -\mathbf{k}}^{(0)} = [\mathcal{N}(\mathcal{N} - 1)]^{-\frac{1}{2}}(q_\mathbf{k} q_\mathbf{k}^* - \mathcal{N})$, $\mathscr{E}_{\mathbf{k}, -\mathbf{k}} = \hbar^2 k^2/m$, whence to first order, $\psi_0 = \psi_0^{(0)} + \sum \langle \psi_{\mathbf{k}, -\mathbf{k}}^{(0)} | V | \psi_0^{(0)} \rangle \, \psi_{\mathbf{k}, -\mathbf{k}}^{(0)}/(\mathscr{E}_0 - \mathscr{E}_{\mathbf{k}, -\mathbf{k}})$, or

$$\psi_0 = 1 - \sum (m/4\hbar^2 k^2) V_\mathbf{k}(q_\mathbf{k} q_\mathbf{k}^* - \mathcal{N}) \tag{60}$$

It follows at once that to first order

$$1 + \mathcal{N}\sigma_\mathbf{k} = 1 - (m\mathcal{N}V_\mathbf{k}/\hbar k^2) \tag{61}$$

Equation (61) clearly has the wrong behavior; it in fact diverges as $k \to 0$, and becomes negative, which is impossible.

The divergence in eq. (61) is accentuated as one goes to higher order. This is not surprising, for if $1 + \mathcal{N}\sigma_\mathbf{k}$ varies as k for $k \to 0$, it cannot be analytic in the vector $\mathbf{k}$ but has at least a square root type of branch point at $\mathbf{k} = 0$; somehow, the corresponding series must be summed up other than perturbationwise. It is perhaps simpler to look at the ground state energy eigenvalue; since the mean potential is clearly $\frac{1}{2}\mathcal{N}(\mathcal{N} - 1) \sum \sigma_\mathbf{k} V_{-\mathbf{k}}$, the "dangerous" terms [48] in the ground state energy development go as $V_\mathbf{k} V_{-\mathbf{k}}/\hbar k^2$, arising from creation of a state pair $(\mathbf{k}, -\mathbf{k})$ from the unperturbed ground state, and a subsequent return to the ground state. From the field quantized point of view, which is particularly convenient to work with, the terms in the Hamiltonian

$$H = \sum (\hbar^2 k^2/2m)a_\mathbf{k} a_\mathbf{k}^* + \tfrac{1}{2} \sum V_\mathbf{k} a_{\mathbf{l}+\mathbf{k}}^* a_{\mathbf{m}-\mathbf{k}}^* a_\mathbf{l} a_\mathbf{m} \tag{62}$$

responsible for creating and annihilating pairs from the unperturbed ground state are

$$V_\mathbf{k} a_\mathbf{k}^* a_{-\mathbf{k}}^* a_0 a_0 \qquad V_\mathbf{k} a_0^* a_0^* a_\mathbf{k} a_{-\mathbf{k}} \tag{63}$$

and these must be treated without perturbation.

Quasi-Particle Approach. One way [48] of achieving this objective is to solve a portion of the Hamiltonian including the dangerous interaction:

$$H_{\text{red}} = \tfrac{1}{2} N(N-1) V_0 + \sum_{\mathbf{k} \neq 0} (\hbar^2 k^2/2m + V_{\mathbf{k}} a_0^* a_0) \, a_{\mathbf{k}}^* a_{\mathbf{k}}$$

$$+ \tfrac{1}{2} \sum_{\mathbf{k} \neq 0} V_{\mathbf{k}} (a_{\mathbf{k}}^* a_{-\mathbf{k}}^* a_0^2 + a_{\mathbf{k}} a_{-\mathbf{k}} a_0^{*2}) \qquad (64)$$

exactly, and then apply the remainder as a presumably legitimate perturbation. Additional terms in H diagonal in a free-particle representation are included in H_{red}; the result excludes only terms less than quadratic in a_0, a_0^*, which certainly tend to be small in a condensed Boson system for which a_0, $a_0^* \sim N^{\frac{1}{2}}$. To solve (64), one introduces particle-conserving annihilators and creators

$$b_{\mathbf{k}} = a_{\mathbf{k}} u_0^* \qquad b_{\mathbf{k}}^* = a_{\mathbf{k}}^* u_0$$

$$u_0^* = N_0^{-\frac{1}{2}} a_0^* \qquad N_0 = a_0^* a_0 \qquad (65)$$

u_0 being the unitary annihilator of state $\mathbf{k} = 0$ ($u_0^* u_0 = u_0 u_0^* = 1$ except when $N_0 = 0$, and this possibility can be neglected); (64) then transforms to

$$H_{\text{red}} = \tfrac{1}{2} N(N-1) V_0 + \sum_{\mathbf{k} \neq 0} (\hbar^2 k^2/2m + V_{\mathbf{k}} N_0) \, b_{\mathbf{k}}^* b_{\mathbf{k}}$$

$$+ \tfrac{1}{2} \sum_{\mathbf{k} \neq 0} V_{\mathbf{k}} (b_{\mathbf{k}}^* N_0^{\frac{1}{2}} b_{-\mathbf{k}}^* N_0^{\frac{1}{2}} + N_0^{\frac{1}{2}} b_{\mathbf{k}} N_0^{\frac{1}{2}} b_{-\mathbf{k}}) \qquad (66)$$

Now $[N_0, b_{\mathbf{k}}] = b_{\mathbf{k}}$ is of order $1/N$ compared to N_0; hence N_0 may be taken as a c-number. But (66), as a bilinear expression, can then be diagonalized by the introduction of normal modes. Since

$$i \hbar \, \dot{b}_{\mathbf{k}} = (\hbar^2 k^2/2m + N_0 V_{\mathbf{k}}) \, b_{\mathbf{k}} + N_0 V_{\mathbf{k}} b_{-\mathbf{k}}^*$$

$$i \hbar \, \dot{b}_{-\mathbf{k}}^* = -(\hbar^2 k^2/2m + N_0 V_{\mathbf{k}}) \, b_{-\mathbf{k}}^* - N_0 V_{\mathbf{k}} b_{\mathbf{k}} \qquad (67)$$

the normal modes or "quasi particles" which diagonalize the Hamiltonian are clearly given (unnormalized) by

$$c_{\mathbf{k}} = b_{\mathbf{k}} + [(1+\gamma_{\mathbf{k}}) - (\gamma_{\mathbf{k}}^2 + 2\gamma_{\mathbf{k}})^{\frac{1}{2}}] \, b_{-\mathbf{k}}^*$$

$$\gamma_{\mathbf{k}} = \hbar^2 k^2/(2mN_0 V_{\mathbf{k}}) \qquad (68)$$

From (67), the excitation energies $\varepsilon(\mathbf{k}) = \hbar \omega_{\mathbf{k}}$ are seen to be

$$\varepsilon(\mathbf{k}) = [(\hbar^2 k^2/2m)^2 + N_0 V_{\mathbf{k}} \hbar^2 k^2/m]^{\frac{1}{2}} \qquad (69)$$

We see that as long as V_{0+} is finite, $\varepsilon(\mathbf{k}) \propto k$ for low k as desired .(and $\sigma_{\mathbf{k}} = \partial E_0 / \partial V_{-\mathbf{k}}$ is found to obey (59) for the ground state). Since the helium potential (55) is quite singular, the zeroth order result (69) can reasonably be used only if its repulsive part is replaced by a pseudopotential or reaction operator; if this is done, the Landau spectrum (Fig. 3) is at least qualitatively reproduced through the roton region. At any rate, there appears to be no fundamental difficulty in continuing the solution of (62) by perturbation.

It is important to note that the spectrum (69) depends on the $k = 0$ occupation number — a primitive saturation effect — and hence in a statistical state upon the temperature. The nature of the transition is then altered from that of a simple Bose condensation, but since it is precisely in the region of low $\mathcal{N}_0$ that the approximations leading to (69) fail, one must be wary of drawing more explicit conclusions.

8. *Level Structure of Superconductors*

Basic Interaction. We shall work with the approximate Hamiltonian of eq. (35), the nature of superconductivity being such that the omitted terms cannot seriously modify the resulting spectrum. The $(\mathcal{N}M)^{-\frac{1}{2}}$ behavior of the coupling constant K_s is to be noted. The isotope effect [49], the variation of the superconducting transition temperature as $M^{-\frac{1}{2}}$ with change of ionic mass, first provoked the realization that the electron-phonon interaction was crucial, unlike its apparently minor modifying effect on equivalent electron potentials in normal metals. From the $\mathcal{N}^{-\frac{1}{2}}$ dependence, each interaction term is seen to be microscopic.

At superconducting temperatures, the lattice is largely in its ground state, and so one might try to eliminate the phonon terms in (35) by simply solving for the phonon ground state energy change due to the electron "sources," and adding it to the electronic part of the Hamiltonian. But this neglects electron recoil, treating the position of the electron as an adiabatic constant; it will turn out that high wave number phonon transfer induces a strongly velocity-dependent electron-electron interaction. Instead, since the conceptual entities are electrons surrounded by phonon clouds and phonons accompanied by virtual electron pairs, the two fluids are properly to be separated by a canonical redescription [50]. After this, some sweeping approximations will be made, but for the complicated structure of (35), painting with a broad stroke at first is the only sensible approach.

It is convenient to rewrite (35) in second quantized form. Thus, in terms of electron annihilators and creators $a_{k\sigma}$, $a_{k\sigma}^*$ (wave vector k, spin σ), and corresponding phonon quantities b_s, b_s^*, eq. (35) becomes

$$H = \sum \mathscr{E}_k a_{k\sigma}^* a_{k\sigma} + \sum (2\pi e^2/k^2)(\rho_k^* \rho_k - \mathcal{N})$$
$$+ \sum \hbar w_k b_k^* b_k + i \sum G_k (w_k/\Omega)^{\frac{1}{2}}(\rho_k b_k^* - b_k \rho_k^*) \qquad (70)$$

where $\rho_s \equiv \sum a_{k-s,\sigma}^* a_{k,\sigma}$ is the electron-density Fourier component, $\mathscr{E}_k = \hbar^2 k^2/2m$, and G_k is approximately a constant depending upon intensive properties of the crystal.

The decoupling transformation is now taken to be of the form

$$H \to H' = e^{-iS} H e^{iS}$$
$$S = \sum g_{ks}(a_{k\sigma}^* a_{k-s,\sigma} b_s + b_s^* a_{k-s,\sigma}^* a_{k\sigma}) \qquad (71)$$

If the Coulomb terms in (70) are tentatively dropped, an easy calculation shows that the phonon-electron interaction in (70) is annihilated by choosing $g_{ks} = G_s(w_s/\Omega)^{\frac{1}{2}}/(\mathscr{E}_{k-s} - \mathscr{E}_k - \hbar w_s)$, and that to second order one then has the decomposed Hamiltonian

$$H' = \sum \mathscr{E}_k a_{k\sigma}^* a_{k\sigma} + \hbar \sum \omega_k b_k^* b_k$$
$$+ \Omega^{-1} \sum G_s^2 w_s \omega_s/[(\mathscr{E}_k - \mathscr{E}_{k-s})^2 - (\hbar \omega_s)^2] a_{1-s,\sigma'}^* a_{k-s,\sigma}^* a_{k\sigma} a_{1\sigma'} \qquad (72)$$

Here $\omega_s = w_s - \sum G_s(w_s/\Omega)^{\frac{1}{2}} g_{ks} \langle a_{k\sigma}^* a_{k\sigma} - a_{k-s,\sigma}^* a_{k-s,\sigma} \rangle$, the renormalized phonon frequency, is actually a q number whose expectation is chosen, and principal-value summations are implied where required. Finally, the Coulomb interaction may be treated along with the rest [51], but instead one may simply add an effective or shielded force to (72)

$$H_{\text{Coul}} = \Omega^{-1} \sum_{s > k_c} (2\pi e^2/s^2) a_{1-s,\sigma'}^* a_{k-s,\sigma}^* a_{k,\sigma} a_{1,\sigma'} \qquad (73)$$

k_c being a screening wave member of the order of but smaller than the top of the Fermi sea. The plasma mode contributions omitted in (73) enter only at a much higher energy than the anticipated gap (but are not trivial for the problem of gauge invariance [52]), and presumably any further errors in (73) (the a's have been transformed) will at least be common to normal and superconductors. Hence the Hamiltonian that we shall consider is $H = H' - H_{\text{phon}} + H_{\text{Coul}}$.

The absence of explicit spin dependence may be noted as one of our assumptions; the profusion of low-lying spin-wave states for (anti-) ferromagnetic substances prevents a ground state energy gap, and hence, superconductivity.

Formation of Energy Gap. We know that many of the properties of superconductors depend vitally on the existence of a macroscopic gap between the ground state and the first excited state. The question is: How can this be brought about by the microscopic phonon-induced interaction, which indeed is attractive only over the small range [see (72)] $|\mathscr{E}_k - \mathscr{E}_{k-s}| < \hbar(\omega_s)_{\max}$. Cooper has pointed out that such a result is not at all unlikely: If one considers $\mathscr{N}$ very closely spaced levels, $\langle m|H_0|n\rangle = C\delta_{mn}$, and turns on a state-independent attractive microscopic interaction, $\langle m|H_1|n\rangle = -V/\mathscr{N}$, the same between any two levels, then, from the fact that $(H_0 + H_1 - C)^2 = -V(H_0 + H_1 - C)$, it readily follows that $\mathscr{N} - 1$ levels are unchanged, while the $\mathscr{N}$th drops by V. Cooper further showed [53] explicitly how an electron pair interacting in a sea of electrons, and thus having momenta below the Fermi momentum excluded, would split off a localized ground state for arbitrarily small attractive interaction.

Returning to the Hamiltonian (72), (73) we isolate those terms responsible for a gap; the remainder may presumably be treated by iteration. One may pick out "dangerous" terms in a fashion similar to that employed [54] in the case of helium, but instead, we observe with Bardeen, Cooper, and Schrieffer [9] that, because in the Cooper pair ground state the electron pair will have zero net momentum and spin, it should be sufficient to consider that part of the Hamiltonian $H' - H_{\mathrm{phon}} + H_{\mathrm{Coul}}$ that involves at most creation or destruction of such pairs, i.e., contains only diagonal operators and the combinations $b_k \equiv a_{k\downarrow} a_{k\uparrow}$, $b_k^* \equiv a_{k\uparrow}^* a_{k\downarrow}^*$. Now this reduced Hamiltonian is clearly

$$H_{\mathrm{red}} = \sum_k \mathscr{E}_k (n_k - 1) - \sum V_{kk'} b_{k'}^* b_k$$
$$V_{kk'} = \Omega^{-1}\{[(\hbar\omega_{k-k'})^2 - (\mathscr{E}_k - \mathscr{E}_{k'})^2]^{-1} G_{k-k'}^2 w_{k-k'} \omega_{k-k'}$$
$$- (k - k')^{-2} 2\pi e^2 \mathscr{Z}(k - k', k_c)\} \quad (74)$$
$$n \equiv a_{k\uparrow}^* a_{k\uparrow} + a_{-k\downarrow}^* a_{-k\downarrow}$$

$\mathcal{E}_{\mathbf{k}}$ here denotes energy with respect to the Fermi energy, $\mathcal{Z}$ is the unit step function, and an additive constant has been tacked on for convenience.

A quick appraisal of the characteristics of (74) is due to Anderson [55], who observes that the $b_{\mathbf{k}}$ and $n_{\mathbf{k}}$ may be represented by commuting vectors $\mathbf{s}_k$:

$$b_{\mathbf{k}} = s_{x\mathbf{k}} + is_{y\mathbf{k}} \qquad b_{\mathbf{k}}^* = s_{x\mathbf{k}} - is_{y\mathbf{k}} \qquad n_{\mathbf{k}} = 1 - 2s_{z\mathbf{k}} \qquad (75)$$

where each $\mathbf{s}_k$ obeys spin commutation relations (in units of $\hbar$); (74) thus becomes

$$H = -2 \sum \mathcal{E}_{\mathbf{k}} s_{z\mathbf{k}} - \sum V_{\mathbf{kk'}}(s_{x\mathbf{k}} s_{x\mathbf{k'}} + s_{y\mathbf{k}} s_{y\mathbf{k'}}) \qquad (76)$$

For fixed particle number, $S_z = \sum s_{zk}$ is of course fixed as well. Now each s_k is in fact seem to represent a direct sum of one spin $\frac{1}{2}$ and two spin 0's, for the eigenvalues of s_{zk} are clearly $-\frac{1}{2}, \frac{1}{2}, 0, 0$. (To enhance confidence, one may write out all operators as 4×4 matrices.) But if the coefficients in (75) are slowly varying, only sums of $s_{\mathbf{k}}$ and thus large spins are really involved, so that (75) may be analyzed as a semiclassical "spin" interaction system. Thus for the ground state, we first rotate each spin coordinate system about the z axis so that $s_{y\mathbf{k}} = 0$ (i.e., define x as transverse to z) and then observe that the effective "field" acting on $s_{\mathbf{k}}$ is $\mathbf{H}_{\mathbf{k}} = \nabla_{s_{\mathbf{k}}} H$, or

$$\mathbf{H}_{\mathbf{k}} = (-2 \sum V_{\mathbf{kk'}} s_{x\mathbf{k'}}, 0, -2\mathcal{E}_{\mathbf{k}}) \qquad (77)$$

For minimum energy, the spins line up with the field and have a maximum amplitude; then, writing $s_{z\mathbf{k}} = \frac{1}{2}\cos\theta_k$, we have $s_{x\mathbf{k}} = \frac{1}{2}\sin\theta_k$, and the ground state equilibrium is determined by the condition that $\mathbf{H}_{\mathbf{k}}$ be parallel to $\mathbf{s}_k$ or

$$\tan\theta_{\mathbf{k}} = \frac{1}{2}\mathcal{E}_{\mathbf{k}}^{-1} \sum V_{\mathbf{kk'}} \sin\theta_{\mathbf{k'}} \qquad (78)$$

Equation (78) could be obtained equally well by direct minimization of H_{red}. We have not yet imposed the condition that S_z is fixed; if it is applied to (76) by a Lagrangian parameter μ, then $\mathcal{E}_{\mathbf{k}}$ in (77) and (78) just changes to $\mathcal{E}_{\mathbf{k}} - \mu$, a simple renormalization of the Fermi level.

In the unperturbed $V_{\mathbf{kk'}} = 0$ case, one knows that $s_{z\mathbf{k}} = -\frac{1}{2}$ in the Fermi sea ($\mathcal{E}_k < 0$) and switches abruptly to $+\frac{1}{2}$ outside it ($\mathcal{E}_k > 0$);

with interaction, a smooth alteration takes place. Now each "spin" $\mathbf{s_k}$ in the direction of its local "field" can make a transition by reversing or, for half as much energy, by dropping to a zero spin component. Hence, for an elementary excitation, two spins $s_{\mathbf{k}}$ and $s_{\mathbf{l}}$ with $\mathscr{E}_{\mathbf{k}} < 0 < \mathscr{E}_{\mathbf{l}}$ drop to zero (conserving S_z by a second-order readjustment) with an obvious increase in orientation energy of $\frac{1}{2}|\mathbf{H_k}| + \frac{1}{2}|\mathbf{H_l}|$, or

$$\varepsilon(\mathbf{k}; \mathbf{l}) = \varepsilon(\mathbf{k}) + \varepsilon(\mathbf{l}) \tag{79}$$

where $\quad \varepsilon(\mathbf{k}) = [\mathscr{E}_{\mathbf{k}}^2 + (\sum V_{\mathbf{kk'}} s_{x\mathbf{k'}})^2]^{\frac{1}{2}}$

These results for the ground state energy [inserting the solution of (78) into (76)] and excitation energies are identical with those of Bardeen, Cooper, and Schrieffer [9] (with corresponding notation $\cos \theta_k \to 2h_k - 1$).

For the sake of clarity, let us regard $V_{\mathbf{kk'}}$ as a constant V in the range $|\mathscr{E}_{\mathbf{k}}|, |\mathscr{E}_{\mathbf{k'}}| < \hbar\omega$, for some mean ω, and zero elsewhere; consideration may then be restricted to the foregoing range, and assuming equal numbers of states on both sides of the Fermi surface for this range, the constant S_z is zero. From (74), one has

$$V \sim \Omega^{-1}[(G/\hbar)^2 - 2\pi e^2/k_c^2] \tag{80}$$

Superconductivity will only occur [9] for attractive interaction, $V > 0$. Now, (78) can easily be solved. If the density of unperturbed spin-up states per unit energy at the Fermi surface is $\mathscr{N}(0)$ (an extensive quantity) and if $\hbar\omega < \varepsilon_f$, then $\varepsilon_0 \equiv \frac{1}{2}V \sum \sin \theta_k = \frac{1}{2}V\mathscr{N}(0) \int_{-\hbar\omega}^{\hbar\omega} \sin \theta_{k(\mathscr{E})} \, d\mathscr{E} = \frac{1}{2}V\mathscr{N}(0) \int_{-\hbar\omega}^{\hbar\omega} (1 + \cot^2 \theta_{k(\mathscr{E})})^{-\frac{1}{2}} \, d\mathscr{E} = \frac{1}{2}V\mathscr{N}(0) \int_{-\hbar\omega}^{\hbar\omega} (1 + \varepsilon_0^{-2}\mathscr{E}^2)^{-\frac{1}{2}} \, d\mathscr{E} = V\mathscr{N}(0)\varepsilon_0 \sinh^{-1}(\hbar\omega/\varepsilon_0)$; hence

$$\tan \theta_k = \varepsilon_0/\mathscr{E}_k \tag{81}$$

where $\quad \varepsilon_0 = \hbar\omega/\sinh[1/V\mathscr{N}(0)]$

Insertion of (81) into (76) and (79) then yields at once

$$E_0 = -2\mathscr{N}(0)(\hbar\omega)^2/[e^{2/V\mathscr{N}(0)} - 1]$$
$$\varepsilon(\mathbf{k}) = (\varepsilon_0^2 + \mathscr{E}_{\mathbf{k}}^2)^{\frac{1}{2}} \tag{82}$$

An energy gap then exists and is given precisely by $2\varepsilon_0$.

If in addition to the constant V of (80), one makes the (infinite mass) approximation that $\mathscr{E}_{\mathbf{k}} = 0$, thereby returning to the point-continuum model of the opening paragraph, the Hamiltonian (76) may be solved exactly, for it takes the form

$$H_{\text{red}} = -V(\mathbf{S} \cdot \mathbf{S} - S_z S_z) \tag{83}$$

where $\mathbf{S} = \sum \mathbf{s}_{\mathbf{k}}$. Since $S_z = 0$, the spectrum is then $E = -VS(S+1)$, where S is an integer (or half integer) up to $S_{\text{max}} = \hbar\omega\mathscr{N}(0)$; each level is of course highly degenerate. This is the strong-coupling limit $\mathscr{N}(0)V \gg 1$, and it is seen that ground state energy $E_0 = -V(\hbar\omega)^2[\mathscr{N}(0)]^2$, and lowest excitation, $\varDelta E = 2V\hbar\omega\mathscr{N}(0)$, both agree with (82) in this limit. Note that if $V < 0$, the spectrum reverses, and $\varDelta E = 2|V|$ is strictly microscopic.

Further Properties. Let us examine the thermal properties of superconductors, as determined by the free energy. Except in the case of infinite mass (83), the excitation energy depends at least on the general level of excitation from the ground state, i.e., on the pre-existing "field" $\mathbf{H}_k$ in the analysis of (76). Rather than obtain this dependence in the fashion of (69), one may observe that certainly for the free energy, which is stationary at its correct value, simulation by a temperature-dependent spectrum of uncoupled excitations should suffice; since the occupation numbers are sharply distributed in a thermodynamic state, other observable quantities may be well reproduced in this manner. The treatments of Bardeen et al. [9] and Valatin [56] are essentially identical, and yield the same results as that of Bogoliubov [57] et al. Indeed, the excitation operator technique of Chap. XIII is also appropriate.

First, we note that the operator which occupies (spin $-\frac{1}{2}$) a previously unoccupied pair (spin $+\frac{1}{2}$) in (76) is $s_{x\mathbf{k}} - is_{y\mathbf{k}} = b_{\mathbf{k}}^*$, so the ground state we obtained, with its relative occupation of $s_{z\mathbf{k}} = -\frac{1}{2}$ and $+\frac{1}{2}$, can be written quantum mechanically as

$$\psi_0 = \prod_{\text{all } \mathbf{k}} (\cos \tfrac{1}{2}\theta_{\mathbf{k}} + \sin \tfrac{1}{2}\theta_{\mathbf{k}} b_{\mathbf{k}}^*)|0\rangle \tag{83}$$

where $|0\rangle$ is the total vacuum. This is not yet an eigenfunction of $S_z = \sum \frac{1}{2}(1 - n_k)$, but S_z does commute with H_{red} [i.e., the result (78) is unchanged by identical rotations of all "spins" about the z axis] and so one may simply project (84) onto the desired state of $\sum n_k = \mathscr{N}$ (i.e., appropriately average z axis rotations). For excited states, one may reverse occupation of both states of a pair, corresponding to a factor $\sin \frac{1}{2}\theta_k - \cos \frac{1}{2}\theta_k b_k^*$, in (83) or have unmixed single occupation of one member, with its factor (all "0-spin" states are pure states) $a_{k\uparrow}^*$ or $a_{k\downarrow}^*$. If we again project onto $\mathcal{N}$ particles, then, since $(sa_{k\uparrow}^* + ta_{-k\downarrow})(ua_{-k\downarrow}^* + va_{k\uparrow})\,|0\rangle = u(t + sb_k^*)\,|0\rangle$, the form

$$\psi = (\prod_{(k\sigma)\,\in\,K} \alpha_{k\sigma}^*)\,|0\rangle \tag{85a}$$

$$\alpha_{k\sigma}^* = \sin \tfrac{1}{2}\theta_{k\sigma}\,a_{k\sigma}^* + \cos \tfrac{1}{2}\theta_{k\sigma}\,a_{-k-\sigma} \tag{85b}$$

where K denotes a set of $\mathcal{N}$ or more one-body spin-momentum configurations, represents all excited-state configurations. If one chooses, as one may, $\theta_{k\uparrow} = -\theta_{-k\downarrow} \equiv \theta_k$, then $\alpha_{k\sigma}^*$ and $\alpha_{-k-\sigma}^*$ commute; further, one then sees that $[\alpha_{k\sigma}^*, \alpha_{k'\sigma'}]_+ = \delta_{kk'}\,\delta_{\sigma\sigma'}$, so that (85) may be regarded as producing any specified occupation of "quasi particles" $\alpha_{k\sigma}^*$.

Now a thermodynamic state of independent excitations is characterized by the mean occupation $g_{k\sigma} = 1 - f_{k\sigma}$ of each $\alpha_{k\sigma}$, as well as by the values of the θ_k which define the $\alpha_{k\sigma}^*$. Using a grand ensemble to avoid specifying the number of real particles, ψ of the form (85a) may be employed as is. Solving (85b), with $\theta_{k\uparrow} = \theta_{k\downarrow} = -\theta_{-k\downarrow}$, we find $a_{k\uparrow}^* = \sin \frac{1}{2}\theta_k\,\alpha_{k\uparrow}^* - \cos \frac{1}{2}\theta_k\,\alpha_{-k\downarrow}$, etc., it follows that the quasi particle-conserving parts of the operators required for the Hamiltonian are

$$\begin{aligned}
a_{k\uparrow}^* a_{k\uparrow} &\to \sin^2 \tfrac{1}{2}\theta_k\,\alpha_{k\uparrow}^*\,\alpha_{k\uparrow} + \cos^2 \tfrac{1}{2}\theta_k\,\alpha_{-k\downarrow}\,\alpha_{-k\downarrow}^* \\
a_{-k\downarrow} a_{k\uparrow} &\to \cos \tfrac{1}{2}\theta_k \sin \tfrac{1}{2}\theta_k(\alpha_{k\uparrow}^*\,\alpha_{k\uparrow} - \alpha_{-k\downarrow}\,\alpha_{-k\downarrow}^*)
\end{aligned} \tag{86}$$

Now $\langle\alpha_{k\sigma}^* \alpha_{k\sigma}\rangle = (1-f_{k\sigma})$, $\langle\alpha_{k\sigma}\alpha_{k\sigma}^*\rangle = f_{k\sigma}$, averaged over the ensemble. Inserting (74), the free energy $F = \langle H - (1/\beta)\kappa S - \mu\mathcal{N}\rangle$ on evaluation thus yields

$$F = 2\sum (\mathscr{E}_k - \mu)(f_k - \tfrac{1}{2}) \cos \theta_k - \sum V_{kk'}(f_k - \tfrac{1}{2})(f_{k'} - \tfrac{1}{2}) \sin \theta_k \sin \theta_{k'}$$
$$- (1/\beta) \sum [f_{k\sigma} \ln f_{k\sigma} + (1-f_{k\sigma}) \ln (1-f_{k\sigma})] \tag{87}$$

where $f_k = \frac{1}{2}(f_{k\uparrow} + f_{-k\downarrow})$. For variations with respect to the θ_k, (87) is identical with (76), except for the use of occupation-weighted kinetic and potential energies; thus, again absorbing μ into $\mathscr{E}_k$, (78) is replaced by

$$\tan \theta_k = -\mathscr{E}_k^{-1} \sum V_{kk'}(f_{k'} - \tfrac{1}{2}) \sin \theta_{k'} \tag{88}$$

Eliminating $V_{\mathbf{kk'}}$ via (88) and varying the $f_{\mathbf{k}\sigma}$ in (87) results in

$$f_{\mathbf{k}\uparrow} = f_{\mathbf{k}\downarrow} = [\exp(\beta\mathscr{E}_{\mathbf{k}}\sec\theta_{\mathbf{k}})+1]^{-1} \tag{89}$$

The distribution (89) is precisely that of a customary system of independent excitations with $\varepsilon(\mathbf{k}) = \mathscr{E}_{\mathbf{k}}\sec\theta_{\mathbf{k}}$. In the special case (80) of constant V, the $\varepsilon(\mathbf{k})$ are easy to find. Eliminating $f_{\mathbf{k}\sigma}$ by means of (89), eq. (88) may be treated precisely as in (81), (82); one now obtains

$$\varepsilon(\mathbf{k}, T) = (\varepsilon_0(T)^2+\mathscr{E}_{\mathbf{k}}^2)^{\frac{1}{2}} \tag{90}$$

where $\quad \int_{-\hbar\omega}^{\hbar\omega} (\varepsilon_0(T)^2+\mathscr{E}^2)^{-\frac{1}{2}} \tanh[\tfrac{1}{2}\beta(\varepsilon_0(T)^2+\mathscr{E}^2)]^{\frac{1}{2}} d\mathscr{E} = 1/V\mathscr{N}(0)$

There is then clearly a temperature-dependent effective spectrum. In particular, the gap $\varepsilon_0(T)$ is temperature-dependent. The transition temperature, at which $\varepsilon_0(T_c) = 0$, is determined by carrying out the integration of (80); although this is not available in closed form, one does readily find [9] that for $\beta_c\hbar\omega \gg 1$ (or $V\mathscr{N}(0) \gg 1$), then

$$kT_c = 1.14\,\hbar\omega \exp[-1/V\mathscr{N}(0)] \tag{91}$$

One consequence of (91) is that, employing (81), the relation $\varepsilon_0 = 1.75\,kT_c$ should hold; this has a fair degree of experimental verification [58].

As for electromagnetic properties, the existence of a uniform current-carrying state must first be established. Taking unit volume, the mean current density $\mathbf{J} = -e\sum\dot{\mathbf{x}}_i$ is not a constant of the motion for the Hamiltonian (74), but the total momentum $\mathbf{P} = \sum\mathbf{p}_i = \sum\hbar\mathbf{k}n_k$ is; one may then simply ask, with Bogoliubov [54], for the lowest state at fixed $\mathbf{P}$. For variational trial functions which need not be eigenfunctions of $\mathscr{N}$ or $\mathbf{P}$, one may introduce a new Lagrangian parameter $\mathbf{v}$, and minimize $\langle H - (1/\beta)kS - \mu\mathscr{N} - \mathbf{v}\cdot\mathbf{P}\rangle$. It is simplest to use the original Hamiltonian (70), for under the unitary transformation $a_{k\sigma} \to a_{\mathbf{k}-m\mathbf{v}/\hbar,\,\sigma}$, $a_{k\sigma}^* \to a_{\mathbf{k}-m\mathbf{v}/\hbar,\,\sigma}^*$ [which will certainly transform one of a class of variational wave functions into another — e.g., one like (85a)], it is clear that $\mathscr{N} \to \mathscr{N}$, $S \to S$, $\mathbf{P} \to \mathbf{P} + \mathscr{N}\mathbf{v}$, while $H - (1/\beta)kS - \mu\mathscr{N} - \mathbf{v}\cdot\mathbf{P} \to H - (1/\beta)kS - \mu\mathscr{N} - \tfrac{1}{2}mv^2\mathscr{N}$. Thus, the transformed wave function is the same as for $\mathbf{v} = 0$, as is any density matrix; since $\langle\mathbf{P}\rangle = 0$ for the $\mathbf{v} = 0$ distribution, the free energy $F = \langle H-(1/\beta)kS-\mu\mathcal{N}\rangle$ of a current-carrying state is increased by $\Delta F = \frac{1}{2}mv^2\langle\mathcal{N}\rangle$, and comment on the metastability of such a state follows as in Sec. 4.

For the description of current density in a real material, and for the resulting Meissner effect, the influence of a magnetic field is required; from a fundamental viewpoint, matters are still not in fully satisfactory state. Certainly, one would want to predict the annihilation of an extended D.C. magnetic field inside a uniform specimen; a simple criterion is due to Schafroth [59]. In the presence of a weak vector potential $\mathbf{A}(\mathbf{x})$, taken in the Lorentz gauge: $\nabla \cdot \mathbf{A} = 0$, a uniform medium will draw an induced current with a tensor admittance for each wave vector: $\mathbf{J}_k^i = \mathbf{F}_k \cdot \mathbf{A}_k$ (equivalent to a general non-local effect of $\mathbf{A}$ on $\mathbf{J}^i$). Suppose the vector potential to be the sum of imposed and internal fields, $\mathbf{A} = \mathbf{A}^0 + \mathbf{A}^i$; since the relation between internal $\mathbf{J}^i$ and $\mathbf{A}^i$, $\nabla^2 A^i = (4\pi/c)\mathbf{J}^i$ or $-k^2\mathbf{A}_k^i = (4\pi/c)\mathbf{J}_k^i$ is of course valid, then

$$\left((4\pi/c)\mathbf{F}_k \cdot +k^2\right)\mathbf{A}_k = k^2\mathbf{A}_k^0 \tag{92}$$

If $\mathbf{F}_0 = 0$ and $\mathbf{F}_k$ is regular in k^2, then as $k \to 0$, $\mathbf{A}_k = $ constant $(\mathbf{A}_k^0)$ as in a normal metal, but if the dyadic $\mathbf{F}_0$ is nonsingular, then necessarily $\mathbf{A}_k \to 0$ as $\mathbf{k} \to 0$ and no field penetrates.

The criterion that $\mathbf{F}_0$ is nonsingular, or for an isotropic medium, simply that the scalar $F_0 \neq 0$, has an unfortunate characteristic: even a small error may cause it to hold and thus give rise to a spurious Meissner effect. Putting it another way, if for any reason $\mathbf{F}_0 \neq 0$, then $\mathbf{J}^i = F_0\mathbf{A}$ for sufficiently long wavelength, and so London's relation is valid.

To compute the $\mathbf{J}$ resulting from a total $\mathbf{A}$ for solutions of the type discussed, it is simplest to include the magnetic field in the Hamiltonian and then use the relation $\mathbf{J} = -(1/c)\, \delta E/\delta\mathbf{A}$. However, one cannot merely make the standard replacement $\psi^* p^2 \psi \to \psi^*(\mathbf{p} + e\mathbf{A}/c)^2\psi$ in (74), first because a canonical transformation has already been made, and second because the approximation (74) is no longer gauge invariant under this replacement. Since the energy then depends on the gauge, the current does too; the approximation is obviously not appropriate to a given gauge, say $\nabla \cdot \mathbf{A} = 0$, and runs the danger of giving F_0 a mythical non-zero value. Several methods of avoiding such difficulties in principle present themselves. For example, one way work in a gauge-independent formulation, using the $\mathbf{x}_i$ and $\mathbf{P}_i \equiv \mathbf{p}_i + e\mathbf{A}(\mathbf{x}_i)/c$ as basic variables, with the modified commutation relations $[P_{i\alpha}, P_{j\beta}] = (\hbar/i)(e/c)\,\delta_{ij}\mathbf{e}_\alpha \times \mathbf{e}_\beta \cdot \mathbf{H}(\mathbf{x}_i)$ for unit vectors $\mathbf{e}_\alpha$. In a more customary fashion, one may carry $\mathbf{J}$ along with H from the outset, transforming both and approximating gauge invariantly at each stage; doing this, with certain additional approximations, Wentzel [60] has reproduced in substance the less rigorously derived results of previous workers.

Notes and References

1. F. London, *Superfluids*, Wiley, New York, 1954, Vol. II.
2. J. G. Daunt and R. S. Smith, *Rev. Modern Phys.* **26**, 172 (1954).
3. J. Wilks, *Repts. Progr. Phys.* **20**, 38 (1957)
4. D. Shoenberg, *Superconductivity*, Cambridge, New York, 1952.
5. M. Von Laue, *Superconductivity*, Academic, New York, 1952.
6. F. London, *Superfluids*, Wiley, New York, 1950, Vol. I.
7. C. Kittel, *Solid State Physics*, Wiley, New York, 1953, Chap. 11.
8. J. Bardeen, *Handbuch der Physik*, Springer, Berlin, 1956, Vol. 15, p. 274.
9. Bardeen, Cooper, and Schrieffer, *Phys. Rev.* **108**, 1175 (1957).
10. R. H. Fowler, *Statistical Mechanics*, Cambridge, New York, 1955, p. 46.
11. K. R. Atkins and M. H. Edwards, *Phys. Rev.* **97**, 1429 (1955).
12. T. D. Lee and C. N. Yang, *Phys. Rev.* **112**, 1419, (1958).
13. R. Peierls, *Quantum Theory of Solids*, Oxford, New York, 1955, Chap. IV.
14. C. Bloch, *Phys. Rev.* **93**, 1094 (1954).
    N. Rosenzweig, *Phys. Rev.* **108**, 817 (1957).
15. F. Seitz, *Modern Theory of Solids*, McGraw-Hill, New York, 1940, Chaps I, XIV.
16. D. ter Haar, *Statistical Mechanics*, Rinehart, New York, 1954, p. 287.
17. L. Landau, *J. Phys. (U.S.S.R.)* **5**, 71 (1941); **11**, 91 (1947).
18. Palevsky, Otnes, Larsson, Pauli, and Stedman, *Phys. Rev.* **108**, 1346 (1957).
19. R. P. Feynman and M. Cohen, *Phys. Rev.* **102**, 1189 (1956); R. P. Feynman, *Phys. Rev.* **94**, 262 (1954).
20. O. Penrose and L. Onsager, *Phys. Rev.* **104**, 576 (1956).
21. R. Peierls, *Ann. Physik* **3**, 1055 (1929).
22. P. A. M. Dirac, *Quantum Mechanics*, Oxford, New York, 1947, 3 rd ed., p. 136.
23. L. I. Schiff, *Quantum Mechanics*, McGraw-Hill, New York, 1949, 1st ed., p. 67.
24. R. P. Feynman, in *Progress in Low Temperature Physics*, C. J. Gorter, ed., Interscience, New York, 1955, Vol. I, Chap. II.
25. O. Penrose, *Phil. Mag.* **45**, 80 (1954).
26. L. Brillouin, *J. Phys. radium* **4**, 334 (1933), Appendix. D. Bohm, *Phys. Rev.* **75**, 502 (1949).

27. R. Peierls, *Proc. Roy. Soc. (London)* **A155**, 613 (1936). L. Landau, *J. Phys. (U.S.S.R.)* **7**, 99 (1943).
28. L. Tisza, *J. phys. radium* **1**, 165, 350 (1940).
29. R. B. Dingle, *Phil. Mag. Suppl.* **1**, 111 (1952).
30. C. J. Gorter, [24], Chap. 1.
31. Huang, Lee, and Yang, Chap. X, this volume.
32. P. S. Epstein, *Thermodynamics*, Wiley, New York, 1937, Chap. VI.
33. L. Landau and I. M. Khalatnikov, J. Exp. Th. Phys. **19**, 637, 709 (1949).
34. L. Tisza, *Compt. rend.* **207**, 1035 (1938).
35. De Klerk, Hudson, and Pellam, *Phys. Rev.* **89**, 326 (1953).
36. J. G. Daunt and K. Mendelssohn, *Nature* **143**, 719 (1939).
37. E. Andronikashvili, *J. Phys. (U.S.S.R.)* **10**, 201 (1946).
38. J. F. Allen and J. Jones, *Nature* **141**, 243 (1938).
39. Allen, Peierls, and Uddin, *Nature* **140**, 62 (1937).
40. C. J. Gorter and J. H. Mellink, *Physica* **15**, 285 (1949).
41. P. M. Marcus and E. Maxwell, *Phys. Rev.* **91**, 1035 (1953).
42. J. Bardeen, *Phys. Rev.* **81**, 469 (1951).
43. A. B. Pippard, *Proc. Roy. Soc. (London)* **A216**, 547 (1953).
44. Becker, Sauter, and Heller, *Z. Physik* **85**, 772 (1933).
45. A. J. Rutgers, *Physica* **1**, 1055 (1934).
46. Hirschfelder, Curtiss, and Bird, *Molecular Theory of Gases and Liquids*, Wiley, New York, 1954, Chap. 14.
47. G. O. Jones, Varenna Conference on Simple Liquids, 1957.
48. See Bogoliubov et al., Chap. XIV, this volume.
49. E. Maxwell, *Phys. Rev.* **78**, 477 (1950); Reynolds, Serin, Wright, and Nesbitt, *Phys. Rev.* **78**, 487 (1950).
50. H. Frohlich, *Proc. Roy. Soc. (London)* **A215**, 291 (1952).
51. S. Nakajima, *Proc. Intern. Conf. Theor. et Phys., Kyoto and Tokyo, Japan*, 916 (1953, 1954); J. Bardeen and D. Pines, *Phys. Rev.* **99**, 1140 (1955).
52. P. W. Anderson, *Phys. Rev.* **110**, 827 (1958).
53. L. N. Cooper, *Phys. Rev.* **104**, 1189 (1956); Chap. XXIV, this volume.
54. N. N. Bogoliubov, *Nuovo cimento* **7**, 794 (1958).
55. P. W. Anderson, Columbia University Physics Seminar, 1958; *Phys. Rev.* **112**, 1900 (1958).
56. J. G. Valatin, *Nuovo cimento* **7**, 843 (1958).
57. Bogoliubov, Zubarev, and Tserkovnikov, *Doklady Akad. Nauk. U.S.S.R.* **117**, 788 (1958).
58. R. E. Glover and M. Tinkham, *Phys. Rev.* **104**, 844 (1956).
59. M. R. Schafroth, *Helv. Phys. Acta* **24**, 645 (1951); *Phys. Rev.* **111**, 72 (1958).
60. G. Wentzel, *Phys. Rev.* **111**, 1488 (1958).

CHAPTER XXIV

Coherent States in a Degenerate Electron Gas

Leon N. Cooper

1. Introduction

I'd like to make some remarks on a different method of calculating some of the properties of an interacting degenerate Fermi gas. Let us keep in mind, in particular, a system of electrons in a metal at very low temperatures, and specifically, the mechanism for the formation of the superconducting phase. Perhaps a review of some of the relevant features of this problem will motivate what was done.

Because of the similarity of the superconducting transition, and of the properties of the superconducting phase, in a wide variety of complicated and differing metals, it is plausible to assume that the details of metal structure do not affect the qualitative features of the phenomena. Our point of view is that the existence of the super-conducting phase must be a rather general property of that system which is common to all metals — a dense, highly degenerate electron gas with interaction — and that complications that make up the details of metal structure can be ignored for a qualitative understanding. Even from this general point of view a criterion can be derived which seems to distinguish the superconducting from the normal metals.

In the primitive model of a metal to be considered, we imagine that the periodic ion potential which produces the band structure and the Bloch Functions can be replaced by a container of volume Ω in which $\mathcal{N}$ electrons are maintained at metallic density. These electrons interact with each other, but in contrast to the nuclear case, the interaction is reasonably well-behaved. One could treat this as a field-theoretic problem with the electrons interacting via an intermediate Boson field, but it is difficult enough if we imagine that the electrons have some effective potential between them.

The existence of the isotope effect leads us to believe that it is the electron-phonon interaction which is responsible for superconductivity. The importance of this interaction in this connection was first emphasized by Frohlich [1] and Bardeen [2]. The exchange of virtual phonons results in an electron-electron interaction [3], [4]; this is rather complicated — attractive in some and repulsive in other regions. Professor Pines mentioned [5] that there is reason to believe that the long-range Coulomb interaction is not the interaction that is important in producing the superconducting phase. However, the residual screened Coulomb interaction which is short-range and not too large, and is repulsive between the electrons, may be of importance in understanding why some metals become superconducting while others do not. For low-lying excitations of the electron system the electron-electron interaction due to phonon exchange is attractive, while the residual Coulomb interaction is repulsive. If the net interaction in this region of excitation is attractive it becomes possible to remove the degeneracy of the unperturbed Fermi sea by the formation of coherent states that will be exhibited below. It is believed that the possibility of producing such states is intimately connected with the occurrence of superconductivity.

2. *Electron Pair Energy Spectrum*

The energy difference between the superconducting and normal states is very small (of the order of 10^{-8} ev per atom). On the other hand the radical change in those metallic properties due to the conduction electrons when one goes through the transition indicates that there is a qualitative change in the electronic wave functions. One wants to understand, therefore, how such a large change can come about in the electronic wave function with such a small gain in energy. Attempts to treat this problem by perturbation theory have all failed. It seems necessary to pick out that part of the interaction that is responsible for the qualitative change in the electron wave function, and to treat this part accurately. A clue to the source of the difficulty lies in the enormous degeneracy of the unperturbed electron levels at the Fermi surface and in the fact that if degenerate levels are connected to one another via non-zero matrix elements they can produce levels which are linear combinations of the unperturbed levels, and which are qualitatively different from the unperturbed levels, while being separated from the unperturbed levels by arbitrary small energies. These coherent levels cannot be obtained by the usual perturbation expansion.

If the interaction is shut off completely, there is an unperturbed Fermi sphere. Now suppose one turns on the interaction very slowly, so that it is a small interaction. Then one might imagine that as one goes a certain depth into the Fermi sphere, the states below this depth will be essentially undisturbed. There are various ways of making this physically plausible. One could say that in the exact solution, the occupation numbers for the plane waves with wave number lower than a given wave number will be all filled up. So one could treat a problem in which electrons interacted above an essentially quiescent sphere; the only thing which the electrons inside the sphere do is provide a bottom to the available phase space.

An attempt to gain an understanding of how such a system would behave near its ground state was made by solving a problem in which two electrons interact above an excluded sphere. Just one essential feature was extracted from the Bardeen-Frohlich interaction — that it is attractive for small excitations of the two-electron system; it was felt that the attractive part of the interaction which connected the degenerate states of the two electron system was the part responsible for the formation of the superconducting state.

The result of the calculation was somewhat surprising. It turned out that if the interaction between the two electrons was attractive in a small shell near the Fermi surface, a single state split off from the continuum by a volume-independent amount [6]. The wave function describing this state was normalizable but decayed asymptotically as $1/r^2$ rather than exponentially. Further, if the binding energy was of the order of kT_c, then the approximate extent of the wave function was $\simeq 10^{-4}$ cm. Since this state occurs only if the net interaction is attractive, if one believes that this type of state is characteristic of a superconductor, then one immediately has a criterion available; clearly the electron-phonon interaction would have to dominate the Coulomb repulsion, or else this state would never appear. This criterion turns out to be numerically equivalent to one proposed previously by Frohlich [1] and Bardeen [2] and does in fact separate the superconducting from the normal metals fairly well.

3. *Formation of the Gap State*

That the formation of this state does not depend on the details of the potential between the two electrons can be shown in the following way. What has been done is to solve the Schrödinger equation for a two-particle system, excluding a certain region, $k < k_F$, of momentum space. The part of the wave function $\chi(\mathbf{r})$ that depends upon the relative coordinate can be written

$$\chi(\mathbf{r}) = \chi_0(\mathbf{r}) - \int d\mathbf{r}' \, Ge \, (\mathbf{r}, \mathbf{r}') \, v(\mathbf{r}') \chi(\mathbf{r}') \tag{1}$$

where $G_e(\mathbf{r}, \mathbf{r}')$ is the Green's function above the excluded sphere and $v(\mathbf{r})$ is the two-body potential. If $v(\mathbf{r})$ is a short-range potential we can find the asymptotic behavior of $\chi(\mathbf{r})$ by determining that of $G_e(\mathbf{r}, \mathbf{r}')$. In fact the asymptotic behavior of the wave function is given by that of the Green's function.

The Green's function $G_e(\mathbf{r}', \mathbf{r}'')$ satisfies the equation

$$(H_0 - E)G_e = 1 \tag{2}$$

and can be written in terms of the solutions of the homogeneous equation as

$$G_e(\mathbf{r}', \mathbf{r}'') = \sum_{\mathbf{k}} \varphi_k(\mathbf{r}') \varphi_k^*(\mathbf{r}'')/(\varepsilon_k - E) \tag{3}$$

where the summation is over all $k > k_F$ and

$$\varphi_k(\mathbf{r}) = \Omega^{-\frac{1}{2}} e^{i\mathbf{k}\cdot\mathbf{r}} \tag{4}$$

We then get, letting $\mathbf{r}' - \mathbf{r}'' = \mathbf{r}$, and the energy in the center of mass system $\varepsilon_k = \hbar^2 k^2/m$,

$$G_e(r) = m/\hbar^2 (1/2\pi)^3 \int_{k>k_F} e^{i\mathbf{k}\cdot\mathbf{r}}/(k^2 - k_0^2) \, dk \tag{5}$$

where $\hbar^2 k_0^2/m = E$ and $\int_{k>k_F} dk$ means an integration over all space excluding the sphere $k < k_F$.

We now want to investigate the asymptotic behavior of $G_e(r)$ as a function of k_0. Performing the angular integration we obtain

$$G_e(r) = m/\hbar^2 \, (1/\pi^2 r) \int_{k_F}^{\infty} k \sin kr/(k^2 - k_0^2) \, dk \qquad (6)$$

When $k_F = 0$ (no excluded sphere) we get the usual behavior: For $k_0^2 > 0$, the poles occur on the real axis at $k = \pm k_0$ and, depending upon how the contour is chosen, we obtain solutions corresponding to incoming or outgoing spherical waves:

$$G_0(r) \sim \text{constant } e^{\pm ik_0 r}/r \qquad (7)$$

For $k_0^2 < 0$ the poles occur on the imaginary axis $k = \pm ik_0$ and the solutions there are normalizable and correspond to bound states:

$$G_0(r) \sim \text{constant } e^{-k_0 r}/r \qquad (8)$$

When $k_F > 0$, however, the situation is radically altered. Now the change in asymptotic behavior occurs when $k_F^2 - k_0^2$ changes sign, or when k_0^2 becomes smaller than k_F^2. For $k_0^2 > k_F^2$, we must again integrate over poles on the real axis, and the various contours give incoming and outgoing spherical waves. When $k_0^2 < k_F^2$, we obtain a normalized solution but its asymptotic behavior is given by

$$G_e(r) \sim \text{constant } \cos k_F r/r^2 \qquad (9)$$

It makes very little difference in this last case if k_0^2 is larger or smaller than zero. The critical change in the Green's function occurs when the energy denominator pole is shifted out of the region of integration, and this occurs at k_F^2. Thus the excluded sphere shifts the point of division between bound and continuum solutions, while, at the same time, changing the asymptotic form of the bound solutions. The fact that $k_F > 0$ is due to the container maintaining the Fermions at a non-zero density. As $k_F \to 0$, or as the volume becomes infinite, one again obtains the usual solutions. In particular, the asymptotic behavior of $G_e(r)$ when $k_0^2 < 0$ again becomes exponentially decreasing.

4. *Extension to Many Electrons*

The solution of the two-body problem with $k_F > 0$ is an attempt to take into account in the simplest possible manner the effect of the interaction on the many Fermions. What has been done is to force the small modifications due to the interaction, which normally take place in all of the electron wave functions, into the wave function of a pair of electrons. The resulting wave function is characteristic of the correlation that would be induced by the interaction between electrons in the interaction region, a correlation which, with the interaction assumed, extends over distances of the order of 10^{-4} cm, drops off algebraically in the asymptotic region, and represents a volume-independent energy shift.

The relation of this result to the solution of the many-electron problem can be seen best by considering the entire configuration Hamiltonian for a degenerate Fermi gas with interactions. In the lowest excitation region — that near the Fermi surface — there will be a vast degeneracy of the levels of this matrix. In particular there will be a large number of degenerate submatrices corresponding to many configurations which differ only in the relative momentum of one pair, and which, via the interactions mentioned above, are connected by slowly varying matrix elements of constant sign. When the potential in the interaction region is attractive, as it seems to be for those metals which become superconducting, we get a qualitatively different ground state of this matrix if we first diagonalize the pair submatrices. Since the number of such submatrices is proportional to $\hbar\omega$, and the energy shift due to the diagonalization of each submatrix goes as $\hbar\omega$ [6], the total energy shift is proportional to $(\hbar\omega)^2$, in agreement with the isotope effect. Further, the exponential factor which occurs in the binding energy of each pair [6] can, with reasonable values of the parameters, make the energy shift due to the diagonalization of the pair submatrices be of the same order of magnitude as that involved in the superconducting transition.

There is a great deal to be understood, of course, about how one should properly attempt to approximate a solution to the many-body problem incorporating these qualitative features which appear to exist under the proper circumstances. Work on such solutions of the many-body problem is underway at present with J. Bardeen and J. R. Schrieffer [7] at the University of Illinois. It is believed that these coherent states, formed when the degeneracy at the Fermi surface is removed by an interaction which is attractive in the region of low lying excitations, are responsible for the superconducting phase.

Notes and References

1. H. Frohlich, *Phys. Rev.* **79**, 845 (1950).
2. J. Bardeen, *Phys. Rev.* **80**, 567 (1950).
3. H. Frohlich, *Proc. Roy. Soc. (London)* **A215**, 291 (1952).
4. J. Bardeen and D. Pines, *Phys. Rev.* **99**, 1140 (1955).
5. D. Pines, Chap. XVI, this volume.
6. L. N. Cooper, *Phys. Rev.* **104**, 1189 (1956).
7. J. Bardeen, L. N. Cooper, and Schrieffer, *Phys. Rev.* **106**, 162 (1957).

CHAPTER XXV

Helium II

LARS ONSAGER

1. *Experimental Background*

I am not certain how great a fraction of the audience is familiar with the experimental facts pertaining to liquid helium. Certainly a good many are, but I suspect that a good many of you are not. I would like briefly to inform those who don't know much about it, and refresh the memories of those who do.

The first thing that distinguishes liquid helium from all other substances is that it remains liquid when cooled under its vapor pressure, or any pressure less than about 25 atmospheres, to within striking range of absolute zero; it shows no signs of crystallizing until you submit it to sufficient pressure — about 25 atmospheres — and this involves a compression of some per cent. Now that is rather remarkable. Moreover, one can find out what its entropy approaches, and that behaves very well — it approaches zero.

As for the specific heat curve, that for He[3] shows nothing very spectacular [1]; that for He[4] looks like this (Fig. 1). The critical point is about 5.2⁰K, but there is also a peak, the lambda point, at which the specific heat becomes infinite. Now such a peak always indicates that something is going on. If you look at helium I as you pump it down through the lambda point, it becomes perfectly obvious that something is going on, because as you approach the lambda point, you are lowering the vapor pressure, and the bubbles get bigger. As soon as you are through the lambda point, the liquid, He II, is perfectly quiet — not a bubble in sight — and yet you know that it is evaporating because the level is falling. This is very dramatic for anyone who has seen it.

If you look into the cause of this steady evaporation and try to

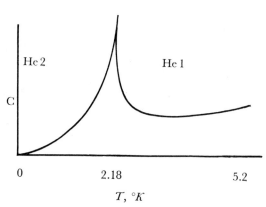

Figure 1. Specific heat of He⁴ (under its own vapor pressure).

measure the thermal conductivity, you find that if you don't try to put too large a heat flux through the liquid, it has no heat resistance at all [2]. Moreover, it can do other funny tricks: you can squeeze it through thin capillaries, jeweler's rouge — tightly packed material that would stop most anything else — but helium below the lambda point goes through with the greatest of ease, almost as if it preferred a thin opening. Here then is a liquid which has no first-order heat resistance, and can flow without dissipation. I should remind you that this is true of the flow only for small velocities; for large velocities, there are some non-linear types of resistance; if nothing else, we know that we might expect some kind of turbulence. But it isn't that simple — the critical Reynold's number in helium is for many purpose rather smaller than that for, say, water flowing in pipes [3]. Moreover, if you measure the viscosity of helium in a rotating viscometer, you find that it has a finite viscosity, comparable to that of a gas [4]. Therefore, He II is a superfluid, but not a superlubricator.

Now if you examine the helium that you have squeezed through a tight filter, you find that it comes through with very little entropy, and with sufficient care, with no entropy at all. You can get the reciprocal (fountain) effect if you heat one side of a filter; the helium will of course try to return to the higher temperature, where the rest of the entropy is, so as to dilute the entropy again — it takes work to squeeze the entropy out of helium. This process can be done almost reversibly, and so you have to a very good approximation an example of a system which can be maintained in chemical equilibrium, although it is not in thermal equilibrium. If you apply the Gibbs-Duhem [5] relation to the appropriate case, you get the relation between pressure difference and temperature difference for samples connected by a fine filter:

$$dP/dT = S/V \tag{1}$$

S and V being specific entropy and volume. This is a perfectly good method for measuring the entropy of helium, and was used by Kapitza.

2. Two-Fluid Model

Since helium II has no heat resistance at all, you can easily obtain a heat flow so great that it has an appreciable kinetic energy. In fact, you can easily find conditions so that just the increment of the kinetic energy and the force on the heat — the temperature gradient — are in dynamic balance. In this way, you set up a wave which is known as second sound; it is excited by an oscillating temperature and detected by any reasonable kind of thermometer. To describe this in detail, various theoreticians, starting with Tisza [6] and Landau [7], developed what might be called the two-fluid theory, or two-fluid model.

Consider two fluids, interconvertible, one a normal fluid, and one a superfluid. The superfluid is characterized by having none of the entropy — the normal fluid has all of that. The superfluid has no viscosity — the normal fluid has. In these terms one can describe the second sound wave equation and various other properties; however, not all of the things that the helium does can be described in terms of such a picture because, the superfluid being regarded as perfectly ideal, the equations always suggest, for example, that the superfluid can never rotate.

Now a few years ago, some young men in Cambridge, England put helium II in a bucket to see if it would rotate with the bucket and it did, although Andronikashvili [8], using a somewhat different set of apparatus, had shown before that if you just persuade helium very gently to rotate, it doesn't follow as readily as an ordinary fluid. But helium does rotate if you persuade it hard enough, and not much persuasion is needed.

I might mention the history of the theory. Landau [9] developed a quantum hydrodynamics that seemed to suggest that all that mattered was that you had a quantum liquid. We know now from experiment that He³ does not do what He⁴ does. At that time, London [10] immediately caught some of the faults in Landau's theory, criticized it severely, and pointed out that some of the commutation rules that Landau had formulated, particularly those involving the vorticity, wouldn't really matter unless something else were true. This was, as London had suggested before, that the momentum distribution of the helium should contain a δ function, which, in a resting liquid, would simply consist of a finite fraction of the particles having no momentum at all. If you can show that this impedes rotation, then it is a pretty good explanation. Moreover, if it is right, you should be able to show from first principles that there ought to be a finite fraction of the particles, not only in the ground state, but a finite temperatures as well, which have no momentum.

Incidentally, in Landau's theory, the normal liquid was more or less associated with excitations above the ground state, and there are methods of computing the effective mass of the excitations from their general dynamical properties. These are generally accepted, except possibly for the superposition principle. When the principle of superposition of excitations is no longer applicable, you really no longer know what to do, and are in for something very much more difficult in the way of theory. Actually, I don't know whether Landau superposed them the right way, so this is still wide open.

3. *Rotation of Helium*

Helium does rotate, but does it rotate normally, or are its properties changed when you make it rotate? Do its properties change significantly? Now within the last few years, Vinen and Hall [11] at Cambridge found indeed that rotating helium does show a significant difference from resting helium. What they did was to study the propagation of second sound, in which the normal fluid and superfluid vibrate against each other, in resting helium and in rotating helium, both along the axis of rotation and perpendicular to the axis of rotation. Perpendicular to the axis of rotation, they did find an attenuation of second sound, and the attenuation was proportional to the absolute value of the velocity of rotation. Along the axis, they found a much smaller degree of attenuation, which might possibly be attributed to inadequate geometrical definition of the setup. From this, they could compute the effective cross section of interaction, and it could be explained in terms of a Feynman [12] theory.

Now, what can you say from first principles about the ability of a superfluid to rotate? If the helium does have a background of particles of vanishing momentum, then it cannot quite rotate like a rigid body. To see that, I have only to look at the one-particle reduced density matrix. If you start out with a one-particle reduced density matrix for a resting solid, $\bar{D}_1(x', x)$, and transfrom to a solid rotating with angular velocity ω, you apply a factor and it looks like this:

$$D_1(x', x) = e^{i(m/\hbar)(x' \times x) \cdot \omega} \bar{D}_1(x', x) \qquad (2)$$

This is perfectly good provided the density matrix for vanishing ω is such that it decreases rapidly enough when x and x' are far apart. But if you have a background of vanishing momentum, then for large $|x - x'|$, $\bar{D}_1$ approaches N_1/N, the fraction of condensed particles, and this is bigger than zero. Then this particular density matrix $D_1(x', x)$ is not a density matrix at all, because you can show that it has negative characteristic values as well as positive, and therefore allows negative probabilities, which is sheer nonsense.

To give meaning to eq. (2), we must improve $D_1(x', x)$, and the cheapest way to improve it is to write instead

$$D_1(x', x) = \exp\{i(m/\hbar)(x' \times x) \cdot \omega - (m\omega/2\hbar)|R' - R|^2\}\bar{D}_1 \qquad (3)$$

Here R means just the distance from the axis of rotation; it's a two-dimensional vector in the plane perpendicular to the axis of rotation, and you can forget the direction parallel to the axis. Now this means that you need some extra energy over and above the normal energy of rotation; this extra energy is just

$$\Delta E = \tfrac{1}{2}N\hbar\omega \qquad (4)$$

If one is really optimistic, only the condensed particles should be counted; this estimate is then a lower bound for the energy needed. It would seem to be enough, and appears to agree quite nicely with the rate of creep, which is one of the most discontinuous phenomena of superflow. On the other hand, I can't quite believe it, because I haven't convinced myself that I can make an N-particle density matrix that will give us this one-particle density matrix. In fact, I've pretty well convinced myself that I can't even make a two-particle reduced density matrix that will conform to this one. The trouble is that the mutual angular momentum of two particles must be even, and that doesn't give me enough flexibility to match this; but that is a detail of the computation.

4. Vortex Lines

On the other extreme, we can get an upper bound for the energy that it takes for helium to rotate. The way to do this is to construct explicitly an N-particle wave function which describes helium with a respectable angular momentum and a macroscopically uniform distribution — and moreover with somewhat greater energy than eq. (4), but not a whole lot. Let us try

$$\psi = e^{i \sum \varphi(\mathbf{x}_j)} \psi_0 \tag{5}$$

where ψ_0 is the ground state wave function, and ψ the wave function of helium in motion. As you know, this describes potential flow, because the local velocity is given by

$$m\mathbf{v} = \hbar\nabla\varphi \tag{6}$$

and if the flow is divergence-free, then the phase is essentially velocity potential — and unless there is a time variation (e.g., a sound wave) it must satisfy Laplace's equation.

Now we have to use brute force to make this rotate — but not very brute. If the helium is rotating, the circulation $\oint \mathbf{v} \cdot d\mathbf{s}$ along a path perpendicular to the axis of rotation must be different from zero, and for uniform rotation would be proportional to the area of the path. To get this, you must have singularities, vortices. The structure right inside the vortex core can't be quite that of ordinary helium; it doesn't matter whether you put a hole in there or you put in solid helium, or something in between, as long as it isn't ordinary liquid. Then if you have a vortex core which the liquid can't reach,

φ can be multivalued. But ψ must be single-valued, so from eq. (5), φ can jump in multiples of 2π, and from eq. (6), the circulation

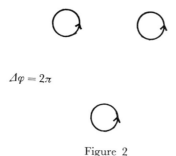

$\Delta\varphi = 2\pi$

Figure 2

$\oint \mathbf{v} \cdot d\mathbf{s}$ is quantized, with h/m as the quantum of circulation:

$$\oint \mathbf{v} \cdot d\mathbf{s} = 2\pi\hbar/m \tag{7}$$

for an elementary vortex.

So we picture helium, in rotation, as disturbed by a set of parallel vortices, each of strength h/m. You can make the energy in the holes finite, and the total energy (above that of a body in uniform rotation) is then of the following order:

$$\Delta E = N(2\pi\hbar\omega) \ln (d/A) \tag{8}$$

Here d stands for distance between vortices, or mean distance, and A stands for something of the size of a vortex core, which would be of the order of a half Angstrom or so. There is only a logarithmic factor times a respectable constant that separates the two reasonably well certified estimates eq. (4) and eq. (8), one a lower bound and the other an upper bound. Now this upper bound suggests some interesting things. It would seem, as Feynman [13] pointed out, very hard to nucleate these vortex lines, to get them away from the wall. On the other hand, it might be very hard to prepare liquid helium without a few scattered vortex lines frozen in, in the first place; it might be very hard to get rid of all of them, and once you have a few, they might breed more, like built-in screw dislocations in a crystal.

5. *Condensed Particles*

Not long ago, with Dr. Penrose [14], I looked into the question of whether helium II ought to have a condensed fraction — a fraction of condensed particles, and this turned out to depend on a very simple condition, namely, in the typical configuration of $\mathcal{N} - 1$ particles, how is the conditional probability of placing the $\mathcal{N}$th particle here or there distributed? If the reasonable places constitute a finite portion of the volume, then you expect momentum space order, otherwise you don't. The first alternative seems reasonable for a liquid and the second for a solid; in fact, one can prove it. This is for a temperature of absolute zero.

Quite recently, I tried to extend the estimate to finite temperatures, and came to the following result. You not only find that a finite portion remains, but that the depletion is in fact proportional to the square of the temperature, and it varies exponentially rather than linearly with the square of the temperature. Therefore, as long as you can superimpose the excitations, you cannot get rid of all of them except by some sort of cooperative effect involving the excitations.

Notes and References

1. F. Hammel, *Progress in Low Temperature Physics*, C. J. Gorter, ed. North-Holland, Amsterdam, 1955, p. 78.
2. W. H. Keesom and A. P. Keesom, *Physica* **3**, 359 (1936).
3. J. F. Allen and A. D. Misener, *Proc. Roy. Soc. (London)* **A172**, 467 (1939).
4. W. H. Keesom and J. E. MacWood, *Physica* **5**, 737 (1938).
5. E. A. Guggenheim, *Thermodynamics*, North-Holland, Amsterdam, 1950, p. 25.
6. L. Tisza, *Nature* **141**, 913 (1938).
7. L. D. Landau, *JETP* **11**, 592 (1941).
8. E. Andronikashvili, *J. Phys. (U.S.S.R.)* **10**, 201 (1946).
9. L. D. Landau, *J. Phys. (U.S.S.R.)* **5**, 71, (1941).
10. F. London, *Revs. Modern Phys.* **17**, 310 (1945).
11. H. E. Hall and W. F. Vinen, *Proc. Roy. Soc. (London)* **A238**, 204 (1956); 215 (1956).
12. R. P. Feynman, *Phys. Rev.* **94**, 262 (1954).
13. R. P. Feynman, *Progress in Low Temperature Physics*, C. J. Gorter, ed. North-Holland, Amsterdam, 1955.
14. O. Penrose and L. Onsager, *Phys. Rev.* **104**, 576 (1956).

CHAPTER XXVI

Boson Field Approach to the Theory of Liquid He II

P. R. ZILSEL

1. *Introduction*

Apparently, there are a great many approaches to the theory of liquid helium, many of which seem to give the same results in first approximation although they use different starting points. I didn't realize just how many of these there were until the present conference.

The approach I want to talk about is not rigorous — one has to use physical, intuitive ideas to get approximate results — but it has the advantage that the validity of the first approximation, which one can calculate, does not depend on the interaction between the particles being weak or the density small. In fact, the approximation is particularly appropriate to the ground state of the system being liquid rather than crystalline or gaseous, that is, to the case of high density without long-range order.

We start from the quantized Boson field describing the system of interacting He atoms, with the Hamiltonian

$$H = \int (\hbar^2/2m)(\nabla\psi^*) \cdot (\nabla\psi)\, d\tau$$

$$+ \tfrac{1}{2}\int d\tau \int d\tau'\, V(\mathbf{r}-\mathbf{r}')\, \psi^*(\mathbf{r})\, \psi^*(\mathbf{r}')\, \psi(\mathbf{r})\, \psi(\mathbf{r}') \tag{1}$$

and the commutation relations

$$[\psi^*(\mathbf{r}),\ \psi(\mathbf{r}')] = -\delta(\mathbf{r} - \mathbf{r}')$$
$$[\psi^*(\mathbf{r}),\ \psi^*(\mathbf{r}')] = [\psi(\mathbf{r}),\ \psi(\mathbf{r}')] = 0 \tag{2}$$

This is, of course, equivalent to the description by the many-body Schrödinger equation in configuration space, with the interaction potential $V(\mathbf{r}_i - \mathbf{r}_j)$ acting between each pair of atoms.

465

It has been pointed out by Bohm [1] that the c-number limit of the field theory given by the Hamiltonian (1) furnishes a hydrodynamic approximation which describes a number of the qualitative features of the superfluid quite well. What I have done now is look into the first approximation that goes beyond the c-number theory, that is, I take into account the quantization of the field, but make approximations which involve the assumption that the quantum fluctuations in the density, at least for long wave lengths, are small compared to the mean density.

2. Extended Hydrodynamic Approximation

In the hydrodynamic approximation, as pointed out by Bohm [1], it is convenient to make a canonical transformation to the density $\rho(\mathbf{r})$ and the phase $S(\mathbf{r})$:

$$\psi = e^{iS/\hbar} \rho^{\frac{1}{2}} \qquad \psi^* = \rho^{\frac{1}{2}} e^{-iS/\hbar} \tag{3}$$

ρ and S are canonically conjugate, and S is the hydrodynamic velocity potential. In the q-number theory, we have

$$[\rho(\mathbf{r}), \, S(\mathbf{r}')] = -\hbar/i \, \delta(\mathbf{r} - \mathbf{r}')$$
$$[\rho(\mathbf{r}), \, \rho(\mathbf{r}')] = [S(\mathbf{r}), \, S(\mathbf{r}')] = 0 \tag{4}$$

and the Hamiltonian in the new variables becomes

$$H = \int d\tau \, \{(\hbar^2/8m\rho)(\nabla\rho)^2 + (1/2m)\rho^{\frac{1}{2}}(\nabla S)^2 \rho^{\frac{1}{2}}$$
$$+ (i\hbar/4m)[\rho^{-\frac{1}{2}}(\nabla\rho) \cdot (\nabla S)\rho^{\frac{1}{2}} - \rho^{\frac{1}{2}}(\nabla S) \cdot (\nabla\rho)\rho^{-\frac{1}{2}}]\}$$
$$+ \tfrac{1}{2}\int d\tau \int d\tau' \, V(\mathbf{r}-\mathbf{r}') \rho(\mathbf{r})[\rho(\mathbf{r}') - \delta(\mathbf{r}-\mathbf{r}')] \tag{5}$$

Any attempt at an approximate solution in this representation runs into the difficulty that the Hamiltonian involves inverse and fractional powers of ρ, and ρ has the eigenvalue zero. On the other hand, one knows that the Fourier components of ρ, at least for long wave lengths, represent approximate normal modes of the system (phonons) and, in fact, diagonalize the interaction part of the Hamiltonian exactly. Keeping in mind the partial validity of the c-number approximation, we can get around the difficulty, in part, by working with smoothed values of the operators:

$$\rho(\mathbf{r}) = u(\mathbf{r})\bar{\rho}(\mathbf{r}) \qquad S(\mathbf{r}) = \bar{S}(\mathbf{r}) + \sigma(\mathbf{r}) \tag{6}$$

where $\bar{\rho}$ and $\bar{S}$ are averages over spheres of radius r_0 (of the order of, but slightly less than, the hard sphere repulsion radius in V) and u and σ contain the high frequency fluctuations only. As long as we are concerned only with low-lying excited states of the system, the high frequency fluctuations will be frozen into their ground state values, so that the operators u and σ can be approximately replaced by their ground state expectation values.

We Fourier analyze $\bar{\rho}$ and $\bar{S}$:

$$\bar{\rho} = \rho_0 + \sum_{\mathbf{k}} \rho_{\mathbf{k}} e^{i\mathbf{k}\cdot\mathbf{r}} \qquad (\rho_{\mathbf{k}}^* = \rho_{-\mathbf{k}})$$
$$\bar{S} = \sum_{\mathbf{k}} S_{\mathbf{k}} e^{i\mathbf{k}\cdot\mathbf{r}} \qquad (S_{\mathbf{k}}^* = S_{-\mathbf{k}}) \tag{7}$$

and obtain

$$[\rho_{\mathbf{k}}, S_{\mathbf{k}'}^*] = (\hbar/i) f(k/k_0) \delta_{\mathbf{k},\mathbf{k}'} \tag{8}$$

where f is a cutoff factor (a c number) arising from the smoothing process, such that

$$f = 1 \qquad \text{for} \qquad k < \sim k_0$$
$$f = 0 \qquad \text{for} \qquad k > \sim k_0$$

and $k_0 = 1/r_0$. In (7) ρ_0 is the average density, which commutes with the Hamiltonian and is simply a number in any particular case. The fluctuations of $\bar{\rho}$ are much less violent than those of ρ so that in (5) we write, approximately

$$\rho^n = u^n (\rho_0 + \sum_{\mathbf{k}} \rho_{\mathbf{k}} e^{i\mathbf{k}\cdot\mathbf{r}})^n$$
$$\sim u^n \rho_0^n [1 + (n/\rho_0) \sum_{\mathbf{k}} \rho_{\mathbf{k}} e^{i\mathbf{k}\cdot\mathbf{r}} + \ldots]$$

Performing the ground state averages, with $\langle u \rangle \sim 1$, $\langle \nabla u \rangle \sim 0$, $\langle \sigma \rangle \sim 0$, one then obtains approximately, to second order in $\rho_{\mathbf{k}}$, $S_{\mathbf{k}}$:

$$H \sim H_0 + \sum_{k < k_0} \tfrac{1}{2} \{[(\hbar^2/4m\rho_0) k^2 + W_k] \rho_{\mathbf{k}} \rho_{\mathbf{k}}^* + (\rho_0/m) k^2 S_{\mathbf{k}} S_{\mathbf{k}}^*\} \tag{9}$$

Here H_0 is the part of the Hamiltonian depending on ρ_0 and the high frequency fluctuations only, and W_k is the Fourier transform of a quantity $W(\mathbf{r})$, which is essentially the interaction potential $V(\mathbf{r})$ cut off for $r < r_0$. More precisely,

$$W(\mathbf{r}) = V(\mathbf{r}) [\langle u(0) u(\mathbf{r}) \rangle - \rho_0^{-1} \delta(\mathbf{r})] \tag{10}$$

where the $\langle \ \ \rangle$ signify the ground state expectation value. Keeping in mind that the smoothing radius r_0 has been chosen to be less than the distance over which V is strongly repulsive, it follows that $W(\mathbf{r}) = 0$ for $r < \sim r_0$. On the other hand, for $r \gg r_0$, $\langle u(0) u(r) \rangle \sim \langle u \rangle^2 \sim 1$, since the correlations over distances $> r_0$ are contained in $\bar{\rho}$ and not in u.

3. *Excitation Spectrum*

The approximate Hamiltonian (9) is a sum of harmonic oscillator terms with excitation energies

$$\mathscr{E}_k = [(\rho_0/m) W_k + (\hbar^2 k^2/4m^2)]^{\frac{1}{2}} \hbar k \qquad (11)$$

Alternatively, since, from (9), the ground state expectation value of $\rho_{\mathbf{k}} \rho_{\mathbf{k}}^*$ is

$$\begin{aligned}\langle \rho_{\mathbf{k}} \rho_{\mathbf{k}}^* \rangle_0 &= \tfrac{1}{2} \mathscr{E}_k [(\hbar^2/4m\rho_0) k^2 + W_k]^{-1} \\ &= \hbar k \rho_0 (4m\rho_0 W_k + \hbar^2 k^2)^{-\frac{1}{2}}\end{aligned} \qquad (12)$$

we have

$$\mathscr{E}_k = (\hbar^2 k^2/2m) \rho_0 / \langle \rho_{\mathbf{k}} \rho_{\mathbf{k}}^* \rangle_0 \qquad (13)$$

in agreement with Feynman's [2] result. Expression (11) agrees with that obtained by Bogoliubov and Zubarev [3], except that because of the smoothing procedure, W_k appears in place of the Fourier transform V_k of the actual interaction potential. Because of the strong repulsion at small distances, V_k is positive for all $\mathbf{k}$ (in fact it diverges strongly if one uses, e.g., the Lennard-Jones potential down to $r \to 0$), whereas W_k becomes negative for $k^{-1} \sim 3$ A, qualitatively reproducing the dip in the energy spectrum corresponding to the "roton" minimum.

In conclusion, it should be pointed out that the approximation used here becomes meaningless for $k > \sim k_0$, since the high frequency density fluctuations do not appear in the $\rho_{\mathbf{k}}$'s, which are the Fourier components of the smoothed density operator $\bar{\rho}$. Thus the asymptotic result

$$\mathscr{E}_k \to \hbar^2 k^2/2m \qquad (k \to \infty)$$

has no meaning in this treatment (and I suspect that the same holds in other treatments). Formally, this limitation shows up through the cutoff factor $f(k/k_0)$ in the commutation relations (8). For high k the Fourier components of the density are not even approximately normal modes.

AUTHOR'S NOTE: No attempt has been made to bring the manuscript up to date. It should be noted, however, that the transformation (3) is not as unproblematical as the text would lead one to believe. In particular, the commutation relations (4) are not exactly but only approximately compatible with (2). For a discussion of the hydro-dynamic representation in terms of the density matrix formalism see T. Nishiyama, *Progr. Theoret. Phys* **8**, (Kyoto) 655 (1952) and **9**, 245 (1953).

Notes and References

1. D. Bohm, unpublished.
2. R. P. Feynman, *Phys. Rev.* **94**, 262 (1954).
3. N. N. Bogoliubov and D. N. Zubarev, *JETP* **28**, 129 (1955). [English translation: *JETP* **1**, 83 (1955)].

CHAPTER XXVII

Round Table on Superfluids

Participants:

E. P. Gross, *Moderator*

J. Bardeen	L. Goldstein
J. M. Blatt	L. Onsager
M. J. Buckingham	D. Pines
K. A. Brueckner	L. Tisza
L. N. Cooper	P. R. Zilsel

A. Superfluid Helium

1. *Specific heat of helium near the λ point*

E. P. Gross: Turning now to the topic of superfluids, there have been some very interesting experiments at Duke recently [1]. I would like to ask Dr. Buckingham to introduce this discussion, since he was associated with doing these experiments.

M. J. Buckingham: I will just state the results briefly, since I don't suppose that you are principally interested in the experimental aspects. This work was performed by W. M. Fairbank, C. F. Kellers, and myself.

The idea was to resolve very sharply in temperature the specific heat of helium near the λ point (subsequently, we hope to do the same for its density). This succeeded, and we now know the specific heat, at the vapor pressure of helium, to within a few millionths of a degree from the λ point. I'll write down an empirical expression which describes this; the results are still really preliminary and it is possible that the numbers may be slightly wrong, but the qualitative shape is given well enough. The specific heat at the vapor pressure in natural units (R per mole) is

$$C = 0.71 f(t) \ln |4.6/(1-t)| - 2.5 \Delta(t) \tag{1}$$

Here $f(t)$ is a smooth function satisfying $f(1) = 1$, t is the reduced temperature $t = T/T_\lambda$, and $\Delta(t) = 0$ for $t < 1$, $\Delta(t) = 1$ for $t > 1$. Thus there is a logarithmic singularity at the λ point and also a discontinuity amounting to a change of specific heat of 2.5 k per particle. The expression holds experimentally to within say 5×10^{-6} degrees on either side of the λ point.

If one puts in for $f(t)$ some smooth function of the reduced temperature (which I have not yet worked out, but it may be something like T^6), then, with expression (1), one can describe the specific heat from 0^0 K right up to 4^0 K. In other words, the logarithmic singularity and the discontinuity mirror all of the singular behavior. We have now a quantitative picture of the transition, and you will notice for example that it doesn't fit into a normal classification of the Ehrenfest type [2]. Since Prof. Tisza does not believe this classification anyway, I think that he has some remarks to make about this.

L. Tisza: The new precision measurement of the λ anomaly of helium is not only an impressive experimental achievement, but promises to be significant for a refinement of our theoretical ideas on phase equilibrium in general, and on the nature of the superfluid state in particular.

A noteworthy aspect of the experiment is that it does not fit into the Ehrenfest scheme of higher order transitions. This scheme was originally advanced under the impact of Keesom's [3] discovery of the λ anomaly of helium some 25 years ago and was meant to fill a gap in the Gibbsian phase theory. But the Ehrenfest scheme envisaged discontinuities of the specific heat, whereas the new measurements seem to suggest a singularity.

The first indication that singularities of the specific heat might have to be considered, instead of or along with discontinuities, arose in connection with Onsager's rigorous calculation [4] of the two-dimensional Ising model. This calculation led to a logarithmic singularity of the specific heat, but it was not entirely evident whether the result was dependent on the special features of the model. The present measurements give support to the view that considers the occurrence of singularities as an effect of basic thermodynamic significance. At the same time, it is possible that discontinuities of the

Ehrenfest type also occur; the case of superconductivity may be a case in point. It would of course be possible to augment the Ehrenfest scheme by simply noting that the classification originally suggested was not inclusive enough. This procedure would be quite in line with the descriptive, taxonomical, attitude taken in most thermodynamic discussions of phase equilibrium.

It may not be unnecessary to point out that the classical phase theory of Gibbs has a more fundamental character. The possible types of dicontinuities in thermodynamic phase space are deduced from principles of thermodynamic stability. I found some time ago [5] that the Gibbsian approach to the theory of phase equilibrium can be extended and λ anomalies integrated into the classical theory, provided that the definition of phase is sharpened to include the specification of the symmetry of the system. This was already recognized several years ago for order-disorder transitions in crystals. The case of helium, however, has quite special characteristics.

Assuming tentatively that the singular character of the helium λ point is confirmed for the entire λ line [6], the experimental findings can be fitted into this generalized phase theory only under the assumption that the superfluid state can exist in two energetically equivalent modifications related to each other by a symmetry operation. The situation would be formally analogous to the case of ferromagnetism, in which the two modifications are provided by the domains, in which the direction of magnetization points to the right and left respectively. This is a surprising result, in contradiction to the perfect symmetry generally assigned to the superfluid. However, the thermodynamic argument gives no clue as to the nature of the asymmetry of the superfluid state. Further progress in this direction would require more incisive methods.

L. Goldstein: I would like to know upon what your statement about temperature differences of the order of 10^{-6} degrees is based. This is the first time any experiment has been made with a temperature difference of this order of magnitude. Can you briefly describe it.

M. J. Buckingham: This was a matter of design of the specimen and method of measurement. What was used here was a closed container, containing approximately 0.06 grams of helium — in fact the absolute values we obtained were not very certain merely because we were not exactly sure of how much helium we had. These results are then accurate to within a few per cent in absolute value, which is all we can expect, and then normalized to the previously measured ones of Keesom at 2.1° K. We are only interested in the shape near the λ point, and so we measured nothing further away than about a tenth of a degree from the λ point. Our relative values of course are much more accurate than the absolute values.

The 0.06 grams of helium is inside a copper container which is sealed, and contains about 200 grams of copper; the specific heat of the copper — which is smooth, anyway, as a function of temperature — contributes to less than 10 % of the total heat capacity. The copper is made with vanes, as it were, inside for thermal contact, in such a way that nowhere is the helium more than 0.003 inches from a copper surface. This was designed (calculated from the heat conductivity of electrolytically pure copper) to give, if one put in 100 ergs per second of heat, no temperature difference inside the copper, due to the heating, of more than 10^{-5} degrees. Actually, the heat input we use is much less than 100 ergs per second, in fact not even 1 erg.

The temperature is measured with a resistance thermometer with a large temperature coefficient of resistance, about 1.5 ohms per 10^{-5} degrees; the absolute value of the resistance is about 75,000 ohms at the λ point. One measures the resistance on a sensitive bridge, using a 10 cps signal, amplified and recorded on an automatic recorder. The measurements were actually made by putting in a constant heating power and recording the temperature as a function of time; numerous runs were made through the lambda point by heating and cooling at various rates, and no difference was observed, so there is no doubt that there was thermal equilibrium. In fact, if one switched off the heat, the apparent temperature, as measured on the recorder, would become constant again within the one second response time of the electronics.

A further corroborating point is that — this is not very accurate — I would say that to within a millionth of a degree, and certainly to within 10^{-5}, which corresponds to a rate of about eight times the noise level, there is no hysteresis of any sort. In other words, if one heats past the λ point and then cools down again, the transition occurs within a millionth of a degree of the same point. I might mention that one is here already approaching a limitation due to the change of the lambda temperature under pressure, because merely from the weight of the helium in the gravitational field (and the maximum dimension was only one centimeter) there is a spatial pressure difference corresponding to a change of about a millionth of a degree in the λ point. If one resolved any further, one would expect to get the curve rounded off anyway.

2. *Excitation spectrum of He II*

K. A. Brueckner: I would like to briefly mention some results that were previously discussed [7] and say to what extent they resemble or differ from Bogoliubov's work [8] of 1947. Bogoliubov observed that the interaction term in the Hamiltonian describes the interaction between superfluid particles, between excited particles, and between excited particles and the superfluid. If one ignores the interaction between excited particles and furthermore observes that the annihilation and creation operators for zero momentum can be replaced by the square root of the particle number when the zero momentum occupation is sufficiently high, then the interaction term in the Hamiltonian reduces to a bilinear form which can be diagonalized by an orthogonal transformation. This gives the spectrum that has been written down several times. Now one can very much improve the calculation by observing that there are two types of higher terms which Bogoliubov ignored, which can really be included in a very simple way [9].

In the first place, the interaction between two particles when they are excited does not have to be completely omitted; at least, the excited particles can be allowed to interact pairwise an arbitrary number of times before returning. The inclusion of these terms replaces the first-order interaction of Bogoliubov essentially by the pseudopotential, the interaction operator, or the reaction matrix — whatever you want to call it — which was actually suggested to Bogoliubov by Landau at the time he wrote his paper. In this way, we remove a very large class of higher order terms from the perturbation theory. The second approximation that one does not need to make is the assumption that the particles which are interacting are really moving as free particles, which is implied when one replaces the interaction potential by the pseudopotential. One can in fact compute the interaction of a pair of particles, taking into account the fact that they are actually in the presence of the superfluid, with its properties of phonon excitation and energy gap against particle excitation.

The only terms which are difficult to take into account are those which describe the remaining interaction, of the excited particles with each other. Now this suggests an approximation that is essentially an expansion in powers of the diluteness of the excited particles, in other words, an expansion in the ratio of normal fluid to superfluid. At low temperatures, of course, this is a very small number, and therefore one does have a convenient parameter in which to expand. The results one gets when one does this are formally somewhat similar to Bogoliubov's, except that one must make the following replacements: If

$$v_{00,00} = (1/\Omega) \int V(\mathbf{r}) \, d^3 r \tag{2}$$

(Ω = normalization volume) is the potential matrix element between superfluid particles, then if one includes first the repeated interaction of this pair of particles when excited, (2) is replaced by $t_{00,00}$, where

$$t_{q-q,00} = v_{q-q,00} + \sum_{q'} v_{q-q,q'-q'} \, (-q'^2/m)^{-1} t_{q'-q',00} \tag{3}$$

$t_{00,00}$ is the same matrix element that occurs in the scattering of two free helium atoms on each other in the limit of zero energy. Then, the inclusion of interactions of the excited particles with the superfluid, i.e., the inclusion of the effect of the superfluid on the propagation of these particles, replaces $t_{00,00}$ by

$$K_{00,00} = v_{00,00} - \sum_{q} v_{00,q-q} [(q^2/m) + 2N(K_{0q,0q} + K_{0q,0q} - K_{00,00})] K_{q-q,00}$$

Here, $K_{0q,0q}$ and $K_{0q,q0}$ describe the interaction of an exciton of momentum q with a superfluid particle, and $K_{q-q,00}$ the excitation of two superfluid particles to excited states q and $-q$; these operators are obtained self-consistently in a fashion similar to eq. (3).

The K operators can thus be said to be generated from V by including first the class of interactions which replace V by the pseudopotential, and second the class of corrections which replace the scattering potential by the operator calculated in the presence of the superfluid. These changes have an effect on the Hamiltonian similar to that of the transformation discussed by Dr. Gross [10]. The transformed Hamiltonian allows one to describe the system with considerable accuracy as long as the percentage of superfluid remains a large fraction of the total, for the essential approximation is the neglect of interaction between excitons. If one now carries out the same transformation that Bogoliubov used, but with the interactions V replaced by the vastly more complicated operators K, then one gets a spectrum (Fig. 1) which is similar to Bogoliubov's at low momentum, but at higher momentum is essentially the spectrum deduced by Landau, with the characteristic dip in the excitation energy.

Now there is one point I would like to raise concerning the spectrum about the dip. Landau has used the word "roton" to describe these excitations. But the transformation which takes one from the original representation to the phonon-roton representation is a transformation which reduces to an identity transformation for high momentum; in the roton region, it is quite close to an identity transformation. Therefore in this region, these excitations are very similar to particle excitations, and so I would like to ask whether there is any evidence for a roton character.

L. Onsager: As long as you use, so to speak, the one-particle approximation to collective excitation

$$\varphi(\mathbf{x}) = \sum e^{i\mathbf{k}\cdot\mathbf{x}_i}\varphi_0(\mathbf{x}) \tag{5}$$

where φ_0 is the ground state, — and this is very good for long-wave phonons — as variational trial function, then the excitation energy is entirely determined [11] by the X-ray scattering function $S(\mathbf{k})$:

$$E(\mathbf{k}) = \hbar^2 k^2/2mS(\mathbf{k}) \tag{6}$$

If you put in an empirical $S(\mathbf{k})$, then, if there is a minimum at all in $E(\mathbf{k})$, the minimum is much too high compared to the Landau value [12]. You must improve (5) and this was done independently by Feynman and Cohen, and by Frohlich and Kuper [13]; they used slightly different trial functions and arrived at much the same result, a characteristic of about 10–11°K, instead of Landau's 9°K.

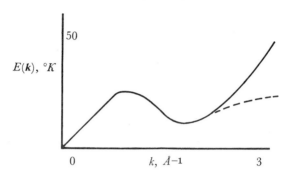

$E(k)$, °K

50

0   k, A^{-1} 3

Figure 1

As regards the principle of superposition of excitations, that is, of describing the relations between the set of excited states and the ground state (but not of getting the description of the ground state, which may be very complicated for strong interactions such as we have in helium), I think that this seems legitimate as long as the general level of excitation is low, and that is the only requirement. Moreover, I think that the distribution of the zero point amplitudes of each excitation will in a sense correspond to just one half quantum. The reason for this is that the amplitude density distribution will have to be Gaussian, because all of the amplitudes are extensive quantities and it seems safe to apply the central limit theorem [14] with the usual limitations, which require among other things that we mustn't go to levels of excitation that are too high.

Now, as regards the shape of the curve (Fig. 1), I don't like it on the high frequency end, where perhaps you consider it most certain, for the following reason. In constructing more and more complicated excitons, involving one, two, or more particles, the complications (and increasing accuracy) arise in a sense from the possibility that a one-particle excitation has of splitting into two, particularly if the energy curve rises steeply for high k, as in Fig. 1. When the curve goes this way, you can split it in two parts in many ways, conserving both momentum and energy. It will be utterly improbable that the process will not occur at all, and so I think you will get an elementary excitation by requiring $E(\mathbf{k})$ to be a minimum for a given $\mathbf{k}$. In a homogeneous liquid, the wave number describes a representation of translational symmetry, so that you can fix $\mathbf{k}$ and find the lowest energy for that $\mathbf{k}$ (dropping pure center of mass motion); in order for an excited state $E(\mathbf{k})$ to be a minimum, it must satisty the inequality

$$E(\mathbf{k}) \leqq E(\mathbf{k}') + E(\mathbf{k}-\mathbf{k}') \tag{7}$$

that the energy corresponding to the sum of two momenta be no greater than the sum of the energies corresponding to the two momenta.

The phonons then are approximately single-particle excitations, but any particle-like excitations for high momentum and energy degrade or split into phonons, vortex excitations (presumably combinations of elementary excitations given by the dotted line in Fig. 1), and . . . junk.

D. Pines: I would say that the high k excitations should properly be regarded as individual-particle excitations, because their energy is quite accurately written as $\hbar^2 k^2/2m^* S(\mathbf{k})$, where m^* is a somewhat larger mass than the free helium atom's mass, because of the phonons the helium atom carries along with it. $S(\mathbf{k})$ essentially represents the fact that the helium atom is interacting with its cloud of nearest neighbors, with the five or six nearest neighbors it has. Its motion is slightly altered by this but we really have here just individual-particle excitations.

L. Onsager: Well, that's a matter of terminology.

P. R. Zilsel: I would like to mention, Professor Onsager, that since this very high k part of the spectrum is in response to k's which are of the order of the reciprocal hard sphere radius of helium, then certainly in any theory like Bogoliubov's or the sort of thing which I have done [15], there will be very high wave number fluctuations in the ground state density. You wouldn't expect such treatments to give a reasonable picture in this limit. As a matter of fact, if one proceeds as I did, averaging over density, then a factor occurs because of this averaging, which brings forth the spectrum of Fig. 1; but that may simply mean that the modes one is using don't properly describe the phenomenon.

L. Onsager: Of course, the size of the sin you commit depends on what you are trying to do. As a matter of fact, the way that the k^2 part of the spectrum appears in Bogoliubov's and Zubarev's [16] paper is very pretty; there, it is a result of statistical fluctuations, so it corresponds to a random distribution of particles and nothing more. Their work converges to something realistic in this fashion; on the other hand, if one really wants to know what the excitations of such high wave number might be, the answer is probably more like what I mentioned previously.

M. J. Buckingham: In connection with the interpretation of the excitations about the energy minimum, one should notice that the group velocity is zero, and to call them single-particle excitations is strange. On the low side, in fact, the harder you push them one way, the slower they go — they go backwards, so I think they are more likely to be like Feynman's backwash [13] on the opposite side. If you like, you could take this into account by a clothed field, perhaps, but not as a single excited particle.

K. A. Brueckner: I suppose that if this is the case, then the transformation which Dr. Gross told us about [10], the sequence U_1, U_2, U_3, really describes a readjustment of the structure as the particle moves through it, giving an effective mass, and one does have a counterflow around it.

E. P. Gross: You certainly have that. I think there is another way of seeing it, which is simply in terms of a classical picture of a subharmonic resonance which comes from the quartic interaction terms. One knows that if you have harmonic oscillators and put in quartic terms, then you not only modify the frequencies of the oscillators, but you produce overtones, subharmonics, resonances. Thus in the treatment I presented, you find terms in both the ground state energy and the excitation spectrum which involve the wave number $k/2$.

Notes and References

1. Fairbank, Buckingham, and Kellers, *Bull. Am. Phys. Soc. Ser.* II, **2** 183 (1957).
2. P. Ehrenfest, *Proc. Roy. Acad. Amsterdam* **36**, 153 (1933).
3. W. H. Keesom and K. Clusius, *Koninkl. Ned. Akad. Wetenschap. Proc.* **35**, 307 (1932)
4. L. Onsager, *Phys. Rev.* **65**, 117 (1944).
5. L. Tisza, in *Phase Transformations in Solids*, R. Smoluchowski, Mayer, and Weyl, ed. Wiley, New York, 1951.
6. See, e.g., F. London *Superfluids*, Wiley, New York, 1954, Vol. II, p. 4.
7. K. A. Brueckner, Chap. III, this volume.
8. N. N. Bogoliubov, *J. Phys. (U.S.S.R.)* **11**, 23 (1947).
9. K. A. Brueckner and K. Sawada, *Phys. Rev.* **106**, 1117 (1957); 1128 (1957).
10. E. P. Gross, Chap. XV, this volume.
11. R. P. Feynman, *Phys, Rev.* **94**, 262 (1954).
12. L. Landau, *J. Phys. (U.S.S.R.)* **5**, 71 (1941); **11**, 91 (1947).
13. R. P. Feynman and M. Cohen, *Phys. Rev.* **102**, 189 (1956). C. G. Kuper, *Proc. Roy. Soc. (London)* **A233**, 233 (1955).
14. See, e.g., W. Feller, *Probability Theory*, Wiley, New York, 1950, p. 192.
15. P. R. Zilsel, Chap. XXVI, this volume.
16. N. N. Bogoliubov and D. N. Zubarev, *ZETF* **28**, 129 (1955) (translation: *JETP* **1**, 83).

B. Superconductivity

1. The Form of the Interaction

E. P. Gross: In the time remaining, we shall turn to the subject of superconductivity, and I think that Prof. Bardeen might summarize the situation as he sees it at this time.

J. Bardeen: We do not as yet have nice solutions for superconductivity, of the type we have been hearing about for liquid helium. What I shall try to do is to indicate the nature of the interaction which we believe is responsible for superconductivity. These considerations are based on work done in collaboration with L. N. Cooper and J. R. Schrieffer. The isotope effect [17] indicates that superconductivity arises from interactions between electrons and phonons — the so-called electron-phonon interaction. We understand now why this interaction, which appears rather weak, actually dominates the Coulomb interaction, which we ordinarily think is rather large. For transitions near the Fermi surface, the phonon interaction is really large, and is the one which we believe gives rise to the transition.

The electron-phonon interaction results in an interaction between electrons in **k** space which can be described roughly by saying that one electron emits a virtual phonon and the other absorbs it, giving a scattering of one electron by the other. The interaction constant which determines the scattering is $2|M_q|^2/\hbar\omega$, where $|M_q|^2$ is the square of the electron-phonon matrix element for phonon wave vector **q**, calculated for zero point energy. A coupling constant may be defined as the product of this expression and the density of states in energy; the criterion for superconductivity given by Frohlich [18] is then that this contant be greater than unity. If the electron-phonon interaction is as large as this, a perturbation theory expansion can not be used, and although an interaction this large suggests that something drastic might happen to the electronic wave functions, it doesn't tell what will happen. Now the phonon interaction is negative, or attractive, when the energy difference between the electron states involved is less than $\hbar\omega$. It is this part of the interaction, between states near the Fermi surface, which we think is responsible for super-conductivity.

Probably the attractive nature of the interaction is important, and the correct criterion is not the one given by Frohlich, but that the phonon interaction dominate the repulsive Coulomb interaction so as to give a net attraction. The Coulomb interaction for a free electron gas is $4\pi e^2/q^2$, where $\mathbf{q} = \mathbf{k} - \mathbf{k}'$. A screened Coulomb interaction should be used; thus in the Bohm-Pines theory [19], plasma oscillations are introduced for q smaller than a critical value q_c. The new criterion may then be expressed in the approximate form:

$$\langle -2|M_q|^2/\hbar\omega + 4\pi e^2/q_c^2 \rangle_{\mathrm{Av}} < 0 \tag{8}$$

When numbers are put in, it turns out that this criterion is actually not much different from that given by Frohlich.

In addition to the true interaction between electrons, the electron-phonon interaction gives a negative self energy of the order of $\hbar\omega$ per electron for electrons within an energy $\hbar\omega$ of the Fermi surface. The total is of the order of $\mathcal{N}(E_F) \cdot (\hbar\omega)^2$, where $\mathcal{N}(E_F)$ is the density of states in energy at the Fermi surface. This is much larger than the energy difference between normal and superconducting states, which is of the order of $\mathcal{N}(E_F)(kT_c)^2$. Thus most of the self energy must occur in the normal state, and only a small fraction, if any, is involved in the transition.

The essential problem is to isolate that part of the electron-phonon interaction that gives rise to the transition and to show how it leads to a coherent many-particle ground state. As Pippard has shown [20], the coherence distance is empirically of the order of 10^{-4} cm in a macroscopic specimen. There is now good evidence for an energy gap for excitations in a superconductor corresponding to those of individual particles in the normal state. These features of the superconducting state probably account for the Meissner effect and other electromagnetic properties of the superconducting state.

ADDED IN PROOF: A theory of superconductivity based on the attractive nature of the phonon interaction has recently been given by Bardeen, Cooper, and Schrieffer [21].

2. Effect of Correlations

J. M. Blatt: I would like to make some comments on the problem of superconductivity. First of all, I think that most people are now agreed on the nature of the interaction (electron-electron interaction via the phonons). There is however considerable disagreement on how one is to stick this interaction into an actual calculation, that is, just how this interaction produces the observed effects. Let me outline the approach which Butler, Schafroth and I have developed [22] in Sydney. This is very crudely the following:

The independent-particle approximation assigns energy levels $E(k)$ to individual electrons, with the total energy E being the sum of the individual electron energies. $E(k)$ may be a complicated function, it may or may not have gaps in it, i.e., ranges of energies which do not occur in $E(k)$ — this does not matter here. What does matter is that the statistical matrix, $\exp(-\beta H)$, under this approximation splits into a direct product of single-particle statistical matrices:

$$\langle k_1 k_2 \ldots k_N | \exp(-\beta H) | k_1' k_2' \ldots k_N' \rangle$$
$$= \langle k_1 | U | k_1' \rangle \langle k_2 | U | k_2' \rangle \ldots \langle k_N | U | k_N' \rangle \qquad (9)$$

This is of course an extremely strong assumption, and there are any number of reasons why it should be very bad. Nevertheless, this is precisely the assumption which corresponds to the band theory of solids, and seems to agree reasonably well with many experimental observations. However, we feel that it does *not* suffice for an understanding of superconductivity, but must be improved for that purpose. In this we differ from others, who maintain that this independent-particle approximation can give superconductivity if only the energy spectrum $E(k)$ is sufficiently complicated.

In order to improve the approximation (9) we add terms in which the pairs of particles are connected. We introduce a pair correlation matrix W with matrix elements $\langle k_1 k_2 | W | k_1' k_2' \rangle$, and generalize the Ansatz (9) to include all possible numbers of factors W, from no W's at all [i.e., the Ansatz (9) itself] to $N/2$ factors W and no U's at all. I write down a few terms below:

$$
\begin{aligned}
\langle k_1 k_2 \ldots k_N & | \exp(-\beta H) | k_1' k_2' \ldots k_N' \rangle \\
&= \langle k_1 | U | k_1' \rangle \langle k_2 | U | k_2' \rangle \ldots \langle k_N | U | k_N' \rangle \\
&+ \langle k_1 k_2 | W | k_1' k_2' \rangle \langle k_3 | U | k_3' \rangle \langle k_4 | U | k_4' \rangle \ldots \langle k_N | U | k_N' \rangle \\
&+ \text{permutations of the above} \\
&+ \langle k_1 k_2 | W | k_1' k_2' \rangle \langle k_3 k_4 | W | k_3' k_4' \rangle \langle k_5 | U | k_5' \rangle \ldots \langle k_N | U | k_N' \rangle \\
&+ \text{permutations of the above} \\
&+ \text{all terms with 3 factors } W \\
&+ \text{all terms with 4 factors } W + \ldots \\
&+ \langle k_1 k_2 | W | k_1' k_2' \rangle \langle k_3 k_4 | W | k_3' k_4' \rangle \ldots \langle k_{N-1} k_N | W | k_{N-1}' k_N' \rangle \\
&+ \text{permutations of the above}
\end{aligned}
\tag{10}
$$

The first term of (10) is identical with the independent-particle model Ansatz (9), so (10) is certainly an improvement in principle over the independent-particle model. The pair correlations included here are over and above everything contained in the band theory of solids.

Now it turns out that the Ansatz (10), that is, the structure of the expression (10), contains within itself the possibility of a thermodynamic transition to a state which is like a Bose-Einstein condensation of these "pairs." The similarity is formal, and the way in which it arises is rather tricky. Furthermore, whether or not such a transition actually occurs depends on the pair matrix W chosen, in particular on the eigenvalue spectrum of a matrix $\tilde{W}$ related to W. I have no time to give details, but let me state some conclusions:

1. The possibility of a transition exists only if the interaction is at least partially attractive.

2. An ordinary (velocity-independent) interaction between electrons would lead to trouble, in the sense that correction terms would become of major importance as the temperature decreases, and the approximation would break down before we reach the condensation temperature. On the other hand, the highly velocity-dependent Frohlich interaction [23] is not necessarily subject to this trouble, and there is some reason to believe that the formal similarity to Bose-Einstein condensation of electron pairs is reasonable if the pairs are produced by such an interaction.

3. If the attractive part of the interaction is strong enough to produce actual bound "pairs," i.e., stable two-electron "molecules," this would be terrible for the theory: in *no* temperature range would the usual band theory of solids make sense. Actually, any reasonable estimate indicates that the electron-electron interaction is *not* strong enough to make bound electron pairs. The "pairs" we talk about are to be understood as something like resonant states in nuclear reaction theory, not as real molecules.

4. If it is really necessary, as we believe it is, to include such pair correlations explicitly, that is, if superconductivity is one phenomenon in solid state physics in which a single-particle approach is not enough, then no single-particle spectrum, with or without a gap in it, would be a correct explanation of superconductivity.

Let me close with some remarks on the relation of our approach to the approach of Bardeen and Cooper about which you have heard here. To the extent that electron pairs are involved, there is agreement. But when we started in this direction two years ago, we realized very quickly that it would not be sufficient simply to write down an interaction between a pair of electrons, incorporate it into a two-particle Hamiltonian, call it H_2, and then look at the eigenvalues and states of this Hamiltonian:

$$H_2\varphi = E\varphi \tag{11}$$

This procedure, and it is in essence the one which Cooper [24] has followed, makes sense for bound molecules, but there is little reason to expect it to be valid for electrons in solids. You will notice that the "pair" terms in our approach, in eq. (10), are introduced not as terms in the Hamiltonian, but as terms in the statistical matrix itself. Of course, if all terms, pairs, triplets, quadruplets, etc., are kept, then it makes no difference. But if one stops with the pair terms, then the approximation of keeping pair terms in the statistical matrix is a very different thing from looking at the eigenvalue spectrum of a pair Hamiltonian.

If you look at what the simplest form of this pair correlation matrix W might be, its relation to a pair Hamiltonian H_2 is rather complicated. Let H_1 be the single-particle Hamiltonian, then the operator U in (9) is

$$U = \exp\left(-\beta H_1\right) \tag{12}$$

and the matrix W is

$$\langle k_1 k_2 | W | k_1' k_2' \rangle = \langle k_1 k_2 | \exp\left(-\beta H_2\right) | k_1' k_2' \rangle - \langle k_1 | U | k_1' \rangle \langle k_2 | U | k_2' \rangle \tag{13}$$

That is, the uncorrelated terms are subtracted, so that W vanishes if there is no interaction between the two electrons. In the theoretical treatment based on (10), what matters finally are not the eigenvalues of the Hamiltonian H_2, nor even the eigenvalues of W, but rather the eigenvalues of a modified matrix $\tilde{W}$, which differs from W by factors which describe the quenching due to the Pauli exclusion principle. There is no simple or sensible relation between the eigenvalues of $\tilde{W}$ and the eigenvalues of H_2, except in the case of bound molecules, which is of no interest in superconductivity. I personally am very doubtful that an inspection of the energy spectrum of H_2 is going to be of any use in superconductivity.

There is a second reason for preferring the Ansatz (10) rather than looking at pair Hamiltonians. So far I have talked as if the labels k_1, k_2, ... describe actual electrons in the solid. If this were to be taken literally, then surely the independent-particle approximation (9) would be absolutely terrible. But we know such an approximation (the band theory of solids) is very good. The solution of this dilemma is now believed to be known, from the work of Brueckner et al. [25]. The "electrons" in the band theory of solid are "effective electrons", with correlations to other electrons hidden in the "single-particle" energy spectrum $E(k)$; the correlation between the effective electrons, unlike the correlations between actual electrons, are what is left over after going through the Brueckner procedure, and it is quite reasonable to assume that these residual correlations are weak; indeed, the entire success of the band theory of solids is strong argument for this position. On the other hand, if the matrix W is to be understood in this way, then it is very likely that there exists no pair Hamiltonian H_2 which can reproduce W via eq. (13).

The effects of electron-electron interactions, including superconductivity, ought to be looked for in terms of pair, and higher, correlation terms in the density matrix $\tilde{W}$ and the modified (quenched) matrix W, and this is what we are planning to do in Sydney.

3. Consequences of Energy Gap

M. J. Buckingham: Our results on the lambda point of helium (see Part A, Sec. 1) show that one has a true transition in the thermodynamic sense, and it is interesting to wonder, as has often been done, about its connection with superconductivity. We propose to measure the superconducting transition similarly, but there are considerably greater difficulties, due to grain boundaries, impurities, and the like. If what is known now is true, there appears to be an ordinary second-order transition, qualitatively different from the one in helium. There is of course a cubic term, due to the lattice specific heat, which in some cases is small, but usually of the same order; subtracting this, the specific heat of a superconductor is essentially exponential $(e^{-a/T})$ at low temperatures, is then a discontinuity, and finally the ordinary linear term of the normal state. The exponential part of course suggests, at least from the thermal point of view, a gap in the spectrum of excitations.

Now I would like to make two remarks, if I may. One is in connection with a statement of Dr. Bardeen. This is that I do not agree that if one can establish a gap by any method, then this necessarily implies the electromagnetic properties of the superconductor. Dr. Bardeen and I have had a number of discussions on the formal reason for this, but I won't go into that, of course. I think that there is a new physical idea involved, if one looks at the problem from a semi-phenomenological point of view, and this can easily be described as follows. (It was, I believe, flrst pointed out in Japan several years ago by H. Frohlich.) First of all, there is one case in which there is a gap — in an insulator — which we know is not a superconductor, and in this case, as for a semi-rigid electron structure, the electron states below the gap in the energy spectrum are tied, by the nature of the interaction that causes the gap, to the positions of the atoms in the lattice. Now something different is required to produce super-conductivity, and this is already strongly implied by the nature of the interaction, in this case unlike the interaction causing ordinary band structure, which is "fixed" to the positions of the atoms in the lattice.

In the superconducting case, the interaction is due to the phonons, namely the displacements of the atoms in the lattice, and there is a qualitative difference here, because there is nothing to give the displacements a fixed origin relative to the lattice. If you have, say, a non-simply connected region, e.g., a ring, there is no reason why the displacements can't move around in phase, although the atoms themselves of course cannot. Now if one did have a structure somewhat like an insulator, where the electrons were all rigidly below some region of energy and it would take a finite amount of energy to remove them, but if this whole structure, in position space, as it were, were linked only to the phases of the displacements of the lattice — to the displacements rather than the positions — then the structure as a whole would be free to move with some additional degree of freedom associated with its total structure. I feel that this qualitative idea is necessary, as well as the existence of a gap, if one looks at it from this point of view.

The second remark I wanted to make ends with a question which I would like to put to the panel. According to what Dr. Blatt says, there is the feeling amongst his group that the phenomenon of Bose condensation is at least closely linked with the phenomenon of super-conductivity. Now we have had quite a lot of discussion on He^4 and its superfluid properties, in all of which the nature of the symmetry requirements plays a dominant role. This gives us a pretty satisfactory picture of the state of affairs, which we feel we understand reasonably well, but central to all is the nature of the statistics. Now of course the electrons in themselves don't have these statistics. In the picture that Dr. Blatt has described, this comes in again in the nature of the statistical mechanical expansion, which appears formally very suggestive, although it remains to be seen whether it can be carried through.

Now the questions I'd like to put are the following: (a) Is this fundamental property of the Bose condensation, which is after all very far removed from any intrinsic properties of the Fermi statistics, really necessary for superconductivity? If not, how close is the analogy between the superproperties in metals and those in helium? (b) I'd like to put a specific question beyond these. If one could measure this — and there may be possibilities of doing so — is there, both in the case of helium and in the case of superconductivity, any resistance at all to flow at very slow velocities? In other words, is the resistance identically zero, or is it just very small and very difficult to measure? For the lifetime of a state in a non-simply connected region, is this lifetime really infinite, or is it finite?

L. Onsager: It is hard to be certain of the connection of the Bose condensation to superconductivity. I rather like the idea of two electrons sticking together. It seems hard to do without, but I'm not certain that all possibilities have been explored.

D. Pines: I would just comment on your remark against the argument of the energy gap; I don't see that it is an argument at all. What you have given is precisely the qualitative picture necessary to explain superconductivity, that of a group electrons which can move together very well, and which respond easily to an external electric or magnetic field in such a way as to give you lossless current or shielding of the external magnetic field. One only has to add to that the reluctance of any given electron to leave its fellow electrons, and that is essentially what one means by an energy gap.

M. J. Buckingham: I am not arguing against an energy gap — the specific heat shows that this is at least one way of describing the situation. What I am saying is that something is needed beyond the mere existence of an energy gap — remember that an insulator is not a superconductor. What you are saying is that the idea I am talking about is already contained in the other, and so doesn't have to be expressed separately. That is a point of view, of course.

P. R. Zilsel: There is the formal theoretical question: given an energy gap, does it imply or does it not imply superconductivity. To that question, I would definitely state my own opinion that it does not imply it; you need additional assumptions of some kind or another, and the assumptions which Dr. Pines has mentioned are of course the conventional ones, but you have not really solved the problem that way — you have just pushed it ahead. Now you have to show in some fashion that these assumptions are reasonable — the energy gap by itself doesn't do it.

J. Bardeen: That is certainly true. I agree that you cannot say that any model with an energy gap is a superconductor, but I think you can also see how to account for the electromagnetic properties from such a model, and it is very likely that if you have a theory which gives the correct energy gap, there will be no further difficulty in accounting for the electromagnetic properties.

E. P. Gross: I think that I would like to close this session now, but before doing so, I would like to express my personal appreciation for all of the obviously back-breaking work that must have been done to arrange the conference.

Notes and References

17. E. Maxwell, *Phys. Rev.* **78**, 477 (1950); Reynolds, Serin, Wright, and Nesbitt, *Phys. Rev.* **79**, 845 (1950).
18. H. Frohlich, *Phys. Rev.* **79**, 845 (1950).
19. D. Bohm and D. Pines, *Phys. Rev.* **92**, 609 (1953).
20. A. B. Pippard, *Proc. Roy. Soc. (London)* **A216**, 547 (1953). A. B. Pippard, *Advances in Electronics* Academic, New York, 1954, Vol. 6, p. 1.
21. J. Bardeen, L. N. Cooper, and R. Schrieffer, *Phys. Rev.* **106**, 162 (1957).
22. Schafroth, Butler, and Blatt, *Helv. Phys. Acta.* **30**, 93 (1957).
23. H. Frohlich, *Proc. Roy. Soc. (London)* **A215**, 291 (1952).
24. L. N. Cooper, *Phys. Rev.* **104**, 1189 (1956).
25. K. A. Brueckner, Chap. III, this volume.

Part Six

CHAPTER XXVIII

Round Table on Statistical Mechanics[†]

Participants:

G. E. Uhlenbeck, *Moderator*

B. J. Alder	K. Huang
T. H. Berlin	J. G. Kirkwood
R. B. Brout	M. Kac
K. A. Brueckner	T. D. Lee
D. Falkoff	E. Montroll
H. Grad	A. J. F. Siegert
M. S. Green	L. Tisza
E. P. Gross	C. N. Yang

G. E. Uhlenbeck: May I bring this meeting to order. This is supposed to be a round table on statistical mechanics, which is a very large subject, and it seems to me that we could talk practically on anything — which we have perhaps done already. I think therefore that perhaps the only way to get something constructive out of it is to use this opportunity essentially to ask questions, not only between members of the panel, but also from the audience — either from the panel to the audience or vice versa, with no one-ways about it. . . . And that we only talk, essentially, about a small number of topics, to see whether we can get to certain statements which one can believe or not believe, but which at least are themselves clear.

1. *Gas of hard spheres*

G. E. Uhlenbeck: I would like to start the discussion with the subject we have talked so much about, namely the hard sphere case — the gas of hard spheres — either Boltzmann or Bose, at low temperature

---

[†] Owing to a confluence of technical difficulties, only a portion of the round table is presented here.

or high. I would perhaps, just for myself, like to open the questions by asking Mr. Lee, Mr. Yang, and Mr. Huang to see if I have really understood some of the points they have made. At a certain moment, they talked about jamming [1] — something at very high density — but I didn't quite understand what it was. So, first question: Is it really true that with these methods of yours, you can treat the high density case and therefore settle the problem, which is more than 10 years old, of whether or not a gas of hard spheres has a transition point? You only have to answer yes or no.

T. D. Lee: No.

G. E. Uhlenbeck: Perhaps I may ask for a slight elucidation. What was the talk about jamming? I was too far in the back to hear it.

T. D. Lee: The first statement is that I have not said anything about jamming.

G. E. Uhlenbeck: Then it was Yang.

C. N. Yang: Yes, I did say something about jamming.

G. E. Uhlenbeck: What did you mean by jamming?

C. N. Yang: What I meant by jamming is that it is too crowded. Let me stress that the remark I made about the jamming situation, the high density end, is not connected with the other remarks I made concerning the low density region. It was only to illustrate the difficulty of the problem that I mentioned that in the jamming end — the end which is almost close-packing — the energy levels look qualitatively completely different from the energy levels in the low density end. We believe that the energy-level distribution at the high density end is very much like what the free-volume theory gives [2], although the free volume theory says that you simply give each particle a finite volume in which it can move; this statement has to be corrected for the reason that you can have correlated movement of all particles together, and this gives you a change of the distribution, but not in a qualitative way — only in a quantitative way.

J. G. Kirkwood: Dr. Yang, are you familiar with the Monte Carlo calculations that Rosenbluth made [3], on the ground state of the Bose hard sphere gas? I don't think he has yet published them. He confirms what you say, that is, he took his energy as a function of volume, and found that at high density it could be represented fairly well by the simple free-volume result, with an effective mass that was not too far from the actual mass.

R. B. Brout: With regard to the problem of communal entropy — if one uses the free-volume theory, one gets no communal entropy. One expects this at close-packed volume, but if you loosen up, you might get some. Such attempts have been made, on the basis of holes in the structure, by Eyring, Mc Pherson, and collaborators [4]. But in my own mind, I suggest that this is not the proper approach, but that the proper approach is what Yang just referred to, namely that one can excite very low-lying states of an oscillatory character, in connection with density fluctuations. I wonder if Dr. Yang has any comments to make on that.

C. N. Yang: Perhaps I can clarify a bit what we meant if you think of a box in which there are N particles that are almost jammed. Now let's say that they are very jammed, such that you cannot exchange the positions of two particles without opening the box first, taking one out, and then doing some switching around. When that is the case, it means that in the $3N$-dimensional configuration space the allowed volume — the allowed positions for the particles — consists of $N!$ independent pockets which are identical in shape with each other, but which are completely separated from each other. To go from one pocket to another pocket, you have to go out of the box; this is the statement that it is very jammed. When this is the case, the energy levels of the system are completely determined by the shape of each of the $N!$ $3N$-dimensional little spaces. Now what does each of the spaces look like? Each of the surfaces is bounded by supersurfaces determined by $|\mathbf{r}_1 - \mathbf{r}_2| = a$; these are supercylinders in $3N$-dimensional space. But each supercylinder has only a very small fraction of itself included in the surface, that is, we have a system of many surfaces, each of which is a supercylinder, but only a very small portion of the cylinder.

Therefore you can replace each of the cylinders in zeroth approximation by a plane. When you do that, the problem becomes a solvable eigenvalue problem in a polyhedron. This problem can be solved by the method of images — if you take the case of simple cubic jamming.

A face-centered cubic jamming unfortunately cannot be exactly solved, because it turns out that you cannot use an image method. But nervertheless, even without being able to solve it, you can easily see what the energy-level structure looks like. It is on such considerations that I made the statement that it looks like a Fermi gas. Now you can always raise the question that this is not a rigorous argument, for the reason that it cannot be that jammed (in order to have it that jammed, you must have the box so close that as N goes to infinity, the jamming increases. That is, you must allow only a leeway of one atomic distance, no matter how big the box is). However, if you allow a leeway which is proportional to $N^{\frac{1}{3}}$, all it means is that the $N!$ pockets get connected by very narrow channels. But these channels do not contribute to the energy at all, because it is evident that the wave function is exponentially small inside the channels. We feel that this kind of approach is another asymptotic expansion.

M. S. Green: I just want to clarify one point. You said that the energy levels are given by the free-volume terms. One cannot compute the energy simply by dividing the phase volume by h^3, for one must allow for diffraction effects in the quantum mechanical ground state.

C. N. Yang: The result is qualitatively the same as the classical free-volume theory, but the coefficients are different. You of course must obtain the energy eigenvalue for the wave equation inside the free volume.

G. E. Uhlenbeck: Perhaps I might ask a second question of Lee. This is for the low density end. I understand that these calculations were made for the ground state, which is to say for temperature zero, but there was also a statement I heard relating to the transition point. Can you really say something about the change of the Bose transition point, and especially about how the interaction affects the nature of the transition?

T. D. Lee: We have observed the change of the transition point due to the interaction. If one considers the system of a hard sphere Bose gas at low energy — this means you try to expand everything in terms of a/λ, where a is the hard sphere diameter and $\lambda = h/(2\pi mkT)^{\frac{1}{2}}$ — then you find [1] at the transition point

$$\lambda^3 p/kT = 1.34 + (2.61)^2\, 2(a/\lambda) + O[(a/\lambda)^{\frac{3}{2}}]$$
$$\lambda^3 \rho = 2.61 \qquad\qquad + O(a/\lambda) \tag{1}$$

The first 1.34 and 2.61 are the same as for an ideal Bose gas. One sees again the characteristic structure, namely the appearance of square roots. As to the nature of the transition point, we believe we will be able to find exactly the nature of the discontinuities, but we have not completed the investigation.

G. E. Uhlenbeck: Especially can you say whether the isotherm at this point has a horizontal tangent or a vertical tangent?

T. D. Lee: It would be rather an easy task to answer this question, for we have the analytical form of p and ρ at this point. It is slightly embarrassing that we have not done it — due to some other activities in other branches of physics [5] — we probably will, or other people will.

G. E. Uhlenbeck: You are excused.

2. *Classical hard sphere gas*

G. E. Uhlenbeck: Recently, there has been some indication, numerically, that a gas of hard spheres has a transition point. I have just heard from Jack Kirkwood that he will talk later [6] somewhat about these numerical calculations, but now I would like him to just draw a rough picture of the results.

J. G. Kirkwood: We are now again speaking of the classical case for hard spheres, and the question comes up as to whether, for sufficiently high densities, the fluid of hard spheres will crystallize. It is possible to set up a criterion which, if fulfilled, will lead to a crystallization. This however involves a transcendental function depending upon the exact radial distribution for a fluid of hard spheres, and since that is not known with precision, one cannot say that the criterion will ever be satisfied. Now the most recent evidence for the existence of the liquid-solid transition was provided by Dr. Alder, who will speak about this later [7]. Following his work, Dr. William Wood of Los Alamos again took up the Monte Carlo calculations relating to the equation of state of a classical fluid of rigid spheres, begun by Rosenbluth, Metropolis, and Teller [8]. He has kindly provided me with figures which I will show you later [6], in which it seems that the Rosenbluth calculations were in error at high densities; there is very definite evidence for a first-order transition, which we would identify as a transition from a solid or crystalline state to a liquid state at a volume of approximately 1.5 times the close-packed volume. This appears as a Van der Waals loop for several reasons. In the first place, the Monte Carlo calculations undoubtedly allow one to go into the metastable region, coming both from the liquid side and the crystalline side, and furthermore because they are carried out with a finite number of particles, one would not expect a sharp transition.

G. E. Uhlenbeck: Last fall, there was something similar — a round table on statistical mechanics at Seattle [9] — and there I finished the discussion on hard spheres with a vote. The vote was simply on the matter of your belief in what you have heard, whether a gas of hard spheres has a transition point or not; at Seattle, the vote was even. Now of course, with Mr. Kirkwood here, we have weighted the evidence a little bit. May I ask first of the panel to put up their hands if they believe there is a transition in the classical case. . . . Now those who believe there is not a transition. . . .   Even, again!

B. J. Alder: May I just say a few words about the numerical calculations and the nature of the transition found by Bill Wood at Los Alamos. It seems that in the particular region where the transition occurs, the number of particles you use in the calculation has a large influence on the results. Now we take 32 up to 500 particles (surface to volume ratio of about 1/3), using a different sort of calculation [7] from the Monte Carlo calculations — following the equations of motion. It seems that with 32, and using periodic boundary conditions, we do not reproduce the results of Wood, although we do get a singularity at a slightly different value of v/v_0. Moreover, it turns out that with 500 particles, there is just barely a transition left; it looks like a second-order transition. What I propose is that if you follow the equations of motion, you can study the diffusion coefficients to advantage, and if there is indeed a liquid to solid transition, the diffusion coefficient should drop by an order of magnitude.

G. E. Uhlenbeck: Do I understand that you therefore throw doubt on the Los Alamos results?

B. J. Alder: I would like to throw doubt on the first-order transition.

G. E. Uhlenbeck: But if you do the calculation with 10,000 particles, everything might disappear.

B. J. Alder: Not quite. I should say that the difference between 256 and 500 particles is very small.

K. A. Brueckner: Let's have a recount!

A. J. F. Siegert: I have some suspicion of the persistance of the result in going to larger and larger numbers, based on the idea that if you took the result of your small box and small number of particles, and then made a very large number of boxes with very many particles all told, but did not take them as an ensemble, then we know that there might not be a condensation. In order to have an actual transition, there must be some interaction, but for pure hard spheres, the interaction, I think, would counteract condensation. Thus for a larger and larger number of particles, one would expect that this effect, certainly the first-order one, would vanish.

J. G. Kirkwood: May I ask you to make a very sharp distinction between condensation and crystallization. We do not maintain that there will be condensation in the fluid of hard spheres, in which you have two fluid phases in equilibrium with each other. That is not possible.

A. J. F. Siegert: Yes, but just for a transition — if we have many boxes without interaction, certainly we know there cannot be a transition because that would be a grand canonical ensemble. We must be able to imagine some interaction which would create the transition if you take many boxes. I am not certain that it has to be an attractive force, but I am just trying to imagine what force could do it.

J. G. Kirkwood: I think it is quite unnecessary to have an attractive force to achieve a crystalline phase, and one can produce simple intuitive arguments for that. Now the question is whether conclusions based on a very smooth but steep repulsion could be carried over to the limit of hard spheres or not.

A. J. F. Siegert: It would seem to me that a repulsion would disfavor, let us say, two densely filled cells next to each other, and would favor something like an antiferromagnet.

G. E. Uhlenbeck: I would like to close this discussion, for I am quite sure that the transition goes a little bit against intuition; that is why so many people have difficulty with it, and surely I am one of those. But this transition — it still might be true, you know — and I don't think one can decide by general arguments.

M. Kac: Before you close the discussion — Dr. Kirkwood was mentioning that you don't have a condensation in the ordinary sense, but a crystallization. I find it difficult in the absence of a gravitational field to really tell the difference. It seems to me that the only way to tell the difference between a gas-liquid transition and a liquid-solid transition is to compute the long-range correlation between particles.

J. G. Kirkwood: The test is that the pair correlation will exhibit long-range order.

M. Kac: Were the Monte Carlo calculations done in two dimensions, or even one dimension, in which we know the answer?

J. G. Kirkwood: All I know is that in the earlier calculations of Rosenbluth, he did two checks. This didn't have to do with the transition, but he did do the linear chain to test his method — there is no transition then, of course — and he got very good agreement.

L. Tisza: I wonder if we can conclude anything from a numerical calculation with any accessible number of particles. For example, when one looks at the finite model of the Yang-Lee lattice gas [10], the metastable states shrink only very slowly towards condensation, towards an actual transition. The overlapping branches swing only with the logarithm of the number of cells in this case.

J. G. Kirkwood: Well, I think we are all aware that we have to take numerical calculations relating to transitions with a grain of salt.

3. *Irreversibility and approach to equilibrium*

G. E. Uhlenbeck: One of the topics which always occurs in statistical mechanics is the relation between it and thermodynamics — and especially nowadays irreversible thermodynamics — and the question of how to look at this relation from a general point of view. Now since the very great amount of work that has been done on this, and notably since the papers of Onsager and Machlup [11], I think the situation is in a more or less finished state. There are of course still many questions to answer, and still the problem of knowing enough about these things to tell them to students, in a simple fashion, without stochastic equations and the like. Perhaps Dr. Tisza will tell in a few minutes some of his ideas about this work, deriving irreversible thermodynamics from simple postulates, on the same level of generalization as the Einstein way of computing probabilities from entropy, by turning around the Boltzmann equation.

[L. Tisza discusses a postulational approach to the Onsager-Machlup formulation for the temporal path of extensive variables in an irreversible process, when the system fluctuations obey Gaussian Markov processes.]

E. P. Gross: I want to make some remarks about the age old problem of the connection of reversibility and irreversibility, where one usually starts from the reversible Liouville equation in $6N$ space and is then supposed to elucidate why and how irreversibility comes about. It would be nice to have models not as complicated as the Liouville equation but which one could solve exactly. There is such a model which was proposed in connection with the theory of plasmas by Vlasov [12] and solved by Landau [13], desolved by Bohm and myself [14], and then resolved correctly by Van Kampen [15]. The following equation has been used to study the classical theory of plasmas. One defines a one-particle distribution function $f(\mathbf{x}, \mathbf{v}, t)$ which satisfies

$$\partial f/\partial t + \mathbf{v} \cdot \nabla f + e\mathbf{E}/m \cdot \delta f/\delta \mathbf{v} = 0 \qquad \nabla \cdot \mathbf{E} = 4\pi e[\int f d^3 v - N] \qquad (2)$$

N is the density of a uniform positively charged background; the force $e\mathbf{E}$ is determined from Poisson's equation. I don't want to discuss in what sense this is or is not an adequate representation of the dynamics of a rarefied electron gas. Let us take it as it stands as a reversible equation describing a hypothetical system, which however is interesting because it is written in an attempt to describe a real plasma.

One can go a great way in studying the exact solutions of this equation for an arbitrary initial distribution. In particular, one approximation which is not serious is to linearize the equation (this can be justified a posteriori). One can get an exact solution subject to arbitrary initial distributions, and one can trace out the interesting things Boltzmann and Ehrenfest said would happen and in fact do happen. But if you take an extremely sharp initial distribution function corresponding to a delta function in velocity, representing a sharp beam, you will never get rid of it. Nevertheless, if you take almost any arbitrary initial distribution, reasonably smooth in velocity, you find that the velocity moments of the distribution, as for example the density, become insensitive to the initial distribution. In spite of this, you never lose the individual particle excitations; they go on forever prescribed by the initial distribution. They simply get out of phase with each other and all averages are insensitive.

J. G. Kirkwood: What you are essentially saying here is that course graining is necessary in order to forget the initial conditions.

E. P. Gross: That's right.

G. E. Uhlenbeck: Since the question of the connection of the Liouville equation with the apparent irreversible nature of the natural phenomena is a really controversial one, before asking questions on the example we heard, I would like Dr. Kac to say a few words about a really simple although academic model [16] in connection with just this point.

M. Kac: The simple model, which however is going to be complicated by Dr. Dresden — and I think will then give even more interesting results — is the following. It is in fact a modification of the wind-tree model [17] of the Ehrenfests. The only difficulty with the Ehrenfest model is that it is still not computable, and so the problem here is to find one which has all the theory of the wind-tree model, but is easily computable.

Suppose you have a circle, and on it a large number n of equidistant points. Then you mark a set S of m points, which are fixed forever. On every point on the circle there sits a ball which is either black or white, and let us say that at the beginning they are all black. Now the dynamics of the model is the following: In each time unit (say, $\Delta t = 1$), each ball moves one step counterclockwise; if it moves from the set S, it changes color — it blushes, so to speak — but if it starts from a point not in S, it maintains color. The question is what is going to happen as time goes on.

Now you can immediately imitate Boltzmann's procedure; you can write conservation equations for the number of black balls and white balls at time t, depending of course on how many black balls and white balls are in the set S at the time. But when you write these equations you clearly find that you can do nothing with them, so you introduce the analog of the Stosszahlansatz [18]: assume that at all times, the number of black balls in S is in the same proportion, m/n, to the total number of black balls, and similarly for the white balls. Then the equations become trivial — ordinary first-order difference equations — and you discover that (assuming $2m < n$), the excess in the number of black balls over the number of white balls, $n_b(t)$, decreases exponentially

$$n_b(t) = n(1-2m/n)^t \qquad (3)$$

Now of course, all the old problems and paradoxes appear, because the model is completely reversible — after $2n$ steps you come right back to where you started — the Poincaré cycle is exactly $2n$, with no fluctuations at all. By a very simple analysis, you can fix it all up in the spirit proposed by the Ehrenfests [17]. Thus you calculate $n_b(t)$ as a functional of the set S, and then average over all possible positions of the set; this really corresponds in Gross' model to integration over S, for you must somehow integrate out information. If you compute this average, assuming all sets S equiprobable, you are led exactly to the result (3) for $\langle n_b(t; S) \rangle_{(S)}$, and if you want to play around a bit more, you will convince yourself that for large n, the fluctuation of this average is extremely small. In other words, there are few possible configurations S which will produce noticeable deviations from the monotonic irreversible decrease of (3). These calculations are all very simple, and can really be presented to students — I mean people with both little preparation and little interest, and maybe completely lacking in intelligence.

Incidentally, one can study this also *à la* Gibbs. The phase space of the model is a discrete space of 2^n points, and one can write down the Liouville equation which in this case, fortunately, is solvable explicitly. One can then average at time t over all original S, and compare with the solution obtained by solving the corresponding transport or master equation — which corresponds to averaging every step. One discovers after a certain amount of hand waving that the solutions are essentially the same, with a few significant differences.

The model suffers from one fundamental defect, that it does not have a density parameter in it. To find out somehow what happens is a gas, one has to be able to trace out the binary collisions in the very dilute case, and then the effect of multiple collisions as the density increases. Consequently, Dr. Dresden proposed to modify the model as follows. First of all, you don't place balls at every point, but for a total of n balls, the circle has $N > n$ points; there is then a black, white, or no ball at all at each point. Next, if a ball moves counterclockwise from a marker (point of S), the marker recoils, moves one step backwards. This is perfectly all right if there was previously at that point a marker and a ball, for the marker will have retreated. But if it finds a marker without a ball, the rule is that it pushes to make room, and the marker it pushes must retreat, . . .

until they all find space, which is soon provided if m and n are small compared to N.

Now, you see, you have a complete analogy with collisions. If only the markers collide and no further shift is necessary, that is a binary collision, and in a dilute situation will be predominant. Of course when you crowd them and get several simultaneous shifts, these correspond to triple and multiple collisions. Unfortunately, the treatment here becomes more complicated, but it is being worked out by Dresden and a student, and it is hoped that they will solve this model which is very close to what is happening in reality. You observe that whereas the simple model corresponds just to collisions against a fixed medium — a simplified Rayleigh gas — the Dresden model sort of indirectly corresponds to collisions as well.

E. Montroll: I think one has to make a distinction between the cases in which there is this mixing bath or scatter, and the case in which there is not. It seems to me a fundamental and difficult problem to relate the two.

H. Grad: I also have my pet example, which is very elementary.

All one needs is a little measure theory and no physics, which makes it, I think, more interesting to me at least.

The problem is that of a Knudsen gas in a box; you have particles which do not collide with one another, they just collide with the walls. The state of the system is then described by particle density. Now you just have a differential equation stating that the number of particles of a given speed does not change and the velocity is altered only by reflection. This is about as reversible as you can imagine, but it is very easy to show, if I call the distribution function $K(\mathbf{v}, \mathbf{x}, t)$ and integrate out the velocity to obtain the density $\rho(\mathbf{x}, t)$ that ρ approaches a constant as t approaches infinity, and no stochastic assumptions have to be made at all. The theorem is that for the initial density taken as any measurable function f, the density ρ approaches a constant — and a little more, $\rho \ln \rho$ approaches its expected value, too.

Now if a system approaches equilibrium, you have obvious ir-reversibility and the question is, what happens to the Poincaré cycle.

But of course it doesn't occur because you have effectively an infinite number of particles. If you have a finite number of particles, this would mean that you are approximating the initial distribution f by a certain number of δ-functions. You can prove that if you approximate more closely by letting the particle number approach infinity, then you will have convergence at any fixed time t, but if you first let t approach infinity for a finite n, then you get, as is well known, no irreversibility.

R. B. Brout: One must be careful in choosing models of irreversibility.

The particular model chosen by Grad is not characterized by a relaxation time, but rather the evolution is governed by the dispersion of velocities in the initial distribution.

A similar model has been considered by Klein and Prigogine in the process of "homogenization" of phonons in crystals. Here the result follows from the dispersion in the frequencies, given an initial envelope of excited phonons.

4. *Reduction of the Liouville Equation*

G. E. Uhlenbeck: It seems to me that the present status of these questions is the following. I think that no one fights any longer over the fundamental reason for irreversibility. We know that there is a Poincaré cycle and that the irreversibility we see is a delusion, simply because the system is so large that one doesn't observe it long enough. At present, the main question, I think, is not so much what happens after a very long interval of time, but how it comes about that after a relatively short time from the initial situation, one can describe the apparent irreversible behavior by more simplified equations than one had to start with. For instance, one knows that instead of the Liouville equation with a great number of variables, one can in certain cases (low density) work with just the Boltzmann equation, which involves many fewer variables, namely only the one-particle distribution; later one doesn't even need that, and only average velocity, temperature, and density are required, which is very much less than the particle-distribution function.

Somehow, it seems to me that at present one is very close to really getting the answer to how it is that one can seek out from the true equations those solutions which depend on fewer variables — those which one really wants. I don't propose to say anything more, because it is still not completely clear and therefore becomes philosophical. But if anyone wishes to say anything about this work, which has been done by a number of people remarkably independently — Bogoliubov [19], and of course Kirkwood [20], Born and Green [21], and recently Green [22] and Brout [23], and also Van Hove [24], and Luttinger and Kohn [25] for the quantum mechanical problem — I will be glad to give him the floor.

R. B. Brout: Let me summarize some recent results on the statistical mechanics of irreversible processes obtained in Brussels in collaboration with Professor I. Prigogine [26].

The first type of system considered was one in which N degrees of freedom were weakly coupled in the manner postulated by Van Hove [24] to account for irreversibility in quantum systems. Essentially any degree of freedom is coupled to any other, either directly or indirectly. The Liouville density is expressed in terms of action and angle variables; the zeroth-order Hamiltonian depends only on the actions $[J_i]$ and the perturbation both on $[J_i]$ and the phases $[\alpha_i]$. The density is Fourier analyzed and it is shown that the phase-independent solution obeys an irreversible Fokker-Planck-type equation for times of the order of the relaxation time. This is valid to lowest non-vanishing order in the coupling parameter. It is proven that only the phase-independent component obeys such an equation. Thus a phase-independent initial ensemble is necessary and sufficient to have irreversibility in weakly coupled classical systems. When gradients exist, the usual treatment of transport phenomena may be justified through the Fourier decomposition of the Liouville density. It may also be shown that the classical Fokker-Planck equation is the classical limit $(\hbar \to 0)$ of the familiar quantum mechanical Poisson irreversible equation which has been derived by Van Hove under initial conditions equivalent to the phase-independent initial ensemble here chosen.

Under some circumstances some consequences of weak coupling may be taken over by changing the expansion parameter. Thus, if collisions are strong in a dilute gas, then one can switch from the coupling parameter to the density. This has been carried out and the usual Boltzmann equation derived in straightforward fashion. The technique is similar to that used by M. S. Green [22].

[M. S. Green discusses his approach [22] to the derivation of the Boltzmann transport equation from the Born-Green hierarchy [21] and its relation to the Bogoliubov hypothesis [19] on the non-equilibrium distribution functions.]

[D. Falkoff shows how the Onsager-Machlup [11] transition probability for a fluctuating variable in an irreversible process may be expressed in simple fashion as a Feynman-type integral over paths (see Hashitsume [28]) and then rigorously as a Wiener integral.]

[After some further discussion, G. E. Uhlenbeck thanks the various contributors and closes the session.]

Notes and References

1. K. Huang, T. D. Lee, and C. N. Yang, Chap. X, this volume.
2. J. G. Kirkwood, *J. Chem. Phys.* **18**, 380 (1950).
3. M. Rosenbluth, private communication.
4. F. Cernuschi and H. Eyring, *J. Chem. Phys.* 7, 547 (1939).
5. T. D. Lee and C. N. Yang, extensive press reports; also *Phys. Rev.* **104**, 254 (1956); etc.
6. See Wood, Parker, and Jacobson, Chap. XXX, this volume
7. B. J. Alder and T. Wainwright, Chap. XXIX, this volume.
8. Metropolis, Rosenbluth, Rosenbluth, Teller, and Teller, *J. Chem. Phys.* **21**, 1087 (1953).
9. Principal papers are in *Revs. Modern Phys.* **29**, (1957).
10. T. D. Lee and C. N. Yang, *Phys. Rev.* **87**, 410 (1952).
11. L. Onsager and S. Machlup, *Phys. Rev.* **91**, 1505 (1953).
12. A. Vlasov, *J. Phys. (U.S.S.R.)* **9**, 25, (1945).
13. L. Landau, *J. Phys. (U.S.S.R.)* **10**, 25 (1946).
14. D. Bohm and E. P. Gross, *Phys. Rev.* **75**, 1851 (1949).
15. N. G. Van Kampen, *Physica* **21**, 949 (1955).
16. See also M. Kac, *Bull, classe sci. Acad. roy. Belg.* (5) **42**, 356 (1956).
17. P. and T. Ehrenfest, *Encykl. math. Wiss.* **4**, No. 32 (1911); see also A. J. F. Siegert. *Phys. Rev.* **75**, 1322 (1949).
18. See e.g., D. ter Haar, *Statistical Mechanics*, Rinehart, New York, 1954, p. 13.
19. N. N. Bogoliubov, *J. Phys. (U.S.S.R.)* **10**, 365 (1946).
20. J. G. Kirkwood, *J. Chem. Phys.* **14**, 180 (1946).
21. M. Born and H. S. Green, *Proc. Roy. Soc. (London)* **A188**, 10 (1946).
22. M. S. Green, *J. Chem. Phys.* **25**, 836 (1956).

23. R. Brout, *Physica* **22**, 509 (1956).
24. L. Van Hove, *Physica* **21**, 517 (1955).
25. W. Kohn and J. M. Luttinger, *Phys. Rev.* **108**, 590 (1957); J. M. Luttinger and W. Kohn, *Phys. Rev.* **109**, 1982 (1958).
26. R. Brout and I. Prigogine, *Physica* **22**, 621 (1956).
27. D. Falkoff, *Progr. Theoret. Phys.* (*Kyoto*) **16**, 530 (1956).
28. N. Hashitsume, *Progr. Theoret. Phys.* (*Kyoto*) **15**, 369 (1956).

CHAPTER XXIX

Investigation of the Many-Body Problem by Electronic Computers

B. J. Alder, T. Wainwright

1. *Introduction*

All the presently available theories regarding the many-body problem neglect some of the correlations that occur in such systems. It has been possible to describe the highly cooperative motions by the so-called collective treatment. The correlations that involve two particles can also be dealt with exactly by means of, for example, the quantum mechanical Brueckner [1] theory or the superposition theory of Kirkwood [2] in statistical mechanics. In these theories correlations between three or four particles are either neglected or approximated. These approximations might involve smoothing, such as expressing three-body correlations by the average effect a third particle has on the remaining two, or expressing higher correlations in terms of lower ones. In any case, the effect these approximations have on any given physical situation has not as yet been illuminated and hence it would be desirable to have a method which makes no such assumptions.

To explicity take into account the interactions of a fairly large number of particles involves either multi-dimensional integrals or differential equations with which analytical techniques are at present unable to cope. Analytical techniques have great difficulty describing the simultaneous interaction of only three isolated particles. Hence, a numerical method involving large scale computing equipment is a natural choice for such problems. For a first attempt in this direction, the classical behavior of a system of molecules appears to be the simplest. A quantum mechanical problem would be very much more difficult to do. Furthermore, particles having long-range forces could not be dealt with exactly unless very large numbers of particles were used.

Even in the classical case the nature of the boundary has to be seriously considered, since of the 500 particles that can be dealt with presently, about half are at the surface. In the calculations described here, periodic boundaries were employed in the hope that they would reduce as much as possible the effect of the smallness of the sample. Although statistical fluctuations are large in small systems, they can be reduced by averaging many examples. This procedure makes more efficient use of calculating time than would be achieved by using a larger system; however, the effects of the boundary may be serious in small systems, and also the inherent fluctuations, such as density fluctuations, are not the same as in large systems. In transition regions the system forms two phases of different density and hence such density fluctuations become very large. These fluctuations might involve more than 500 particles in a macroscopic system, but such fluctuation cannot take place when only that many particles are strictly confined in a box. Hence the nature of the phase change may depend strongly upon the number of particles used.

2. *Method of Calculation*

The dynamics of motion were followed for a system of hard sphere particles and for particles having square well attractive interaction potentials with a hard repulsive core. These interaction potentials have the property that the particles do not experience any force unless they are separated by a distance at which there is a discontinuity in the potential. The machine is made to calculate exactly, to the number of significant figures carried, the shortest time at which any two particles approach such a distance. This requires examination of the projected particle paths of all possible pairs of particles in the system and is the most time-consuming step in the calculation, involving the solution of $N(N-1)/2$ second-order algebraic equations (N is the number of particles). Once this time has been found, all particles are advanced at constant velocity to this time and the velocity changes for the two colliding particles are then evaluated according to the discontinuity in the potential involved. The process is then repeated. The machine calculations can, however, be speeded up [3] by some elementary considerations, and it has thus been possible to deal with larger systems in·reasonable calculating times.

The problem has been set up on the IBM-704 machine. Starting with some initial distribution in space (usually a face-centered cubic arrangement) and in velocity (usually a δ function), the system is allowed to proceed to equilibrium and then to run further to obtain the equilibrium properties. For a 500-particle system on the IBM-704 machine, about two mean collision times per particle can be handled in an hour, and several mean collision times are necessary before all the equilibrium properties can be meaningfully calculated. Hence, such a problem requires several hours to run. However, when the system is not near a transition, fewer particles appear to be sufficient and then many more mean collision times can be calculated in an hour. For 100 particles the rate is about 40 mean collision times per hour.

As the calculation of the motion of the many-particle system proceeds, the history of each particle is recorded on magnetic tape. At the same time the potential energy of the system and the equation of state are evaluated. The potential energy for square-well molecules is simply proportional to the number of pairs of particles whose separation is less than the outside diameter of the square well. The pressure is calculated directly from the virial of the internal forces. A function, Σ, is defined by:

$$\Sigma = \sum_i (\mathbf{r}_{a_i} - \mathbf{r}_{b_i}) \cdot \Delta\mathbf{v}_{a_i} \tag{1}$$

where $\mathbf{r}_{a_i}$ and $\mathbf{r}_{b_i}$ are the positions of the particles a_i and b_i that are involved in collision i. $\Delta\mathbf{v}_{a_i}$ is the change of velocity of particle a_i, which is equal and opposite to the change in velocity of particle b_i. The virial theorem then relates Σ to the pressure by the time derivative of Σ:

$$(pv/RT) - 1 = -1/N \langle v^2 \rangle \, (d\Sigma/dt) \tag{2}$$

As the particle histories are generated the collision rate is also simultaneously determined. However, a separate process later analyzes the data for various other numbers that may be desired, and also for some distribution functions. For example, the distribution in velocity, $f(v)$, is of interest for the evaluation of the Boltzmann H function

$$H = \int f(v) \ln f(v) \, d\mathbf{v} \tag{3}$$

The spatial distribution function, $f(r_{12})$, is evaluated in a straight-forward way. Furthermore, the triplet spatial distribution function, $f(r_{12}, r_{13}, r_{23})$, can also be evaluated and can be used to judge theories that neglect or smooth out correlations higher than pair correlations.

Only one other function, the velocity auto-correlation function, of the many that can be obtained will be mentioned here, since it has direct bearing on the multiple correlation problem. The velocity auto-correlation function, $\rho(s)$, is defined as a function of time, s, as follows:

$$\rho(s) = \sum_{i=1}^{N} \mathbf{v}_i(t+s) \cdot \mathbf{v}_i(t) / \sum_{i=1}^{N} v_i^2(t) \tag{4}$$

where t is some base time in the equilibrium state of the system. The self-diffusion coefficient can be immediately calculated from $\rho(s)$ by

$$D = (kT/m) \int_0^\infty \rho(s) \, ds \tag{5}$$

An alternative way to evaluate the diffusion coefficient is by noting the distance particles move in known time intervals; that is

$$D = \langle \sum [\mathbf{r}_i(t+s) - \mathbf{r}_i(t)]^2 \rangle / 6t \tag{6}$$

3. Results

The results will be presented mainly in graphical form, to illustrate the qualitative features that have to be considered in the behavior of a many-body problem. The few quantitative results (because insufficient statistics are presently available) should be considered to be provisional.

Figure 1 shows the rapid monotonic decrease of the H function for a system of 100 hard sphere particles at $v/v_0 = 14.14$, where v_0 is the close-packed volume, from an initial condition where all the velocities squared were the same but the velocities were in random directions. The horizontal line in Fig. 1 represents the equilibrium value (544.6) in the arbitrary units employed, that is, the H that would be calculated if the Maxwell-Boltzmann velocity distribution had been established. It can easily be demonstrated that the reason that the H calculated for the 100-particle system levels out somewhat higher than the equilibrium value is that, in a 100-particle system, there are no particles in the very high-energy region. That is, if it is assumed that the equilibrium distribution is Maxwellian with the high-energy

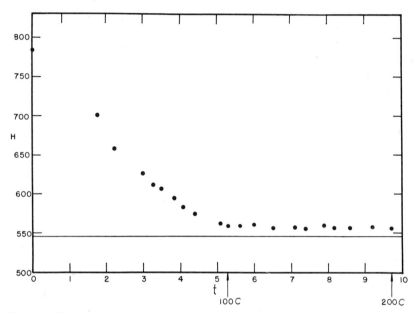

Figure 1. The behavior of the Boltzmann H function with time, t, or collision number, C, for 100 hard spheres at $v/v_0 = 14.14$. The horizontal line represents the equilibrium H value. (Reprinted with permission from *UCRL Livermore Report No, MUL—2255*).

tail cut off at four or five times the mean energy, the H function should level out in the neighborhood of the value found. A similar study at different densities has shown that the H function, and hence the velocity distribution, assumes the equilibrium configuration rapidly and monotonically in about two to four mean collision times in the hard sphere system.

The H function for the square well potential case behaves quite differently, as can be seen in Fig. 2. The solid line represents the H function for a density of $v/v_0 = 5.0$ and a reduced temperature, $T^* = kT/V$ of 0.9, where V is the depth of the potential well. The horizontal line represents the equilibrium value of H, which is reached only after 4000 collisions or 80 mean collision times. This illustrates how slowly, compared to the velocity distribution, the spatial distribution of molecules comes to equilibrium. The crosses in Fig. 2 correspond to the H function that is calculated under the assumption of an

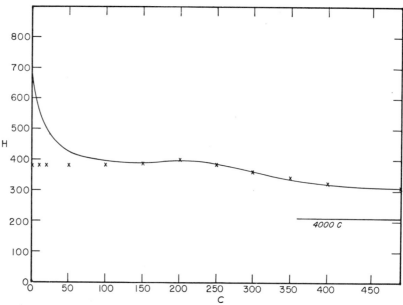

Figure 2. The H function for molecules with square well potentials at $v/v_0 = 5.0$ and $T^* = 0.9$ as a function of collision number (solid curve). The horizontal line represents the equilibrium H value. The crosses represent the values of H under the assumption of a local equilibrium temperature.

instantaneous equilibrium temperature; that is, from the instantaneous value of the calculated potential energy the kinetic energy can be calculated and hence, if a Maxwell-Boltzmann distribution is assumed, a temperature can be defined and an H function calculated. Hence, once the crosses coincide with the real H function (solid curve), the assumption is that a Maxwell-Boltzmann distribution has been established. Here the interesting thing that can be observed is that the velocity distribution, initially peaked at one velocity, again reaches a Maxwell-Boltzmann distribution after about

150 collisions (three mean collision times), but that thereafter the mean of this Maxwell-Boltzmann distribution shifts to its final equilibrium value in about 4000 collisions. Again the H function decreases mono-

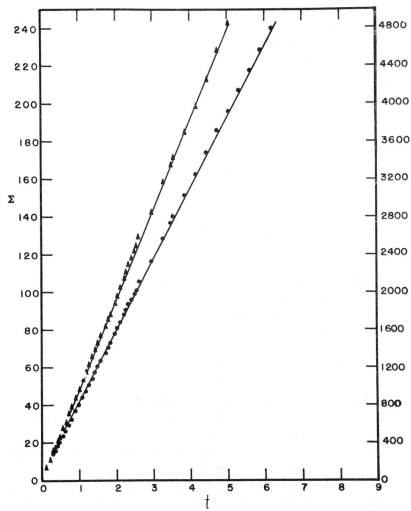

Figure 3. A plot of the virial (triangles), Σ, and the collision number (circles), C, as a function of time for a system of 100 hard sphere particles at $v/v_0 = 2.00$. The solid line for the collision rate is calculated from Enskog's theory. (Reprinted with permission from *UCRL Livermore Report No. MUL—2257*.)

tonically, but this cannot be expected to be always true for molecules with attractive potentials.

Fig. 3 shows how well the pressure can be determined by means of eq. (2) for hard-core particles at a density corresponding to $v/v_0 = 2.00$. The figure also shows how the collision rate, Γ, is determined. The solid line is a theoretical line obtained from the transport theory of Enskog for a dense hard sphere system. This theory takes into account the finite size of the spheres through a factor Υ which is related to the equation of state by

$$\Upsilon = [(pv/RT) - 1]/\tfrac{2}{3}\pi N d^3 \tag{7}$$

Thus

$$\Gamma = 2N(N-1)\,d^2\,\sqrt{(\pi/3)}\,\sqrt{\langle v^2\rangle}\,\Upsilon \tag{8}$$

where d is the diameter of the hard sphere molecules. A comparison of the hard sphere collision rate with that calculated from the Enskog theory [4] for a wide range of densities less than $v/v_0 \sim 2$ shows remarkable numerical agreement. Equation (8) can also be shown to be a direct consequence of the virial theorem for hard spheres and hence this numerical agreement is not surprising. Nevertheless it can be concluded from evidence to be presented further on, that the Enskog theory which neglects velocity correlations between successive collisions represents, in the wide density region quoted above, a good approximation for hard spheres for the properties so far evaluated. Another way of stating this is that the molecular chaos approximation or the Markoff chain representation for hard spheres is valid up to quite high densities. At very high densities it will be shown that higher velocity correlations become important. Furthermore, it can be expected that the presence of an attractive well will cause the molecular chaos approximation to break down at much lower densities.

The equation of state for hard spheres is shown in Fig. 4. The dotted line represents the four-term virial expansion. At low densities, agreement with the virial expansion is obtained, and that region is not plotted. The solid line and the corresponding triangles refer to a 500-particle system, the squares refer to 256 particles, and the circles refer to 108 particles. On either side of the transition, at about $v/v_0 = 1.7$, the same pressure is obtained regardless of the number

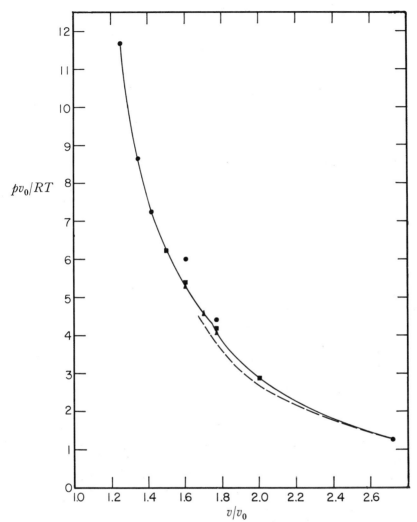

Figure 4. The hard sphere equation of state: pv_0/RT versus v/v_0; the circles represent 108 particles, the squares 256 particles; and the solid line is drawn through the triangular points for 500 particles. The dotted line is the four-term virial expansion.

of particles used. In the region of the transition the pressure is mark-edly dependent on the number of particles used, and this in itself, as mentioned in the introduction, is evidence of the presence of a transition in which fluctuations are influenced by the number of particles used. Although the quantitative aspects of the transition are not as yet firmly established it is encouraging to note that the difference between 256 and 500 particles is relatively small. Whether the 500-particle behavior closely resembles that of an infinite system is an open question at the moment, but it is clear that some transition is occurring in that region, presumably a first order one from a

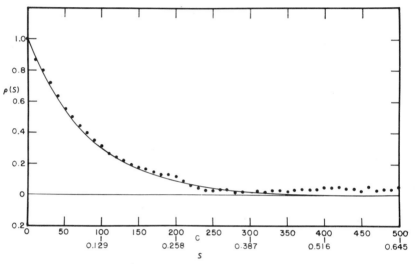

Figure 5. A comparison of the velocity auto-correlation function, $\rho(s)$, with an exponential decay (solid line) at $v/v_0 = 2.0$ for hard spheres. The abscissa is given in terms of collision number, C, and time, s. (Reprinted with permission from *UCRL Livermore Report No. MUL—2262*).

fluid to a solid phase. It is also interesting to note that higher virial coefficients of the hard sphere system could be positive up to the transition, where presumably the virial expansion breaks down. This conclusion is different from the published Monte Carlo [5] results. These results however, are presently being reinvestigated by Dr. W. Wood at Los Alamos. Analytical theories which take into account only single or pair correlations exactly, such as the free-volume theory [6] and the superposition theory of Kirkwood [2], are considerably off in this intermediate-density region below the transition.

The velocity auto-correlation function has been evaluated by means of eq. (4) for hard spheres. Figure 5 shows its behavior at $v/v_0 = 2.0$.

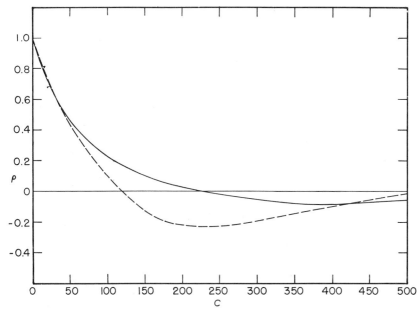

Figure 6. The velocity auto-correlation function, ρ, versus collision number for hard spheres at $v/v_0 = 1.60$ (solid line) and $v/v_0 = 1.03$ (dotted line).

The calculated points agree remarkably well with an exponential decay (solid line).

$$\rho(s) = e^{-\beta s} \tag{9}$$

where β is an effective friction constant, that is,

$$D = kT/m\beta \tag{10}$$

This exponential decay is the direct result of the fact that the relaxation can be described by a Markoff process. However, at densities above the transition for hard spheres, the auto-correlation function develops wiggles as shown in Fig. 6 for $v/v_0 = 1.60$ and $v/v_0 = 1.03$. These wiggles suggest that at high densities two particles collide again after only a few collisions with other molecules, and these correlations are negative, since a particle at high density is forced by its neighbors to reverse its velocity into a narrow range of angles. It is, however, interesting to note that these correlations are not built up until a short time has elapsed. Thus, as Table I shows, the initial decay of the auto-correlation function, even at high densities, is given correctly by the

Enskog theory as an exponential decay; that is, the diffusion coefficient from the initial decay (column 1) and the Enskog theory (column 4) agree within the accuracy of the calculation. However,

TABLE I

Comparisons of the Diffusion Coefficients [a]

v/v_0	Eq. (10)	Eq. (5)	Eq. (6)	Esnkog	Boltzmann
14.141	2.9(2)	—	3.2(2)	3.4(2)	3.9(2)
2.000	3.1(3)	3.4(3)	3.4(3)	3.3(3)	1.1(2)
1.767	2.4(3)	2.0(3)	2.0(3)	2.4(3)	—
1.600	1.9(3)	1.3(3)	1.3(3)	1.9(3(	—
1.031	1.7(4)	—	—	1.9(4)	—

[a] The number is parentheses is the negative power of 10 by which the accompanying number must be multiplied.

the value of the diffusion coefficient calculated from eq. (5) and eq. (6) are different from Enskog's theory. At lower densities all these values agree within present accuracy. The fifth column shows that the Boltzmann [7] theory is only valid at quite low densities.

ACKNOWLEDGEMENTS: We wish to thank the computing group for the tremendous cooperation they have given us, and in particular Dr. Sidney Fernbach for generously making machine time available. Only the extremely competent coding of Shirley Campbell and Mary Shephard have made these results possible.

Notes and References

1. K. A. Brueckner, *Phys. Rev.* **97**, 1353 (1955).
2. J. G. Kirkwood, *J. Chem. Phys.*, **3**, 300 (1935).
3. Proceedings of I.U.P.A.P. on *Statistical Mechanical Theory of Transport Properties* in Brussels (to be published).
4. D. Enskog, *Kgl. Svenska Vetenskapsakad. Handil.*, **64**, 4 (1932).
5. B. J. Alder, S. P. Frankel, and V. A. Lewinson, *J. Chem. Phys.* **23**, 417 (1955); N. Metropolis, A. Rosenbluth, M. Rosenbluth, A. Teller, and E. Teller, *J. Chem. Phys.* **21**, 1087 (1953); M. N. Rosenbluth and A. W. Rosenbluth, *J. Chem. Phys.* **22**, 881 (1954).
6. J. Lennard-Jones and A. Devonshire, *Proc. Roy. Soc. (London)*, **A163**, 53 (1937).
7. S. Chapman and T. Cowling, *The Mathematical Theory of Non-Uniform Gases*, Cambridge, New York, 1939.

CHAPTER XXX

Recent Monte Carlo Calculations of the Equation of State of Lennard-Jones and Hard Sphere Molecules*+

W. W. Wood, F. R. Parker and J. D. Jacobson

Abstract

The more important results of these investigations which will shortly be published in detail, are described. The method, which for systems of sub-thermodynamic extent can be exact, but in which approximations are necessary to obtain results applicable to macroscopic systems, is briefly described. Results for the two types of molecules obtained to date indicate that the approximations introduce only slight errors, but further calculations will be required to verify this conclusion, particularly in the region of the first order phase transitions. The existence of the latter is inferred from breaks in the p-v isotherms for both kinds of molecules. The Lennard-Jones isotherm is above the critical temperature, and the phase transition occurs in the approximate neighborhood suggested by experimental freezing data for argon. Experimental p-v-T data for the latter are also compared with the calculated results.

In addition, the calculated radial distribution function of liquid argon is compared with that estimated from x-ray scattering data.

The hard sphere results are in good agreement with the similarly exact molecular-dynamics calculations of Alder and Wainwright. While the results are quite detailed in the neighborhood of the phase transition, they are still insufficient to determine the properties of the coexistent phases.

---

* Work performed under the auspices of the United States Atomic Energy Commission.

+ Presented, in summary, at the Symposium, by J. G. Kirkwood.

CHAPTER XXXI

One Hundred Years of Statistical Mechanics

ELLIOTT MONTROLL

The organizers of this conference on the many-body problem should be complimented on the shrewdness with which they selected its date. It falls on the 100th birthday of statistical mechanics. This birthday has been assigned by no lesser authorities than Maxwell and Gibbs.

Maxwell, after reviewing the primitive ideas of Bernoulli, LaSage, Herapath, and Joule, states in a popular article in the *Encyclopedia Britanica* entitled "Molecules", "the further development of the theory is generally supposed to have begun with Krönig, who has not as far as I can see made any improvement on what has gone before. Professor Clausius, the principle founder of the kinetic theory of gases, tells us what is meant by the heat in a body, namely its mean kinetic energy". Gibbs in his Clausius obituary notice calls him the "Father of statistical mechanics" and says that we may regard the Clausius paper, "On the Nature of the Motion we Call Heat", as marking his entrance into the field. This paper was, contrary to a recommendation made by Professor Wigner in his retiring address as Chairman of the American Physical Society, published twice; once in English in the *Phil. Mag.* in August, 1857; and once in German in *Poggendorf Annalen*. The manuscript was mailed from Zurich on the 5th of January.

This paper also marks the birth of modern physics in that it introduced "the microscopic" (as well as statistics) into natural philosophy in more than a speculative manner. The concept of the mean free path and the first analysis of transport processes appeared in a 1859 Clausius article.

The work of Clausius attracted Maxwell to the field. He entered the scene in 1860 with his great memoir "Illustrations in the Dynamical Theory of Gases". There the familiar Maxwell velocity distribution was derived and various remarks on transport processes made. Freshman physics students would be happy to hear that the Maxwell estimate of the heat conductivity of air was too large by a factor of 1000 because of an improper conversion of pounds to kilograms and the erroneous use of hours instead of seconds in the calculations.

Boltzmann's contributions started in the late 1860's with his famous transport equation as well as a discussion of the equipartition theorem.

While the kinetic theory was growing to maturity in the period 1857–90 an old but pertinent manuscript written by one James Waterston lay collecting dust in the archives of the Royal Society. It was finally brought to light by Lord Rayleigh in 1891 after a 45 year burial. To quote Rayleigh, "My attention was attracted in the first instance to Waterston's work upon the connection between molecular forces and the latent heat of evaporation and thence to a paper in *Phil. Mag.* (1858) 'On the Theory of Sound', where he alludes to the theory of gases and a paper entitled 'On the Physics of Media That Consists of Perfectly Elastic Molecules in a State of Motion', which was placed in the archives of the Royal Society in 1845". Rayleigh, then being secretary of the Royal Society, had little difficulty locating the manuscript as well as a referees report which contained the opinion that "the paper is nothing but nonsense, unfit even for reading before the Society". Rayleigh then stated that the omission to publish the manuscript was a misfortune that probably retarded the subject by 10 or 15 years and that it is singular that Waterston appears to have advanced no claim for subsequent publication.

The memoir was finally published in 1891 with introductory remarks by Rayleigh. Several bits of advice to young authors appeared in this introduction ". . . a young author who believes himself capable of great things would usually do well to secure favorable recognition of the scientific world by work whose scope is limited and whose value is easily judged, before embarking upon higher flights . . . One circumstance which may have told unfavorably upon the reception of Waterson's paper is that he mentions no predecessors. Had he put forward his investigation as a development of the theory of D. Bernoulli a referee might have hesitated to call it nonsense". When you curse referees and long waiting times for publication, think of Waterston.

The Waterston manuscript identified the temperature of a gas with the mean kinetic energy of its component particles, discussed the equipartition theorem, Graham's law of diffusion, and various other points about diffusion and heat conduction. It also contained the first calculation of a molecular velocity. In fact most of the early ideas of the kinetic theory (with the exception of the Maxwell velocity distribution) were mentioned.

Since Waterston's life story is not well known, a few remarks about him are in order. His father was a well-known manufacturer of sealing wax but at too early an era for this to have had any bearing on John James' choice of profession. His mother was a sister of George Sandeman, the founder of a well-known firm of London wine merchants. As is evident from the New Yorker ads which weekly depict a mysterious Spanish-looking character, the firm still flourishes.

Waterston's mother was also the niece of Robert Sandeman, who, with his father-in-law John Glas, founded a small but despised religious sect known as Glasites or Sandamanians. This sect believed that one should be subject to no league (including the British Government) or covenant but only to the doctrines of Christ and his apostles. It had no ordained minister or paid preachers and would suffer no differences of opinion from its members. The London membership never exceeded twenty families. It, however, contributed more than its due share to the fraternity of natural philosophers (and indeed it has in its proportion outdone the oft-quoted Reed College). Its two offerings were James Waterston and Michael Faraday.

Faraday was a highly respected elder and lay preacher of the sect, but was stricken from its list for absenting himself from services one Sunday to obey a command to lunch with Queen Victoria. After fifteen years of patient attendance at services as a visitor, he was finally reinstated as an elder.

To return to Waterston, his first remarks on the kinetic theory of gases actually preceded the preparation of his forgotten manuscript. They appeared in the appendix of a book entitled *Thoughts on the Mental Function*, which was published in 1843 but which fell even flatter than his paper on the kinetic theory.

J. S. Haldane, the British physiologist states (in an introduction to Waterston's collected works) that this book contains discussions of the

central nervous system and various other connections between phys-
iology and the senses that were even more ahead of his time than was
his kinetic theory. Waterston was convinced (at a time when few even
believed in atoms or molecules) that problems of life and conscious
behavior must ultimately be bound up with molecular or atomic
phenomenon. It was these supposed connections which stimulated
him to develop parts of his kinetic theory and to append them to his
book.

Because of his inability to get his papers published and the lack of
interest in his book, Waterston never graced an academic chair in
England. He was a Naval Instructor at Bombay to the East India
Company Cadets. After returning to England he lived on his family
income, taught mathematics to his nieces and nephews, was critical
of people like Lord Kelvin because of their too close connection with
industrial applications of science, and made rude remarks unbecoming
to an English gentlemen when the Royal Society was mentioned.

Maxwell's contributions to Statistical Mechanics diminished after
his appointment as Cavendish professor. He devoted his few years at
that post to the development of a laboratory teaching program (which
was the precursor of the modern elementary physics laboratory)
and to the editing and interpreting of Cavendish's unpublished notebooks. After the completion of this work, he was stricken with a fatal
illness and died at the age of 48 at the height of his powers.

At the turn of the century the subjects of kinetic theory and statistical mechanics seemed on the verge of collapse. Attacks against
them were proceeding successfully on two fronts. The first was started
by Loschmidt and followed up by Zermelo. Their camp could not
conceive of a peaceful coexistence of the reversible equations of motion
of gas molecules and the irreversible transport equations of Boltzmann.
The second attack led by Kelvin resulted from the violation of the
equipartition theorem (which relates the heat capacity of a polyatomic
gas to its number of degrees of freedom) by diatomic gases such as
hydrogen.

Zermelo, armed with proofs of the existence of Poincaré cycles,
claimed that since closed systems display a quasi-periodic behavior,
they have no equilibrium states. Boltzmann countered this argument
by estimating the period of a Poincaré cycle of a cubic centimeter

of gas to be more reminiscent of the age of the universe than the duration of an experiment. Although Zermelo concentrated his attack on Boltzmann, he had sufficient leisure to write a derogatory review of Gibb's *Statistical Mechanics*.

These attacks left Boltzmann in a state of despondency and induced a persecution complex. In the introduction of the first volume of his treatise *Vorlesung über Gastheorie* (1897) he states apologetically that he is publishing the book even though "kinetic theory seems to have gone out of style in Germany". After defending himself for several years, he writes in the introduction of his second volume (1904), "Even while the first part of this book was being printed the manuscript of the second and last part was almost completed . . . Just at that time, however, the attacks against the kinetic theory increased. I am convinced that the attacks rest upon misunderstandings and that the role of the kinetic theory is not yet played out. In my opinion it would be a blow to science if the contemporary opposition were to cause the kinetic theory to sink into the oblivion which was the fate suffered by the wave theory of light through the authority of Newton. I am aware of the weakness of an individual against the prevailing currents of opinion. In order to insure that not too much will have to be rediscovered when people return to the study of the kinetic theory I will present the most difficult and misunderstood parts of the subject in as clear a manner as I can".

Boltzmann somewhat overestimated his opposition, for his cause was successfully taken up by Smoluchowski and Ehrenfest who invented models which showed how dynamics and statistics could coexist. The last word has not yet been spoken on the nature of irreversibility and transport equations, but the overwhelming mass of experimental evidence gives us great confidence in the kinetic theory and statistical mechanics. Einstein, in his theory of Brownian motion, quieted the objections of another class of critics, the Energeticists led by Ostwald, finally convincing them of the existence of atoms and molecules.

Kelvin's attack on the kinetic theory found sympathetic ears in those who were more concerned with agreement between experiment and theory than with philosophical foundations. He objected to the equipartition theorem on the grounds that some degrees of freedom seem to be frozen in polyatomic molecules (H_2 being the classical case). Although he viewed this difficulty as being quite serious, he was even more alarmed at the absence of any contribution of the degrees of freedom responsible for the spectrum to the heat capacity of monatomic as well as polyatomic gases. The basis of atomic spectra was not understood in 1900 but he as well as Stokes and Kirchoff were convinced that every atom had an internal structure which was somehow responsible for its spectrum. While Rutherford was just outgrowing his knee pants, Kelvin suspected that an atom had a heavy central core and that light "satellites" composed of the "ions" of J. J. Thompson revolved in stable orbits about the central core. He felt that if the equipartition theorem was correct these "ions" should all contribute to the heat capacity of a gas. Kelvin's search for faults in the various derivations of the equipartition theorem was fruitless but he put his finger on one of the important paradoxes which required the quantum theory for its clarification.

These difficulties as well as those concerning the ether (which were to some extent resolved by the quantum theory and the theory of relativity) are discussed in great detail in Kelvin's 1900 article entitled "19th Century Clouds over the Dynamical Theory of Heat and Light". This can be found in Appendix B of Kelvin's *Baltimore Lectures*.

Although Kelvin's contributions to the kinetic theory and statistical mechanics were critical and not of the same fundamental nature as those of the other authors quoted above, this report would not be complete without some remarks on the part played in 19th century physics by the man whose name along with Boltzmann's is read in every statistical mechanical formula (. . . where k is Boltzmann's constant and T, degrees Kelvin). In the words of J. J. Thompson, "Any notice about the progress of physics in the later part of the last century would be like the play of Hamlet without the Prince of Denmark, if it did not deal with the part played in it by Lord Kelvin, who for more than forty years before his death in 1907 had been the most potent influence in British physics". It is hard to imagine anyone today with his influence; he was the Einstein, Fermi and Steinmetz of his time all rolled in one.

The 19th Century public's estimate of Kelvin's value in dollars and cents can be appreciated in terms of his contract for the delivery of fifteen lectures in two weeks (twenty lectures were actually delivered in the period Oct. 1–17) at the then newly formed Johns Hopkins University. After some negotiation, President Gilman offered him $2000 plus traveling expenses from Glasgow, an amount comparable to the annual salary of most of the faculty members. The Baltimore lectures were attended by all the important American physicists of the period. The stenographic report of the lectures was taken by Mr. A. S. Hathaway and immediately papyrographed (the papyrograph being a primitive ditto machine, printing in purple) and circulated to the community of natural philosophers as the first machinemade "preprint". Kelvin describes the details of the final publishing as follows: "The printing of the present volume began in August 1885; and it has gone on at irregular intervals during the 19 years since that time, in a manner which I am afraid must have been exceedingly inconvenient to the printers".

Kelvin's researches encompassed practically all branches of physics and engineering. His 661 papers form a substantial part of that which has become classical physics-thermodynamics, electricity and magnetism, hydrodynamics and elasticity — the references to his publications outnumber those of practically all other authors cited in the great, black, Cambridge University press volumes which were studied so avidly twenty-five years ago. Almost all important papers of his time start with phrases such as "According to Thompson . . ." or, "Thompson has posed the question . . .".

Kelvin's first paper, written at the age of 17, was a reply to a book by one Mr. Kelland, who claimed that Fourier's *Analytic Theory of Heat* was full of incorrect series expansions. Kelvin rederived many of the expansions by methods more modern than the original ones of Fourier. His second paper contained the theory of images and the first application of Fourier Analysis to electrostatics. From this Maxwell derived his initial inspiration for his electromagnetic theory — "It was this paper which introduced into mathematical science the idea of electrical action being carried on by means of a continuous medium . . .". Kelvin's fame as an undergraduate was so widespread that at 22 he became Professor of Natural Philosophy at Glasgow University, a chair which he occupied until his promotion to Chancellor at 70.

Kelvin's education might be educational for educators. He was one of seven children. His mother died when he was six, leaving his father (who was Professor of Mathematics at Glasgow) with a brood to be taken care of between arduous teaching duties. The children did not attend school. However, in the absence of a baby sitter they were sometimes kept in papa's sight by being seated in the rear of his classroom. The professor was surprised one day when little Willie, 10, volunteered the answer to a difficult problem which stumped the regular university students. Little Willie was soon enrolled as a Freshman. Most of the undergraduate prizes went his way, but he refrained from taking the final examinations which would have awarded him a degree so that he could go down to Cambridge as an undergraduate. Upon entering Cambridge at 16, he had already studied the works of Laplace, Lagrange, Poisson, Fourier, etc. Unlike most prodigies he was quite normal in his social behavior and outlook.

Kelvin, as his protégé, Maxwell, 9 years later, was second wrangler in the mathematical tripos at Cambridge. As was frequently the case, the first wrangler sank into the oblivion of a country parish while the second wrangler spent the rest of his life proving that he was more competent than the first. Since many of the tripos questions were based on the current literature, Kelvin had an opportunity to rederive some results of one of his own papers on the examination. Unfortunately, he did not bone up on his own research while his competitor studied it very carefully.

As is clear to anyone who tries to write 661 papers, Kelvin calculated and wrote continuously. He was most productive while at tea parties, faculty and board of directors meetings (being on the board of most of the prominent English engineering and electrical firms); and he didn't do badly on trains and in hansom cabs either. His specially designed oversized coat pockets always contained his famous large green notebooks which, in turn, always contained several unfinished articles.

Kelvin was knighted for his contributions to the first successful laying of an Atlantic cable. For this purpose he was the first to use stranded wire as an electric conductor (to insure a more uniform resistance) and invented many of the precision instruments (Kelvin Bridge, Kelvin galvanometer, etc.) required for cable operations. The tension and monotony of the cable-laying operation on the Great

Eastern was broken by Kelvin with the writing of several papers.

Although he was one of the greatest masters and developers of macroscopic and applied physics, Kelvin was personally most interested in the problems of the nature of atoms and molecules, and of the ether. It was his great enthusiasm in discussing these subjects, and his great public esteem, which gave the study of these highly speculative topics an air of respectability, and paved the way for the development of modern physics.

In conclusion, I thank the organizers of this conference for arranging a most stimulating and interesting program and for providing the facilities for a most pleasant meeting.

Author Index

535

Subject Index